Artillery and Ammunition of The Civil War

Artillery and

Ammunition of The Civil War

Warren Ripley

 VAN NOSTRAND REINHOLD COMPANY
NEW YORK CINCINNATI TORONTO LONDON MELBOURNE

To my wife, Quintillia Shuler Ripley, and children, William Young Warren Ripley Jr. and Clements Ripley.

Van Nostrand Reinhold Company Regional Offices:
   Cincinnati, New York, Chicago, Millbrae, Dallas
Van Nostrand Reinhold Company Foreign Offices:
   London, Toronto, Melbourne

Library of Congress Catalog Card Number: 75-90331

Published simultaneously in Canada by
D. Van Nostrand Company (Canada), Ltd.

Published by Van Nostrand Reinhold Company
450 West 33rd Street, New York, N. Y. 10001

10   9   8   7   6   5   4   3   2   1

Contents

Preface

EACH YEAR THOUSANDS OF AMERICANS visit the nation's military parks where Blue and Gray once fought and died in the bitterness of civil war.

To most it's a restful interlude in the annual race we call vacation. A chance to relax amid carefully manicured surroundings and even absorb a bit of history. A few, and their numbers grow each year, are genuinely interested in the tales the parks have to tell. They push a button, stand quietly, almost reverently, while a recorded voice narrates events of a bygone day. They buy a guidebook with its capsule version of the battle—what's more, they read it.

For people in the latter category this book is written in the hope it will give more meaning to two groups of objects in almost every military park which are largely overlooked by both recording and guidebook—cannon and ammunition.

Information on Civil War small arms is readily available in many fine, modern works. But anyone seeking data on artillery is forced to dig it out of 100-year-old texts, or collect various articles on specific types of weapons. The former are difficult to find, and modern works, paradoxically, are either too general or too specific for the novice cannon hunter.

This book is designed to bridge the gap between; to give the reader who knows nothing about artillery a fighting chance to identify various types of Civil War ordnance with, in certain instances, a bit of history on a few weapons thrown in.

Writing a book of this sort inevitably brings up certain problems. First is the matter of conflicting evidence. To ensure accuracy, Civil War texts, with few exceptions, have been used in preference to modern. Unfortunately, however, our forefathers left unsaid much that should have been, and said a great deal that shouldn't—even the Official Records contain statements diametrically opposed and obviously one or the other must be in error. In certain of these instances, both sides will be given and the reader can choose. In others, the author has selected a preferred version and takes full responsibility for so doing. At these places in the text, such irritating words as "the author believes" are inserted, not to establish the writer as an "expert" in a field almost devoid of such, but to point out that controversy does exist and although there are grounds for believing the proposition can be defended, it may still be open to argument.

Second is the matter of missing evidence. Information, particularly on ammunition, has been lost or destroyed during the years or often not recorded in the first place. Letters, books, and other documents of the 1800s often tantalize the researcher with small bits of information—clues, not solutions.

Occasionally, further reading will solve the problem, a joyful day in the annals of the researcher. More often, the single clue remains alone in its file, a frustrating reminder that Civil War ordnance is an extensive subject in which many facets are still unknown. In such cases, where evidence is insufficient, weapon identification is stated as tentative.

Finally, there is the problem of presenting a thoroughly chaotic subject in some semblance of order—a chapter arrangement that will enable the reader to examine a given weapon, then identify it without leafing through the entire book.

If the reader can do this—and enjoy doing it—then the book has accomplished its purpose and the author can feel successful.

Acknowledgments

RESEARCH HAS MANY COMPENSATIONS, not the least being the pleasant discovery that in this day of self-service and commercialism, people are essentially considerate and kind. Throughout the country dozens of men and women have given unstintedly of their knowledge and time to furnish the innumerable bits of information that have gone into preparation of this book.

The assistance of a number is acknowledged in footnotes. To them and to the others I am exceedingly grateful and especially to three fellow ordnance enthusiasts without whose help many, if not all, chapters would have suffered considerably.

In the early stages of research some years ago I discovered that every tough ordnance question addressed to museum or park invariably came back with a negative answer and the suggestion ". . . Ask Dr. James C. Hazlett of Wheeling, W.Va."

Eventually, I took the advice and initiated correspondence which has continued unabated through the years. Over and again Dr. Hazlett has furnished information obtainable from no other source—generosity doubly appreciated since the data, amassed only through arduous study, was given to a competitor, for the doctor is also a writer of ordnance articles published in the "Journal of the Company of Military Historians," and "Civil War Times Illustrated."

One of the major problems of an identification book is finding specimens to identify, particularly when they are scattered throughout many states. In this the assistance of a Pennsylvanian, Edwin H. Olmstead of Mount Holly Springs, has been especially welcomed and the inclusion of many rare weapons is due to his unselfish efforts in furnishing data and photographs.

Sydney C. Kerksis of Atlanta, Ga., who is well-known to ammunition collectors for his knowledge of this field, not only has been extremely helpful in solving a number of particularly tough problems, but was kind enough to read the ammunition section in rough draft—no mean chore in itself—and point out portions needing elaboration or correction.

Consequently, to these three men, Dr. Hazlett, Mr. Olmstead, and Mr. Kerksis, I owe a debt of gratitude which can never be repaid, but can, at least, be acknowledged.

Park Service personnel have without exception cheerfully rendered any requested assistance and although it is impossible to list all, I especially wish to thank the following: James F. Kretschmann of Vicksburg; Martin R. Conway, Gettysburg; John T. Willett, Petersburg, and W. Glen Gray, formerly at that park; Francis P. Wilshin, Manassas; Hobart Cawood and Raymond J. Geerdes, Chickamauga-Chattanooga;

Bernard Goodman, Kennesaw Mountain; James N. Haskett, Fort McHenry; Edward E. Tinney, Shiloh; Paul C. Swartz and George Condon, both of Fort Sumter, and Omega East, formerly of Sumter, and Edwin C. Bearss, Division of History Office of Archeology and Historic Presentation, Washington, D.C., and Mrs. Bearss.

In addition, Chief A. G. Fuller, U.S. Naval Historical Display Center, Washington Navy Yard; Robert H. Burgess, Mariners Museum, Newport News, Virginia; Dr. Chester D. Bradley, Casemate Museum, Fort Monroe, Virginia; Leslie Bright, Fort Fisher, (North Carolina) Preservation Laboratory; E. Milby Burton and John D. Miller, Charleston (South Carolina) Museum; Mrs. Wade L. Murray, UDC Museum, Charleston; Gerald C. Stowe, United States Military Academy Museum, West Point, and Egon Weiss of the Academy's Library; Captain Elton Manuel, Newport, Rhode Island Artillery Co. Museum; Mrs. Roger Lee Kirkland, Fort Morgan Historical Commission; Miss Virginia Rugheimer, Mrs. Pringle Haigh, and Mrs. Beulah T. Sheetz, all of the Charleston Library Society; Mrs. Granville T. Prior, South Carolina Historical Society; Waverly K. Winfree, Virginia Historical Society; Mrs. Stuart Gibson, the Valentine Museum, Richmond; Dorrell E. Garrison, John M. Browning Museum, Rock Island, Illinois; Mrs. Bessie Sasser, Friedman Library, Tuscaloosa, Alabama; Milton C. Russell, Virginia State Library, Richmond; Carl M. Becker, Miami University of Ohio, Dayton, Ohio; Eddie J. Nesmith, Fort Gadsden State Park, Sumatra, Florida; R. H. Taliaferro, the Jordan High School, Columbus, Georgia; Miss N. Ruth Hudson, Centre Hill Mansion Museum, Petersburg, Virginia; The Citadel Museum and Library staffs, Charleston; Public Information Departments of the U.S. Army Artillery and Missile Center, Fort Sill, Oklahoma, and the Norfolk Naval Shipyard, Portsmouth, Virginia; Mr. and Mrs. Albert J. Aronstamm, Long Island, New York; Mrs. William B. King, Washington, D.C.; Mrs. Philip Hewitt-Myring, Thetford, England; and David Maybank Jr., Dr. and Mrs. Albert Cannon and Miss Josephine Cannon, Dr. and Mrs. J. Moultrie Townsend, Mr. and Mrs. Randell C. Stoney, Park H. Mikell, and Eddie Phillips, all of Charleston, South Carolina.

Finally, I would like to thank my employers, the Evening Post Publishing Co. for the use of photographic equipment and files as well as members of the staff: Robert A. Nettles, J. Richard Burbage, Dewey A. Swain, William A. Jordan, Myles E. Smoak, William J. Murton, Gene Evans, Thomas K. Peck Jr., Ernest M. Glover, and Lewis M. Weston.

THE MAJORITY OF PHOTOGRAPHS WERE TAKEN by the author or obtained from ancient texts. However, a number were furnished by individuals or institutions and are gratefully acknowledged in this section by chapter and number rather than with the illustrations in an effort to keep captions as brief as possible.

Similarly, statistics have been restricted to those considered essential for identification. An attempt has been made to include all pertinent marks. However, in a few cases such identification was omitted by the founder, in some it has been obliterated by the ravages of man and weather, and in a great many presumably is present, but unobtainable due to concealment by paint, rust, or form of carriage.

Measurements are those of the illustrated weapon and may not conform exactly to statistics in Appendix C.

All weapons are assumed to be muzzle-loading unless otherwise indicated.

Source books are listed by author or title and will be found in the bibliography.

Since rust makes exact measurement of ammunition difficult if not impossible, projectiles are listed according to weapon caliber and actual diameter, unless otherwise indicated, will be a tenth or so less.

Abbreviations have been used as follows:
Length O/A—Overall length from muzzle face to tip of cascabel.
v. ————Indicates distance from muzzle face to vent measured atop the tube. Other bore lengths are interior measurements.
Cwt. ————Hundredweight of 112 pounds.

In many cases two names are given. The first, Identification, is technically descriptive. The second, Common Name, may not be technically accurate, but is generally used for convenience.

Illustrations by:
U.S. Army—I–35. V–3. VI–10. VIII–28.
The National Archives, Washington—III–17, 18, 21. IV–5, 6, 11. V–7, 11, 15. VI–2, 8. VIII–42, 46. X–22, 23. XI–21. XIII–1.
North Carolina Department of Archives and History, Raleigh, N.C.—I–43, 45, 47.
Library of Congress, Washington—I–23, 28, 40, 50. II–7. III–2, 8, 19. IV–7, 24. V–8, 9, 18, 25. VI–20, 28, 31. VII–12. VIII–12, 16. IX–7, 12, 45. X–13, 20, 28, 31, 34, 36, 37, 52, 57, 61, 62. XI–18, 22, 23, XII–23, 24.
Florida Board of Parks and Historic Memorials, Tallahassee—XII–17, 31.
Mariners Museum, Newport News, Va.—III–14.
U.S. Navy—VI–12, 13, 18.
Edwin H. Olmstead—I–13, 14, 22, 41. II–11, 15, 16, 17. III–12, 13, 15. IV–2, 21, 23. V–20, 21, 22. VII–7, 8. VIII–26, 30. IX–1, 8, 9, 19, 43, 44. X–44, 54.
National Park Service (Vicksburg NMP)—I–44. X–47.
William Y. W. Ripley Jr.—III–11.
Smithsonian Institution, Washington—I–29. II–13. III–10. X–10, 12, 21, 24, 25, 30, 40. XI–1, 3, 4, 5, 6, 7, 14, 17, 23, 24. XII–1, 5, 6, 8, 20.
Valentine Museum, Richmond, Va.—VIII–41.
Lewis Weston—I–52.
West Point Museum.—I–1. IV–14. XII–7, 16, 19, 57. XIII–14, 21, 22, 26, 31, 32, 36, 39, 42, 43, 44, 46, 49, 53, 69, 70, 72, 74, 76, 79, 80, 81, 89, 103, 124, 125, 133, 138, 139, 141, 152, 153, 154, 155, 157, 158, 159, 160, 166, 167, 168, 169, 170, 172, 175, 177, 179, 182, 186, 187, 188, 189, 190, 197, 198. XIV–4.

Introduction

CIVIL WAR CANNON HUNTING IS A HOBBY that, like any other, offers returns in proportion to time and effort invested. Basic equipment is inexpensive and simple—a six-foot rule, notebook, and pencil are the essentials. However, the serious hobbyist will soon find a camera helpful since without photographic evidence it is often difficult to remember days, or even hours, later the configuration of a specific weapon. Once equipped, however, remaining expenses are almost entirely those incidental to travel and this can be as extended as pocketbook and time permit.

The majority of weapons are in national, state or municipal parks and the collections of a few museums. These are generally accessible to the public at little or no charge and specimens of almost all common weapons and quite a few rare ones can be found by scheduled stops at these points.

The remaining pieces offer a greater problem. They are scattered mainly up and down the Atlantic seaboard and spotting them is a game in which the novice has as much chance as the experienced ordnance fan, and either may turn up a real "find." Among the author's proudest discoveries, for instance, are an 8-inch seacoast howitzer at a country cemetery in Connecticut, a pair of beautiful little Blakely rifles outside a small South Carolina muse-um, unrecognized and unappreciated by the owners, and an unusual caliber Parrott rifle resting on a courthouse lawn.

Fortunately, since the cannon hunting fraternity is relatively small, and the Atlantic seaboard rather a large stretch of territory, there are doubtless far more unusual and interesting weapons waiting to be "discovered" than one would suppose. Many small towns have a cannon or two rusting on the village green and sometimes these are quite rare weapons. Cemeteries often prove lucrative locations and every now and then a weapon will be found mounted on the lawn of a private dwelling. Civil War monuments are well worth checking as are grounds of public buildings. Service station operators can often say quickly whether or not their town has any weapons and policemen are an even better source of information.

Estimates of the total number of Civil War cannon extant are hazardous in the extreme. Dr. James C. Hazlett of West Virginia, whom the author considers the nation's top authority on field calibers, has catalogued more than 2,000 weapons. Taking his figure as a rough base and adding an arbitrary 25 per cent, we arrive at 2,500 which, give or take a hundred or two, is probably fairly close for surviving weapons used during the war. If we include Revolutionary War pieces and those of Spanish American and World War I vintage, the number would have to be juggled upward substantially.

The size of the number and the very fact that it is entirely indefinite are two factors tending to increase, rather than mitigate, the pleasure of the hobby. The beginner, by visiting various parks, can start building a collection of photographs and data at a great rate thus furthering initial enthusiasm. Later, as experience is gained, he will find the search becomes increasingly complicated and difficult, with the rarer specimens few and far between.

The collection can be an aim in itself, or just a starting point for extensive research into history. Cannon and their markings are clues which can send the fan interested in history into hours of research which many times results in tracing the weapon's story from place and date of manufacture to its use and final disposition.

An instance of this is discussed fully in Chapter IV, but a synopsis will illustrate the point. Measurements and markings of a cannon mounted today in Fort Sumter show that the weapon, a 10-inch columbiad, was made in Boston in 1846. Various records place the piece in Fort Sumter during the initial bombardment of 12-13 April 1861. It later was used by the Confederates against attacking ironclads 7 April 1863, and then was transported to the City of Charleston where it was rifled and banded. It was sent to Fort Johnson, one of the fortifications in Charleston Harbor that took part in the initial bombardment of Sumter, where it served during the remainder of the war. Years later the piece was returned to Sumter and placed on display. The histories of many other weapons are similarly recorded, awaiting enthusiastic "buffs" who will spend the necessary hours of armchair detective work.

Assuming the neophyte cannon hunter has the necessary equipment, enthusiasm—and a cannon, how does he determine its identity? Unfortunately, almost all subjects have initial steps that must be understood before proceeding, and Civil War artillery is no exception. Consequently, the following information is general and basic in nature and the experienced ordnance fan may wish to skip the remainder of this section.

Not so the novice. He should at least understand the principles advanced here before proceeding. In addition, since every hobby, including ordnance, has its peculiar terminology, the beginner should become familiar with the description of parts and terms as explained in Appendix A.

The term "Civil War cannon" is used throughout this book in relatively loose fashion to include all weapons served or available for service during the conflict although many were manufactured several decades before the war and a few before the turn of the century.

Cannon were made in a variety of shapes and sizes and may be separated into categories based on one or more of the following: 1. The size of the bore, or opening from which the projectile is ejected, 2. Type of bore, 3. Type of weapon, 4. Material, 5. Model, 6. Employment, 7. Name of inventor, 8. Method of loading, 9. Army or Navy, 10. Union or Confederate.

1. The size of the bore is included in the basic description of any weapon. It is expressed in one of two ways: inches, such as "10-inch columbiad," or, surprisingly, in pounds. The latter is based on the weight of the projectile the weapon fired— "32-pounder gun." This method worked fine in the early days of artillery when smoothbore cannon fired mainly solid iron spherical projectiles since the diameter of the shot, and hence that of the bore, remained constant for a given weight. Thus the bore diameter of a "32-pounder" was always 6.4 inches (diameter of the shot was a fraction less so that it could be inserted).

However, when the system was extended to rifled weapons, which fired elongated projectiles, lengthening or shortening the shot changed the weight although the bore diameter remained constant. This led to such confusing situations as the same 8-inch Parrott rifle being called a "200-pounder" by the Army and a "150-pounder" in the Navy. The original projectile weighed 200 pounds, but was later shortened which reduced the weight to 150 pounds for use by both services. The Navy adapted terminology to fit the new weight, but the Army retained the original designation. This state of confusion continued throughout the war, but today most ordnance enthusiasts prefer to express bore diameter in inches except for extremely common varieties.

Note that the word is "pounder," not "pound," when used to describe bore size or type of weapon. The "32-*pounder* gun" fired roughly a 32-*pound* solid shot. The gun itself weighed several thousand *pounds*.

2. Type of bore. Civil War weapons were either smoothbore or rifled. The former were characterized by smooth internal surface of the tube, or barrel, and the latter by one of several systems of "grooves" (indentations) and "lands" (raised portions) in the bore known as "rifling."

The smoothbore was designed for spherical projectiles, but could also fire specialized elongated forms described in the ammunition section. Projectiles for rifles were generally elongated although most such weapons were capable of firing spherical ammunition in emergency. Both smoothbore and rifled artillery used a wide variety of ammunition.

Unfortunately, type of bore is not a clear-cut category. When the war started, the rifle was relatively new in this country and in an effort to obtain a number of them quickly, many smoothbores were sent to the shops and rifled. The reverse also occurred occasionally in the South, where a rifle was reamed to larger caliber smoothbore.

3. Type of weapon. Smoothbore cannon may be classified as guns, howitzers, mortars, or columbiads and although there are many exceptions, normally the weapons within each class are basically similar in appearance. This is particularly true of *guns* which are long-barreled weapons designed to throw a solid shot with heavy charge of powder at long range using a low angle of elevation.

Howitzers have shorter barrels. They fired shells and other types of ammunition with lower charges than guns and at higher elevation. They are lighter than guns of the same caliber and had less range.

Mortars are stubby weapons designed to project large shells with light charges of powder at very high elevation. Having a high trajectory, they utilized the force of fall as well as the force of the powder within the shell to inflict damage.

Columbiads combine qualities of all three. They are relatively long-barreled pieces capable of firing large shot or shell with heavy charges at high elevation.

4. Civil War cannon were made of bronze, or "brass" as it often was called in ordnance circles of the day, cast iron, wrought iron, and steel, either alone or in combination. There is one piece in the United States Military Academy Museum collection which is said to be made of German silver, and a few mortars were made of wood. From a practical standpoint, the cannon hunter is not equipped to determine whether a piece is made of cast iron, wrought iron, or steel, and a simple decision between bronze and iron in most cases will be sufficient.

5. Weapons often underwent model changes as the years passed. Some were minor, others major, but for purposes of this book, usually only those will be considered which noticeably altered the appearance of the piece.

6. Civil War artillery, smoothbore and rifled, also was characterized by its employment—field, siege or garrison, mountain or prairie, and seacoast.

Field artillery included light weapons of high maneuverability capable of keeping up with normal troop operations in the field.

Siege and garrison weapons were a bit heavier and slower of movement. The same pieces were considered "garrison artillery" if used to defend a fortification and "siege artillery" if for knocking it down.

Mountain service demanded a specialized weapon capable, with its carriage, of being taken apart and transported on pack animals. Fitted with a four-wheel "prairie carriage," the same piece could be used in defense of frontier forts and camps against Indian attack.

Seacoast artillery was the heaviest ordnance used by the Army. These were weapons of position, mounted with considerable time and effort in the forts along the coast. Although employed occasionally against land targets, their primary use was defense against naval attack.

7. Name of inventor. A few classes of cannon, generally of distinctive appearance, are known by the name of their inventor. They are normally identified by the bore diameter and the inventors' last name as: "7-inch Brooke," a Confederate weapon developed by Lieutenant John M. Brooke, CSN.

8. Method of loading. Most cannon of the day were muzzle-loaders: the charge and projectile were inserted at the mouth of the bore. A few, generally foreign weapons, were breechloaders, the method used in modern weapons. Unless otherwise indicated, it will be assumed herein that all weapons are muzzle-loading.

9. Most weapons were used interchangeably by Army and Navy. However, in United States service, the Dahlgrens and Rodmans were designated Navy and Army weapons respectively. The rule was not entirely rigid, however, and there are instances of Dahlgrens being used ashore. The reverse also may have been true although the author is not aware of its occurrence. The Confederacy, limited in its ordnance supplies, used weapons where needed without regard to specific service.

10. Several types of weapons may be classified as Union or Confederate. Of these, a very limited number—all large seacoast or Navy weapons—may be considered as definitely used by one side alone. The others, particularly field calibers, were subject to capture. The North, especially late in the war when excellent ordnance was available in abundant supply, generally scorned use of captured material as inferior and a needless complication of ammunition supply problems.

Not so the South. Confederate field batteries often were armed with captured weapons many of which Southern artillerymen prized far more than those of home manufacture. Consequently, although a weapon may bear U.S. markings, it may well have spent most of its career being served by Southern gunners against the original owners.

The foregoing is a very basic introduction to a hobby that, like any other, requires a certain amount of study. If the beginner reads this far and rushes out to the nearest national park to identify fifty or a hundred cannon, he will find the subject thoroughly confusing.

If, on the other hand, he finishes the book to get some idea of the types of cannon and their chapter locations for quick reference, he should find identifi-cation of the majority fairly easy, others a bit more difficult, and a few that probably no one can identify with absolute assurance.

Chapters XII and XIII are devoted to ammunition, both for the casual interest of the cannon fan who wants to know what was fed into the various weapons and for the artillery ammunition collector.

Today many people own metal detectors, and checking old battlefields for projectiles and other artifacts is a growing hobby in itself. Unfortunately, much ammunition lacks positive identification due to loss of records. However, photographs and sketches of many "unknowns" are included to illustrate the multitude of varieties used, particularly by the South.

W.R.

Chapter 1

The Gun

GUNS ARE AMONG THE EASIEST of Civil War cannon to identify. Most follow standard configurations that once understood are simple to recognize, for although artillery development through the years brought numerous models, all fall within a limited number of categories based on bore diameter. This once varied widely, but long before the war had been restricted to a relatively small number of calibers in the interests of weapons standardization and simplification of ammunition supply.

Limited quantities of non-standard 4-, 3-, and even 1-pounders are reported in militia inventories at the outbreak of war, but these were relics of a bygone era and although technically available for service, it is doubtful if many saw combat in the 1860s.

Consequently, the identification problem is simplified and, with a few exceptions, restricted to gun models of the following calibers specified in ordnance manuals of 1861:

Field . . . . 6- and 12-pounders of bronze.
Siege and Garrison . 12-, 18-, and 24-pounders, all of iron.
Seacoast . . . 32- and 42-pounders, both of iron.
Navy . . . . 32- and 64-pounders, both of iron.

All were smoothbore initially, a form that was obsolescent if not obsolete before the first shot was fired. As the war progressed, smoothbores of larger caliber and rifles took precedence in fort and field and the old guns were either relegated to secondary roles, or rifled in a makeshift attempt to utilize existing materiel.

Rifling beefed up projectile weight to roughly double, turning a smoothbore 24-pounder into a 48-pounder, for instance. But such rifles were only partially successful and as soon as possible they were supplanted by improved weapons of other types. However, until the foundries could begin extensive production, both sides frantically rifled the old guns, from 6-pounder to 42, and even after Appomattox, the North continued to rifle 32s and 42s in seacoast forts although it was clearly recognized as a stopgap measure pending development of more adequate weapons. In the South, where production never kept pace with demand, many of the old guns, both rifle and smoothbore, were still in use at the end of the war, but even the Confederates tried to replace them as much as possible at major points of defense.

On occasion, rifled smoothbores turned in quite creditable performances—Fort Pulaski, for instance, where in April, 1862, their fire helped breach the walls and bring the downfall of that Georgia bastion. Their work from 2,000 yards was exceptional in the light of textbook breaching ranges for smoothbores which started at an ideal 40 yards for minimum expenditure of ammunition and increased to 500 or 600 yards with a tremendous additional cost in powder and shot.

Yet less than eighteen months later on Morris Island, these makeshift weapons were hopelessly outclassed by heavy Parrott rifles that systematically pounded Fort Sumter into rubble from up to 4,000 yards and lofted 150-pound shells about 8,000 yards into the City of Charleston.

The obsolescence of the gun, while no doubt deplored by Civil War artillerymen, had one happy effect for modern cannon enthusiasts—the siege and seacoast calibers often were shunted off to secondary defensive works. These were generally small, out of the way positions of little real military value.

When the war neared its end, the cannon were worth neither saving by the retreating Confederates nor salvaging by the victorious Federals. They were usually spiked and left to rust on their carriages. Being far from main roads, the weapons were either overlooked by junk dealers or considered not worth the effort of dragging to the melting pot. Wooden carriages rotted with time. The guns slipped to the ground and were forgotten; half-buried they lay until rescued and mounted by a later generation.

The smallest regulation gun caliber of the war was the 6-pounder (3.67-inch bore) which falls into three general categories: 6-pounder, bronze, Models 1839 and 1841, U.S.; 6-pounder, cast iron, Models 1819 and 1831, U.S.; and Confederate 6-pounders.

The Model 1841 (Fig. I-1) is the 6-pounder most prevalent in the National Parks commemorating field engagements, particularly battles early in the war such as Manassas. The illustrated piece is in the extensive weapons collection of the U.S. Military Academy at West Point. The plaque states: "Lost without dishonor at the Battle of Buena Vista [22–23 Feb. 1847] by a Company of the 4th Artillery. Recaptured with just pride and exultation by the same Regiment at Contreras [20 Aug. 1847]." Ordnance Manual weights and measurements of these and other weapons will be found in tables of Appendix C. Actual measurements are listed with photographs of the piece.

The Model 1841 is found both smoothbore and rifled. The weapon began as a smoothbore, but shortly before and during the war a number were grooved by the North in what is known as the James System of rifling. General Charles Tillinghast James was the inventor of a type projectile described in Chapter XIII. It required a special type rifling which in the 6-pounders consisted of 15 lands and grooves (Fig. I-2) although most other small caliber rifles of the

FIGURE: I-1 LOCATION: West Point, N.Y. IDENTIFICATION: Gun, Field, 6-Pounder, Model 1841, Bronze. BORE: Diameter — 3.67. Smoothbore. Length — 57.5. LENGTH O/A: 65.6. TRUNNIONS: Diameter — 3.67. Length — 2.8. MARKINGS: Left Trunnion — 1842. Right Trunnion — N.P. Ames, Founder, Springfield, Mass. Cascabel — 881 (Weight). Tube — U.S. COMMON NAME: 6-Pounder, Model 1841.

FIGURE: I-2 LOCATION: Chickamauga-Chattanooga, Ga.-Tenn. IDENTIFICATION: James Rifling, 6-Pounder, Model 1841. BORE: Diameter — 3.67. Rifling — 15 x 15 (straight). MARKINGS: Muzzle Face — J.W.R. 121. Left Trunnion — 1844. Right Trunnion — N.P. Ames, Founder, Springfield, Mass. Tube — U.S. COMMON NAME: (Of the weapon) — 6-Pounder, Model 1841, Rifled.

day had from three to seven lands and grooves.

The 6-pounders (and other cannon rifled for the general's projectiles) are often called "James Rifles." This, in the author's opinion, is as improper as referring to the old 32- and 42-pounders, banded and rifled by the Confederacy in the Brooke pattern as "Brookes" (q.v.). In both cases it is a needless confusion of nomenclature which, unfortunately, our ancestors were not above perpetuating in their records. The confusion is compounded since there are other James rifles which are distinctly different.

By rifling the bronze 6-pounder, for instance, we obtain—in theory if not always in practice—a gun firing an elongated James projectile about double the weight of the ball, or 12 pounds. This is 2 pounds less than the theoretic weight of the James projectile for the 14-pounder bronze field rifle generally known as the "James Rifle" (q.v.). This piece has an entirely different appearance from the rifled 6-pounder, and when a report in the Official Records refers to "James Rifle," it often takes considerable checking to determine which rifle is under discussion.

Numerous rifled 6-pounders, a designation the author prefers[1] will be found in the nation's parks. Those bearing pre-war dates were doubtless grooved later to utilize General James' projectiles. However, a large number stamped on the trunnions "M Greenwood, Cincinnati, Ohio" were both cast and rifled during the early stages of the war. Miles Greenwood (1807-1885) was a native of New Jersey who moved to Ohio and established the Eagle Iron Works in 1832. The firm rapidly became the largest in the West and during 1861-62 turned out 161 bronze field pieces—rifled and smoothbore—scores of gun carriages, and rifled some 26,000 smoothbore muskets.[2] External measurements of all Model 1841 6-pounders, whether rifled or smooth, conform to those of the West Point piece.

The Model 1839 is exactly the same as the 1841, according to the Ordnance Manual,[3] with the exception of the muzzle molding which consists of "an echinus, a fillet, and a cavetto" in the early model compared to "two echinus" for the 1841. Fortunately, dates are usually easy to read on bronze weapons and are a lot easier to interpret.

Although the majority of Civil War 6-pounders found today are bronze, there are a few legitimate U.S. 6-pounders of cast iron and a number of others of this metal that presumably were either militia or Confederate weapons. The explanation for the U.S. guns goes well back into history. Both bronze and cast iron could be utilized in the manufacture of field pieces and weapons of the Revolutionary War period will be found of both metals. However, between 1775 and the end of the century, bronze was favored since it was felt to be less subject to bursting.

In 1801, Secretary of War Henry Dearborn held up the casting of more bronze weapons pending tests to determine which was the better material. Heavy weapons, 24- and 32-pounders, had long been made of cast iron and the excellent results obtained with 6-pounders turned out during this period brought about some thirty-five years of what may be called the "Iron Age" for United States weapons. Motives behind the move were based on economy and national defense. The cost of bronze, or brass as it is also called, was five or six times that of iron. In addition, while this country produced some of the best iron ore in the world, sufficient deposits of copper and tin—metals necessary for the manufacture of bronze—had not been developed. We were forced to rely upon foreign sources and these probably would be cut off in time of war leaving us in a precarious position.

Consequently, with exception of a few orders, the manufacture of bronze weapons ceased in 1801 and was not resumed until 1836. The return to bronze was decided by the Ordnance Board of 1835. This body, in accordance with a recommendation of the preceding board (1831), was ordered to test the two metals and determine the better. Actually, since there were no recently made American bronze weapons to test, the board subjected iron 6- and 12-pounders to what it considered proper trial, passed off the howitzers of similar material as not worth the labor and expense of proving, and resolved, rather arbitrarily under the circumstances, that iron was not a proper material for field pieces and that they should instead be made of bronze.[4]

The 1835 board's report was approved 8 July 1836, marking the date of authorization for the future use of bronze for field pieces.[5] Approval, however, by no means ended the fight over the proper metal and proponents of iron kept up the struggle even after their weapons showed a discouraging tendency to explode during testing of both materials by the Ordnance Board of 1838.[6]

Finally, a commission of ordnance officers—consisting of Major R. L. Baker, Captains Alfred Mordecai and Benjamin Huger, and a Mr. (probably William) Wade, a practical founder and former captain of ordnance—were sent to Europe.[7] They spent nine months of 1840 visiting foundries, arsenals, and armories and upon their return, the Ordnance Board 2 January 1841, confirmed former recommendations. From this date until 1861, bronze ruled undisputed as the proper metal for field pieces.

Figure I-3 shows one of the rare Model 1819 iron 6-pounders which, because of their extreme length, became known as "walking sticks."[8] This smoothbore, now in private hands,[9] measures 71.25 inches overall in contrast to the 65.6 of the bronze, Model 1841, and the 59 inches of the iron weapon in Figure I-4. The latter piece, mounted at Fort Pulaski, is dated 1836 and presumably is one of the last to be cast during the "Iron Age." It differs in several respects, other than metal, from the bronze model of 1841, notably in the addition of lock piece and reinforce band, a somewhat differently shaped breech, and reduction of some 6 or 7 inches in length to reduce weight.

Model year of the Fort Pulaski gun is doubtful, but since the 1819 system fell apart in 1827[10] and a change was made in iron field ordnance in 1831, it is quite possible the weapon is one of the Model 1831 6-pounders and has been listed tentatively in this category.

FIGURE: I-3 LOCATION: Morris Plains, N.J. (private collection). IDENTIFICATION: Gun, Field, 6-Pounder, Model 1819, Iron. BORE: Diameter — 3.75. (originally 3.67). Smoothbore. Length — 62 (estimated). LENGTH O/A: 71.25. TRUNNIONS: Diameter — 3.67. Length — 3. MARKINGS: Left Trunnion — McC. Pitt. Right Trunnion — 1821. Tube — U.S. REMARKS: Because of their length, these guns were known as "Walking Sticks." COMMON NAME: 6-Pounder, Model 1819.

FIGURE: I-4 LOCATION: Fort Pulaski, Ga. IDENTIFICATION: Gun, Field, 6-Pounder, Model 1831 (tentative), Iron. BORE: Diameter — 3.67. Smoothbore. Length — 47.5v. LENGTH O/A: 59. TRUNNIONS: Diameter — 3.67. Length — 3. MARKINGS: Muzzle Face — 23. Left Trunnion — 1836. Right Trunnion — J.M., C.F. Tube — U.S. COMMON NAME: 6-Pounder, Model 1831.

Although the commission of 1840 was instrumental in furthering the ascendancy of bronze, it did leave us at least one quite interesting weapon of the other metal. This is a 6-pounder of American model cast in Europe. Since Sweden was the leading European exponent of iron, the commission had several cannon of United States pattern cast in that country and subjected them to extreme proof along with similar weapons made of American iron. The trials showed our iron compared favorably with the European, but the results were largely academic since bronze had already won the victory. One of these smoothbores (Fig. I-5) is preserved in the West Point collection and is very similar to the bronze Model 1839 with exception of a flat chase ring in lieu of astragal and fillets.

In addition to United States iron 6-pounders, some were no doubt made for militia units both during and after the "Iron Age." One of the latter, in the author's opinion, is an extremely interesting rifled 6-pounder at Newport, Rhode Island (Fig. I-6). Markings show the gun was made, presumably as a smoothbore, by Cyrus Alger & Company of Boston in 1854. The piece is rifled in the James manner indicating alteration during the early part of the war. It is probable that the iron reinforcing band over the breech was added at the same time to provide additional strength.

Note that the piece, discounting the band and type of metal, differs from the bronze Model 1841 in slighter muzzle swell and lack of molding and reinforce. It may have had a base ring. If so, it was turned off during the process of banding. Barring size and reinforcing band, the piece has marked external resemblance to a little bronze 6-pounder (Fig. I-7) in the Petersburg National Military Park.

FIGURE: I-6 LOCATION: Newport, R.I. IDENTIFICATION: Gun, Field, 6-Pounder, Iron, Banded and Rifled. BORE: Diameter — 3.75 (originally 3.67). Rifling — 15 x 15 (James, straight). LENGTH O/A: 62.75. TRUNNIONS: Diameter — 3.67. Length — 3.5. MARKINGS: Left Trunnion — 1854. Right Trunnion — C.A. & Co., Boston. REMARKS: Original smoothbore banded and rifled, probably during the early part of the war. COMMON NAME: 6-Pounder, Banded and Rifled.

FIGURE: I-7 LOCATION: Petersburg, Va. IDENTIFICATION: Gun, Field, 6-Pounder, Bronze, Light. BORE: Diameter — 3.67. Smoothbore. Length — 44. LENGTH O/A: 51.5. TRUNNIONS: Diameter — 2.8. Length — 2.5. MARKINGS: Left Trunnion — 1851. Right Trunnion — C.A. & Co., Boston. COMMON NAME: 6-Pounder Cadet Gun.

FIGURE: I-5 LOCATION: West Point, N.Y. IDENTIFICATION: Gun, Field, 6-Pounder, Experimental, Iron. BORE: Diameter — 3.67. Smoothbore. Length — 57.5. LENGTH O/A: 65.5. TRUNNIONS: Diameter — 3.67. Length — 2.5. MARKINGS: Not available. REMARKS: Cast in Sweden apparently on slightly modified U.S. Bronze, Model 1840 pattern. COMMON NAME: 6-Pounder, Experimental.

This unusual smoothbore, made by Cyrus Alger in 1851, is only 51.5 in long and has a base ring, but no muzzle molding, astragal and fillets, or reinforce joint. The muzzle has a more pronounced swell than the Newport weapon. When examined in 1965, the Petersburg piece, which was not on display, bore a plaque identifying it as a 6-pounder Napoleon used for training purposes.

Any connection with the Napoleon (q.v.) is entirely erroneous although the weapon was made in limited numbers for training. Colonel Cary S. Tucker, USAR (Ret.)[11] has published correspondence which shows the 6-pounder was developed at the instigation of Virginia Military Institute. It seems the school, unlike West Point, was not assigned horses, and the cadets were having a tough time dragging standard 6-pounders around the drill field practicing maneuvers. It wasn't that the VMI cadets lacked brawn, but their field was hilly and some 1,800 pounds of gun and carriage was a heavy load. Consequently, four "light 6-pdr. guns" as they were called in those days, or "cadet guns" as they are better known today, were cast by Alger. The weapons, weighing 462 pounds each, were delivered to VMI in June 1848 and were used by the cadets until the war when they were taken into service.

Dr. Hazlett[12] later discovered that two cadet guns—of which the Petersburg piece is one—were made for the Arkansas Military Institute in 1851 and four for the State of Georgia in 1852. All ten were made by Alger and varied only 8 pounds in weight.

Another short 6-pounder[13] entered the service in 1838. This bronze smoothbore of 14 calibers (51.38 inches) of bore was designed for use with the highly maneuverable horse artillery in which all cannoneers were mounted. The piece was never popular and before long manufacture was discontinued. The author has never seen one of these guns but, based on bore length, estimates it was about 59.5 inches overall.

The period 1835-39 was one of great change and in addition to standard weapons numerous models were attempted or tried in field service although not officially adopted.

Confederate 6-pounders may be either bronze or iron, the former generally conforming to the U.S. Model 1841 pattern, the latter quite often not. The Confederacy also, of course, used captured U.S. weapons.

Several excellent Confederate bronze weapons of the U.S. Model 1841 type are in the West Point collection. One (Fig. I-8), cast by John Clark of New Orleans, has a wide base ring inscribed "Jeff Davis." The astragal is heavier than a U.S. 6-pounder and the muzzle swell more bulbous—differences probably due more to the Confederacy's lack of exact patterns to give founders than a planned model change. It was captured by Federal troops along the Mississippi where it presumably lost its cascabel. Three others at West Point, cast by another New Orleans firm, Leeds & Co., were bored initially to 3.3-inch rifles and although of conventional 6-pounder appearance are relegated to the miscellaneous rifle category of Chapter IX along with a Fort Monroe rifle of similar pattern bored to 3-inch.

The most perfect Confederate 6-pounder the author has seen is mounted at Vicksburg (Fig. I-9). This bronze smoothbore of superb craftsmanship was made by the Tredegar Co. of Richmond, Virginia, in 1862. It differs from the U.S. model primarily in having molding with sharp edges as compared to rounded as in the Federal weapons.

Confederate iron 6-pounders often lack sufficient marks for positive identification. This is true of the three weapons that follow. Available evidence would place them in the Confederate column but the listing must remain tentative pending discovery of absolute proof.

The first two are in the cemetery of Chalmette National Military Park at New Orleans. That shown

FIGURE: I-8 LOCATION: West Point, N.Y. IDENTIFICATION: Gun, Field, 6-Pounder, Bronze, Confederate. BORE: Diameter — 3.67. Smoothbore. Length — 55.75. LENGTH O/A: 61.75 to end broken cascabel. Probably 65.6 complete. TRUNNIONS: Diameter — 3.67. Length — 2.75. MARKINGS: Identification data not readable. Base Ring — Inscription, "Jeff Davis." REMARKS: Plaque states weapon was made by John Clark of New Orleans and captured by federal troops along the Mississippi River. COMMON NAME: 6-Pounder, Confederate.

in Figure I-10 was made by T.M. Brennan of Nashville, Tennessee, who is known to have made weapons for the South. Unfortunately, Mr. Brennan failed to affix a date which would have clearly established the piece as Confederate. There are two of these weapons, apparently identical, mounted a few feet apart, both breeches buried in concrete. Figure I-11 shows a similar, but slightly shorter weapon mounted a few steps from the Brennan guns. The trunnions are well down in concrete and markings, if any, are obscured. The third type (Fig. I-12) outside the information center at Fredericksburg, Virginia, has the general appearance and measurements of the U.S. bronze Model 1841, but no apparent markings.

The initials "U.S.," which would establish the weapons as Federal, are lacking on all three. In addition, they are iron, not bronze, and of 1841 or later model. Taken together, these facts virtually eliminate the federal government as a contender leaving the alternatives of milita or Confederate. The general lines of the Chalmette guns and absence of moldings (the strap around the chase of the Brennan piece is relatively modern) indicate they were built

FIGURE: I-10 LOCATION: Chalmette (Cemetery), New Orleans, La. IDENTIFICATION: Gun, Field, 6-Pounder, Iron, Confederate. BORE: Diameter — 3.7 (originally 3.67). Smoothbore. TRUNNIONS: Diameter — 3.67. Length — 2.75. MARKINGS: Right Trunnion — T. M. Brennan, Maker, Nashville, Tenn. REMARKS: Band around chase is modern. COMMON NAME: 6-Pounder, Iron, Confederate.

FIGURE: I-9 LOCATION: Vicksburg, Miss. IDENTIFICATION: Gun, Field, 6-Pounder, Bronze, Confederate. BORE: Diameter — 3.67. Smoothbore. Length — 57.5. LENGTH O/A: 65.6 TRUNNIONS: Diameter — 3.67. Length — 2.8. MARKINGS: Muzzle Face — 1541. Left Trunnion — 1862. Right Trunnion — J.R.A. & Co. REMARKS: Vent is not bushed. Fillets of muzzle and chase molding are sharp at edges instead of rounded as in most Union 6-pounders. COMMON NAME: 6-Pounder, Confederate.

near the beginning of or during the war. Lack of any state name or device, while far from conclusive, also lends credence to the theory that these weapons were Confederate.

The Fredericksburg gun is somewhat more doubtful. It might have been cast between 1841 and the start of the war. However, most weapons manufactured during this period of peacetime were by the larger founders who generally affixed their mark. Absence of such identification can in no way be considered proof that the weapon was not militia, but it does serve as an indication that the gun was probably Confederate. Lack of state initials and devices also would tend to bear out this theory as would the knowledge that firms such as Clark, Leeds, and Tredegar cast bronze 6-pounders of this pattern for the Confederacy and they, or others, might well have made similar weapons of iron.

FIGURE: I-11 LOCATION: Chalmette (Cemetery), New Orleans, La. IDENTIFICATION: Gun, Field, 6-Pounder, Iron, Confederate (Tentative). BORE: Diameter — 3.67. Smoothbore. LENGTH O/A: 65. TRUNNIONS: Diameter — 3.67. Length — 2.75 MARKINGS: Not available. COMMON NAME: 6-Pounder, Iron, Confederate.

FIGURE: I-12 LOCATION: Fredericksburg, Va. IDENTIFICATION: Gun, Field, 6-Pounder, Iron, Confederate (Tentative). BORE: Diameter — Plugged, but apparently 3.67. Smoothbore. LENGTH O/A: Cascabel broken, but apparently originally was 65.6. TRUNNIONS: Diameter 3.67. Length 3.5. MARKINGS: Not available. REMARKS: Apparently cast in the U.S., Bronze, Model 1841 pattern. COMMON NAME: 6-Pounder, Iron, Confederate (Tentative).

The converse, slightly modified, may have been true in the case of the bronze 6-pounder (Fig. I-13), one of twin smoothbores at Ft. McHenry, Maryland. Both guns have 3.67-inch bores 57.5 inches long, are 66 inches overall, have trunnions 3.67 inches in diameter, 2.8 inches long, and a maximum diameter of roughly 10 inches. They show a marked resemblance to the Chapter IX sketch of the Model 1861 Confederate iron 3-inch rifle taken from the Southern Ordnance Manual.[14] Although a rifle, measurements show the piece must have been almost identical to a straight muzzle, iron 6-pounder smoothbore, probably Model 1861, also listed in the manual. In fact, other than caliber, the only difference seems to be about an inch greater length for the rifle.

No specimen of the iron 6-pounder has been found, but measurements include bore diameter 3.67 inches, bore length 62.45 inches, length overall 70.71 inches, trunnion diameter 3.67 inches and length 2.75 inches, and maximum diameter 11.5 inches. Measurements and appearance lead to speculation that the McHenry pieces were cast in the iron 6-pounder pattern scaled down a bit to conserve metal and conform more closely to conventional bronze 6-pounder size.

The next larger gun—4.2-inch or 9-pounder—introduced about 1831[15] had been out of service some twenty-three years by the start of war. Being non-standard, its use was limited and both iron and bronze models are extremely rare. The latter was authorized by the board of 1835 as a Model 1836. However, the piece was not generally accepted and was suppressed by the board of 1838.[16] The Naples, New York, weapon (Fig. I-14) is stamped 1838 and no doubt was among the last of this caliber made. All bronze 9-pounders were cast with handles over the center of gravity as an aid in mounting. Two 9-pounders, termed "nondescript" by the Confederates, were left in Fort Donelson.[17] They may have been bronze or the iron Model 1831 which possibly resembled the previously described Fort Pulaski 6-pounder of this era.

Little is known of the Model 1819 and 1831 12-pounders, but like other field weapons, the piece followed the vicissitudes of the "Iron Age" and change back to bronze, culminating in the Model 1841 which followed the Model 1840 which in turn succeeded the Model 1836 (Fig. I-15). All three were basically the same and differences were very minor. Like the 9-pounder they were equipped with handles over the center of gravity. Two of the Model 1841 guns, known in later years after development of the Napoleon as the "heavy" 12-pounder, are located at Gettysburg. Unfortunately, they are used as markers in front of General Lee's Headquarters and are buried, breech down (Fig. I-16) in cement. The illustrated piece was made by the Ames Co. in 1858. All 12-pounders have a 4.62-inch bore and both the illustrated 1836 model, which was cast in 1837 and is now at Manassas, and the 1841 are 85 inches overall.

FIGURE: I-15 LOCATION: Manassas, Va. IDENTIFICATION: Gun, Field, 12-Pounder, Model 1836, Bronze. BORE: Diameter — 4.62. Smoothbore. Length — 74. LENGTH O/A: 85.25. TRUNNIONS: Diameter — 4.62. Length — 3.1. MARKINGS: Left Trunnion — 1837. Right Trunnion — N.P. Ames, Founder, Springfield, Mass. Tube — U.S. COMMON NAME: 12-Pounder, Model 1836.

FIGURE: I-13 LOCATION: Fort McHenry, Md. IDENTIFICATION: Gun, Field, 6-Pounder, Bronze, Confederate. BORE: Diameter — 3.67. Smoothbore. Length — 57.5. LENGTH O/A: 66. TRUNNIONS: Diameter — 3.67. Length — 2.8. MARKINGS: Muzzle Face — 773. COMMON NAME: 6-Pounder Confederate.

FIGURE: I-14 LOCATION: Naples, N.Y. IDENTIFICATION: Gun, Field, 9-Pounder, Model 1836, Bronze. BORE: Diameter — 4.2 Smoothbore. Length — 66v. LENGTH O/A: 77.25. TRUNNIONS: Diameter — 4.2. Length — 3.1. MARKINGS: Left Trunnion — 1838. Right Trunnion — N.P. Ames, Founder, Springfield, Mass. Cascabel — 3, 1376, G.T. Tube between handles — H.A. C.G., S.N.Y. COMMON NAME: 9-Pounder, Model 1836.

FIGURE: I-16 LOCATION: Gettysburg, Pa. IDENTIFICATION: Gun, Field, 12-Pounder, Model 1841, Bronze. MARKINGS: Left Trunnion — 1858. Right Trunnion — Ames Co. REMARKS: Measurements unobtainable. See Appendix C for Ordnance Manual specifications of this model. COMMON NAME: 12-Pounder, Model 1841. Or: Heavy 12-Pounder.

An iron 12-pounder in the extensive collection of the Historical Display Center, Washington Navy Yard (Fig. I-17), can be tentatively identified as a field weapon. The piece has no marks and is 84 inches long—1 inch shorter than the bronze field guns and far less than the 116-inch iron siege and garrison 12-pounder at Vicksburg (Fig. I-18). Muzzle face and chase closely resemble the "Iron Age" 6-pounder at Fort Pulaski (Fig. I-4). However, reinforce molding and lack of rimbase would indicate earlier vintage, around 1810. It was rifled and banded during the war, probably by the Confederates.

The 12-pounder, as previously mentioned, was also used as a siege and garrison weapon and the gun for this was the iron Model 1839. The piece in Figure I-18 is in the Vicksburg National Military Park, mounted on a field instead of a siege carriage. It is smoothbore, but this type will be found rifled in both James and Brooke (q.v.) style. It also may, or may not, be banded.

The next cannon in the 12-pounder class goes by a variety of names including "Gun-Howitzer," "Light 12-Pounder," and "12-Pounder Gun, Model 1857." However, North and South it was best known as the "Napoleon." The weapon was developed in France as a result of tests initiated by Louis Napoleon in 1850 to design a single piece of medium weight and 12-pounder caliber capable of using both shot and shell, which would substitute for the 8- and 12-pounder guns and 24- and 32-pounder howitzers then in use in his country. Since in Europe it took the place of both gun and howitzer, it was known as the "Canon-Obusier" or "Gun-Howitzer." However, the Napoleon has no chamber and technically is a gun. When introduced into our service, it replaced only the 12-pounder, bronze field gun Model 1841, so the term "Gun-Howitzer" has little actual meaning in this country.

Dr. Hazlett without question has done more research than anyone on American Napoleons and to him and to his articles, which are listed in the bibliography, the author is indebted for much of the following information. Dr. Hazlett traced the first Napoleon made in this country to Petersburg National Military Park where it is now displayed. The weapon (Fig. I-19) was made at the Ames Manufacturing Co. of Chicopee, Massachusetts in 1857 and technically is the only true Napoleon made in America. Apparently it had certain undesirable characteristics for all other weapons produced in 1857 or later are termed "modified." These are some three inches longer, an alteration which increased the weight, reduced the preponderance, and seems to have eliminated the initial defects.

FIGURE: I-17 LOCATION: Washington Navy Yard, D.C. IDENTIFICATION: Gun, Field, 12-Pounder, Iron. BORE: Diameter — 4.62. Rifling — 5 x 5, straight. Length — 72.75v. LENGTH O/A: 84. TRUNNIONS: Diameter — 4.62. Length — 4.5. MARKINGS: None visible. REMARKS: Note lack of rimbases indicating the piece is quite old, probably ca. 1810. It was banded and rifled by the Confederates during the war.

FIGURE: I-18 LOCATION: Vicksburg, Miss. IDENTIFICATION: Gun, Siege & Garrison, 12-Pounder, Model 1839, Iron. BORE: Diameter — 4.62. Smoothbore. LENGTH O/A: 114.25. TRUNNIONS: Diameter — 4.62. Length — 4.5. MARKINGS: Muzzle Face — R.L.B. No. 21. Left Trunnion — 1846. Right Trunnion — W.P.F. COMMON NAME: 12-Pounder Siege Gun.

FIGURE: I-19 LOCATION: Petersburg, Va. IDENTIFICATION: Gun, Field, 12-Pounder, Model 1857, Bronze. BORE: Diameter — 4.62. Smoothbore. Length — 61. LENGTH O/A: 69.5. TRUNNIONS: Diameter — 4.2. Length — 3.25. MARKINGS: Muzzle Face — No. 1, B.H., 1187. Left Trunnion — 1857. Right Trunnion — Ames Co., Founders, Chicopee, Mass. REMARKS: Only true Napoleon made in this country. All others were modified by lengthening. COMMON NAME: Napoleon No. 1.

The first Napoleon, as well as the next thirty-five "modified" weapons, were made with handles. One of these early pieces (Fig. I-20) has been preserved at Fort Wadsworth on Staten Island, New York, but the federal weapon usually seen today is the "modified" model with handles omitted (Fig. I-21) which was standard in United States service. Muzzle swell is often said to differentiate these "Northern Napoleons" from their Southern contemporaries. However, although the best-known Confederate variety (Fig. I-22) has a straight muzzle, the South also made at least two bronze types with muzzle swell, one with muzzle band, and designed, but may not have produced, a type with both muzzle swell and handles. This abundance of models depreciates the muzzle swell identification rule's value and makes a check of measurements and marks mandatory for positive determination.

The Confederates also used many captured weapons as evidenced by the line of guns taken by Union troops 25 November 1863 at the Battle of Chattanooga (Fig. I-23). Those as far as the soldier, in the center of the picture, are straight muzzle and presumably Confederate, while those beyond have a noticeable swell and could be Southern models, or, more likely, captured Yankee pieces.

A very few standard Napoleons were experimentally rifled on the James plan in the North and, following the reasoning applied to the rifled 6-pounders, probably should be called "rifled Napoleons" in preference to the often used, and misleading, "24-pounder James." On the other hand, a limited number of 3-inch rifles which have a general resemblance to the 12-pounder and are sometimes called "rifled Napoleons" are probably better described as "experimental 3-inch Rifles" and are so designated in Chapter IX. Consequently, with exception of the few experimentally rifled standard weapons, the Napoleon may be considered a smoothbore and without equivocation, a favorite of both sides.

The U.S. piece weighed a bit more than 1,200 pounds yet could burn a 2.5-pound charge of powder for solid shot or case, the same charge used in the Model 1841 "heavy" 12-pounder which weighed roughly 1,750 pounds. With such a charge, the Napoleon was deadly in the relatively wooded country in which the Civil War was fought and where field engagements beyond the weapon's 1,680-yard range were few. It could handle shot, shell, and spherical case with equal facility and loaded with canister against personnel at a quarter mile, it was downright vicious.

Moreover, the Napoleon was an extremely safe

FIGURE: I-20 LOCATION: Fort Wadsworth Staten Island, N.Y. IDENTIFICATION: Gun, Field, 12-Pounder, Model 1857 (Modified), Bronze. BORE: Diameter — 4.62 Smoothbore. Bore plugged, length, muzzle face to vent — 62.5. LENGTH O/A: 72. TRUNNIONS: Diameter — 4.2. Length — 3.25. MARKINGS: Muzzle Face — G.T.B., 18. Left Trunnion — 1861. Right Trunnion — Ames Co., Founder, Chicopee, Mass. Tube — U.S. REMARKS: The first few (estimated 36) "modified" Napoleons were cast with handles over the center of gravity. (Note illustrated piece is No. 18). COMMON NAME: Napoleon With Handles.

FIGURE: I-21 LOCATION: Fort Moultrie, S.C. IDENTIFICATION: Gun, Field, 12-Pounder, Model 1857 (Modified), Bronze. BORE: Diameter — 4.62. Smoothbore. Length — 62.5v. LENGTH O/A: 72.5. TRUNNIONS: Diameter — 4.2 Length — 3.1. MARKINGS: Muzzle Face — No. 273, HNH & Co., 1231 Lbs. 1863, T.J.R. Tube — U.S. REMARKS: This is type U.S. "Light 12-Pounder" or "Napoleon" usually seen. COMMON NAME: Napoleon. Or: Light 12-Pounder. Or: 12-Pounder, Model 1857.

FIGURE: I-22 LOCATION: Warsaw, N.Y. IDENTIFICATION: Gun, Field, 12-Pounder, Bronze, Confederate. BORE: Diameter — 4.62. Smoothbore. LENGTH O/A: — 72. TRUNNIONS: Diameter 4.2. MARKINGS: Muzzle Face — No. 29, F.C.H., C.S. Arsenal, Columbus, Ga., 1216. Tube — C.S. REMARKS: Usual type "Confederate Napoleon." COMMON NAME: Confederate Napoleon.

FIGURE: I-23 IDENTIFICATION: Weapons captured by United States forces at the Battle of Chattanooga 23 Nov. 1863. Straight muzzle Confederate Napoleons to the point where the soldier is standing. The remainder probably are recaptured federal weapons.

piece in a day when many weapons had a disconcerting tendency to explode in the faces of their cannoneers. Its record led Brigadier General George D. Ramsay, federal Chief of Ordnance to write 4 July 1864: "No instance has occurred during the war . . . of the 12-pounder bronze gun (the Napoleon) having worn out or of its bursting . . . ."[18]

While the Napoleon, as General Ramsay stated, may be properly called a bronze gun, here again we run into exceptions. As the war progressed, the Confederacy became exceedingly hard pressed for the main ingredients of bronze, copper and tin. In fact, after the battles in the vicinity of Chattanooga near the end of 1863 and the resultant loss of Tennessee copper mines began to pinch, copper liquor stills of North Carolina were literally pressed into duty as caps for smallarms.[19] Consequently, since copper for a 1,200-pound gun was a heavy drain on supplies, the Confederacy turned to another material—iron.

The resulting weapon (Fig. I-24) was turned out by the Tredegar Foundry at Richmond and was termed an "Iron Napoleon" in foundry records. Bore length is the same as the bronze gun, but the piece, due to material and the 2-inch thick reinforcing band, is considerably heavier. The illustrated weapon is one of two fine specimens at Wilmington, Delaware. It was made at Tredegar and, although paint obscures the date, probably after 1 January 1864 when the foundry stopped casting bronze cannon. Another of these rare guns is in the Petersburg National Military Park collection.

The iron Napoleon seems to have been quite successful for we find a letter[20] of Confederate Ordnance Chief, Brigadier General Josiah Gorgas, dated 13 October 1864, which states: "From deficiency in the supply of copper, the manufacture of bronze field pieces is suspended and an iron gun, tightly banded, substituted for the 12-pdr. Napoleon, which gives entire satisfaction . . . ." In addition, the 28 April 1865 report[21] of materiel captured at Tredegar Foundry lists: ". . . three small guns, supposed to be

FIGURE: I-24 LOCATION: Wilmington, Del. IDENTIFICATION: Gun, Field, 12-Pounder, Iron, Confederate. BORE: Diameter — 4.62. Smoothbore. Length — 63.6. LENGTH O/A: 72. TRUNNIONS: Diameter — 4.2. Length — 3.25. MARKINGS: Right Trunnion — J.R.A., T.F. REMARKS: Banded "Iron Napoleon" replaced the bronze model in the copper-starved Confederacy in 1864. Left trunnion, covered by heavy coats of paint, probably carries 1864 date. COMMON NAME: Iron Napoleon.

light 12-pounders cast and one cast and bored. They are cast iron smoothbore with wrought iron reinforce. Made to fit (the) 12-pdr. carriage."

Space prohibits further discussion of the Napoleons, but the reader interested in these fascinating weapons is advised to obtain Dr. Hazlett's articles. His work, particularly in the field of Confederate Napoleons, is the product of exceptionally fine research and must be required reading for any comprehensive study of the subject.

Confederate leaders in the Charleston area pressed into service a few guns which may have set some sort of record for age. One in particular (Fig. I-25) was an antique when the war started. This British 12-pounder siege piece, now in private hands at Charleston,[22] bears the "G.R." (Georgius Rex) and crown in the form used by George II (1727–1760). Although far from identical, molding and shape have a marked resemblance to the stubbier weapon (Fig. I-26) copied from a 1757 publication.[23]

The drawing, caliber unspecified, apparently was intended to represent brass and iron guns in general rather than a specific piece. However, measurements for an iron 12-pounder listed elsewhere in the same text conform closely to those of the Charleston cannon and since such weapons in 1757 were termed "Old Battering Pieces," the South Carolina specimen may date from the early years of Charles' reign rather than the upper limit.

Two other English 12-pounders which also saw war duty and have survived the ravages of time and scrap drives are now displayed at the Old Powder Magazine in Charleston. These guns differ from the other in elimination of considerable molding and are later models, which bear the device of George III (1760–1820).

One (Fig. I-27) has been banded and rifled with very shallow lands and grooves which due to rust and scaling defy accurate count. The bore of the other is plugged, but since it is not banded, chances

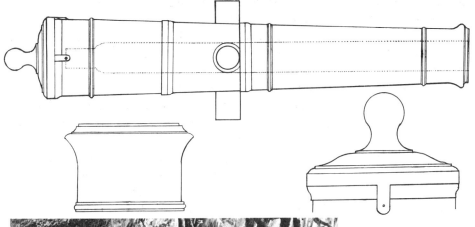

FIGURE: I-26 IDENTIFICATION: Gun, English. SOURCE: Muller, *A Treatise of Artillery,* 1757. Plate 1. REMARKS: Caliber not specified. Piece seems designed to represent the type weapon of an era rather than a specific piece and is reproduced here to illustrate the form of molding. See Fig. I-25.

FIGURE: I-25 LOCATION: (Privately owned), Charleston, S.C. IDENTIFICATION: Gun, Siege & Garrison, 12-Pounder, English, Iron. BORE: Diameter — 4.62 (approximate measurement due to rust). LENGTH O/A: — 117.5. TRUNNIONS: Diameter — 4.5. Length — 4.5. MARKINGS: Tube (above trunnions) — Monogram of George II. Small "2" at left of it, and farther to rear, the Broad Arrow. Breech — Apparently "9-1-5", but more likely in a piece this size, "29-1-5" (3,281 lbs). REMARKS: Weapon probably dates from early part of reign of George II (1727–1760). COMMON NAME: Old English 12-Pounder.

FIGURE: I-27 LOCATION: Powder Magazine, Charleston, S.C. IDENTIFICATION: Gun, Navy, 12-Pounder, English, Iron. BORE: Diameter — 4.75 (originally probably about 4.62), Rifling — Light lands and grooves, too rusted to count. LENGTH O/A: 115 (includes estimated length of broken cascabel). TRUNNIONS: Diameter — 4.75. (both broken flush with the tube). MARKINGS: Tube over trunnions — Monogram of George III. REMARKS: Banded and rifled by Confederates.

are the weapon was left a smoothbore. Breeching loops on both would indicate they were Navy pieces. In addition to the king's monogram, the British Broad Arrow, denoting government property (see Appendix B), is stamped on both smoothbores and probably was on the rifle, but now covered by the band.

The guns, though old, were apparently highly regarded by the Confederates for the Official Records[24] mention an "Old English 12-Pounder" being sent to the Arsenal in Charleston to be banded (and obviously rifled). In addition, there is a letter from Colonel A. J. Gonzales, chief of artillery in the Charleston Department, to General Gorgas 17 October 1863, which states:[25] "The old 18-pounder mentioned by Maj. [John G.] Barnwell, being old is rather in its favor. These old guns are very good guns notwithstanding, if sound. The rifled 12-pounder gun he mentions at Royals [near Charleston] is very old, but reported a very good gun. It is one of those long 12-pounder English siege guns recommended by me to the commanding general [P.G.T. Beauregard] to be banded, which was then approved. I do not know what connection the 24-pounders mentioned by Maj. Barnwell as being in the same work as this 12-pounder at Royals have with the matter of rifling and banding as they are not recommended by the board for either. . . ."

Every now and then a particular weapon catches the public fancy. World War I had its "Big Bertha" employed against Belgian fortifications in 1914. "The Anzio Express" played a limited role in World War II. And "Excalibur" seems to have done its bit for King Arthur. Certainly the Civil War was no exception and the name "Whistling Dick" has come down to us linked to the siege of Vicksburg in 1863 where apparently the peculiar sound of its projectiles in flight made an unforgettable impression.

Unlike most "named" guns, "Whistling Dick" was known by the same title on both sides of the line although it is not entirely certain that both always referred to the same weapon. In fact, judging from the number of references in federal records, the name may have been applied to several weapons tossing shot and shell at the attackers. For purposes of identification, Confederate sources may be somewhat more accurate—after all, they owned the piece. Consequently, believing the owners undoubtedly knew what they were shooting, the author has relied primarily on Southern records, specifically reports of Major Samuel H. Lockett, C.S. Engineers, and Colonel Edward Higgins, C.S. Artillery, commander of the River Batteries.

In a report[26] written after the fall of the city, Major Lockett said that on 29 May 1863 ". . . a new battery was made in rear of the line, left of Hall's Ferry Road; the new battery in rear of General Lee improved, and 'Whistling Dick' (an 18-pounder rifled piece) put in position. . . ." The parentheses are the major's.

Colonel Higgins, in a similar report,[27] listed weapons in batteries along the three miles of river front, some thirty-one pieces, including one 18-pounder rifle. The colonel also recalled the repulse of four ironclads and one wooden gunboat after an hour and a half engagement 22 May[28] in which he claimed two of the ironclads were severely damaged and ". . . our casualties were only two wounded during the fight; one 10-inch columbiad and the 18-pounder rifled gun temporarily disabled. . . ." Apparently the damage was repaired for 28 May[29] ". . . the 18-pounder rifled gun was sent to the rear lines. . . ."

Specific mention of "Whistling Dick" as an 18-pounder rifle, the listing of only one such piece in the River Batteries, and the use of the article "the" on two other occasions, make this identification of the weapon plausible. This also is the conclusion reached by Edwin C. Bearss, historian with the National Park Service. His article in the *Journal of Mississippi History*[30] goes extensively into fact and fiction regarding the weapon and should be read by anyone wishing more information than it is possible to give here. Bearss also proved that a 7.5-inch gun at West Point, which bore the identification "Whistling Dick" was, in reality, another famous "named" gun, the "Widow Blakely" (q.v.). This weapon, properly titled, is now on display at Vicksburg where it gained its name.

"Whistling Dick" was rifled, so say the reports and Mr. Bearss quotes a post-war newspaper story which corroborates this. It records a statement by a lieutenant of the battery in which the gun was said to have been located, saying in part: ". . . the real 'Whistling Dick'. . . was an eighteen-pounder, old fashioned smoothbore, which had been rifled and reinforced by a jacket at the breech."

Although probably correct, the statement was made from memory some thirty-seven years after the fact and thus may be subject to error. That the piece was rifled is mentioned so often that it may be taken as fact. Banding, however, like the model, must remain tentative pending more evidence, or, better still, discovery of the actual weapon. Until then, evidence points to "Whistling Dick" being a banded and rifled 18-pounder, iron siege (garrison might be more technically apt in this case since it was in a defensive position) gun, probably Model 1839 which remained standard from that date until 1860. If the piece had been an older model, mention of it would have been probable.

From the point of view of the romanticist, this identification has certain drawbacks; it is irreconcilable with many so-called "facts" concerning the weapon which have been perpetuated through the years.

Two of these Mr. Bearss has effectively laid to rest. One, erroneous identification of the "Widow Blakely" as "Whistling Dick" has been mentioned. The other was identification in a book by Lamar Fontaine[31] of "Whistling Dick" as an 8-inch Whitworth. Mr. Bearss' article takes Fontaine's statement apart bit by bit. It will suffice here to mention only that no such rifle existed in the Vicksburg defenses.

The third "fact" the author believes erroneous is a photograph (Fig. I-28) which, in this and a similar view showing a soldier sighting the same piece, has

appeared in numerous publications since the Civil War, particularly during the recent Centennial. Cutlines proclaim the piece "Whistling Dick" and often an "18-pounder rifle," identifications subject to doubt on both counts. The gun appears to be a Navy 32-pounder, Model 1845-47. However, the muzzle has been cut back and the weapon banded, an alteration which makes determination of the specific weight of the piece doubtful.

The base of the breech is the main giveaway. All iron siege and garrison weapons—12-, 18-, and 24-pounders—have an easily identifiable base of the breech. It slants in an almost straight line from the base ring to the neck of the cascabel knob. (Figs. I-29 and I-18). The base of the breech of the 32-pounders, both Army and Navy, is rounded. Moreover, to judge from contemporary publications, the Navy made no 18-pounders in this model and any such calibers used would have been Army weapons with knob-type cascabel, or older Navy pieces of

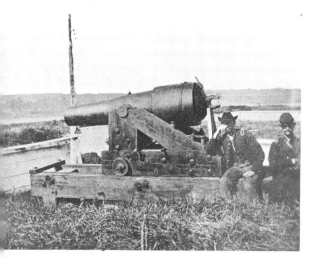

FIGURE: I-28 IDENTIFICATION: Civil War photograph of weapon erroneously identified as Vicksburg's celebrated "Whistling Dick."

FIGURE: I-29 IDENTIFICATION: (Top) Gun, Siege & Garrison, 24-Pounder, Model 1839, Iron. (Bottom) Gun, Siege & Garrison, 18-Pounder, Model 1839, Iron. SOURCE: Mordecai, 1849. COMMON NAME: 24-Pounder, Model 1839. 18-Pounder.

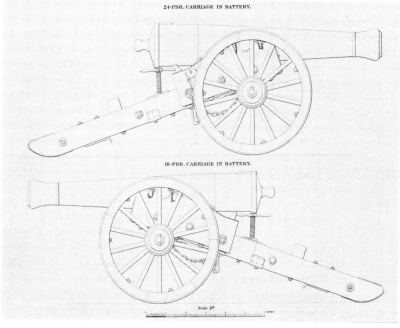

31

totally different general appearance. Consequently, if, as previously established, "Whistling Dick" was an 18-pounder and if the gun in the photograph clearly isn't an 18-pounder, then it follows that the photograph is something other than "Whistling Dick."

A possible explanation lies in the 32-pounder (Fig. I-30). This gun, according to the superintendent of Vicksburg National Military Park,[32] was placed in the Water Battery at the park about 1962 after being in the nearby cemetery since 1874. Documentation of its use during the siege has not been established although, since it was in Vicksburg only eleven years later, this seems a reasonable assumption.

The author makes no pretence at certifying the two are the same gun. However, a close inspection of both tubes will show that if we take out the removable cascabel block and pin of the gun at Vicksburg today and remove the vent cover and sights from the contemporary photograph, the two weapons appear identical. Measurements also tend to bear out this supposition although identification based on such evidence remains speculative due to lack of exact scale of the Civil War picture.

Although a few 18-pounder siege guns, Model 1839, were used during the war, particularly by the Confederates, the weapon was pretty well outmoded by this time and existing specimens are rare. In fact, despite diligent search, the only such piece found by the author is at West Point (Fig. I-31).

Twenty-four-pounders (5.82-inch) on the other hand, were far more prevalent in 1861 and still are fairly common. At the start of the war, they were pressed into service and when rifled in the James manner threw a projectile weighing in the neighborhood of 48 pounds. A single rifled 24 was in General Gillmore's siege batteries for the reduction of Fort Pulaski[33] and apparently did creditable work lobbing shell and shot against the walls. A James 5.82-inch shell, which was excavated at Pulaski and likely was intended for this weapon, is illustrated in Chapter XIII. Other 24s were in New England forts and a number were no doubt rifled as an expedient pending manufacture of larger cannon. However, artillerymen of both sides were under few illusions as to their worth in comparison to more modern weapons, and the old guns, both rifled and smoothbore, generally wound up in secondary positions.

Standard weapon of the caliber is the 24-pounder, iron siege and garrison gun, Model 1839, although the illustrated piece (Fig. I-32) was cast in 1851 by Tredegar Foundry. Now located at Waycross, Georgia, it was placed during the war on

FIGURE: I-30 LOCATION: Vicksburg, Miss. IDENTIFICATION: Gun, Navy, 32-Pounder, Iron (Model and weight undetermined). BORE: Diameter — 6.4. Rifling — 7 x 7, Brooke type. LENGTH O/A: 102 (See Remarks). TRUNNIONS: Diameter — 6.4. Length — 6. MARKINGS: Left Trunnion — P. J.S.C. Right Trunnion — 32, 1849. REMARKS: Banded and rifled by the Confederates. Several inches of the muzzle have been removed so length overall today is not original.

FIGURE: I-31 LOCATION: West Point, N.Y. IDENTIFICATION: Gun, Siege & Garrison, 18-Pounder, Model 1839, Iron. BORE: Diameter — 5.3. Smoothbore. Length — 109. LENGTH O/A: 124. TRUNNIONS: Diameter — 5.3. Length — 4.75. MARKINGS: Left Trunnion — 1841. Right Trunnion — W.P.F. Tube — U.S. Breech — 4,889 lbs. COMMON NAME: 18-Pounder.

the bank of the Altamaha River to defend a drawbridge which lay along Sherman's route to the sea, but was taken and spiked by the invaders. Left in position, it was believed dangerous and ignored for years. Finally, in 1887, an enterprising railroad official had the weapon loaded on a wreck train and brought to Waycross[34] where it is now mounted in front of a Confederate monument. A similar, 1851 Tredegar gun is in private hands[35] near Charleston (Fig.

I-33). Both weapons are stamped on the tube "S.C." and were part of an order for the State of South Carolina.

It is ironic that although both are in an excellent state of preservation today, their worth was very lightly regarded during the war. A 4 November 1863 report[36] by Major John G. Barnwell, ordnance inspector, to his district chief at Charleston states: ". . . the 24-pounders of 1828, and especially those of 1848 and 1851 marked S.C., are not made of the best iron and most of them are defective in the bore . . ."

Despite the major's belief, the gun in Figure I-33 has been banded and rifled in typical "Brooke" fashion of 7 lands and grooves. This and a companion piece were mounted in a two-gun battery on the Ashepoo River to prevent access of federal gunboats to the nearby Charleston and Savannah Railroad which served as a lifeline between those two cities. The other gun (Fig. I-34), also a 24-pounder, is by fortunate coincidence dated 1828 and presumably is another type 24-pounder disliked by Major Barnwell. This piece, left as a smoothbore, was made by Columbia Foundry for the federal government, identified by the U.S. on the tube. Both guns have been spiked and the rifle is also plugged with a number of solid shot as in Figure XIII-54 which was found in position with the piece.

Although the major's terminology would lead one to accept his dates as model numbers, the author feels he referred purely to year of manufacture and the 1828 gun is actually a Model 1819, cast in 1828,

FIGURE: I-33 LOCATION: Charleston, S.C. (Privately owned) IDENTIFICATION: Gun, Siege & Garrison, 24-Pounder, Model 1839, Iron, Banded and Rifled. BORE: Diameter — 5.82. Rifling — 7 x 7, Brooke Type. Length — 107 (estimated, see Remarks). LENGTH O/A: 123. TRUNNIONS: Diameter — 5.75. Length — 5. MARKINGS: Left Trunnion — 1851. Right Trunnion — T.F. Tube — S.C. REMARKS: Bore is plugged with projectiles similar to that in Fig. XIII-54. Piece was banded and rifled by Confederates. COMMON NAME: 24-Pounder, Model 1839, Banded and Rifled.

FIGURE: I-34 LOCATION: Charleston, S.C. (privately owned) IDENTIFICATION: Gun, Seacoast, 24-Pounder, Model 1819, Iron. BORE: Diameter — 5.82. Smoothbore. Length — 108. LENGTH O/A: 124. TRUNNIONS: Diameter — 5.82. Length — 5. MARKINGS: Left Trunnion — I.M., C.F. Right Trunnion — 1828. Tube — U.S. COMMON NAME: 24-Pounder, Model 1819.

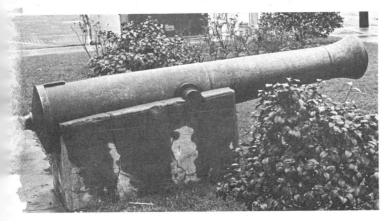

FIGURE: I-32 LOCATION: Waycross, Ga. IDENTIFICATION: Gun, Siege & Garrison, 24-Pounder, Model 1839, Iron. BORE: Diameter — 5.82. Smoothbore. Length — 108. LENGTH O/A — 123.5. TRUNNIONS: Diameter — 5.82. Length — 5. MARKINGS: Left Trunnion — 1851. Right Trunnion — T.F. Tube — S.C. (South Carolina). COMMON NAME: 24-Pounder, Model 1839.

and the 1848 and 1851 guns are Model 1839, cast in those years. A similar weapon to the 1828 piece is in the collection of the U.S. Army Artillery and Missile Center Museum, Fort Sill, Oklahoma. This gun (Fig. I-35) also was made by Columbia Foundry in 1828. Another Model 1819 at West Point is dated 1826 and was rifled, but not banded, during the war.

Differences between the Models 1839 and 1819 are relatively minor.[37] With exception of an inch and a half thicker base ring for the 1839, measurements are less than a quarter inch apart and may be overlooked for all practical purposes. Weights also are close, 5,500 pounds for the Model 1819 and a hundred more for the other. Appearance, however, is different. The 1819 has no lock piece or chase ring and the muzzle molding consists of a fillet only. The muzzle swell is shorter and sharper in the 1819.

A particularly interesting Navy 24-pounder (Fig. I-36) is mounted at Fort Pulaski. The bore measures roughly 6.5 inches at the muzzle face—within range, give or take a bit of rust, of 6.4-inch, 32-pounder caliber. However, there is a decided taper to the bore and within 6 inches or so it narrows to the 5.82-inch, 24-pounder size. This straight muzzle with flare is illustrated in Lieutenant Simpson's book as a type in use prior to 1845. The author has run across two other weapons of this general form, a 32-pounder at Fort Fisher, North Carolina and an 8-inch shellgun at West Point. The Fort Fisher gun is dated 1842. The trunnion which apparently held the date of the West Point piece (Chapter V) has been destroyed, but through identification of the inspector's initials found on the weapon, it probably is about the same, perhaps a year earlier. However, in view of the jagged metal on the base of the breech and cascabel knob of the Pulaski gun, evidence of a former breeching loop, the author would surmise this weapon predates the other two and likely was made during the 1830s.

The 24-pounder, although listed in the Ordnance Manual of 1861 as a siege and garrison piece, was until 1850 specified also for seacoast defense and was the heaviest in that category between 1816 and 1829 when the 32-pounder was reintroduced into the land service. (The 32-pounder had been developed before the turn of the century and the 42-pounder added in 1801. However, the contingency for use of heavy guns in the forts was considered so remote that it was not provided for in the systems of 1816 and 1821).[38]

The same 24-pounder apparently was used in both seacoast and siege and garrison service for it is listed under both categories in 1818 as "heavy 24-pounder guns," in the Army Regulations of 1835 as "24-pounder cannon," and in 1839 as "24-pounder guns." The Ordnance Manual of 1841 carries the 1819 as "seacoast" and the new model in a single column as "Seacoast (and) Siege and Garrison."

In 1850, the 24-pounder, although still listed under siege and garrison weapons, is missing from the seacoast category. However, changes on paper and physical changes were often far apart and although stripped from seacoast duty officially, 24-pounders remained in many of the forts and were so listed in ordnance inventories at the start of the war. Many of these weapons were earmarked for

FIGURE: I-35 LOCATION: Fort Sill, Okla. IDENTIFICATION: Gun, Seacoast, 24-Pounder, Model 1819, Iron. BORE: Diameter — 5.82. Smoothbore. Length — 108. LENGTH O/A: 123.25. TRUNNIONS: Diameter — 5.82. Length — 5. MARKINGS: Muzzle Face — J.B., No. 43. Left Trunnion — 1828. Right Trunnion —I.M., C.F. Tube — U.S. COMMON NAME: 24-Pounder, Model 1819.

FIGURE: I-36 LOCATION: Fort Pulaski, Ga. IDENTIFICATION: Gun, Navy, 24-Pounder, Iron. BORE: Diameter — 5.82, flared to 6.4 at muzzle face, Smoothbore. Length — 75v. LENGTH O/A: 91.5. TRUNNIONS: Diameter — 5.82. Length — 5.6. MARKINGS: Tube — Pf. No. 56, 3132, I.C., B.F. REMARKS: Piece probably was made in the 1830s.

rifling and continued on duty pending replacement by heavier pieces.

Although not reintroduced in the land service until 1829, 32-pounders had continued part of the Navy's arsenal, and one of these weapons, dated 1821 (Fig. I-37), is today in Fort Pike State Park near New Orleans.

A wartime photograph (Fig. I-38) depicts a similar piece mounted aboard the *Freeborn* with the crew demonstrating how their commander, James H. Ward, was killed while pointing the gun. Records show the vessel, officially *U.S.S. Thomas Freeborn*, was purchased by the Navy Department in May, 1861 for $32,500. She was a wood, sidewheel steamer of 269 tons, length 143′ 4″ and beam 25′ 6″. Although her battery was subsequently changed, at the time Ward was killed she mounted a 32-pounder of 60 cwt. (the piece shown) and a 32 of 27 cwt.[39]

Commander Ward, flotilla commander on the Potomac as well as skipper of the *Freeborn*, decided to emplace a gun at Mathias Point. He led a party of men ashore in the morning of 27 June 1861, threw out skirmishers, and drove in the Confederate pickets.[40] However, within a short time he was notified of the approach of several hundred Southerners and told his men to take to the boats and lie off shore while he went aboard the *Freeborn* and shot up the woods a bit with her guns. This action seems to have dispersed the Confederates for the men in the boats were soon ordered back to the beach where they worked all day building the battery until recalled about 5 P.M. During the retreat they received heavy fire which proved especially annoying since anticipated covering fire from the *Freeborn* failed to materialize. Ward, who had remained aboard during the day, apparently was trying to furnish the fire for about 6 P.M. he ". . . was struck by a musket ball while sighting his forward gun. He died about an hour later. . . ."

The Fort Pike gun is marked on the tube near the breech "No. 210, 60-12." The first combination is the number of the piece and the latter two figures the weight in hundredweight, generally abbreviated "cwt." and pounds. The hundredweight used for cannon at this period was 112 pounds, hence the weight of the piece is 60 x 112 = 6,720 pounds plus 12 pounds, or 6,732 total. In most cases another number

will be found inserted between hundredweight and pounds, i.e., 60-3-12. The center number represents quarters (qrs.) of a hundredweight or 28 pounds. The total weight in this hypothetical case would be 6,816 lbs. Obviously, the center number should never exceed 3, nor the final number 27.

Since 1821 is the earliest available date for this type 32-pounder, as well as a companion 42 which will be discussed later in the chapter, it has been ascribed tentatively as a model year for convenience of reference. The reader is warned, however, that both calibers had long been part of naval armament and the model may well pre-date 1821.

This type 32 may be easily differentiated from the next by molding near the vent and on the chase. Both are absent from the model in Figure I-39, one of a pair mounted at Fort Moultrie. They are dated 1830 and are the earliest of this pattern found thus far. However, this, the author believes, is the Model 1829 referred to previously. The weapons have a breeching loop for shipboard use, but contemporary photographs show they were used in land fortifications and many bear marks of Army inspectors. Consequently, it is probable that, like the larger caliber Parrott rifles of later years, they were designed to be

FIGURE: I-38 IDENTIFICATION: Gun, Navy, 32-Pounder, Model 1821 (tentative), Iron. SOURCE: *Photographic History of the Civil War*, edited by Miller, 1911. Vol. 6. Cutline states crew of the Freeborn demonstrate how Cmdr. James H. Ward was killed. REMARKS: This is probably one of the few photographs of the "Novelty Carriage" developed by Cmdr. Ward prior to the war. The carriage (Fig. X-56) was not adopted into general service. It consisted of a standard 4-Truck Navy Broadside Carriage modified to utilize a slide.

FIGURE: I-37 LOCATION: Fort Pike, La. IDENTIFICATION: Gun, Navy, 32-Pounder, Model 1821 (tentative), Iron. BORE: Diameter — 6.4. Smoothbore. LENGTH O/A: 121.5. TRUNNIONS: Diameter — 6.25. Length 6.5. MARKINGS: Left Trunnion — 32. Right Trunnion — 1821. Tube — Pf. No. 210, 60–12. Breech — C.F., I.M., G.1. REMARKS: Although cast for the Navy, these weapons were later used in the land service. COMMON NAME: 32-Pounder, Model 1821.

FIGURE: I-39 LOCATION: Fort Moultrie, S.C. IDENTIFICATION: Gun, Seacoast, 32-Pounder, Model 1829, Iron. BORE: Diameter — 6.4, flared about last half-inch to 7, Smoothbore, Length — 107.5. LENGTH O/A: 125. TRUNNIONS: Diameter — 6.4. Length 6. MARKINGS: Muzzle Face — J.B., No. 163. Left Trunnion — I.C., B.F. Right Trunnion — 1830. Tube — U.S. REMARKS: Also used by Navy. COMMON NAME: 32-Pounder, Model 1829.

FIGURE: I-40 IDENTIFICATION: Gun, Seacoast, 32-Pounder, Model 1829, Iron. REMARKS: 32-Pounders in Fort Totten, part of the Washington defenses, mounted on wood, front pintle, barbette carriages. With the aid of a magnifying glass, the initials "C.F." can be discerned on the trunnion face of the near piece. COMMON NAME: 32-Pounder, Model 1829.

used interchangeably between Army and Navy. A Civil War photograph (Fig. I-40) shows several of these guns in Fort Totten, Washington, mounted on wood, front pintle, barbette carriages.

Both services shifted to their own models in the 1840s. At the start of the decade, the Army came out with a model that a year later, with changes so slight as to be inconsequential, became the Model 1841 (Fig. I-41) which remained a standard seacoast weapon[41] until the war when it was used extensively by both sides in smoothbore and rifled form. The illustrated gun at St. Augustine, Florida, was cast in 1846 and rifled during the war.

The Navy used the 32-pounder (Figs. I-42 and I-43), a Fort Fisher piece mentioned previously in the section on 24-pounders. The gun is dated 1842 and was a type produced between 1841 and 1845. It is easily recognized by the straight muzzle and unusual cascabel.

During 1845-47, the Navy adopted a series of 32-pounders of similar design, but varying weights. They were also used on land during the war and will be found in original smoothbore condition as well as rifled, banded or not. All are of similar appearance, but dimensions vary considerably.

This is not only true for the six weight categories, but also occurs within several of the classes, for during the years the 27 cwt. and 42 cwt. were lengthened approximately an inch and a half and the 42 later may have been cut back about 3 inches. The 33 cwt., which is carried in certain texts as a 32 cwt., seems to have been shortened .06 inch, but this is so negligible an amount one wonders if the change didn't occur in the tables rather than the metal.

FIGURE: **I-41** Location: St. Augustine, Fla. Identification: Gun, Seacoast, 32-Pounder, Model 1841, Iron. Bore: Diameter — 6.4. Rifling — 9 x 9, straight. Length — 107.5v. Length O/A: 126.5. Trunnions: Diameter — 6.4. Length — 6. Markings: Muzzle Face — 5, A.M. Left Trunnion — 1846. Right Trunnion — J.R.A., T.F. Tube — U.S. Breech — 7215. Remarks: Original smoothbore rifled by Confederates. Common Name: 32-Pounder, Model 1841.

FIGURE: **I-44** Location: Vicksburg, Miss. Identification: Gun, Navy, 32-Pounder, 42 cwt. Model 1845, Iron. Bore: Diameter — 6.4. Smoothbore. Length — 90.75. Length O/A: 106.4. Trunnions: Diameter — 6.4. Length — 5.5. Markings: Left Trunnion — P., S.B. Right Trunnion — 32, 1845. Base Ring — W.P.F.A., No. 276, 42-2-21 (4,781 lbs.). Common Name: 32-Pounder of 42 cwt.

FIGURE: **I-42** Location: Fort Fisher, N.C. Identification: Gun, Navy, 32-Pounder, Model 1841, Iron. Bore: Diameter — 6.4. Smoothbore. Length — 90.75v. Length O/A: 106. Trunnions: Diameter — 6.4. Length — 5.5. Marking: Left Trunnion — 32, A.S.W. Right Trunnion — P., 1842. Base of Breech — P.F. No. 59. Remarks: When photographed, weapon was undergoing treatment at the Fort Fisher Preservation Laboratory. The marking on the base of the breech, P.F., may have been originally "W.P.F." Common Name: 32-Pounder, Navy, Model 1841.

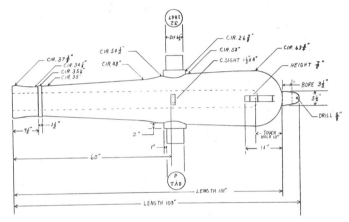

FIGURE: **I-45** Identification: Gun, Navy, 32-Pounder, 42 cwt. Model 1847, Iron. Remarks: Drawing of weapon undergoing preservation at Fort Fisher, N.C. Common Name: 32-Pounder of 42 cwt.

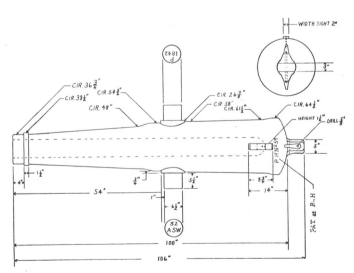

FIGURE: **I-43** Identification: Gun, Navy, 32-Pounder, Model 1841, Iron. Remarks: Drawing of weapon in Fig. I-42 at Fort Fisher Preservation Laboratory. The author feels the base ring marks are P.F. rather than as indicated. However, they are indistinct and either could be correct. Common Name: 32-Pounder, Navy, Model 1841.

Two types of 42 cwt. 32-pounders exist and, although hundreds of miles apart, are available for comparison. The Model 1845 (Fig. I-44) is one of half a dozen of this pattern salvaged from the Union gunboat *Cairo* at Vicksburg in an operation best described in Bearss' book *Hardluck Ironclad*. Measurements vary slightly, but those of the illustrated piece seem about standard at 106.38 inches overall and 90.75 inches in the bore. The base ring is quite pronounced. The Model 1847 (Fig. I-45) at Fort Fisher measures 108 inches overall with a 92-inch bore (91 to vent). The breech is more rounded with less pronounced base ring. The cascabel tapers vertically and muzzle molding is omitted. The 1861 Ordnance Manual (Army)[42] lists the 42 cwt. (presumably the latest model) at 105 inches overall and 90.5 inches bore. Normally this would indicate a third

37

model, but since an 1866 Navy text refers to "old" and "new" patterns of this weight, thus implying only two types, the author feels the 1847 may have been changed without calling it a new model.

Assuming the Fort Fisher gun was deemed too long, the alteration could have been accomplished by casting new weapons in the 1847 mold, but 3 inches shorter from the muzzle, then reaming the bore 1.5 inches deeper to conform to the specifications listed in 1861. This would have changed neither the general appearance nor ballistic qualities of the piece materially, and the weapon many have continued to carry the 1847 model designation, but with new dimensions. Fortunately, despite alterations in the 27 and 42 cwt., there is sufficient length variation to distinguish one weight category from another. In addition, many, but by no means all, are marked with the weight.

Trunnions of the 27 cwt. are 5.82 inches in diameter compared to 6.4 for all the others. This piece also seems to be the sole exception to the definition of a gun. The 27 cwt. is chambered like certain 8-inch shellguns, yet is listed in the gun category of all contemporary ordnance works, Army and Navy, that the author has examined. Even Simpson,[43] who mentions the chamber, calls it a gun, stating: "All shellguns in the U.S. Navy are cham-bered, also howitzers and mortars. The only solid shot gun in the Navy which is chambered is the 32-pounder of 27 cwt. This gun as well as the shellguns of 8-inch caliber, have the chambers cylindrical and they are united with the large cylinder by a conical surface called the slope. . . ."

Specifications of the various guns are given in the appendix tables. The 27 and 33 cwt. pieces (Fig. I-46) are in the Washington Navy Yard collection and the 51 cwt. (Fig. I-47) at Fort Fisher.

The 57 cwt. (Fig. I-48) is often referred to as a "Long 32-Pounder." The illustrated piece is in the Portsmouth Naval Shipyard Museum collection. A similar gun that has been rifled and banded (Fig. I-49) is mounted at Washington Navy Yard. The bore is plugged and the type rifling could not be discerned. Records at the Yard, however, state the weapon was banded and rifled by the Confederates which would make it probable that the Brooke form of 7 lands and grooves was used.

The three Fort Fisher 32-pounders (Figs. I-43, I-45, I-47) were originally aboard the *U.S.S. Peterhoff*, a blockade runner which had the misfortune to be picked up in February, 1863, by a federal warship. Armed and turned into a blockader, the 210-foot, 800-ton vessel[44] put out 28 February 1864 from Hampton Roads, Virginia, on her last voyage. She was

FIGURE: I-46 LOCATION: Washington Navy Yard, D.C. IDENTIFICATION: (Top) Gun, Navy, 32-Pounder, 27 cwt., Model 1846, Iron. BORE: Diameter — 6.4. Smoothbore. Length — 68.5v. LENGTH O/A: 76 to base of breech. TRUNNIONS: Diameter — 5.82. Length — 5. MARKING: Left Trunnion — P. Right Trunnion — 32. Breech — W.P.F.? (probably A), No. 122, 27-3-10 (3-118 lbs.). REMARKS: Only gun with a chamber. Trunnions probably hold additional information, unobtainable due to paint. Note small diameter trunnions in this model. COMMON NAME: 32-Pounder of 27 cwt.

IDENTIFICATION: (Bottom) Gun, Navy, 32-Pounder, 33 cwt., Model 1846, Iron. BORE: Diameter — 6.4 Smoothbore. Length — 75.8v. LENGTH O/A: 86.5 to base of breech. TRUNNIONS: Diameter — 6.4. Length — 5.5. MARKINGS: Left Trunnion — P., ?.S.?. Right Trunnion — 32, 1846. Tube — Anchor. Breech — F.P.F., 32-2-0 (3,640 lbs.). REMARKS: Undetermined initials on left trunnion obscured by paint. COMMON NAME: 32-Pounder of 33 cwt.

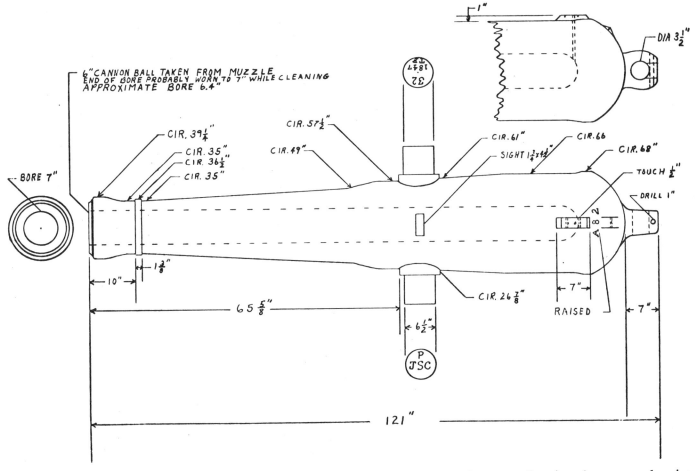

FIGURE: I-47 IDENTIFICATION: Gun, Navy, 32-Pounder, 51 cwt., Model 1846, Iron. REMARKS: Drawing of weapon undergoing preservation at Fort Fisher, N.C. COMMON NAME: 32-Pounder of 51 cwt.

FIGURE: I-48 LOCATION: Portsmouth Naval Shipyard Museum, Portmouth, Va. IDENTIFICATION: Gun, Navy, 32-Pounder, 57 cwt., Model 1846, Iron. BORE: Diameter — 6.4. Smoothbore. Length — 107v. LENGTH O/A: 124.5. TRUNNIONS: Diameter — 6.4. Length — 6. MARKINGS: Left Trunnion — P., J.S.C. Right Trunnion — 32, 1848. Tube — Anchor. Base Ring — T.F., No. 38, 57-2-18 (6,458 lbs.). COMMON NAME: 32-Pounder of 57 cwt. Or, Long 32-Pounder.

FIGURE: I-49 LOCATION: Washington Navy Yard, D.C. IDENTIFICATION: Gun, Navy, 32-Pounder, 57 cwt., Model 1846, Iron, Banded and (presumably) Rifled. BORE: Diameter — 6.4 Rifling — Undetermined, bore is concreted flush. Length — 107.5v. LENGTH O/A: 125.5. TRUNNIONS: Diameter — 6.4. Length — 6. MARKINGS: Muzzle Face — C. 42. Left Trunnion — P., G.W.S. Right Trunnion — 32, 1852. REMARKS: Probably rifled and banded by the Confederates. COMMON NAME: 32-Pounder of 57 cwt., Rifled and Banded.

rammed early in the morning of 6 March by another blockader, the *U.S.S. Monticello,* and sent to the bottom in some 4½ fathoms.[45]

The *Monticello,* 180-foot, wood, screw steamer of 655 tons[46] was headed south for Beaufort, South Carolina, to replenish her coal supply and entered within the inner line of blockade ships where she had no business to be before daylight. The commander of the *Peterhoff* was absolved of guilt and blame laid to the "inefficiency and carelessness" of the deck officer aboard the *Monticello.* All officers and crew of the *Peterhoff* were rescued and to prevent salvage by the Confederates, a party was sent the following day to the site not far off Fort Fisher. This group cut away spars and masts, carried off such rigging as was useful and spiked and threw over the side two of the vessel's weapons, a 30-pounder Parrott and a 12-pounder howitzer on the quarter deck. The main battery was about 5 feet under water and although immediate salvage was deemed feasible, the guns were left alone to remain submerged until a few years ago when they were dragged ashore and the lengthy process of preservation started at Fort Fisher.

A Civil War photograph of an 1845-47 32-pounder (Fig. I-50) shows the piece in Fort Moultrie. The weapon has been banded, presumably rifled, and has a trunnion band—affixed no doubt to place the gun back in service after breaking one of the original trunnions. The 32-pounder gun, although still in service, was obsolescent toward the end of the war and Charles Knap of the Fort Pitt Foundry[47] testified before a Senate committee in 1864 that the government was no longer ordering them.

However, 32-pounders will be found which are similar in many respects to the 1845-47 models, but bear dates of 1865-66 and, probably, 1864. This is the "new model 32-pounder of 4,500 pounds" designed by Admiral John A. Dahlgren. Since the piece has a chamber and is classified in Navy records as a shellgun, it is discussed in Chapter V on the Dahlgrens.

Twelve days before the start of hostilities, the Virginia Assembly in a joint resolution took action which, while probably legal, was certainly high-handed to say the least. Excitement in the commonwealth was at fever pitch when April arrived in 1861, for while the state deliberated its future course, war clouds were visible just above the horizon. The Old Dominion had not yet seceded and legally was still part of the Union even though popular sentiment favored attachment to her sister states farther south.

Then into the Assembly's discussions was thrust a problem that required immediate solution. Dr. Junius L. Archer, proprietor of Bellona Foundry near Richmond, had completed "a large number of heavy guns" under contract from the Ordnance Department at Washington.[48] The weapons had been ordered sent to Fort Monroe where, in the Assembly's words: ". . . they can only be needed for the purpose of intimidation and menace to Virginia at present and of actual hostilities in a certain contingency that may change her future relations to the federal government and the anti-slavery sentiment it represents. . . ."

This, the Assembly decided, it must prevent and directed the governor to seize the guns in the event the federal government attempted to move them. This qualification of the order was largely a face-saving gesture for obviously if the guns were not moved, they were as good as in state possession. However, although firmly determined to have the weapons, the Virginians were far too gentlemanly to confiscate federal ordnance without compensation. In the final section of the resolution the Assembly directed payment to Dr. Archer of the remainder due on the contract, $7,872—and reimbursement to the government in Washington of $13,024, already paid to Archer.

The author believes the weapon in Figure I-51 is one of these guns. The piece, a 42-pounder seacoast gun, Model 1841, is now in the Washington Navy Yard collection. Records at the museum there state the weapon was captured from a Confederate battery on the Potomac River in July, 1862. Stamped on the left trunnion is "1860" and on the right "BF JLA," on the breech 8590, and on the tube, U.S. From this data it is clear that the gun, weighing 8590 pounds, was made for the federal government in 1860 by Bellona Foundry, owned by Junius L. Archer.

It is true the date is the year preceding the joint resolution. However, a study of the text lends substance to the belief that this is one of the weapons involved. For instance, the resolution mentions "a large number of heavy guns." Use of the specific word "guns" in preference to a general term such as "cannon" and the adjective "heavy" certainly would fit the 42-pounder category, while mention of a "large number" indicates the completion of the contract took far longer than the three months preceding April 1.

The amount of the contract, $20,896, is further evidence of a sizable number for although the cost per gun charged by Dr. Archer is not available, a rough approximation may be made with a similar weight, cast iron weapon, the 8-inch Rodman columbiad. This piece weighed slightly under 8,500 pounds and the cost was $825.[49] Even if we add $75 to this and use $900 as a round figure, we arrive at a

FIGURE: I-50 IDENTIFICATION: Gun, Navy, 32-Pounder (weight and model undetermined), Iron. REMARKS: Banded and presumably rifled piece in Fort Moultrie mounted on a wood, front pintle, barbette carriage probably about 1865. Note trunnion band –– one method of repairing a weapon with damaged trunnions.

contract for some twenty-three guns, an order that a foundry such as Bellona in pre-war days probably would have taken a number of months to fill.

The text indicates the order was completed by April 1, and shipping instructions received from Washington. This doubtless involved communication between Bellona and the Ordnance Department, generally a red-tape process seldom noted for speed. It also involved a "leak" of information to the Assembly and drafting of the resolution. Taken together, the facts represent a series of actions that may have required anything from a few days to several weeks with a consequent narrowing of the three months available in 1861.

Moreover, even with a certain number of Dixie sympathizers in the federal government, it is doubtful if such a contract would have been given a Virginia firm after secession of Southern states began. Add the "U.S." stamped on the tube, and the preponderance of evidence seems favorable to listing this as one of the "purchased" weapons, although in view of the firing on Sumter April 12, it is doubtful whether the federal government ever got its money.

The 42-pounder, as previously mentioned, was adopted in 1801, then dropped from weapons specified for land service until 1831 when it again entered the list of seacoast cannon.[50] Not so in the Navy where this caliber continued in service as evidenced by a specimen (Fig. I-52) at Fort Pike which, like the previously illustrated 32-pounder at that park, is dated 1821. Vent and chase molding (astragal and fillets) differentiate this model from later types which have a chase ring or lack all such ornamentation.

FIGURE: I-51 LOCATION: Washington Navy Yard, D.C. IDENTIFICATION: Gun, Seacoast, 42-Pounder, Model 1841, Iron. BORE: Diameter — 7. Smoothbore. Length — 109. LENGTH O/A: 128. TRUNNIONS: Diameter — 6.9. Length — 6.5. MARKINGS: Left Trunnion — 1860. Right Trunnion — B.F., J.L.A. Tube — U.S. Breech — 8,590. COMMON NAME: 42-Pounder, Model 1841.

FIGURE: I-52 LOCATION: Fort Pike, La. IDENTIFICATION: Gun, Navy, 42-Pounder, Model 1821 (tentative), Iron. BORE: Diameter — 7. Smoothbore. Length — 101.5v. LENGTH O/A: 121. TRUNNIONS: Diameter — 7. MARKINGS: Right Trunnion —1821. Breech — 70-1-2 (7,870 lbs.), P., G. (other initials concealed), No. 169. Base Ring — I.C. & Co., B.F. REMARKS: Note broken breeching loop. COMMON NAME: 42-Pounder, Model 1821.

The 42-pounders of the '30s, like contemporary 32-pounders, had a breeching loop and, the author believes, were used indiscriminately in land and sea service. One of these 1831 models (Fig. I-53) is mounted at Fort Pulaski. It was cast at Columbia Foundry in 1836. Another of these rare weapons, cast in 1839 at West Point Foundry, but banded and rifled during the war, is still at West Point, but in the U.S. Military Academy collection.

The Model 1831 had no chase ring or molding and the lock piece was raised above the level of the base ring. The Model 1841 added a chase ring, but initially removed the lock piece which is missing from the 1845 weapon (Fig. I-54) at West Point. The lock piece returned later, now level with the base ring as in the Bellona Foundry piece (Fig. I-51).

Specifications[51] differ slightly with the 1831 having a bore and trunnion diameter of 7.018 inches, length overall 129.4, and bore length 109 as compared to 7, 129 and 110 inches respectively for the 1841. Standard weights are 8,688 pounds for the 1831 compared to 8,465 for the later model. Between them was an 1840 model which had almost identical specifications to the 1841, but was 165 pounds lighter.

The 42-pounders were suppressed by order of 9 February 1861,[52] however they were used in smoothbore and rifled form by both sides throughout the war, and Benton[53] mentions 32- and 42- pounders "rifled for temporary purposes" still mounted in our seacoast forts in 1875.

On the other hand, since the Confederate Ordnance Manual of 1863, which is largely a copy of the United States Manual of 1861, also mentions suppression of the gun,[54] and since gun metal could be put to better use in other weapons, it is doubtful if any 42-pounders were made after 1861—in fact the Bellona, 1860 gun probably was one of the last of this caliber.

Two heavy Navy guns were a 10-inch, or 125-pounder, which will be discussed further in Chapter V on the Dahlgren, and a 64-pounder, or 8-inch, developed in 1849 as a pivot gun for the largest class of steamers.[55] This restriction as well as increasing acceptance of shellguns, limited production of the 64-pounder to a relatively few weapons and only a handful are listed aboard ship during the Civil War.

The 1861 Ordnance Manual[56] lists the weight as 11,872 pounds which, divided by 112, gives a total of 106 cwt., a figure also used by Brandt[57] in 1864. However, Dahlgren[58] in 1856 described the gun as 105 cwt. as did Lieutenant Simpson[59] in 1862. Such discrepancy could indicate either typo-

graphical errors, or modification of the piece, obviously slight in view of the small weight change in a gun of this size. Bore length was 124.2 inches and length overall 140.95. The breech was rounded like the 32-pounders, but the cascabel (Fig. I-55) was a button type, split in the center by a vertical line of ratchets cut into the breech for the elevating mechanism and similar in appearance to that of certain Army columbiads. The Navy quickly discarded this type elevation although it was retained in the Army. The 64-pounder burned a 12-pound charge in normal operation firing a shot weighing 63.75 pounds and shell of 51.5.[60]

FIGURE: I-53 LOCATION: Fort Pulaski, Ga. IDENTIFICATION: Gun, Seacoast, 42-Pounder, Model 1831, Iron. BORE: Diameter — 7. Smoothbore. Length — 109.25v. LENGTH O/A: 128.5. TRUNNIONS: Diameter — 7. Length — 6.5. MARKINGS: Left Trunnion — 1836. Right Trunnion — J.M., C.F. REMARKS: No chase ring. Raised lock piece. COMMON NAME: 42-Pounder, Model 1831.

FIGURE: I-54 LOCATION: West Point, N.Y. IDENTIFICATION: Gun, Seacoast, 42-Pounder, Model 1841 (initial form), Iron. BORE: Diameter — 7. Smoothbore. Length — 110. LENGTH O/A: 129. TRUNNIONS: Diameter — 7. Length — 6.5. MARKINGS: Left Trunnion — 1845. Right Trunnion W.P.F. REMARKS: West Point records list weight as 8,466 lbs. Statistics of this early type appear identical to those of the 42-Pounder, Model 1841 listed in the 1861 Ordnance Manual (See Appendix C). Only visible differences between this specimen and weapons cast shortly before the war (Fig. I-51) seem to be addition of lock piece and slightly narrower base ring in the later form. COMMON NAME: 42-Pounder, Model 1841.

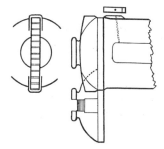

FIGURE: I-55 IDENTIFICATION: Breech of Gun, Navy, 64-Pounder (8-inch), 106 cwt., Model 1849, Iron. SOURCE: Simpson. REMARKS: Also listed as 105 cwt. Note button cascabel and ratchet form of elevation, both unusual in naval weapons. COMMON NAME: 8-Inch of 106 cwt. Or, 64-Pounder.

NOTES

1. "Rifled 6/12" also has been suggested as a method of identification giving initial and final pounder designation.
2. Mr. Carl M. Becker, Department of History, Wright State University, Dayton, Ohio, who wrote the chapter, "Miles Greenwood," in *For The Union, Ohio Leaders in The Civil War*, pp. 259–319, informed the author that based on U.S. House of Representatives Document No. 99, 2nd session, 40th Congress, 1867–68, Washington, 1868, p. 754, Greenwood's production amounted to 161 pieces. These were forty-six 6-pounder smoothbores, fifty-one 6-pounder rifles, fifty 12-pounder Napoleons, and fourteen 12-pounder field howitzers.
3. *Ordnance Manual for The Use of Officers of The United States Army*, 1861, pp. 16–17.
4. William E. Birkhimer, *Historical Sketch of The Organization, Administration, Materiel and Tactics of The Artillery, United States Army*, 1884, pp. 258–263, 280–282.
5. *Ibid.*, p. 263.
6. *Ibid.*, p. 264.
7. *Ibid.*, p. 265.
8. *Ibid.*, p. 279.
9. Dr. Robert H. MacLeod of Morris Plains, N.J.
10. Birkhimer, *loc. cit.*, p. 262.
11. Col. Cary S. Tucker, USAR (Ret.), "Virginia Military Institute Cadet Battery Guns," *The Military Collector and Historian*, Vol. XIII, 1961, journal of The Company of Military Historians.
12. Dr. James C. Hazlett, Wheeling, W. Va.
13. Birkhimer, *loc. cit.*, pp. 281–282.
14. *Ordnance Manual for The Use of Officers of The Confederate States Army*, 1863, pp. 9, 13.
15. Birkhimer, *loc. cit.*, p. 280.
16. *Ibid.*, pp. 263–264, 281.
17. *Official Records*, Series IV, Vol. 2, p. 65, "Estimates of Losses at Forts Henry and Donelson."
18. *Ibid.*, Series III, Vol. 4, p. 469.
19. William LeRoy Broun (sic), "The Red Artillery, Confederate Ordnance During The War," *Southern Historical Society Papers*, Vol. XXVI, 1898, p. 368.
20. Josiah Gorgas, "Contributions to The History of The Confederate Ordnance Department," *Southern Historical Society Papers*, Vol. XII, 1884, p. 93.
21. *Official Records*, Series I, Vol. 46, Part 3, p. 1009, report of Capt. Daniel W. Flagler, 28 April 1865.
22. Dr. Pierre Jenkins, Charleston, S.C.
23. John Muller, *A Treatise of Artillery for Use of The Royal Academy of Artillery*, 1757.
24. *Official Records*, Series I, Vol. 28, Part 2, p. 284.
25. *Ibid.*, p. 415.
26. *Ibid.*, Vol. 24, Part 2, pp. 331–332.
27. *Ibid.*, pp. 336–337.
28. *Ibid.*, p. 337.
29. *Ibid.*, p. 338.
30. Edwin C. Bearss, "The Vicksburg River Defenses and The Enigma of Whistling Dick," *The Journal of Mississippi History*, Vol. XIX, No. 1, January, 1957, p. 21.
31. Lamar Fontaine, *My Life and Lectures*, p. 176.
32. Letter to the author dated 6 November 1964 from Park Supt. Jack K. Anderson.
33. *Official Records*, Series I, Vol. 6, pp. 144–165, reports of Brig. Gen. Quincy A. Gillmore, U.S.A., of operations against Fort Pulaski 28 January–11 April 1862, specifically p. 154. The breaching batteries also included two rifled 32-pounders, a pair of rifled 42-pounders, and five 4.2-inch Parrott rifles.
34. Laura Singleton Walker, *History of Ware County, Georgia*, 1934, p. 262.
35. Mr. David Maybank, Lavington Plantation, Charleston County, S.C.
36. *Official Records*, Series I, Vol. 28, Part 2, p. 485.
37. *Ordnance Manual for The Use of Officers of The United States Army*, 1841, specifications of the Model 1819 and Model 1839, which is listed here as Model 1840, pp. 2, 4.
38. Birkhimer *op. cit.*, pp. 277, 280.
39. *Official Navy Records*, Series II, Vol. 1, p. 223.
40. *Ibid.*, Series I. Vol. 5, various reports, pp. 537–546, 645. Reports are conflicting as to date, some saying 26, others 27. The latter has been selected as the more probable.
41. *Ordnance Manuals*, 1841 and 1861, *op. cit.*
42. *Ibid.*, 1861, p. 492.
43. Edward Simpson, *A Treatise on Ordnance and Naval Gunnery*, 1862, pp. 58–62.
44. *Official Navy Records*, Series II, Vol. I, p. 176. Also, *The Hebe Skirmish Centennial and the Fort Fisher Visitor-Museum Groundbreaking Program*, 1963.
45. *Ibid.*, Series I, Vol. 9, pp. 535–537.

46. *Ibid.,* Series II, Vol. 1, p. 150.

47. Reports of committees of the U.S. Senate, 2nd session, 38th Congress, "Heavy Ordnance," p. 90, testimony, Charles Knap (also spelled Knapp), proprietor of Fort Pitt Foundry, 4 February 1864.

48. *Official Records,* Series IV, Vol. 1, pp. 203–204.

49. Alexander L. Holley, *A Treatise on Ordnance and Armor,* 1865, p. 131.

50. Birkhimer, *loc. cit.,* p. 277.

51. *Ordnance Manual,* 1841, *loc. cit.,* pp. 2, 4.

52. *Ordnance Manual,,* 1861, *op. cit.,* p. 14.

53. J. G. Benton, *A Course of Instruction in Ordnance and Gunnery Composed and Compiled for Cadets of The United States Military Academy,* 1875, pp. 193, 247.

54. *Ordnance Manual* (Confederate, 1863), *op. cit.,* p. 9.

55. J. A. Dahlgren, *Shells and Shellguns,* 1856, pp. 23, 26.

56. *Ordnance Manual,* 1861, *op. cit.,* p. 492.

57. J. B. Brandt, *Gunnery Catechism as Applied to the Service of Naval Ordnance,* 1864, pp. 112, 193.

58. Dahlgren, *loc. cit.,* p. 26.

59. Simpson, *loc. cit.,* p. 62.

60. Dahlgren, *loc. cit.,* p. 26.

Chapter 2

The Howitzer

COMPANION WEAPONS TO CIVIL WAR GUNS were howitzers—smoothbore cannon, as a rule, designed to throw large projectiles with comparatively light charges of powder concentrated at the bottom of the tube by means of a chamber. They were lighter than guns of the same caliber and at short ranges with shell, case, grape, or canister were considerably more effective. They also had a higher trajectory and were able to reach objects in greater defilade than could guns.

The value of these weapons in the Richmond campaign was cited by a Union general[1] in these words:

"For defending positions against assault . . . no artillery can be more efficient than the 32-pdr. or 24-pdr. field howitzer. The former . . . throws very large case shot and canister and from its light weight may be kept out of sight and danger until the assault is delivered when it can suddenly be run into battery and served with murderous effect.

"This was shown on June 2, 1865, when the 22nd S.C. Regiment . . . made a determined assault upon the small, advanced redoubt Dutton on our Bermuda front. . . . It was then incomplete (and garrisoned by one company of the 1st Conn. Artillery with a few dismounted cavalry supports), but armed with two 32-pdr. and one 24-pdr. brass howitzers. Only two of them could be brought to bear on the assaulting party, but so rapid a canister fire was maintained as to repulse the column with severe loss . . . so demoralized was . . . (the) command that a lieutenant and 22 enlisted men surrendered rather than attempt to retreat under the fire. . . ."

Caliber of howitzers followed standard cannon sizes and was expressed in terms of the weight of solid shot for lighter weapons and in inches for large bores.

To limit the number of types of carriages, howitzer trunnions were turned to fit the same carriage of the guns they often accompanied and complimented. This was particularly true in field and siege models. The 12-pounder howitzer had the same 3.67-inch diameter trunnions as the 6-pounder gun. The 24-pounder field howitzer with 4.2-inch trunnions fit the 9-pounder gun carriage—although the gun itself had been suppressed—which later was used for the "light" 12-pounder, or Napoleon. The 32-pounder's 4.62-inch trunnions permitted use on the carriage of the "heavy" 12-pounder, Model 1841. The 8-inch siege howitzer had 5.82-inch trunnions that fit the carriage of the 24-pounder siege gun, although it was necessary to use a quoin to elevate the piece which was too short to reach the screw set for the 24-pounder.

The 8-inch seacoast howitzer used the 32-pounder gun, barbette carriage (trunnions 6.4-inch) and the 10-inch howitzer with 8-inch trunnions was mounted on the barbette carriage of the 8-inch columbiad after this weapon was adopted in 1844. Between 1841 and 1844, the barbette carriage normally used for the 32-pounder and 42-pounder guns probably served with a change of trunnion plates and a few other minor alterations.

The little 12-pounder mountain howitzer with 2.7-inch diameter trunnions had its own special carriage. However, the 2.25-inch Confederate mountain rifle also had 2.7-inch trunnions and utilized the same carriage. Standard U.S. field and mountain howitzers are bronze, the siege and garrison pieces and seacoast, iron. All but the seacoast have characteristic straight muzzles with muzzle band which aids in identification, particularly at a distance. Most prevalent today of these weapons is the 12-pounder field howitzer, Model 1841. This bronze piece will be found in most national parks commemorating field engagements, often mixed in batteries with field guns.

Figure II-1 shows a standard 12-pounder obtained from Watervliet Arsenal in 1929 and now mounted on The Battery at Charleston. Trunnion markings reveal the weapon was manufactured by Ames Co., Chicopee, Massachusetts, in 1851, and the palmetto tree and "S.C." on the tube identify it as a South Carolina piece, although made on the same pattern as the U.S. model. It was captured by federal forces on nearby James Island during the war and taken north where it eventually wound up at Watervliet.

There were two bronze models prior to 1841—1836 and 1839. The first was almost identical to the standard pattern, but the 1839 was considerably shorter.[2] Appearance was similar, but the piece was only 55.5 inches overall compared to 58.6 for the 1841. It was an experimental weapon that quickly gave way to the longer form and although a few were made and may be encountered in the national parks, it is considered a rarity today.

Although the Confederates made and used the standard 12-pounder, they also developed their own weapon which differed materially. This was an iron 12-pounder field howitzer which the Confederate Ordnance Manual of 1863 describes[3] as Model 1862. One of these (Fig. II-2) at Petersburg conforms accurately to official specifications laid down in the manual: length, 64.4 inches, bore diameter 4.62, trunnion diameter 3.67, and weight 837 actual compared to a specified 850 pounds. A footnote in the manual states the weapon was ". . . made and used in the service, but not considered as permanently adopted."

FIGURE: II-1 LOCATION: Charleston, S.C. IDENTIFICATION: Howitzer, Field, 12-Pounder, Model 1841, Bronze. BORE: Diameter — 4.62. Smoothbore. Length — 50.50. LENGTH O/A: 58.6. TRUNNIONS: Diameter — 3.67. Length — 2.8. MARKINGS: Muzzle Face — 32. Left Trunnion — 1851. Right Trunnion — Ames Co., Founders, Chicopee, Mass. Tube — Palmetto Tree and S.C. (South Carolina). COMMON NAME: 12-Pounder Howitzer, Model 1841.

FIGURE: II-2 LOCATION: Petersburg, Va. IDENTIFICATION: Howitzer, Field, 12-Pounder, Model 1862, Confederate, Iron. BORE: Diameter — 4.62. Smoothbore. Length — 55.8. LENGTH O/A: 64.5. TRUNNIONS: Diameter — 3.67. Length — 2.8. MARKINGS: Muzzle Face — J.R.A. & Co., 1481 (weapon number), 837 (weight). Left Trunnion — 1862. COMMON NAME: 12-Pounder Confederate Howitzer.

FIGURE: II-3 LOCATION: Beaufort, S.C. IDENTIFICATION: Howitzer, field, 24-Pounder, Model 1841, Bronze. BORE: Diameter — 5.82. Smoothbore. Length — 61. LENGTH O/A: 71.5. TRUNNIONS: Diameter — 4.2. Length — 3.25. MARKINGS: Left Trunnion — 1847. Right Trunnion — N.P. Ames, Founder, Springfield, Mass. COMMON NAME: 24-Pounder Field Howitzer.

Data on the muzzle face records that the Petersburg piece was cast by J. R. Anderson & Co. (Tredegar Foundry, Richmond, Virginia). The date apparently is on the left trunnion which, when the cannon was photographed, was jammed against another weapon and impossible to read. However, park records list it as 1862.

The bronze 24-pounder field howitzer (Fig. II-3) was cast by Ames Co. in 1847. Nothing has been discovered of its early history, but during the Civil War it showed up aboard the *U.S.S. George Washington,* an Army vessel, variously called a steamer and an armed transport, operating in the Beaufort, South Carolina, area.

The *Washington* and the Navy steamer *E.B. Hale* set out 8 April 1865 from Beaufort to reconnoiter nearby tidal rivers.[4]

Both vessels made their way up the Coosaw until the *Hale* grounded about 1:30 P.M. and despite efforts of the *Washington* remained fast on a mud bank throughout the afternoon and until 11 o'clock that night.

Once more afloat, her pilot preferred to brave the tricky navigation of the river in daylight, so the *Hale* dropped anchor near the *Washington* and both vessels lay quietly through the night not far from shore and close to a wooded area offering excellent concealment for any Confederates caring to take advantage of the situation. Realizing the potential danger, Lieutenant Edgar Brodhead, skipper of the *Hale,* weighed anchor about 4:30 A.M. and felt his way upstream leaving the *Washington* behind.

At daylight, the *Washington* got under way only to have shot and shell crash aboard from a Confederate battery that had been brought up under cover of darkness and emplaced in woods about a mile astern. The first shot knocked out the rudder and the second got the magazine setting the ship afire. With no means of navigation and his vessel burning, Captain Thomas B. Briggs considered discretion the better part and struck his flag.

The Confederates immediately ceased fire, but without boats, they had no way of actually taking possession of the surrendered steamer and while they sought smallboats, the vessel drifted in the fast-moving tide. Rudderless, she swept toward the opposite shore from the Confederates—the side toward Beaufort which, by virtue of patrol activity, was under nominal federal control. Before long she grounded against mud and marsh. Whereupon a general hegira ensued from her burning decks as officers and crew sought escape across the marsh to friendly territory.

Seeing their prisoners escape through what they considered downright ungentlemanly conduct, the Confederates danced in frustration and reopened fire as the fleeing Yankees fought their way through the mud toward land. Most seem to have made it, including Captain Briggs, for the majority of casualties reportedly occurred during the explosion of the magazine.

Finally, rescue hove in sight—the *Hale,* white wave curling from her bow, stack spouting smoke and sparks, straining to her full eight knots. Her skipper had heard the firing, but presumed the *Washington* was shooting up the woods a bit as she cruised up and down the river. Then a federal soldier rowed out from shore to report a vessel in trouble, and the *Hale* was on her way. She arrived to find the *Washington* had burned to the waterline and sunk in four feet of water. By this time a truce was in effect, so the *Hale* took aboard several injured men and headed for home.

Back in the safety of the federal base at Hilton Head, recriminations flew thick and fast. The Army hurried an investigation which censured Briggs for surrendering and then escaping under the white flag—terming his conduct "unjustifiable and reprehensible"—but blamed the loss of the *Washington* on the *Hale* for sneaking off in the dark without notifying her companion vessel.

Furious over the charge, the Navy convened its own board of inquiry and pointed out that the *Hale* left with no attempt at secrecy, passing close enough for any Army lookout to have spotted the move. Furthermore, the Navy intimated that if Army skippers were so stupid as to spend an afternoon and night in the lee of an enemy shore and still be there at daylight, Navy men were not, and concluded by completely exonerating the *Hale.* Finally, as is often the case, both sides were happy to let the affair die quietly and get on to more pressing business.

As for the *Washington,* the *Hale* went back to the site to guard an Army salvage crew, but apparently nothing was attempted. Later the Confederates took a crack at it from small boats and hauled out one of her cannon which they dragged ashore, then hastily buried fearing the momentary appearance of a Union gunboat. It presumably still awaits a finder for there is no mention of its being recovered either during the war or later.

The weapon in Figure II-3, however, was still aboard the *Washington.* It was spotted some years ago by a man catching crabs amid the wreckage of the vessel. He knocked the oyster shells off a large piece of metal and recognized it as a cannon and a brass one at that. He notified authorities in Beaufort who raised the piece, cleaned and mounted it at the town museum where it stands today, a monument to an engagement which had overtones of a Gilbert and Sullivan operetta, yet took the lives of men who were just as dead as those who fell at Gettysburg.

The standard U.S. field 24-pounder is easily recognized by its handles placed over the center of gravity as an aid in lifting the piece. The Confederates, however, made some of these bronze weapons without handles and an excellent example of this type is in the Petersburg collection. The piece (Fig. II-4) was made in 1862 by the Tennessee firm of Quinby and Robinson and the handles presumably were omitted as having little real value and no doubt lessening the strength of the casting. Close examination shows a few other differences—such as shallower recess and base ring and a trifle more space between the chase ring and muzzle band on the Confederate piece—but these are minor and probably due to lack of exact specifications for the founder.

The South also seems to have made an iron field model, but appearance is entirely conjectural since sole reference[5] thus far is Flagler's list of weapons captured at Tredegar: ". . . and three 24-pounder, iron field howitzers, newly completed. . . ."

Handles also were cast on the 32-pounder field howitzer, another standard U.S. bronze piece which is further identified by a heavy band marking the front end of the recess and serving to reinforce the forward portion of the chamber where it joins the bore. This weapon was introduced several years later than the other field howitzers and is listed as a Model 1844. The one illustrated (Fig. II-5) is at Petersburg and was cast by Ames in 1851.

Final U.S. bronze cannon of this class is the 12-pounder mountain howitzer, Model 1841 (Fig. II-6), a dual purpose weapon used in the highly contrasting terrains of mountain and prairie. Although having the standard 12-pounder bore of 4.62 inches, the tube is but 37.21 inches long and weighs only 220 pounds, a convenient load for a pack animal. The carriage, a smaller, simplified version of the field carriage, breaks down into several parts which may be loaded on another mule. With ammunition and other battery equipment similarly packed, the entire unit could operate easily in mountainous country that would be extremely difficult if not utterly impossible for a field outfit. When mounted on the carriage, no limber was used. Instead the howitzer was hauled by a single animal using two shafts attached to the stock near the trail plate.

The mountain howitzer was especially favored in

FIGURE: II-4 LOCATION: Petersburg, Va. IDENTIFICATION: Howitzer, Field, 24-Pounder, Confederate, Bronze. BORE: Diameter — 5.82. Smoothbore. Length — 61. LENGTH O/A: 71.5. TRUNNIONS: Diameter — 4.2. Length — 3.25. MARKINGS: Left Trunnion — 1862. Right Trunnion (face) — Quinby & Robinson, Memphis, Tenn. Right Trunnion (top) — A.W. McConnell. COMMON NAME: 24-Pounder Confederate Field Howitzer.

FIGURE: II-5 LOCATION: Petersburg, Va. IDENTIFICATION: Howitzer, Field, 32-Pounder, Model 1844, Bronze. BORE: Diameter — 6.4. Smoothbore. Length — 71. LENGTH O/A: 82. TRUNNIONS: Diameter — 4.62. Length — 3.5. MARKINGS: Muzzle Face — J.W.R. Left Trunnion — 1851. Right Trunnion — Ames Co., Founders, Chicopee, Mass. Tube — U.S. COMMON NAME: 32-Pounder Howitzer.

FIGURE: II-6 LOCATION: Kennesaw, Ga. IDENTIFICATION: Howitzer, Mountain, 12-Pounder, Model 1841, Bronze. BORE: Diameter — 4.62. Smoothbore. Length — 31. LENGTH O/A: 37.5. TRUNNIONS: Diameter — 2.7. Length 2.25. MARKINGS: Muzzle Face — 1863, A.M.Co., A.B.D., 221 (weight), No. 104. REMARKS: Iron, reproduction carriage. COMMON NAME: Mountain Howitzer.

the Mexican War where its small size and light weight facilitated employment from rooftops during street fighting.[6] Equipped with a light, four-wheel "prairie carriage," it later proved excellent for operating against Indians on the Western frontier. An 1865 photograph (Fig. II-7) shows one of these little pieces on the walls of Fort Sumter. Note baskets of earth, termed "gabions," with which Confederates reinforced the walls.

Siege and garrison howitzers were of two calibers, 24-pounder and 8-inch, the former (Fig. II-8) differed from its field counterpart primarily in material—all siege howitzers were made of cast iron—by absence of handles, and in lack of recess. General appearance is similar, but dimensions differ a bit, the most important for purposes of identification being a somewhat shorter length for the siege 24-pounder, 69 inches compared to 71.2 for the field model, and larger trunnions, 4.62 inches as against 4.2 for the bronze howitzer which, as previously mentioned, was designed to fit the 9-pounder gun carriage.

There is a certain amount of confusion over when the 24-pounder siege and garrison howitzer was introduced. Birkhimer[7] states the weapon was added by the board of 1838 and lists it in ordnance approved by the War Department in 1839. The Ordnance Manual of 1861 refers to it as a Model 1841, but terms the 24-pounder bronze field howitzer, which Birkhimer also includes in the 1839 list, as a Model 1844.

The 1841 Ordnance Manual, while it lists the 24-pounder field howitzer as well as other weapons specified by the War Department in 1839 (it even includes the 10-inch seacoast howitzer which Birkhimer says was added in 1841), makes no mention of either the 24-pounder siege and garrison howitzer or the 32-pounder field howitzer, a weapon which both Birkhimer and the 1861 manual agree came in later. The 1841 manual also fails to acknowledge the existence of the flank casemate carriage, a special type for use with the 24-pounder garrison piece, yet mentions the carriage for the field 24-pounder on several occasions.

In view of this somewhat sketchy evidence, the author feels that while the 24-pounder garrison howitzer possibly was approved in 1839, it may not have been adopted for use until later and the 1861 manual has erroneously switched dates. If this be true, then the siege and garrison 24 should be identified as a Model 1844, a description the author will use pending discovery of one of these weapons bearing a prior date.

FIGURE: II-7 IDENTIFICATION: Howitzer, Mountain, 12-Pounder, Model 1841, Bronze. REMARKS: Fort Sumter, 1865. Note basket-like "gabions" plugging breach in wall. COMMON NAME: Mountain Howitzer.

FIGURE: II-8 LOCATION: Chalmette Cemetery New Orleans, La. IDENTIFICATION: Howitzer, Siege & Garrison, 24-Pounder, Model 1844, Iron. BORE: Diameter — 5.82. Smoothbore. Length — 58. LENGTH O/A: 69. TRUNNIONS: Diameter — 4.62. Length — 3.25. MARKINGS: Left Trunnion — 1847. Right Trunnion — C.A. & Co., Boston, Mass. COMMON NAME: 24-Pounder Siege Howitzer.

The 24-pounder, although technically a siege and garrison howitzer, was generally used in the latter fashion. Mounted on the flank casemate carriage (q.v.) the piece was designed, as the terminology indicates, to guard the flanks of fortifications against infantry assault. The weapon in Figure II-8 is one of four affixed to a monument in Chalmette National Military Park Cemetery near New Orleans and was made in 1847 by Cyrus Alger. Two others (Fig. II-9) are mounted in front of the Wilmington, North Carolina, library. These weapons, made by Robert P. Parrott at the West Point Foundry in 1858 and inspected by Benjamin Huger, are the same as the Chalmette howitzers with exception of the chase ring which is a bit closer to the muzzle band, a discrepancy which the author feels was rather a matter of founder inconsistency than a model change.

The 8-inch siege howitzer, Model 1841 (Fig. II-10) now at the Washington Navy Yard, figured in a Confederate attempt to duplicate a feat which initially won them a gunboat. The Southerners at Charleston under General P.G.T. Beauregard, during the latter part of 1862, noticed that one of the federal gunboats operating in the Stono River a few miles from the city was considerably more brave—or foolhardy—than the others. This vessel, the 453-ton *Isaac Smith,* secure in her eight 8-inch broadside shellguns and a single 30-pounder Parrott rifle mounted as a pivot,[8] was in the habit of poking her bow far up the Stono. In fact, the trip often became so dull, she would drop anchor while her officers went ashore and engaged in a bit of target practice with their pistols.

With the turn of the year and as January days slipped by, the Confederates watched the *Smith* and laid plans to end her pleasant cruising.[9] They noticed that the vessel generally dropped back downstream each afternoon to spend the hours of darkness safe in Union territory at the mouth of the river. So Confederate artillerymen spent several nights building siege gun platforms at strategic points along both sides of the river. Shortly before dawn, they would lay down their tools, conceal all evidence of work and take cover for the day in convenient barns or thickets.

By 30 January the trap was ready and when the *Smith* came slowly upriver, the Southerners graciously let her pass. As soon as she moved from sight, guns—rifled 24-pounders on siege carriages—rolled out of hiding and were emplaced on the platforms, two on one side of the river, three on the other, with lighter guns and picked smallarms marksmen scattered between. The 24-pounders probably were Model 1839, banded, and when the three-gun battery

FIGURE: II-9 LOCATION Wilmington, N.C. IDENTIFICATION: Howitzer, Siege & Garrison, 24-Pounder, Model 1844, Iron. BORE: Diameter — 5.82. Smoothbore. Length — 58. LENGTH O/A: 69. TRUNNIONS: Diameter — 4.62. Length — 3.25. MARKINGS: Muzzle Face — 17. Left Trunnion — 1858. Right Trunnion — R.P.P., W.P.F. Tube — U.S. REMARKS: Ornamental iron stand inscribed: W.L.I. (Wilmington Light Infantry) 1853–1909. COMMON NAME: 24-Pounder Siege Howitzer.

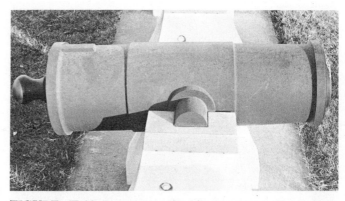

FIGURE: II-10 LOCATION: Washington Navy Yard, D.C. IDENTIFICATION: Howitzer, Siege & Garrison, 8-Inch, Model 1841, Iron. BORE; Diameter — 8. Smoothbore. LENGTH O/A: 62. TRUNNIONS: Diameter — 6. Length — 5.5. REMARKS: Bore plugged. Marks concealed by paint. COMMON NAME: 8-Inch Siege Howitzer, Model 1841.

opened at less than 500 yards, the *Smith* was seriously damaged before she could even reply.

She got off a few rounds of grape and canister and tried to make a run for it. But her eight broadside pieces, which together could hurl roughly 400 pounds of iron at a single discharge, were next to useless in a running engagement since they could only be trained on targets almost directly abeam. Her 30-pounder pivot, while capable of wider deflection, was no match alone for the storm of incoming shot and shell.

The *Smith* made a brave fight of it for about a mile. Then a Confederate shell got the engine and the battle was over. The vessel surrendered and the Southerners came aboard to examine their prize—a 171-foot propeller steamer with armament intact and a crew of eleven officers, one hundred and five enlisted men and three Negroes, of whom twenty-five were dead or wounded. The Confederates lost only one man.

Towed to Charleston, the *Smith* was renamed *Stono* and converted to a blockade runner while her cannon went into the forts. But bad luck continued to dog her. Loaded with cotton, she set out the night of 5 June 1863, but ran afoul of a blockader and was chased back toward the harbor. In the dark, apparently due to error on the part of her helmsman, she rammed ashore on Sullivan's Island and was lost although much of her cargo was salvaged.[10]

Spectacular success in capturing the *Smith* led the Confederates toward the end of 1863 to consider repetition of the exploit and with this in mind began eyeing two gunboats which lay off the small community of Legareville on the Stono. The vessels, both formidable opponents, were the *Marblehead* and *Pawnee*.[11] The former, a 158-foot two-masted screw steamer of 507 tons, mounted four 24-pounders (probably howitzers), an 11-inch Dahlgren smoothbore, and a 20-pounder Parrott rifle. The *Pawnee*, a 1,289-ton twin-screw steamer, had an impressive battery of eight 9-inch Dahlgrens in broadside, a 100-pounder Parrott rifle and a 50-pounder Dahlgren rifle.

Legareville was held by a small federal garrison and the Southern plan was to overwhelm this outfit with infantry supported with field artillery while two 8-inch siege howitzers knocked off the gunboats.[12] Once more the cannon were brought up under cover of night and about dawn Christmas Day opened at roughly 1,000 yards on the *Marblehead* which had the bad luck to have her starboard boiler down for repairs. Consequently, it took some twenty minutes to get up steam while shells screamed in from the howitzers.

Not so the *Pawnee*. She slipped her cable and was under way within five minutes, headed straight for a flanking position where she dropped anchor, swung with the tide and enfiladed the Southern batteries with the devastating fire from her port broadside backed up with the two rifles. Even with light

breastworks, the barrage was too hot and the Southerners pulled back leaving the two howitzers, a dead cannoneer, and eight dead horses. Both the *Pawnee* and *Marblehead* harassed the retreat and were soon joined by the schooner *C. P. Williams*[13] which came under sail some four and a half miles to add her 13-inch mortar to the shooting gallery.

The assault against the troops in Legareville never got started. It was discovered they were ensconced on a small island approached by a narrow causeway and could only be attacked after the *Marblehead* had been driven off or sunk. With the gunboat still very much in action, the attack was abandoned and the infantry retreated along with the field guns which were saved.

That afternoon a federal attempt was made to take possession of the abandoned howitzers, but it was frustrated by the necessity of dragging them across a wide expanse of marsh and mud. With night coming on, the weapons were spiked, the carriages overturned and the wheels lugged off with the salvage party as it returned to the protection of the ships.

The Confederates came back after dark to retake the weapons, but could do nothing in the face of the damaged carriages. They left before dawn to obtain suitable equipment and try again the next night. Unfortunately for the Southerners, equipment was slow to arrive and by the time it appeared on the 28th, men from the *Marblehead* had discovered a small creek which snaked through the marsh close enough for them to pick up both weapons by boat. It was a fitting triumph for the vessel which had taken seven casualties, picked a dozen shot from her hull, and seen another eighteen rip through her upper works and aloft. Yet the Confederates believed the vessel hadn't been touched and blamed failure of the expedition on poor shooting.

Actually, the attempt was doomed from the start. This was no case of a careless *Isaac Smith* blundering into a trap and hemmed in by river banks to straightaway flight. These were two wide-awake vessels operating in home waters with room to maneuver and bring to bear the awesome power of broadsides backed up with pivot guns. Within a matter of minutes the *Pawnee* had slipped into the enfilading position which turned the rest of the engagement into simple gunnery practice.

The lost howitzers were taken to Washington where both are displayed today at the Navy Yard. One, according to Lieutenant Commander Richard W. Meade Jr., skipper of the *Marblehead*, fired quite an interesting projectile. Although the howitzer is a

51

smoothbore, from it was drawn, instead of a ball, a ". . . cylindrical, conical projectile with a soft metal base . . . (which) weighed 100 pounds and was fuzed (sic)."

The 8-inch siege howitzer, although used by both sides during the war as necessity dictated, was designed primarily for ricochet firing and to batter down the fragments of masonry and earth left standing after breaching guns had finished their job on the walls of fortifications. The Model 1841 had a cylindrical chamber, capable of holding exactly four pounds of powder, which joined the bore with a spherical curve shaped to fit the shell. This form was used to enable the projectile to fit flush against the charge without an intervening wooden cartridge block or sabot. This customarily used device was omitted since the piece was often fired over the heads of friendly troops who would be endangered by bits of wood. An exception to the rule was made in the case of canister which spit out balls like a shotgun and was too risky to use over one's own infantry.

As previously mentioned, the weapon was mounted on the 24-pounder siege gun carriage and by reversing its direction on the carriage, could be made to fire at very high angles of elevation in the fashion of a mortar giving a minimum range of 300 and a maximum of roughly 1,600 yards. The Confederate Ordnance Manual[14] mentions that a few of these 8-inch siege howitzers were rifled with a bore of 4.62 inches as an experiment. However, no report of the results has been found.

The 1841 howitzer is easily distinguished from the model adopted by the U.S. in 1861 (Fig. II-11). The illustrated piece is one of a pair at Temple, New Hampshire. Both were made by Cyrus Alger in 1864 and weigh roughly 2,550 pounds each. Unlike the older model, they have an elliptical chamber although 4 pounds of powder remained the standard charge. The new model also used the 24-pounder siege carriage and could be reversed in the trunnion plates for use as a mortar giving roughly 300 yards minimum and 1,900 extreme range.[15]

Largest weapons in the howitzer category were the 8- and 10-inch seacoast pieces. The 8-inch was introduced by the board of 1838 and approved for the land service by the War Department in 1839. The 10-inch was introduced two years later, but for practical purposes, the 1841 and 1861 Ordnance Manuals designate both pieces as Model 1841. With exception of the obvious difference in size and weight, the weapons are identical in appearance. Both howitzers, along with the 42-pounder guns, were suppressed by order of 9 February 1861. However, they were used on each side throughout the war and even in 1875 Benton[16] mentions 8-inch seacoast howitzers still in the nation's forts pending replacement by more modern weapons.

An excellent specimen of the 8-inch (Fig. II-12) is in a cemetery near Cornwall Hollow, Connecticut, about six miles from Goshen and approximately a mile off Connecticut Route 63. Markings of manufac-

FIGURE: II-11 LOCATION: Temple, N.H. IDENTIFICATION: Howitzer, Siege & Garrison, 8-Inch, Model 1861, Iron. BORE: Diameter — 8. Smoothbore. Length — 46.5. LENGTH O/A: 59.5. TRUNNIONS: Diameter — 5.82. Length — 5. MARKINGS: Muzzle Face — 37, C.A. & Co., 2554, R.M.H., 1864. Tube — U.S. COMMON NAME: 8-Inch Siege Howitzer, Model 1861.

FIGURE: II-12 LOCATION: Cornwall Hollow (Goshen), Conn. IDENTIFICATION: Howitzer, Seacoast, 8-Inch, Model 1841, Iron. BORE: Diameter — 8. Smoothbore. Length — 93. LENGTH O/A: 109. TRUNNIONS: Diameter — 6.4. Length — 6. MARKINGS: Muzzle Face — ?.?.R., No. 4. Left Trunnion — W.P.F. (tentative). Right Trunnion — 1839. REMARKS: Introduced in 1839, but for practical purposes called Model 1841 in later ordnance manuals although apparently there was little or no change in the weapon. COMMON NAME: 8-Inch Seacoast Howitzer.

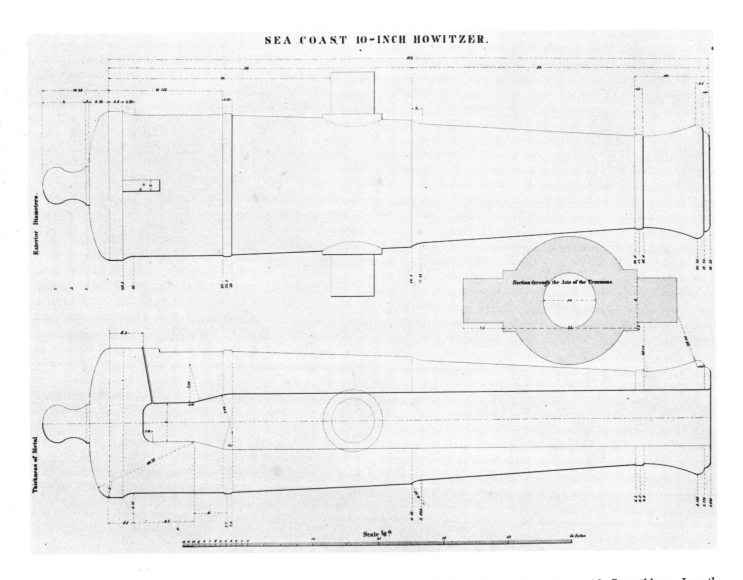

FIGURE: II-13 IDENTIFICATION: Howitzer, Seacoast, 10-Inch, Model 1841, Iron. BORE: Diameter — 10. Smoothbore. Length — 101.5. LENGTH O/A: 125.25. TRUNNIONS: Diameter — 8. Length — 7.5. SOURCE: Mordecai. COMMON NAME: 10-Inch Seacoast Howitzer.

turer and inspector are nearly obliterated, but the number 4, and date, 1839, are easily readable and place the piece as one of the earliest made. No 10-inch seacoast howitzer has been found, but a sketch (Fig. II-13) from Mordecai's book[17] will show its appearance.

Before leaving howitzers, several unusual specimens should be mentioned. The first, a 12-pounder, bronze field piece (Fig. II-14) initially appears to be a slightly obese 6-pounder, Model 1841 gun. However, examination reveals the 4.62-inch bore is chambered and specifications conform closely to the 1841 field howitzer. Difference, of course, is in the muzzle

FIGURE: II-14 LOCATION: Petersburg, Va. IDENTIFICATION: Howitzer, Field, 12-Pounder, Confederate, Bronze. BORE: Diameter — 4.62. Smoothbore. Length — 48.5v. LENGTH O/A: 58.5. TRUNNIONS: Diameter — 3.67. Length — 2.8. REMARKS: No apparent marks, but a few identical weapons have been found which were made by John Clark of New Orleans, La.

swell and molding which, for some undisclosed reason, was substituted for the standard muzzle band and chase ring. The Petersburg weapon is unmarked, but identical to several others cast by J. Clark of New Orleans and presumably also was made in that shop.

Shiloh has two rare 12-pounders which differ from the norm primarily at the breech. Figure II-15 has the deep recess more characteristic of larger field howitzers than this caliber. The piece is Confederate, an 1862 product of S. Wolfe & Co. of New Orleans. The other (Fig. II-16) is unmarked, but probably also is Confederate. Measurements are about standard, but the base ring is a major departure being much larger and with straighter lines than usual.

An iron 24-pounder field howitzer at St. Augustine, Florida (Fig. II-17) is a type in use during the "Iron Age" and might have been emplaced by the South during the war. Marks, if any, are obscured by paint, but the piece is identical to the field howitzer (Fig. II-18) in an 1834 text[18] specified for South Carolina Militia along with the Gribeauval carriage—not replaced in national service until 1836—and the "Walking Stick" 6-pounder, Model 1819 gun.

Discounting length, the howitzer has a marked similarity to the "Walking Stick" as well as the 24-pounder gun of the same vintage and presumably is the 24-pounder howitzer listed for field use in 1819 by the Ordnance Board of the previous year. Two other howitzers, an Austrian 24-pounder, and the "Ripley" 8-inch—which probably never existed—are discussed in the miscellaneous cannon category of Chapter IX.

FIGURE: II-16 LOCATION: Shiloh, Tenn. IDENTIFICATION: Howitzer, Field, 12-Pounder, Confederate, Bronze. BORE: Diameter — 4.62. Smoothbore. Length — 50.25v. LENGTH O/A: 59.5. TRUNNIONS: Diameter — 3.75. Length — 2.75. REMARKS: Only mark seems to be 799 on cascabel knob.

FIGURE: II-17 LOCATION: St. Augustine, Fla. IDENTIFICATION: Howitzer, Field, 24-Pounder, Model 1819, Iron. BORE: Diameter — 5.82. Smoothbore. Length — 31v. LENGTH O/A: 39.25. TRUNNIONS: Diameter — 3.5. Length — 3.5. COMMON NAME: 24-Pounder Howitzer, Model 1819.

FIGURE: II-15 LOCATION: Shiloh, Tenn. IDENTIFICATION: Howitzer, Field, 12-Pounder, Confederate, Bronze. BORE: Diameter — 4.62. Smoothbore. Length — 50. LENGTH O/A: 58.7. TRUNNIONS: Diameter — 3.67. Length — 2.75. MARKINGS: Left Trunnion — S. Wolfe & Co., N.O., 1862. Right Trunnion — S. Wolfe & Co., N.O., 1862.

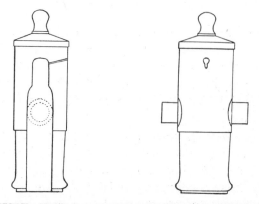

FIGURE: II-18 IDENTIFICATION: Howitzer, Field, 24-Pounder, Model 1819, Iron. SOURCE: Wilson. COMMON NAME: 24-Pounder Howitzer, Model 1819.

NOTES

1. Henry L. Abbot, "Siege Artillery in The Campaigns Against Richmond With Notes on The 15-Inch Gun," *Professional Papers No. 14, Corps of Engineers,* 1867, p. 48.
2. Identification of this model was established by Dr. James C. Hazlett, Wheeling, W. Va., who first discovered the piece.
3. *Ordnance Manual for The Use of Officers of The Confederate States Army,* 1863, pp. 9, 13.
4. Various reports, including *Official Navy Records,* Series I, Vol. 14, pp. 114–121, *Official Records,* Series I, Vol. 14, pp. 280–284, and *Official Records,* Series I, Vol. 53.
5. *Official Records,* Series I, Vol. 46, Part 3, pp. 1007–1010, report of Capt. Daniel W. Flagler, 28 April 1865.
6. J. G. Benton, *A Course of Instruction in Ordnance and Gunnery Composed and Compiled for Cadets of the United States Military Academy,* 1861, p. 176.
7. William E. Birkhimer, *Historical Sketch of the Organization, Administration, Materiel and Tactics of The Artillery, United States Army,* 1884, pp. 282–283.
8. *Official Navy Records,* Series II, Vol. 1, vessel statistics.
9. Various reports of the engagement including: *Official Records,* Series I, Vol. 14, pp. 119, 200–203, 756, 773, *Official Navy Records,* Series I, Vol. 15, pp. 189, 195–196, and *Official Navy Records,* Series I, Vol. 13.
10. The story of her loss has been taken from *The Charleston Daily Courier,* 8 June 1863, p. 1, and is believed to be more accurate than the *Official Records'* version (*Official Navy Records,* Series II, Vol. 1, vessel statistics) which states she served as a harbor craft until February 1865, when she was burned at the evacuation of Charleston.
11. *Official Navy Records,* Series II, Vol. 1, vessel statistics.
12. *Official Records,* Series I, Vol. 28, Part 1, pp. 181–188, 747–750. *Ibid.,* Part 2, pp. 435–438, 591–593.
13. *Official Navy Records,* Series II, Vol. 1, vessel statistics.
14. *Ordnance Manual* (Confederate, 1863), *op. cit.* p. 10.
15. Another pair of these 1861 howitzers in excellent condition is at Johnstown, Pa. According to Councilman Addison A. Wagner, director of parks, they were made by Alger in 1864 and are stamped with the weights, 2,548 and 2,549 pounds. Numbers are 47 and 57 respectively and the inspector was Richard M. Hill who, incidentally, also inspected the Temple howitzers.
16. J. G. Benton, *A Course of Instruction in Ordnance and Gunnery Composed and Compiled for Cadets of the United States Military Academy,* 1875, p. 247.
17. Alfred Mordecai, *Artillery for The United States Land Service,* 1849, Plate XV.
18. John L. Wilson, *Abstract of a System of Exercise and Instruction of Field Artillery and The Exercise of Heavy Artillery in Battery . . . for Use of South Carolina Militia,* Plate II.

Chapter 3

The Mortar

MORTARS ARE SHORT CANNON designed to throw large, hollow projectiles at high elevations with a small charge of powder. Although there is evidence that the Confederates used a rifled mortar on Sullivan's Island near Charleston in 1864 and there may have been other isolated cases, for all practical purposes, the mortar of the Civil War era may be considered a smoothbore weapon. Designed primarily to fire shells, it also could handle carcasses, grape, both light and fire balls, and one type could even toss a basket of stones.

In addition, federal forces experimented with spherical case for 10-inch mortars.[1] The trial firing was in October, 1863 at Fort Scott in the Washington defenses using a standard 10-inch mortar shell loaded with twenty-seven 12-pounder, iron canister balls (diameter 1.46 to 1.49 inches, weighing .43 pounds each) and a bursting charge of 2.5 pounds of powder sprinkled loose among them. The complete round weighed 104 pounds and fired from a Model 1861, 10-inch siege mortar with 1 pound 6 ounces of powder, gave a range of 800 yards and a 13-second time of flight.

Since the bursting charge merely destroyed the case with little scattering of the balls, they fell within a circle roughly equal in diameter to the height of the burst above ground, and struck with sufficient force to kill. This was especially valuable since exact control of height of burst was difficult if not impossible and prior experience with mortar shell had proved that unless the projectile was almost a direct hit, it was relatively harmless to personnel. This was because shell, with a heavier bursting charge, dispersed its fragments over a large area. High air bursts often caused little damage to men directly beneath while shells that buried into the ground before exploding did even less.

Success of the experiment led to employment of spherical case in the Battle of Petersburg Mine where the artillery was ordered to use every effort to keep enemy batteries silent. Ten mortars fired at a Confederate salient battery from which a great deal of trouble had been expected. Not a shot came from it after the mortars had zeroed in, and Southern officers later said it was impossible for gunners to work their weapons amid the shower of balls falling from shells bursting overhead about once every thirty seconds.

However, although success proved spectacular,

the projectile fell into disfavor. It was occasionally used during the remainder of the siege, but a few premature bursts near the muzzles of the pieces soured the gunners on it. No casualties resulted and the problem was probably due more to expediencies used in preparation of the shell—particularly loose powder and perhaps the wooden fuse cases—than to design failure. Had the balls been fixed in place by sulphur, the powder confined to a drilled hole, as in other spherical case, and a different type fuse used, the projectile might have proved an efficient form of ammunition.

Although the first round of the war—the shell that signaled the bombardment of Fort Sumter—was fired from a mortar, the potential of the weapon apparently was more or less overlooked in the East until the spring of 1864.

The Union had emplaced mortars at Yorktown[2] and experienced considerable discomfort during this campaign from a single Confederate 8-incher, but generally speaking mortars were relegated to the background until, according to Abbot:

". . . the advance of the Army of the Potomac from the Rapidan in the spring of 1864 . . . Gen (Henry J.) Hunt, chief of artillery, had procured eight Coehorn mortars to accompany the movement and had included in . . . my siege train many 10-inch and 8-inch siege mortars and Coehorns. It was a new arm to the troops and excited much interest and attention from both officers and men.

"After the failure of the first assault upon the Confederate position on the Heights of Petersburg, the siege train was called into active service and then began for the first time in the experience of armies operating in Virginia, a really heavy mortar fire.

"The result of their sudden and unexpected opening on the Petersburg lines was appalling. Having no mortars wherewith to reply and no bombproofs for cover, and yet being compelled by the proximity of the main lines (only 200 yards apart in the nearest place) to keep their own fully manned in order to guard against assault, the enemy suffered severely for the first few days and the moral effect was extremely depressing.

"As soon as the enemy could obtain mortars, they placed them in position and from that time until the evacuation, the fire was frequent and severe. . . . Our expenditures (of ammunition) amounted to over 40,000 rounds and their's were not much less. . . ."

Lack of mortar fire, particularly on the part of the Confederates, was cited on several occasions as an important factor in engagements.

Johnson,[3] for instance, emphasized this point in his discussion of the fall of Battery Wagner on Morris Island, South Carolina, in 1863:

FIGURE: III-1 LOCATION: Petersburg, Va. IDENTIFICATION: Mortar, Siege & Garrison, 24-Pounder, Model 1841, Bronze, Coehorn. BORE: Diameter — 5.82. Smoothbore, Length — 13.07. LENGTH O/A: 16.32. TRUNNIONS: Diameter — 2.75. Length — 2.5. MARKINGS: Muzzle Face — A.M. Co., A.B.D., 163 (weight), No. 49, 1862. REMARKS: Reproduction bed. COMMON NAME: Coehorn. (Name used alone refers only to this weapon –— Southern models should be termed "Confederate Coehorn" of specific caliber, 12 or 24-pounder.)

"It may be candidly admitted that in two particulars pointed out by Gen. Gillmore [Maj. Gen. Quincy A. Gillmore, USA] the special defense of Battery Wagner was faulty—viz: The disuse of vigorous night sorties and of mortar firing. From numerous admissions in the reports of federal officers, it is plain that if even the single mortar occasionally fired from Wagner had been well served upon the sappers, they would have been seriously delayed . . . while if the Confederates had mounted four or five mortars to the rear of the gorge . . . and had served them with any spirit, it is highly probable that the approach of the sap over the narrow front could have been entirely arrested. . . ."

Johnson felt it necessary to explain later[4] that the Confederates were aware of this and blamed failure to rectify the deficiency on lack of ammunition and not ordering the correct type of mortars (Coehorns).

Similarly Abbot[5] called attention to lack of mortar fire in the Fort Fisher, North Carolina, engagement and stressed the fact in connection with what he considered an essential use of large mortars—seacoast defense, particularly of harbor installations. Although acknowledging several factors involved in the loss of Fisher, he pointed out that a few well-served mortars would have frustrated the main plan of the U.S. Navy. This consisted in bringing up ironclads and a few gunboats to close range outside the traverse of most of the water batteries. These vessels anchored to insure accurate firing and systematically knocked out the Confederate weapons, all mounted in barbette. Meanwhile, thinner-skinned vessels lay off at distant range and by a hot, although random fire, protected the ironclads by keeping Southern gunners away from their pieces.

Abbot felt that while guns would have had trouble penetrating the thick turrets and sides of the monitors, a few mortars firing from defiladed positions could have dropped shells on the lightly clad decks and perhaps changed the outcome of the battle. He added that even had the fleet possessed mortars, counterbattery fire from rolling decks of ships would be too inaccurate to be dangerous. Continuing in this vein, he urged consideration of heavy mortars for U.S. harbor defense installations which due to their accuracy, high trajectory, and the relatively thin deck plating of existing ironclads, would prove extremely formidable weapons.

Mortars, like guns and howitzers, were made in various models, but most conform to a few general types and recognition of these is relatively easy. A light mortar used by both sides during the war was the bronze Coehorn, Model 1841, which bore the Anglicized name of its Dutch inventor, Baron van Menno Coehoorn (1641-1704).[6] The tube weighed about 164 pounds and mounted on its wooden mortar bed (Fig. III-1) had an overall weight of 296 pounds, give or take a pound or two. Handles on the side of the

bed permitted two men to carry it for short distances, although the standard crew of four could do a better job.

The piece fired a standard 24-pounder shell (weight 16.8 pounds) and a half-pound of powder delivered a maximum range of 1,200 yards. In federal service, the projectile was loaded by means of tin straps, a system which Abbot termed "clumsy" in comparison to the Confederate practice of casting the shells with ears as was usually done by both sides with larger mortar ammunition. The ears consisted of a hole on either side of the fuse into which the points of shell hooks, that resembled ice tongs, could be inserted to facilitate loading. Careful loading of shell was essential to insure that the fuse pointed outward when the projectile came to rest at the bottom of the bore. If reversed, the force of the propellant would drive the fuse into the shell resulting in an explosion which might destroy cannon and crew.

Although the weapon in Figure III-1 is generally referred to when speaking of Civil War Coehorns, the Confederates during the siege of Petersburg turned out 24- and 12-pounder Coehorns, both of iron, which apparently were highly successful.[7] The author believes one of these weapons, probably the 24-pounder, is in the foreground of Figure III-2, mounted on a seemingly sturdy, albeit crude, mortar bed. The mortar at right is an 8-inch, Model 1841 siege mortar and the gun on the broken carriage a

FIGURE: III-2 IDENTIFICATION: Weapons captured at Richmond, 1865. REMARKS: Mortars (bottom) are a siege and garrison, 8-inch, Model 1841 (right) and Confederate-made, iron "Coehorn", probably the 5.82-inch model. Center on damaged carriage is a 32-Pounder, Model 1846, 27 cwt. (the weight, 27-2-11, is stamped clearly on the base ring and the date, 1846, indistinctly on the visible trunnion). In line over the chase and muzzle are three standard Coehorns, 5.82-inch. The line of weapons at rear include Parrotts and Confederate Parrotts, caliber undetermined, and three 8-inch, siege and garrison howitzers, Model 1861. The piece on the ground, lower left, is a 30 or 50-pounder Dahlgren rifle.

32-pounder of 27 cwt., Model 1846. On carriages at rear are a number of Parrott rifles and immediately behind the 32 are three 8-inch siege howitzers, Model 1861. Below them and directly over the chase ring of the 32 are three standard 24-pounder Coehorns. The weapons were captured at the fall of Richmond.

The Confederate 12-pounder Coehorn drew special praise from Abbot who urged adoption of a similar caliber into the federal service, observing: "For practice against troops, the 12-pounder Coehorn is decidedly more deadly than the 24-pounder as its shell, when the fuse burns too slowly, does not bury itself on striking and the fragments thus scatter widely."

Another small mortar, the eprouvette (Fig. III-3), was never intended for use against an enemy and by the time of the Civil War had fallen sufficiently into disuse that it is not even listed in the Ordnance Manual of 1861.[8] Made of iron, the eprouvette was used solely to test powder. It was cast with an iron bed-piece or "sole," countersunk into a bed-plate, generally also of iron, which gave the mortar an elevation of precisely 45°. Theoretically, when loaded with an ounce of powder, the eprouvette would fire a carefully weighed, 24-pounder shot a given distance— not less than 225 yards for acceptable powder and preferably 250 or more. Good cannon powder ranged 280 to 300 yards and small grain types 300 to 320.[9]

However, it was discovered that the theory behind this form of proving was faulty for the power of powder did not progress uniformly as quantity increased and the force exerted by a pound was generally far greater than sixteen times that established for an ounce. Moreover, fast-acting powder imparted its total velocity to the ball within the short confines of the eprouvette while slower burning cannon powder would need a longer tube to be entirely consumed. As a consequence, results were misleading and the little mortar was, in most cases, set aside in favor of improved testing methods, although it continued to be used occasionally to check the relative strength of two lots of powder.

The eprouvette illustrated is at the Washington Navy Yard and was made in 1816 by Columbia Foundry. It is stamped USND (U.S. Navy Department). There are several of these mortars at the yard as well as a bronze type (Fig. III-4). These differ somewhat in appearance from the standard iron model and probably were cast at the yard. This identification, however, is tentative since at the time they were examined, heavy tampions covered markings, if any, that might lead to a more positive determination. The illustration is included since ordnance enthusiasts visiting the Yard will observe these intriguing little mortars and perhaps have better luck at identification.

With exception of the eprouvette, which in a

FIGURE: III-3 LOCATION: Washington Navy Yard, D.C. IDENTIFICATION: Mortar, Eprouvette, 5.655-Inch, Iron. BORE: Diameter — 5.655. Smoothbore. Length — 11.5v. LENGTH O/A: 13.5 (Muzzle face to estimated end of breech). MARKINGS: Tube — 1816, I.M., U.S.N.D. (U.S. Navy Department), Col. Foun. (Columbia Foundry). REMARKS: Not a weapon. Used for testing powder. COMMON NAME: Eprouvette.

FIGURE: III-4 LOCATION: Washington Navy Yard, D.C. IDENTIFICATION: Mortar, Eprouvette, 5.655-Inch (assumed), Bronze. BORE: Diameter — 5.655 (assumed, bore plugged). Smoothbore. Length — 11.5v. LENGTH O/A: 13 (Muzzle face to estimated base of breech). REMARKS: Not a weapon. Used for testing powder. No marks apparent, but probably cast at Washington Navy Yard for use at that facility, and not a standard model. COMMON NAME: Bronze Eprouvette.

FIGURE: III-5 LOCATION: West Point, N.Y. IDENTIFICATION: Stone Mortar, Siege & Garrison, 16-Inch, Model 1839, Bronze. BORE: Diameter — 16. Smoothbore. Length — 26.75. LENGTH O/A: 31. TRUNNIONS: Diameter — 8. Length — 6.5. MARKINGS: Muzzle Face — J.W.R. Left Trunnion — 1840. Right Trunnion — N.P. Ames, Founder, Springfield, Mass. Base of Breech — 1496. COMMON NAME: Stone Mortar.

technical sense was not a weapon, all mortars were either siege and garrison or seacoast. Listed under the former were the 24-pounder Coehorn, already discussed, 8- and 10-inch siege mortars (termed "light"), and the 16-inch stone mortar. Seacoast pieces were 10- and 13-inch (heavy) mortars.

Since the 8-, 10- and 13-inch mortars went through several model changes, most of which were used during the war, the stone mortar, largest of the lot, will be taken up first. Recommendation for a 15-inch stone mortar was made by the Ordnance Board of 1818, but the proposal died a-borning and the piece was omitted from the list of ordnance approved in 1819. Twenty years later, the idea was revived by the board of 1838 and the 16-inch stone mortar was adopted by the War Department in 1839 for siege and garrison use.

It was a bronze piece designed to throw 120 pounds of stones from 150 to 250 yards with a charge of one and a half pounds of powder. The stones were placed in a basket, made to fit the bore, which sat on a circular piece of wood covering the entrance to the conical or Gomer chamber. Strictly an anti-personnel weapon, it was supposed to be fired by the besiegers to clear the breach, made by other weapons, in a fortification just before the final assault. Conversely, the besieged were to use the weapon to stop just such an attack.

When loaded with stones, the piece was elevated to 60° which gave the missiles sufficient height of fall to attain killing velocity. Instead of stones, the mortar could be loaded with 6-pounder shells. Fifteen of these shells, each with a 15-second fuse, could be fired using a 1-pound charge at 33° elevation to give a range of 50 to 150 yards. The lower elevation was used to prevent the shells from burying if they failed to explode before impact. Since the chances were rather good that one or more of the 6-pounders would explode near the muzzle, the mortar, when using this type ammunition, was fired by a slow match attached to a quick match which gave the cannoneers time to get under cover.

Taken as a whole, the stone mortar was more impressive to look at than a danger to the enemy, and the piece was abandoned in 1861. It was omitted from the Ordnance Manual of that year and the author has found no evidence of the weapon being used during the war. The illustrated piece (Fig. III-5) is in the West Point collection and was made by N. P. Ames in 1840. It is 31.55 inches long and since the trunnion diameter is the same as that of the Model 1841, 10-inch siege mortar—8 inches—it utilized a similar type bed.

The remaining siege and seacoast mortars were made of iron and, as has been previously mentioned, were standard in three calibers—8, 10, and 13 inches. Mortars in these as well as other calibers had been used on and off since well before the turn of the century, but the Ordnance Board of 1818, in an attempt to standardize and reduce the number of different size weapons, dropped the 8- and 13-inch mortars and recommended that only the 10-inch be used. Consequently, for many years, the Army had

FIGURE: III-6 LOCATION: West Point, N.Y. IDENTIFICATION: Mortar, Siege & Garrison, 10-Inch, Model 1819, Iron. BORE: Diameter — 10. Smoothbore. Length — 23.5v. LENGTH O/A: 31.25. TRUNNIONS: Diameter — 8. Length — 6. COMMON NAME: 10-Inch Siege Mortar, Model 1819.

FIGURE: III-7 LOCATION: Fort Sumter, S.C. IDENTIFICATION: Mortar, Seacoast, 10-Inch, Model 1819, Iron. BORE: Diameter — 10. Smoothbore. Length — 35.25. LENGTH O/A: 45.5. TRUNNIONS: Diameter — 10. Length — 9. MARKINGS: Tube — HF, No. 4, 34-1-25 (3,861 lbs.). COMMON NAME: 10-Inch Seacoast Mortar, Model 1819.

FIGURE: III-8 IDENTIFICATION: Mortar, Seacoast, 10-Inch, Model 1841–44, Iron. REMARKS: Mortars being emplaced at Butler's Crows Nest, Dutch Gap. Note clevis and bolt attached to mortar ears. COMMON NAME: 10-Inch Seacoast Mortar, Model 1841–44.

only two pieces in this category, the 10-inch, Model 1819 siege mortar (Fig. III-6), and the 10-inch, Model 1819 seacoast mortar (Fig. III-7).

The siege piece illustrated is in the U.S. Military Academy collection. A mate to it formerly was also at West Point, but now is on display at Fort Pulaski, Georgia. Markings, if any, on both these weapons are concealed and data on when and by whom they were made is not available. They are approximately 31.25 inches long with trunnion diameter of 8 inches. This length is considerably less than the 45.5-inch seacoast model, a difference quite evident in a comparison of the photographs which also show a somewhat different positioning of the trunnions.

The seacoast piece, at Fort Sumter, is reported to be the type which fired the first round of the war, an identification that appears to have been based more on availability of a mortar to exhibit than documentary evidence. Whether this was the first shot and who fired it is an argument outside the province of this book, so for the sake of brevity, the shell which burst over Sumter at 4:30 A.M. 12 April 1861 will be assumed to have opened the war, and who touched it off will be pointedly ignored. The piece that fired it, however, merits somewhat more consideration.

Unfortunately, both sides were far too busy shooting to bother noting such irrelevant information as types of weapons. Consquently, although reams have been written about the event, accurate ordnance data is extremely sketchy. Based on the Official Records and various eyewitness accounts, there seems little doubt that the projectile was a shell and that it came from a 10-inch seacoast mortar battery at Fort Johnson. But what kind of seacoast mortar? Three types of 10-inch were used during the war although one, Model 1861, may be eliminated immediately as not being available in the area at this time. That leaves the Model 1819 and a 10-inch seacoast mortar which is termed Model 1844 by the Ordnance Manual of 1861. However, there is also a Model 1841 listed in the manual of that year which differs so little in appearance and statistics that for purposes of this book, the weapons will be considered one and called Model 1841-44.

No specimen has been found, but a number of Civil War photographs of the piece are available. Several pictures are of batteries in the Charleston harbor defenses and definitely establish this type as being used in the area. One even shows three of these mortars at Fort Johnson, but it is an 1865 view and hence of doubtful reliability regarding armament of the fort four years earlier. Unfortunately, quality of the Charleston photographs is not of the best, so for illustrative purposes, an 1864 shot of a federal battery being emplaced in Virginia (Fig. III-8) has been substituted.

The picture shows two 10-inch seacoast mortars, Model 1841-44, at Butler's Crows Nest, an observation point near Dutch Gap. The pronounced upswept forward ends of the mortar bed cheeks were separated by a wood transom through which a screw held the piece at elevation. Traverse was by working handspikes under a long maneuvering bolt extended through the lower nut near the front of each cheek and a projection at the rear.

Photographs placing the Model 1819 in the Charleston area have not been discovered, but the sketch (Fig. III-9) purports to be drawn from a photograph and the weapons are clearly 1819s. These pieces, while not in Fort Johnson, were on nearby Morris Island in one of the ring of batteries which joined in the bombardment of federal forces in Sumter.

Consequently, both models were used in the area and the unfortunate lack of specific information makes any selection extremely hazardous. However, since the Model 1819 was quite old and most ordnance in Charleston defenses was of more recent vintage, and since wartime photographs show a preponderance of the newer model, the author leans toward the Model 1841-44 as the more likely weapon used for the initial shot.

In addition to the 10-inch seacoast, 1841 mortars included two in the siege category 8- and 10-inch— and another seacoast piece, a 13-inch. Neither an exist-

ing weapon nor a Civil War photograph of the 13-inch has been found, but the drawing (Fig. III-10) shows that in appearance this 1841 model resembled the 10-inch 1841-44 very closely and differences, other than size, may have been due to slight changes which ap-

FIGURE: III-9 IDENTIFICATION: Mortar, Seacoast, 10-Inch, 1819. Iron. SOURCE: *Battles and Leaders,* Vol. 1. Confederate mortar battery on Morris Island, S.C. 1861. COMMON NAME: 10-Inch Seacoast Mortar, Model 1819.

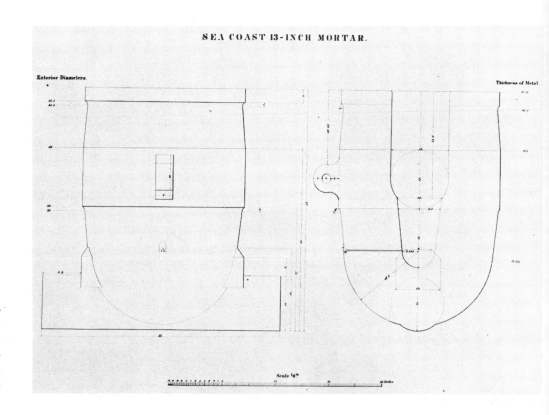

SEA COAST 13-INCH MORTAR.

Exterior Diameters.

Thickness of Metal

Scale 1/6

FIGURE: III-10 IDENTIFICATION: Mortar, Seacoast, 13-Inch, Model 1841, Iron. BORE: Diameter — 13. Smoothbore. Length — 39. LENGTH: O/A: 53: TRUNNIONS: Diameter — 12. Length — 8.5. SOURCE: Mordecai. COMMON NAME: 13-Inch Seacoast Mortar, Model 1841.

parently were made to the 10-inch in 1844. All of these 1841 (44) models have one easily distinguishing feature—the trunnions are at the base of the piece. The seacoast types are also longer and have an ear at the center of gravity which is omitted in the siege pieces.

The Model 1841 siege pieces are the 8- and 10-inch. One of the former (Fig. III-11) is at Providence, Rhode Island, and a 10-inch, mounted on an original carriage (Fig. III-12), is at Fort Barrancas, Florida. Another of these weapons, the 8-inch to judge by the size, is illustrated in Figure III-2.

Although the North came out with a new series of mortars in 1861, the Confederates continued with the 1841 models, listed as standard in their Ordnance Manual of 1863. This manual, incidentally, lists the 10-inch seacoast mortar, Model 1841-44, as Model 1841. The 1861 series of mortars retained the same calibers as the older model—8 and 10 inches for the siege pieces and 10 and 13 for the seacoast. However, their appearance was considerably different. All molding was stripped from the new weapons and the trunnions were enlarged and moved to the approximate center of balance. This permitted setting elevation by means of a ratchet and handspike at the rear instead of wood quoins under the front as was the practice with older types. The chamber was omitted and the bottom of the bore made elliptical. This allowed the shell to rest against the charge resulting in increased range over previous models, particularly when light charges were used.

With exception of the 10-inch seacoast (Fig.

III-13) which was slightly elongated, the weapons were similar in appearance. Specimens of the 8- and 10-inch siege models, identical except for size, are rare, but one of the former (Fig. III-14) is displayed at the Mariners Museum, Newport News, Virginia. A Civil War view of another 8-inch is shown in Figure X-28. Fort Macon, North Carolina, has the 10-inch (Fig. III-15), one of a pair cast in 1862 by Cyrus Alger.

The ratchet of the 10-inch seacoast and both siege weapons was enclosed while that of the 13-inch was open. Both siege and seacoast models were equipped with an ear cast on top of the tube although it has been removed from the illustrated 10-inch and from one of the 13-inchers (Fig. III-16) mounted on The Battery at Charleston. The 1861 Ordnance Manual description[10] of the siege mortars omits the appendage. However, it is clearly evident in the manual drawings of these pieces,[11] was mentioned by Benton in his 1875 edition,[12] and can be seen in both the Mariners Museum and Fort Macon pieces as well as the Civil War photograph of Chapter X—sufficient evidence, the author feels, to establish the ears were cast on the siege mortars as well as seacoast.

Specimens of the 13-inch are by far the most common today with six in the Charleston area alone. Four on The Battery, of which three are in Fig. III-16, were made at Fort Pitt in 1861-62 and range in weight from 17,100 to 17,200 pounds.

Although the Confederates presumably captured

FIGURE: III-11 LOCATION: Providence, R.I. IDENTIFICATION: Mortar, Siege & Garrison, 8-Inch, Model 1841. BORE: Diameter — 8. Smoothbore. Length — 16. LENGTH O/A: 22.5. TRUNNIONS: Diameter — 6. Length — 4. COMMON NAME: 8-Inch Siege Mortar, Model 1841.

FIGURE: III-12 LOCATION: Fort Barrancas, Fla. IDENTIFICATION: Mortar, Siege & Garrison, 10-Inch, Model 1841, Iron. BORE: Diameter — 10. Smoothbore. Length — 18.75v. LENGTH O/A: 28.25. TRUNNIONS: Diameter — 8. Length — 5. MARKINGS: Muzzle Face — 6, J.W.R. Left Trunnion — 1842. Right Trunnion — C.A. & Co., Boston. Tube — 1832 (weight), U.S. COMMON NAME: 10-Inch Siege Mortar, Model 1841.

FIGURE: III-13 LOCATION: St. Augustine, Fla. IDENTIFICATION: Mortar, Seacoast, 10-Inch, Model 1861, Iron. Bore: Diameter — 10. Smoothbore. Length — 30v. LENGTH O/A: 46. TRUNNIONS: Diameter — 12. Length — 3.25. MARKINGS: Muzzle Face — No. 8, C.A. & Co., ton, 7640, T.J.R., 1862. Tube — REMARKS: Ear has been removed. COMMON NAME: 10-Inch Seacoast Mortar, Model 1861.

FIGURE: III-14 LOCATION: Mariners Museum, Newport News, Va. IDENTIFICATION: Mortar, Siege & Garrison, 8-Inch, Model 1861., Iron. BORE: Diameter — 8. Smoothbore. Length — 14v. LENGTH O/A: 22. TRUNNIONS: Diameter — 10. Length — 2.5. MARKINGS: Muzzle Face — C.A. & Co., Boston, 995, T.J.R., 1862. Tube — U.S. REMARKS: Tube (rear) is 4-foot section of 16-inch rifle of battleship South Dakota. COMMON NAME: 8-Inch Siege Mortar, Model 1861.

FIGURE: III-15 LOCATION: Fort Macon, N.C. IDENTIFICATION: Mortar, Siege & Garrison, 10-Inch, Model 1861, Iron. BORE: Diameter — 10. Smoothbore. Length — 20.5. LENGTH O/A: 28. TRUNNIONS: Diameter — 12. Length — 3.5. MARKINGS: Muzzle Face — No. 7, 1966 Lbs., C.A. & Co., Boston, T.J.R., 1862. COMMON NAME: 10-Inch Siege Mortar, Model 1861.

FIGURE: III-16 LOCATION: Charleston, S.C. IDENTIFICATION: Mortar, Seacoast, 13-Inch, Model 1861, Iron. BORE: Diameter — 13. Smoothbore. Length — 33v. LENGTH O/A: 54.5. TRUNNIONS: Diameter — 15. Length — 3.5. MARKINGS: Muzzle Face (Piece in foreground) — 17,200 lbs., No. 41, J.R.M.M., Fort Pitt, Pa., 1862. Tube — 7?7 (missing number probably 8). Muzzle face (Second piece from front) — 17,196 lbs., No. 101, Fort Pitt, Pa., 1862. Tube — 929 (preponderance). REMARKS: Ear has been removed from second piece from foreground. This weapon also has handles attached to trunnions for ease in setting elevation. Shot and shell in right foregound are 10-, not 13-inch. COMMON NAME: 13-Inch Seacoast Mortar, Model 1861.

a few Model 1861 siege mortars, there is no record of their having obtained one of these seacoast monsters which with 20 pounds of powder could hurl a 218-pound shell some 4,200 yards.[13]

Figure III-17 illustrates an ingenious arrangement for one of these mortars devised by the federals during the siege of Petersburg. But let Abbot[14] tell it:

"The great weight of the 13-inch mortar (17,000 pounds) renders it difficult to move and some satisfactory experiments were made with a novel platform. An ordinary railroad platform car (eight wheels) was strengthened by additional beams tied strongly by iron rods and was plated on top with iron. The mortar was placed upon the car (top of mortar nine feet above the tracks) and run down on the Petersburg and City Point Railroad to a point near our lines where a curve in the track afforded facilities for changing the plane of fire by advancing the car or drawing it back.

"The mortar fired with 14 pounds of powder recoiled less than two feet on the car which moved 10 or 12 feet on the track. The effect of the charge was taken up without damage to the axles, even when the full allowance of 20 pounds of powder was used. This mortar, whose shell would crush and explode any ordinary field magazine, excited dread among the Confederate gunners and was effective in inducing their enfilading batteries on Chesterfield Heights to discontinue fire upon the right of our line.

"Its practice was excellent . . . of course with this platform, the plane of fire must be nearly paralled to the track or the mortar will be dismounted, but by placing the car on a curve, a very considerable traverse can be secured without difficulty."

This was the celebrated "Dictator" which today is preserved at Hartford, Connecticut.

A number of these weapons were mounted on mortar barges during the Vicksburg campaign and were also used by the Navy in mortar schooners. The platform used for this latter service (Fig. III-18) was equipped with eccentric wheels which, when engaged, permitted the top of the platform and the piece to revolve for traversing and when thrown out of gear let the top rest on the bottom of the platform and the deck which was reinforced below to stand the shock of firing. The vessel shown was a guard boat at Alexandria, Virginia. Needless to say, all gear aloft had to be cleared away before firing.

FIGURE: III-17 IDENTIFICATION: Mortar, Seacoast, 13-Inch, Model 1861, Iron. REMARKS: "The Dictator", 13-Inch mortar emplaced on a railway car, was used by the Federals during the siege of Petersburg. The piece today is mounted at Hartford, Conn. COMMON NAME: 13-Inch Seacoast Mortar, Model 1861.

FIGURE: III-18 IDENTIFICATION: Mortar, Seacoast, 13-Inch, Model 1861, Iron. REMARKS: Mortar mounted aboard guard boat at Alexandria, Va. Note square opening in circular platform through which levers worked the eccentrics for use during traverse. COMMON NAME: 13-Inch Seacoast Mortar, Model 1861.

FIGURE: III-19 IDENTIFICATION: Mortar, Seacoast, 13-Inch, Model 1861, Iron. REMARKS: Mortars emplaced to bombard Yorktown which was evacuated 4 May 1862 before they were ready to fire. Note method of using ratchets for elevation, eccentrics, platforms, and excellent defilade of position. COMMON NAME: 13-Inch Seacoast Mortar, Model 1861.

A number of these 13-inch mortars (Fig. III-19) were emplaced during the siege of Yorktown, but just when they were ready to open fire, the Confederates abandoned the town and the work of the Northern gunners went for nought. The picture, in addition to depicting a well-defiladed position, illustrates the method of elevation and shows a standard platform used in the field.

A 12-inch mortar saw limited use during the war. It was an experimental U.S. model which at 45° elevation with 20 pounds of powder and a 200-pound shell could deliver a range of 4,625 yards.[15] The Official Records list at least two instances of 12-inchers being used in battle and presumably these were the experimental weapon. One, possibly two, were used by the Confederates during the siege of Fort Pulaski[16] and another was used by United States troops at Fort Pickens[17] to bombard Southern lines 22-23 November 1861.

The author has heard of no 12-incher extant and has found no description of its appearance. However, since the weapon is mentioned in Gibbon's book, dated 1860, and omitted from the 1861 Ordnance Manual, it more likely resembled the 1841 (44) type with breech trunnions than the 1861 model. This theory is borne out to a certain extent by a statement in the Records[18] regarding the Fort Pickens firing: ". . . early in the day, the elevating screws began to bend and by means of blocks and quoins the 13-inch mortar was kept at an elevation of about 40 degrees and was fired at that elevation during the afternoon when the screw broke off entirely. About 3 P.M. the elevating screw of the 12-inch mortar broke off and the mortar rested on the bolster and was not used for the rest of the day. . . ." This would indicate the mortar was held at elevation from the front, as in the older mortars, rather than with a ratchet at the rear.

No discussion of mortars would be complete without mention of the wooden "Coehorns" which seem to have been used on occasion by both sides. Grant[19] refers to their use in the Vicksburg Campaign: "There were no mortars with the besiegers, except what the Navy had in front of the city; but wooden ones were made by taking logs of the toughest wood that could be found, boring them out for six or twelve-pounder shells, and binding them with strong iron bands. These answered as Coehorns, and shells were successfully thrown from them into the trenches of the enemy. . . ." General Andrew

67

FIGURE: III-20 IDENTIFICATION: Mortar, Siege & Garrison, 12-Pounder, Wood. SOURCE: *Battles and Leaders*, Vol. 3. REMARKS: 4.62-inch mortars made of hollowed logs strapped with iron bands were a field expedient employed by federal forces during the Vicksburg Campaign as a substitute for Coehorns which were not available. COMMON NAME: Wood Mortar.

Hickenlooper, chief engineer with the 17th Corps during the same campaign, stated[20] they were made from "short sections of gum-tree logs" and that they "proved exceedingly effective." Figure III-20 is a sketch of one of these Vicksburg wooden mortars.

No such success crowned Confederate attempts to use wooden mortars during the Petersburg Campaign.[21] These were made in substantially the same fashion, but proved a complete flop. Even at short distances, as General E.P. Alexander put it: ". . . when they did not split, the ranges were so irregular that they could not be made useful. . . ."

In addition to designed mortars, various types of other cannon were used on occasion in this fashion. The 8-inch siege howitzer, as previously mentioned, and the 12-pounder Napoleon were both especially adaptable for this service and there are instances where 8- and 10-inch columbiads were fired as mortars by propping up the front or digging in the rear of the carriage.

A case in point is illustrated in Figure III-21, a photograph of Fort Sumter taken shortly after Ander-

son's surrender 13 April 1861. At far left are three 8-inch columbiads, dug in as mortars and aimed, but not fired, at Morris Island.[22] The structure slightly right and rear of the pieces is a hot shot furnace, which will be discussed more fully in a later chapter.

A 10-inch Model 1844 columbiad, although not dug in, was mounted to fire at mortar elevation on the City. The piece rested on its top carriage similar to that in Fig IV-4, and, in unbanded, smoothbore condition, could have been the identical weapon. The 10-inch, like the 8s, remained silent during the bombardment.

Although traditionally a smoothbore during the war, there is at least one reference to a rifled mortar. The report,[23] dated 17 August 1864 from Sullivan's Island simply states: "Ten shots were fired from the rifled mortar out of which 5 burst well. . . ." No other reference has been found to the piece and this isolated report remains to tantalize the ordnance enthusiast. Caliber, appearance, specifications must all await the day when further evidence becomes available.

FIGURE: III-21 IDENTIFICATION: Columbiad, 8-Inch. Model 1844 (tentative), Iron. REMARKS: 8-inch columbiads (left) dug in as mortars by Maj. Robert Anderson's command at Fort Sumter. They were aimed, but not fired, at Morris Island. Photograph was taken in 1861 shortly after Anderson's surrender. Burned out west barracks (left) with nearby hot shot furnace. North channel face at right.

NOTES

1. Henry L. Abbot, "Siege Artillery in The Campaigns Against Richmond With Notes on The 15-Inch Gun," *Professional Papers No. 14, Corps of Engineers,* 1867, pp. 26–28.
2. *Ibid.,* pp. 17–19.
3. John Johnson, *The Defense of Charleston Harbor, 1863–65,* 1890, p. 154; Q. A. Gillmore, *Engineer and Artillery Operations Against The Defenses of Charleston Harbor, 1863,* 1865, pp. 213–216.
4. Johnson, *op. cit.,* p. 269.
5. Abbot, *op. cit.,* p. 44.
6. *Encyclopaedia Britannica,* 1946, Vol. 5, p. 963.
7. E. P. Alexander, "Confederate Artillery Service," *Southern Historical Society Papers,* Vol. XI, 1883, p. 110.
8. *Ordnance Manual for The Use of Officers of The United States Army,* 1861, p. 13.
9. J. G. Benton, *A Course of Instruction in Ordnance and Gunnery Composed and Compiled for Cadets of the United States Military Academy,* 1861, p. 29; John Gibbon, *The Artillerist's Manual, Compiled From Various Sources and Adapted to The Service of The United States,* 1860, p. 27.
10. *Ordnance Manual for The Use of Officers of The United States Army,* 1861, p. 15.
11. *Ibid.,* Plate I.
12. J. G. Benton, *A Course of Instruction in Ordnance and Gunnery Composed and Compiled for Cadets of The United States Military Academy,* 1875, p. 187.
13. *Ordnance Manual,* 1861, *op. cit.,* p. 34, 390. Gibbon, *op. cit.,* Appendix, p. 46, lists weight of shell 200, charge 20 pounds, range, 4,325 yards.
14. Abbot, *op. cit.,* pp. 22–24.
15. Gibbon, *op. cit.,* Appendix, p. 46.
16. *Official Records,* Series I. Vol. 6, p. 149, report of Gen. Q. A. Gillmore, U.S.A., 20 October 1865 lists two 12-inch mortars. Page 169, report of Brig. Gen. Alexander R. Lawton, C.S.A., 14 April 1862 lists one.
17. *Ibid.,* p. 487, report of Capt. Matthew M. Blunt, 12th U.S. Infantry, 25 November 1861 at Fort Pickens: "The battery consists of one 13-inch and one 12-inch seacoast mortars. . . ."
18. *Ibid.,* p. 487.
19. *Battles and Leaders of The Civil War,* 1887, p. 522.
20. *Ibid.,* p. 540.
21. Alexander, *loc. cit.,* p. 110.
22. *Official Records,* Series I, Vol. 1, p. 215.
23. *Official Records,* Series I, Vol. 35, Part 1, p. 251.

Chapter 4

The Columbiad

COLUMBIADS COMBINE CERTAIN FEATURES of all the preceding weapons. They are large-caliber, long pieces capable of firing shot and shell with heavy charges at high angles of elevation. Originally they were chambered, like the howitzers, but this feature was dropped in later models. Heavy caliber, long range, and high elevation made them ideally suited for defending narrow channels as well as distant roadsteads and for many years the safety of American seacoasts hinged on these weapons. They are, with a few exceptions noted later in this chapter, smoothbore.

The columbiad made its appearance in 1811 as a 50-pounder, the invention of Colonel George Bomford (1780-1848)[1] and saw use for firing solid shot during the War of 1812 only to be set aside in 1821. One of these early model columbiads, identified by the United States Military Academy and in the West Point collection (Fig. IV-1) has a bore diameter of roughly 7.25 inches and a 74-inch overall length. Weight, clearly stamped "55-5-12" on the breech is a puzzle since under the hundredweight theory, 5 quarters are clearly redundant. Probably the solution is no more complicated than a mixup of "3" and "5" stamps which would make the true weight 55-3-12 or 6,256 pounds. It also could have been a way of adding 1 cwt. after the 55 had been erroneously marked to give the same result as 56-1-12, or 6,312 pounds. In either event, the error is interesting, but academic since as far as can be determined, the

FIGURE: IV-1 LOCATION: West Point, N.Y. IDENTIFICATION: Columbiad, Seacoast, 50-Pounder, Model 1811, Iron. BORE: Diameter — 7.25. Smoothbore. Length — 63.5v. LENGTH O/A: 74. TRUNNIONS: Diameter — 6.5. Length — 6.25. MARKINGS: Breech — 55-5-12 (6,312 lbs.). REMARKS: Note lack of rimbase. See text for possible explanation of 5-quarter weight listing. COMMON NAME: 50-Pounder Columbiad.

columbiad in this form saw no action during the Civil War and is included solely to illustrate development of a major form of antique ordnance.

In 1844 the columbiad once again was adopted into the land service, but with a longer bore and considerably different appearance. Both 8- and 10-inch models were made and were similar other than size. Litchfield, Connecticut has an 8-inch, Model 1844 (Fig. IV-2) made at West Point Foundry in 1845. Although of smaller size, the form is identical to the original appearance of the next two pieces, one of which (Fig. IV-3) ranks among the most valuable Civil War weapons in the nation.

The piece, now mounted in Fort Moultrie, originally was a standard 10-inch, Model 1844 columbiad. Manufacturer and date are unknown since the trunnions, on which the information was recorded, were removed during the war. However, the initials J.W.R. on the muzzle face established that the weapon was inspected by James W. Ripley who served as superintendent of Springfield Armory, Massachusetts, 1841-54, and during the war became Chief of Ordnance.

The other piece (Fig. IV-4) at Fort Sumter is the same caliber and model weapon. It was made for the U.S. Government by Cyrus Alger & Co., Boston, Mass., in 1846, but surprisingly, lacks inspection marks. It does, however, have the numeral "9" on the muzzle face in exactly the same location and in the same style and size as the figure "7" on the muzzle face of the Fort Moultrie piece.

This, admittedly, is nebulous evidence. However, to it may be added certain other clues. Both columbiads were together at the outbreak of the war and could well have been part of the same shipment to Charleston some years previously and it is known that one was sent from Boston. Moreover, Ripley, whose initials are on the other, was stationed for years in Massachusetts and inspected cannon during this period for his initials are found on a 32-pounder field howitzer (Fig. II-5) made by Ames Co., Chicopee (Springfield) Massachusetts in 1851. Taken together the evidence is sufficient for a rough guess that the Fort Moultrie piece also was made by Alger in 1846.

Both weapons were in Sumter during the initial bombardment of 1861, but took no part in the fight. Taken over by the Confederates at the surrender of Major Anderson, their history during the next two years is largely conjectural. The Fort Moultrie piece, which turns up with a broken trunnion in 1863, probably received the damage in the 1861 action and lay useless during the years in some out of the way

spot on the Fort Sumter parade ground. The other columbiad, still a smoothbore, is believed to have been used on Fort Sumter in a 7 April 1863 engagement known as "The Ironclad Attack."

Some months prior to the battle, however, General Beauregard had realized the need for heavy rifles to combat the ironclads and had started improving

FIGURE: IV-2 LOCATION: Litchfield, Conn. IDENTIFICATION: Columbiad, Seacoast, 8-Inch, Model 1844, Iron. BORE: Diameter — 8. Smoothbore. Length — 111. LENGTH O/A: 124. TRUNNIONS: Diameter — 8. Length — 6.5. MARKINGS: Muzzle Face — R.L.B., No. 21. Left Trunnion — 1845. Right Trunnion — W.P.F. Tube — U.S. Breech — 9082 (weight). Front Sight — 8. COMMON NAME: 8-Inch Columbiad, Model 1844.

FIGURE: IV-3 LOCATION: Fort Moultrie, S.C. IDENTIFICATION: Columbiad, Seacoast, 10-Inch, Model 1844, Iron, Banded and Rifled. BORE: Diameter — 10. Rifling — 15 x 15, straight. Length — 110.5v. LENGTH O/A: 126. TRUNNIONS: Diameter — 10.5 Length — 9. MARKINGS: Muzzle Face — 7, J.W.R. (original foundry marks). Left Trunnion — J.M. Eason & Bro., 1863, Charleston, S.C. (stamped after banding and rifling). Trunnion Band — C.S. (Stamped neatly by the Eason firm or Confederate gun crew), U.S. (Crude work by Federal captors). REMARKS: Bronze trunnion band and method of attachment make this Confederate conversion of a standard Model 1844 columbiad one of the most valuable of Civil War weapons. See text for history. COMMON NAME: 10-Inch Columbiad, Model 1844, Banded and Rifled.

Charleston harbor defenses by banding and rifling old smoothbores. Although manufacture of heavy caliber rifles began early in both North and South, initial efforts at rifling existing smoothbores extended mainly to guns which were considered strong enough to stand the conversion. Beauregard, always one to try something new, wanted even heavier rifles than the largest available guns, 42-pounders, and decided to try rifling and banding 8-inch columbiads, probably the Model 1858.

Success of the experiment led to attempts with even larger weapons and incidentally embroiled Beauregard in an argument with the Ordnance Bureau in Richmond to which we are indebted for much of the data that has come down to us on the two 1844 10-inchers.[2] The entire correspondence has not been found, but based on what is available, it is apparent that Beauregard tried to get bureau approval to have certain 8-inchers banded and rifled at the Charleston Arsenal. The attempt seems to have bogged in red tape amid bureau hesitation to risk valuable weapons to an untried process without prolonged testing.

Although Beauregard no doubt would have objected, the author feels there was some justification for Richmond's position and bureau officers were not quite the villains the general would have us believe. They recalled the disastrous failure of attempts early in the war to build rifles on a columbiad model—although apparently not banded—so their hesitation under the circumstances is understandable if not commendable.

But their action was not even understandable to Beauregard. He was charged with defense of a section of coastline in danger of imminent attack. To delay through months of testing was unthinkable. He needed heavy rifles and he needed them now. So without bureau approval, Beauregard had the job done by a private firm in Charleston. This provided him with needed rifles, but also with a bill for the work which, duly approved by local ordnance men, he sent off to Richmond for payment. This the Ordnance Bureau, since it had not authorized the conversions, absolutely refused to pay and a pen and ink battle raged bitterly until Beauregard was forced in the end to get congressional approval for payment.

An interesting letter regarding the transaction is quoted here in full since it reveals Beauregard's feelings on the subject even several years after the war. It is addressed to the Reverend John Johnson, Camden, South Carolina, from Beauregard who was at Alleghany Spa, Virginia, and is dated 21 September 1869. The original is in the collection of Johnson papers owned by the South Carolina Historical Society at Charleston and is reproduced here with the society's permission:

"In writing to you a few days since, I forgot to state (where I refer to the War Department having refused to furnish me at Charleston any assistance to rifle and band our heaviest smoothbore guns for the defense of that harbor) that shortly after I had had those guns thus improved, the forts were attacked [by the ironclads] and the enemy signally defeated, the bill for rifling and banding the guns used so successfully on that occasion was then presented, duly certified to by the Ordnance Officers of the district department and approved by me, to the Ordnance Department at Richmond for payment. This was refused on the ground that the improvement of these guns had not been ordered by it nor made under its supervision.

"The matter was referred by me to the War Department, which sustained, to my surprise, that iniquitous decision, and it was not until some members of Congress, especially Col Wm. Porcher Miles, chairman of the Mili-

FIGURE: IV-4 LOCATION: Fort Sumter, S.C. IDENTIFICATION: Columbiad, Seacoast, 10-Inch, Model 1844, Iron, Banded and Rifled. BORE: Diameter — 10. Rifling — (probably 15 x 15 straight). LENGTH O/A: 126. TRUNNIONS: Diameter — 10. Length — 9. MARKINGS: Muzzle Face — 9. Left Trunnion —1846. Right Trunnion — C.A. & Co., Boston. Tube — U.S. Rear, Inner Band — J.M.E. & Bro. (J.M. Eason & Bro., Charleston, S.C.). COMMON NAME: 10-Inch Columbiad, Model 1844, Banded and Rifled.

tary Committee of the House, actively interfered in the matter, threatening an exposure in Congress of the whole nefarious transaction, that said bill was reluctantly paid. Such is the succinct history of one of the many discreditable acts of the War Department towards me, not only during the memorable siege of Charleston, but also on several other occasions during nearly the whole of the war.

"I hope to be in Washington on the 30th instant when I intend calling on General [William T.] Sherman to have my stolen papers returned to me—Should I succeed, I will gladly see what can be done with regards to yours. I remain, yours very truly—[signed] G. T. Beauregard."

Against this background, it is apparent that when Beauregard—flushed with the success of his 8-inchers, but faced with the fact that the work was not authorized—started looking for a 10-inch, his eye fell on the Model 1844 with broken trunnion lying in Fort Sumter. Here was an ideal subject for the experiment. If successful, a useless arm would be restored to the firing line. If the attempt failed, Beauregard could not be blamed for ruining good ordnance.

He had the piece hauled to the Charleston shops of the Eason Brothers, who had done the other work, where it was rifled with 15 straight type lands and grooves. Rifling the piece was relatively easy. The hard part was how to replace a broken trunnion. The problem was solved in a way that makes the piece unique. Both the good trunnion and presumably a broken stub of the other were sawed off and the rough edges turned true. At the same time, the base ring was removed and the reinforces turned to form a cylinder with gradually decreasing diameter toward the rear. Over the cylinder was slipped an interior band of iron extending from almost the start of the chase to the end of the breech and tapered on the inside to fit. This resulted in the outside diameter of tube and band being about the same throughout its length. This was further strengthened by an exterior iron band from the rear of the trunnion band to the end of the breech. Both bands are wrought iron and were shrunk on after heating.

Now, since a wrought iron trunnion band would have been difficult to make and one of cast iron too weak, both trunnions and band were made in a single piece of cast bronze which contrasts clearly with the black painted iron in the photograph. The problem of holding it on was solved by backing the exterior iron band with a base plate, or ring, almost 2 inches thick which just covers the band leaving the interior reinforce clearly visible beneath. Both base plate and trunnion band have four equi-distant projections, threaded on the inside, and the two bands are squeezed together by heavy bolts. Probably friction alone was sufficient to hold the unit against the shock of discharge, but as additional precaution, the meeting surfaces of the two iron bands may have been given a slight taper. The conversion increased the weight of the piece from approximately 15,000 to 22,000 pounds.

Apparently the bronze was not painted during the war for an 1865 photograph (Fig. IV-5) of the rifle in Battery Bee, about 900 yards from Fort Moultrie, dimly reveals a difference between the trunnion band and the iron. However, a 1915 picture in the author's possession shows the piece near the entrance to Moultrie completely covered with black paint. This concealed the bronze and its true nature was not discovered until 1964 when the trunnions were scraped by the writer in a search for markings. Inscribed on the left trunnion in letters 5/32 inch high is "J.M. Eason & Bros., 1863, Charleston, S.C." On top of the band between the trunnions are the well-formed initials "C.S." and nearby, also on the bronze, a roughly inscribed "U.S.," obviously placed there after capture by some enthusiastic federal soldier.

The piece was finished by the Eason Brothers and mounted in Battery Bee toward the end of 1863 for

FIGURE: IV-5 IDENTIFICATION: Columbiad, Seacoast, 10-Inch, Model 1844, Iron, Banded and Rifled. REMARKS: View of Battery Bee on Sullivan's Island, S.C., shortly after the war shows at far right the rare, Confederate banded weapon now mounted at Fort Moultrie (Fig. IV-3) which is one of the distant works in the far left center of the picture. COMMON NAME: 10-Inch Columbiad, Model 1844, Banded and Rifled.

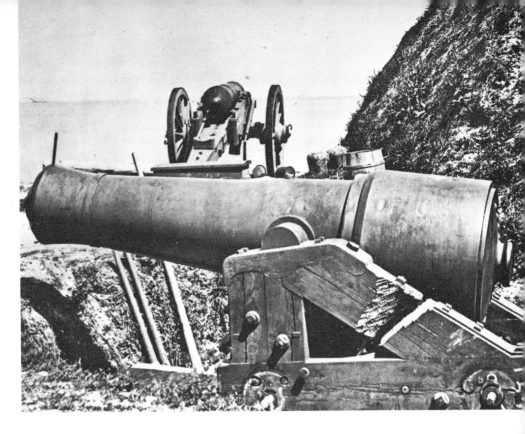

FIGURE: IV-6 IDENTIFICATION: Columbiad, Seacoast, 10-Inch, Model 1844, Iron, Banded and Rifled. REMARKS: Civil War view of weapon believed to be Fig. IV-4 in Water Battery of Fort Johnson, S.C. Note method of disabling carriage. Piece in background is an 8-Inch, Siege and Garrison Howitzer, Model 1841. COMMON NAME: 10-Inch Columbiad, Model 1844, Banded and Rifled.

statements of test firing 16 December are found in the Records. There are minor discrepancies between Beauregard's report and Brigadier General R.S. Ripley's,[3] but the rifle seems to have delivered ranges from 1,100 to 1,800 yards with elevations from 1 to 5 degrees and charges of 14 to 16 pounds of powder. The projectiles were flat-headed Harding bolts weighing from 225 to 240 pounds. Both officers felt the firing was completely successful and Ripley expected to get slightly better range with pointed bolts.

The Fort Sumter columbiad, since both trunnions were intact, was banded in standard fashion at the Charleston Arsenal increasing the weight to about 20,000 pounds. Rifling was by the Eason Brothers, their work attested by half-inch initials at the breech edge of the interior reinforcing band: "J.M.E. & Bros." Presumably it has the same 15 lands and grooves of the other, but this cannot be ascertained since the bore has been plugged with a roundshot and the interstices cemented flush.

After rifling, the piece was mounted in Fort Johnson and tried with Harding projectiles of 215 pounds and Parrotts of 250. The former failed to take the grooves and, with 16-pound charges, broke up. The Parrotts, however, gave "excellent results,"[4] although the Records omit mention of what they were.

Figure IV-6 shows what is believed to be this weapon in the Fort Johnson Water Battery in 1865.

If correct, and close study reveals identical marks in the 1865 picture and the columbiad in Fort Sumter today, then it was moved after the war for records list no rifled 10-inch in Sumter at the fort's evacuation during the night of 17 February 1865. With the passage of years, the rifle has lost its sight piece and picked up a few rust pits, but by and large there is little doubt the Fort Sumter columbiad and that in the 1865 photograph are the same.

Initial success in the 1840s of the 8- and 10-inch led to development of a 12-inch columbiad, presumably on the 1844 pattern, which Mordecai[5] in 1849 described as "promising favorable results." However, within a year of his book, tests showed all the 1844 models were weak and in 1858 they were downgraded to shellguns and their places supplied by an improved type.[6]

The new weapons—8- and 10-inch, often called 64- and 128-pounders respectively—had a more streamlined appearance and put additional strength in the breech by shortening the bore and terminating it in a hemisphere. The chamber, present in previous columbiads, was omitted in these and future models. For the sake of clarity, this "New Columbiad" as it was known, is called a Model 1858 based on the year of its ascendancy. However, it should be understood that the piece was developed gradually between 1850 and 1858 and no doubt underwent minor changes in the process although the general form probably remained fairly constant.

FIGURE: IV-7 IDENTIFICATION: Columbiad, Seacoast, 8-Inch, Model 1858, Iron. REMARKS: Battery Magruder, Yorktown. Weapons were spiked and abandoned by the Confederates at the evacuation of Yorktown in May, 1862. COMMON NAME: 8-Inch Columbiad, Model 1858.

Consequently, a close examination of the weapons in Figures IV-7 and IV-8 reveals a slight difference at the breech. The former shows 8-inch columbiads in Battery Magruder at Yorktown which were spiked by the Confederates at their abandonment of the town in May, 1862. The breech of these pieces is clearly rounded between base ring and button cascabel which was split to permit use of ratchet-type elevation.

Yet Figure IV-8 of Fort Moultrie in 1861 after its occupation by the Confederates 27 December 1860, shows 8-inch columbiads which have a slanted breech. This is even more evident in Figure IV-9 of an 8-inch which, as mentioned in the discussion of the Model 1844, was rifled and banded by Beauregard and stated by him to have been in Fort Moultrie.[7] It was made at West Point Foundry, but the trunnion which bore the date has been damaged and the year of manufacture is not available.

Differences in shape of the breech may have been due to founder inconsistency, or to the Moultrie

FIGURE: IV-8 IDENTIFICATION: Columbiad, Seacoast, 8-Inch, Model 1858, Iron. REMARKS: Fort Moultrie in April, 1861. 32-Pounders at rear. Note palmetto log and sandbag traverses. COMMON NAME: 8-Inch Columbiad, Model 1858.

FIGURE: IV-9 LOCATION: Fort Moultrie, S.C. IDENTIFICATION: Columbiad, Seacoast, 8-Inch, Model 1858, Iron, Banded and Rifled. BORE: Diameter — 8. Rifling — 8 x 8, hook-slant or "Brooke" type. Length — 110.75v. LENGTH O/A: 121 (Muzzle face to base of breech). TRUNNIONS: Diameter — 8. Length — 6.5. MARKINGS: Muzzle Face — 89, B.H. Left Trunnion — R.P.P., W.P.F. Tube — U.S. REMARKS: Date obliterated by pitting of right trunnion. Cascabel broken. COMMON NAME: 8-Inch Columbiad, Model 1858, Banded and Rifled.

FIGURE: IV-11 LOCATION: Fort Pulaski, Ga. IDENTIFICATION: Columbiad, Seacoast, 8-Inch, Model 1858, Iron, probably Confederate. BORE: Diameter — 8 (estimated). TRUNNIONS: Diameter — 8. Length — 6.5 MARKINGS: Left Trunnion — 1861. Right Trunnion — J.R.A., & Co., T.F. Breech (top) — 9460 (weight). REMARKS: Based on date and manufacturer, the piece probably was cast under the Confederacy in the U.S. Model 1858 mold, altered to knob-type cascabel. COMMON NAME: 8-Inch Columbiad, Model 1858 (Confederate).

FIGURE: IV-10 IDENTIFICATION: Columbiad, Seacoast, 8-Inch, Model 1858, Iron, (probably Confederate made). REMARKS: Location of fort not identified.

pieces being an intermediate form during development. In either case, the answer must await discovery of additional records or dated weapons of each type. Until then, for the purposes of this book, both will be called Model 1858.

An interesting variation of the Model 1858, probably a Confederate version, is illustrated in Figures IV-10 and IV-11. The Civil War view, from the Brady Collection in the National Archives, does not have a caption stating location, but does show the entire piece which in general appearance, with exception of cascabel and lack of ratchet, seems a fair duplicate of the Model 1858 at Yorktown.

One of these columbiads, or more likely part of it, is buried muzzle down outside the walls of Fort Pulaski. Wartime photographs show the fort had at least two of this type and one is believed to have lost its muzzle during the bombardment preceding capture of the bastion in 1862. Figure IV-11 is thought to be this weapon, emplaced near the walls as a cemetery marker during Union occupation of the premises. Although the muzzle may be broken, the trunnions are in good shape and since they measure 8 inches in diameter, the bore probably is the same. One trunnion bears the date 1861 and the other "J.R.A. & Co., T.F.," one of the signatures of Richmond's Tredegar Foundry.

This leads to assumption that the piece was cast in the 1858 molds—which Tredegar no doubt had since it made cannon for the United States before the war. It probably was an interim form cast early in the year before patterns were obtained for the Model 1861, or Confederate version of the U.S. Rodman. The change to the easily manufactured, knob-type cascabel may have been due to utilization of a simple quoin method of elevating the piece (Fig. IV-10). This would have eliminated the necessity of the more complicated ratchet and split button form of cascabel in the U.S. version.

No 10-inch Model 1858 has been found, but a sketch (Fig. IV-12) shows this caliber resembled the 8. The Model 1858 gave way to what the Ordnance Manual[8] calls Model 1861, although some of these weapons appear to have been made a year previously.[9] A smoothbore, it was made in 8-, 10-, 13-, 15-, and even 20-inch caliber and is generally known as the "Rodman Columbiad" for the inventor of the process which made such huge weapons possible.[10]

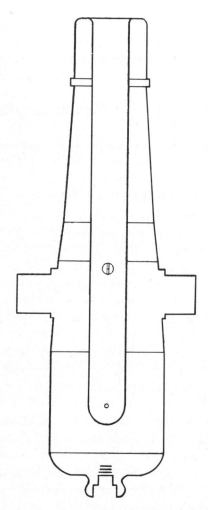

FIGURE: IV-12 IDENTIFICATION: Columbiad, Seacoast, 10-Inch, Model 1858, Iron. BORE: Diameter — 10. Smoothbore. Length — 101.17. LENGTH O/A: 128.82. TRUNNIONS: Diameter — 10. Length — 9. SOURCE: Gibbon. COMMON NAME: 10-Inch Columbiad, Model 1858.

Lieutenant T.J. Rodman in 1844–45 developed a method which permitted the casting of large units. In those days, manufacture of cast iron cannon depended on pouring a block in the general shape of the piece, then turning off the exterior roughness in a lathe and drilling out the bore. This worked fine for small weapons, but large castings developed cracks and weak spots that made manufacture of heavy weapons a chancy business. A few had been made, particularly in Europe, but seldom with marked success. Rodman, after deciding that stresses due to cooling from the exterior inward were causing the trouble, developed a way of reversing the process and thereby, theoretically at least, forcing the stresses of cooling to aid in holding the tube together, rather than tearing it apart, thus improving its resistance to the shock of firing.

Since he was in the Army, Rodman offered the process on several occasions during 1846–47 to his superior, Colonel George Talcott, later general and Chief of Ordnance, but was turned down. Finally, he asked if there would be any impropriety in taking out patents and having the invention tried by a private firm. Talcott told him to go ahead, and, Rodman testified later, seemed relieved to be rid of an annoying problem and its persistent proponent.

Thereupon Rodman worked out a business agreement in 1847 with Charles Knap of the Fort Pitt Foundry to take out patents and try the process— an experiment believed fraught with the very real danger of burning down the plant. However, the gamble paid off and cannon cast by the Rodman method, when proved on the range, outlasted those cast by conventional procedures. It was during these trials, incidentally, that the Model 1844 columbiads were found to be structurally weak, a discovery which led to development of the Model 1858 and later to the Model 1861 designed by Rodman.

In addition to the Rodman columbiads, the process was used on many other weapons including the 13-inch, Model 1861 mortars, certain Navy weapons, and even Parrott's larger rifles. The patents continued to be held by the Pittsburg firm, to which they were conveyed by Rodman about 1861, but other major Northern manufacturers were permitted to use the method to speed the build-up of heavy ordnance necessitated by the war.

The process consisted in casting the tube around a hollow core, or pipe, which was closed at the bottom and into which was inserted a smaller pipe to within a few inches of the base. After the molten metal was poured into the mold, water was turned into the smaller pipe. It flowed out the bottom, filled the larger pipe, and ran off at the top away from the casting and not touching the hot metal. Meanwhile, coals were heaped around the exterior of the casting to insure that cooling spread outward from the interior.

All calibers of the Rodman, other than size, appear identical and are easily recognized by smooth, flowing lines culminating in an almost flat breech notched for a ratchet-type elevating method. Their clean-cut look is exemplified by the 8-inch (Fig. IV-13) one of three identical pieces at Soldiers' and Sailors' Monument on Riverside Drive, New York City. Two 10-inchers (Fig. IV-14) overlook the Hudson River at West Point. The left piece was made by Alger in 1866 and the right in 1865 at the West Point Foundry, also called Cold Spring Foundry, located at Cold Spring, New York on the east side of the Hudson River about one half mile north of West Point.

Production of the 13-inch seems to have been limited and the piece is not listed in the 1861 Ordnance Manual. Specifications in the appendix were taken from an 1875 text[11] and an 1865 sketch[12] shows it to have been identical in appearance to other Rodmans. It was classed with these weapons in testimony before a U.S. Senate committee in February, 1864,[13] and Benton[14] in 1875 listed a 13-inch Rodman in U.S. seacoast armament.

FIGURE: IV-13 LOCATION: Soldiers & Sailors Memorial Monument, New York, N.Y. IDENTIFICATION: Columbiad, Seacoast, 8-Inch, Model 1861, Iron. BORE: Diameter — 8. Smoothbore. Length — 104.25v. LENGTH O/A: 120.5. TRUNNIONS: Diameter — 8. Length — 3.25. MARKINGS: Muzzle Face — S.C.L., S.McM. & Co., 1865, 8508 lbs., 31. Tube — U.S. COMMON NAME: 8-Inch Rodman.

FIGURE: IV-14 LOCATION: West Point, N.Y. INDENTICATION: Columbiad, Seacoast, 10-inch, Model 1861, Iron. BORE: Diameter — 10. Smoothbore. Length — 116.75v. LENGTH O/A: 136.5. TRUNNIONS: Diameter — 10. Length — 3.25. MARKINGS: Listed in museum records, location not stated, as follows: Left piece — W.P.F., 1865, 14932 lbs. Right piece — C.A. & Co., 1866, 15110 lbs. REMARKS: Measurements approximately the same for both. COMMON NAME: 10-Inch Rodman.

Far more prevalent is the next larger model, the 15-inch. The first of these weapons (Fig. IV-15) was cast at Fort Pitt in 1860 and taken to Fort Monroe where it was mounted on an iron, center pintal barbette carriage for testing. It was fired 350 times with charges averaging 35 pounds and shells varying from 305 to 335 pounds. The service charge was later established at 50 pounds with shot weighing in the neighborhood of 440 pounds. The piece is still at Monroe although no longer mounted on the carriage. It measures 190 inches overall and has a maximum exterior diameter of 48 inches and weight of 49,099 pounds. These figures are carried in the 1861 Ordnance Manual for 15-inch statistics. However, later weapons were about 2 inches longer and averaged approximately 50,000 pounds. In addition, trunnion length was reduced from 6.5 to 4.5 inches. A Civil War photograph (Fig. X-37) shows one of these columbiads at the outskirts of Alexandria, Virginia and Figure X-38 a similar piece today at Fort McHenry.

Weight of the 15-inch was less than half that of the 20-inch Rodman cast at Fort Pitt in February, 1864. A contemporary newspaper story[15] states the huge cannon was cast in twenty-two minutes from 173,000 pounds of metal melted in three furnaces which fed into a reservoir and then into the mold. After cooling, it was turned down to 115,000 pounds with a length of 243.5 inches, a bore of 210, and maximum diameter of 64 inches.[16]

Mounted at Fort Hamilton, New York, the piece was fired only a few times since no target could be found sufficiently tough to resist the impact of 1,080-pound solid shot propelled by 100-pound service charges.[17] It was fired four times after mounting and four more in 1867. The latter practice, with 125 pounds of powder, gave a range of 6,144 yards and with 200 pounds, 8,001 yards. Elevation in both instances was 25°.[18] The piece today (Fig. IV-16) is mounted in a small park at 4th and 101st Streets Brooklyn, just outside the Fort Hamilton gate. Measurements conform to those of the newspaper article although weight, stamped on the muzzle face, is 116,497 pounds. Also marked there is No. 1, Fort Pitt Pa., 1864.

FIGURE: IV-16 LOCATION: 4th and 101st, Brooklyn, N.Y. IDENTIFICATION: Columbiad, Seacoast, 20-Inch, Model 1864, Iron. BORE: Diameter — 20. Smoothbore. Length — 203v. LENGTH O/A: 243.5. TRUNNIONS: Diameter — 18. Length — 6. MARKINGS: Muzzle Face — No. 1, 116497 (weight), Fort Pitt, Pa., 1864. COMMON NAME: 20-Inch Rodman.

FIGURE: IV-15 LOCATION: Fort Monroe, Va. IDENTIFICATION: Columbiad, Seacoast, 15-Inch, Model 1861, Iron. BORE: Diameter — 15. Smoothbore. Length — 165. LENGTH O/A: 190. TRUNNIONS: Diameter — 15. Length — 6.5. MARKINGS: Muzzle Face — 1, T.J.R. Left Trunnion — 1860. Right Trunnion — F.P.F., K.R. & Co. Breech — 49,099 (weight). REMARKS: Although piece was cast in 1860, model is listed as 1861. Weapons cast in same pattern later seem to run about 2 inches longer. COMMON NAME: 15-Inch Rodman.

Quite a number of Rodmans were made, but since they were primarily designed for seacoast defense of Northern fortifications, they saw little if any action during the war. The 15-inchers, certainly, were never fired in anger.[19]

Despite lack of use, foundry production continued after the war and for some years the Rodmans were considered our primary seacoast weapon although, in retrospect, it should have been apparent that the day of the smoothbore had ended. By the 1870s, even ardent adherents of the Rodman system recognized the superiority of rifles, but economy dictated an attempt be made to salvage something from the large number of these venerable relics arming the nation's coastal fortifications. Consequently, a misguided attempt was made late in the decade to convert the 10-inchers into rifles by inserting a wrought iron sleeve.[20] This turned the pieces into 8-inch rifles, but the system blew apart, literally, on the Sandy Hook proving ground in the fall of 1881.[21]

A number of these conversions are still around—reminders that stinginess seldom pays in national defense. One (Fig. IV-17) at Fort Monroe is dated 1884, three years after the Sandy Hook fiasco, and weighs 15,800 pounds, about 750 more than it did as a smoothbore. However, since another at Fort McHenry is stamped 15,925 and a Mobile, Alabama, piece 16,120, weight probably averaged about 16,000 pounds. All three have a fascinating oblong cascabel (Fig. IV-18) presumably attached during conversion as a purchase for machining. It could have been left in this shape for attachment of an experimental elevating mechanism, but more likely, since the weapons were under test and might need additional work, it was retained in expectation of being returned to the lathe.

The knob and its supporting rings, or washers, partially cover the original elevating ratchets indicating the appendage was affixed later, not cast with the piece. Moreover, since cast iron is difficult to weld, chances are the breech was drilled and threaded for attaching the knob as a screw.

The bore was converted by reaming it to 12-inch diameter, inserting the sleeve, then rifling in the usual manner. Specimens have been found with both 15 and 24 straight-type lands and grooves. One of the former at West Point (Fig. IV-19) retains the conventional ratchet base of the smoothbore columbiads without additional cascabel.

There was also a war-time attempt to build Rodman rifles. Two experimental pieces were made in 1861 by casting a columbiad with the exterior dimensions of the 10-inch smoothbore, but with 8-inch bore, which was then rifled, and a 15-inch cast with 12-inch bore and rifled. Both were sent to Fort Monroe for testing. No performance data is available on the 8-inch and by January, 1864, the 12-inch had been fired only a few times. James projectiles were used, but the rotating device stripped off and the rounds tumbled giving poor results. The following month, Rodman, now a major, stated[22] that he had sent twenty-five 8-inch and the same number of 12-inch projectiles to Monroe to be tried in the weapons. These were grooved bolts designed to lock into the rifling of the piece and doubtless were similar to the Washington Navy Yard 12-inch Rodman illustrated in Chapter XIII that may have been part of the original shipment.

Benton in 1875 remarked[23] that a 12-inch rifle having the exterior form of the 15-inch columbiad

FIGURE: IV-17 LOCATION: Fort Monroe, Va. IDENTIFICATION: Columbiad, Seacoast, 10-Inch, Model 1861, Sleeved to 8-Inch Rifle, Iron. BORE: Diameter — 8. Rifling — 15 x 15, straight. Length — 117v. LENGTH O/A: 144. TRUNNIONS: Diameter — 10. Length — 3.25. MARKINGS: Muzzle Face — 1884, 68, 15800, D.A.L., S.B.I.W. REMARKS: Bore was reamed to 12-inch diameter, then sleeved to 8-inch and rifled. Number 1884 is date of conversion. COMMON NAME: 10-Inch Rodman Sleeved to 8-Inch Rifle.

FIGURE: IV-19 LOCATION: West Point, N.Y. IDENTIFICATION: Columbiad, Seacoast, 10-Inch, Model 1861, Sleeved to 8-Inch Rifle, Iron. BORE: Diameter — 8. Rifling — 15 x 15, Straight. Length — 114v. LENGTH O/A: 137. TRUNNIONS: Diameter — 10. Length — 3.25. MARKINGS: Muzzle Face — W.P.F., 1878, No. 2, 16065. REMARKS: Cascabel unchanged from original condition. COMMON NAME: 10-Inch Rodman Sleeved to 8-Inch Rifle.

FIGURE: IV-18 IDENTIFICATION: Columbiad, Seacoast, 10-Inch, Model 1861, Sleeved to 8-Inch Rifle, Iron. REMARKS: Cascabel of Fort Monroe weapon, Fig. IV-17.

had been fired 420 times without injury with charges varying from 40 to 120 pounds and with projectiles ranging from 475 to 620 pounds. Presumably this was the Monroe rifle although identification is not certain.

Before leaving Rodman's columbiads, it should be emphasized that for purposes of this book, only those pieces having the exterior design of the Model 1861 columbiad are so identified. Yet anyone who delves into Civil War era books on ordnance will soon find many officers and writers considered Rodman's *Process* a guiding factor and their terminology reflects this belief to the extent of calling other types of cannon "Rodmans" simply because they were cast on his principle. This was particularly true in regard to the 15-inch Navy Dahlgren and will be discussed at greater length in the chapter on those weapons.

Various locations in the South boast what appear to be roughly-made Rodman columbiads. These are Confederate columbiads, Model 1861,[24] which resemble the Rodman, particularly at the breech and are generally called "Confederate Rodmans" although with little real title to the name since they were cast solid and not by his process. As a rule, the pieces are smoothbores of 8- and 10-inch caliber. The Confederate Ordnance Manual of 1863 lists a 15-inch columbiad, but specifications merely echo those of the federal Rodman and although Southern forts were armed with U.S. 15-inchers after the war, the Confederates had no 15-inch columbiads of any type.

The 8-inch Confederate model 1861 columbiad conforms so closely in size to the U.S. Rodman that general appearance is deceptively similar. Ordnance tables, for instance, list length of the Southern model as 120.5 inches compared to 119.475 for the U.S., roughly an inch variation. Maximum diameter of the federal piece is 25.6 inches, only two-tenths larger than the Confederate. Such measurements are far too close for identification purposes even if all weapons were made exactly to manual specifications—which seldom was the case. Consequently, other factors must be considered. Marks, such as foundry initials and date, generally offer positive identification, but if these are covered by paint, different methods must be tried.

Trunnion length, dictated by the type carriage used, is often an excellent way of separating the two weapons. Columbiads usually were mounted on seacoast carriages and in the North during the war these were made of wrought iron. This material, much stronger than wood, permitted relatively thin cheeks and trunnions only 3.25 inches long were habitually used. The Confederacy, with iron in short supply, could hardly afford to waste it on carriages when wood served reasonably well. But wood cheeks had to be much thicker to stand the weight and trunnion length increased accordingly—to 6.5 inches for the 8-inch, although it varied a bit between pieces. Such trunnions are evident on the 8-inch (Fig. IV-20) in Fort Darling, between Petersburg and Richmond, which is mounted on a reproduction wood, center pintle, barbette carriage.

Although long-trunnion 8-inchers are undoubtedly Confederate, the converse does not hold true for a St. Augustine, Florida, piece (Fig. IV-21) and its mate have trunnions only 3 inches long yet are clearly marked "C.S." on the tubes. Cast at Bellona in 1861, both have identical statistics conforming exactly to neither Northern nor Southern manual specifications, but ranging closer to those of the three 8-inch Rodmans at Soldiers' and Sailors' Monument in New York than to the long-trunnion Confederate piece at Fort Darling.

Probably they are early attempts at manufacturing the new model and short trunnions may be blamed on too strict adherence to drawings obtained from the North before alteration to meet Southern needs. The obvious presumption that, like the Bellona 42-pounder of Chapter I, they were intended for the U.S. and picked up by the Confederates, is untendable in this case since Bellona was not equipped for hollow-core casting, a prerequisite of federal Rodmans.

FIGURE: IV-20 LOCATION: Fort Darling, Va. IDENTIFICATION: Columbiad, Seacoast, 8-Inch, Model 1861, Confederate, Iron. BORE: Diameter — 8. Smoothbore. Length — 108. LENGTH O/A: 119.5. TRUNNIONS: Diameter — 8. Length — 6.5. MARKINGS: Muzzle Face — No. 66 (Possibly 86). Left Trunnion — 1862. Right Trunnion — B.F., J.L.A. Tube — C.S. Breech — 8800 (weight). REMARKS: Note long trunnions in comparison to similar piece, Fig. IV-21. COMMON NAME: 8-Inch "Confederate Rodman."

FIGURE: **IV-21** LOCATION: St. Augustine, Fla. IDENTIFICATION: Columbiad, Seacoast, 8-Inch, Model 1861, Confederate, Iron. BORE: Diameter — 8. Smoothbore (tentative). Length — 104.5v. LENGTH O/A: 121.5. TRUNNIONS: Diameter — 8. Length — 3. MARKINGS: Left Trunnion — 1861. Right Trunnion — No. 27, B.F., J.L.A. Tube — C.S. Breech — 8750 (weight). REMARKS: Compare trunnion length with similar piece, Fig. IV-20. COMMON NAME: 8-Inch "Confederate Rodman."

FIGURE: **IV-22** LOCATION: Charleston, S.C. IDENTIFICATION: Columbiad, Seacoast, 10-Inch, Model 1861, Confederate, Iron. BORE: Diameter — 10. Smoothbore. Length — 103.5v. LENGTH O/A: Left Piece — 125. Right Piece —123.5. TRUNNIONS: Diameter — 10. Length — 9. MARKINGS: Muzzle Face — Left Piece 1863, 13945, No. 20, R.M.C., B.F.; Right Piece 1678. Left Trunnion — Left Piece J.L.A.; Right Piece 1862. Right Trunnion — Left Piece J.L.A.; Right Piece J.R.A., & Co., T.F. REMARKS: Note sight piece on tube just forward of trunnions on Tredegar (right) piece, and absence of this feature on Bellona weapon. COMMON NAME: 10-Inch "Confederate Rodman."

Exterior finish often assists in columbiad identification. Federal Rodmans were turned on a lathe after casting, a procedure which added nothing to the weapon but a smooth surface and was omitted by the South as a needless luxury. Consequently, rough appearance, particularly casting lines around the chase and the curve of the breech, is a trademark of "Confederate Rodmans." Recognition of the 10-inch Model 1861 (Fig. IV-22) is considerably easier than the 8. Rough appearance, including casting lines, holds true for this weapon and trunnions are even longer—9 inches compared to 3.25 for the U.S. 10-inch. In addition, overall length of the Confederate columbiad is listed at 122.5 inches compared to 133.66 for the federal model, a difference of roughly 11 inches which, with maximum diameter approximately the same for both, gives the Southern weapons a stubby appearance. Actual length of the Confederates sometimes runs an inch or two longer, but they still fail to achieve the slim, streamlined look of the true Rodman.

The illustrated pieces are at Charleston, which has an excellent collection of these weapons with eight in the vicinity. All were cast by Tredegar or Bellona Foundries between 1862 and 1864 and have similar measurements although differing slightly in that the former have a sight piece (for the front sight) cast on top of the tube just forward of the trunnions and are often equipped with an additional sight on the left rimbase. Bellona weapons are smooth on top and utilized rimbase—or trunnion sights as they are generally called—exclusively. This is evident in the illustrated weapons. That in foreground was made at Bellona in 1863 and is smooth on top; the other, cast at Tredegar in 1862, has both tube sight piece and a trunnion sight.[25]

Location can also be a help in columbiad identification. This is not to imply that all north of Messers. Mason's and Dixon's survey stakes are Rodmans and south are the Confederate model. But the pieces are heavy—15,059 and 8,465 pounds for the 10- and 8-inch United States weapons and 13,320[26] and 9,020 for the Confederate—and difficult to move. Hence any "Confederate Rodman" found in the North should get more than a cursory examination before identification—and vice versa.

During the early part of the war, a few Confederate columbiads were cast with smaller bore and rifled. The 8-inch smoothbore was grooved to 5.8 inches, or 24-pounder caliber, and the 10-inch became a rifled 32-pounder with 6.4-inch bore. This permitted use of solid projectiles weighing roughly 64 pounds in the 5.8-inch and an estimated 80 or so pounds in the 6.4-inch.

A 6.4-inch (Fig. IV-23) salvaged from the site of Fort Powell in Mobile Bay today is mounted at Olde Fort Alabama near Coden. Neither this model nor the 24-pounder was successful and frequent bursting caused discontinuance of the experiment.[27] These were the pieces, incidentally, the Ordnance

FIGURE: IV-23 LOCATION: Olde Fort Alabama near Coden, Ala. IDENTIFICATION: Columbiad, Seacoast, 10-Inch, Model 1861, Confederate, Rifled to 6.4-Inch, Iron. BORE: Diameter — 6.4. Rifling — 5 x 5, Straight, Length — 105v. LENGTH O/A: 123. TRUNNIONS: Diameter — 10. Length — 9. MARKINGS: Muzzle Face — 1285. Left Trunnion — 1861 (noted at time of salvage, but obliterated during moving). Right Trunnion — J.R.A. & Co., T.F. Tube — C.S.A. Cascabel, Top — 14850 (weight). REMARKS: Salvaged from Mobile Bay at site of Fort Powell where it had lain for years exposed at all but highest tides. COMMON NAME: 10-Inch "Confederate Rodman" Rifled to 6.4-Inch.

Bureau in Richmond remembered when squabbling with Beauregard over rifling the 1858 and 1844 models.

The "Confederate Rodman" (note long trunnions) in Figure IV-24 may be one of these rifles. However, since the Alabama piece is unbanded and such reinforcement is mentioned neither in the Official Records nor contemporary ordnance literature, the weapon probably was unbanded initially and returned to the shops in an effort to make it safe to fire. It could, of course, have been an original 10-inch smoothbore later banded and rifled in that caliber, but the possibility is remote.

Shortly before Richmond surrendered, the Confederates poured a pair of 12-inch cannon at Tredegar. Although termed "guns" in available records, these were more likely columbiads and of the "Confederate Rodman" pattern. Flagler's report[28] of ordnance captured at Tredegar mentions: "There are two 12-inch smoothbore guns, cast and boring nearly completed. Guns of this and other large calibers have not been turned on the exterior surface except at the trunnions and near the muzzle. . . ." This description, of course, precisely fits the 8- and 10-inch Confederate Model 1861 columbiads which presumably are the "other large calibers" to which he refers.

Abbot, who doubtless had access to Flagler's report and may also have seen the weapons, stated[29] in reference to a huge sling cart with 10-foot diameter wheels found at Richmond: ". . . this cart was designed for the two 12-inch guns cast at Tredegar Works just before the evacuation. They were cast solid and bored out, weighing nearly 50,000 pounds. . ."

However, General Gorgas' papers[30] mention that just before the end of the war, Tredegar cast its first 12-inch piece after the method of Rodman. Gorgas, who certainly was more familiar with operations in his own department than Abbot, is probably more accurate in regard to the cooling method. Abbot's error—if error it was—could have been due to Flagler's report. Even if the weapons were cast hollow, the bores had to be dressed on a boring machine to proper diameter and Flagler, who was too good an ordnance man to be fooled, could, by his words "cast and boring" have misled Abbot into thinking the weapons were cast solid.

FIGURE: IV-24 IDENTIFICATION: Civil War view of Columbiad, Seacoast, Model 1861, Confederate, Iron, Banded and (presumably) Rifled of undetermined caliber. Probably it was the 10-inch bored to 6.4 and rifled then banded later when this innovation exhibited a tendency to burst. Other possibilities are 8-inch rifled to 5.82 and later banded or — and very unlikely — original 8- and 10-inch smoothbore later banded and rifled in the respective caliber.

NOTES

1. William E. Birkhimer, *Historical Sketch of The Organization, Administration, Materiel and Tactics of The Artillery, United States Army,* 1884, p. 277.
2. *Official Records,* Series I, Vol. 35, Part 1, pp. 514–515.
3. *Ibid.,* pp. 514–515 and footnote 515; *Ibid.,* Series I, Vol. 28, Part 2, p. 565.
4. *Ibid.,* Series I. Vol. 35, Part 1, p. 514.
5. Alfred Mordecai, *Artillery for The United States Land Service,* 1849, p. 3. John Gibbon, *The Artillerist's Manual, Compiled From Various Sources and Adapted to The Service of The United States,* 1860, Appendix, p. 46, states a 12-inch columbiad with 28 pounds of powder, 180-pound shell, elevation 39 degrees delivered a range of 5,761 yards.
6. J. G. Benton, *A Course of Instruction in Ordnance and Gunnery Composed and Compiled for Cadets of The United States Military Academy,* 1861, p. 182; Birkhimer, *op. cit.,* p. 283; Gibbon, *op. cit.,* pp. 67–68, Plate V.
7. *Official Records,* Series I, Vol. 35, Part 1, p. 514.
8. *Ordnance Manual for The Use of Officers of The United States Army,* 1861, pp. 13, 18.
9. J. G. Benton, *A Course of Instruction in Ordnance and Gunnery Composed and Compiled for Cadets of The United States Military Academy,* 1875, p. 553 lists 8- and 10-inch columbiads as Model 1860.
10. Reports of committees of the U.S. Senate, 2nd session, 38th Congress, "Heavy Ordnance," pp. 84–85, testimony of Charles Knap, proprietor of Fort Pitt Foundry, 4 February 1864, and of Major T. J. Rodman, p. 98. Also, testimony Capt. Alfred Mordecai, p. 54, regarding 13-inch columbiad. This weapon was authorized, but apparently few were made during the war.
11. Benton, 1875, *loc. cit.,* p. 553.
12. Alexander L. Holley, *A Treatise on Ordnance and Armor,* 1865, Fig. 78, p. 109.
13. Reports of committees of the U.S. Senate, *op. cit.,* testimony of Capt. Mordecai 1 February 1864, p. 54.
14. Benton, 1875, *op. cit.,* p. 190.
15. *Frank Leslie's Illustrated Newspaper,* 9 April 1864, p. 36.
16. Benton, 1875, *loc. cit.,* p. 553.
17. Leslie's, *loc. cit.,* notes the piece also was to have a shell weighing 750 pounds, but whether or not it was made seems to be unrecorded.
18. Benton, 1875, *loc. cit.*
19. Birkhimer, *op. cit.,* p. 291 footnote.
20. *Ibid.,* p. 272.
21. *Ibid.,* p. 270.
22. Reports of committees of the U.S. Senate, *op. cit.,* pp. 12, 87, 103, 174, 176.
23. Benton, 1875, *op. cit.,* pp. 551–553.
24. *Ordnance Manual for The Use of Officers of The Confederate States Army,* 1863, pp. 9, 13.
25. The author is indebted to Mr. Edwin H. Olmstead of Mount Holly Springs, Pa., who discovered this easy, visual method of differentiating between the two foundries.
26. Weight stated in *Ordnance Manual* (Confederate, 1863), *loc. cit.,* p. 13. Specimens examined seem to run 500 to 600 pounds heavier.
27. *Official Records,* Series I, Vol. 11, Part 3, p. 461, letter dated 24 April 1862 from D. H. Hill at Yorktown, Va., to Secretary of War G. W. Randolph in which Hill complains: "Another 24-pdr. rifle burst today and one of Pierson's 6.4-inch guns. We have but one gun now to keep the shipping at a distance. The smoothbore guns have no range. . . . There must be something rotten in the Ordnance Department. It is a Yankee concern throughout and I have long been afraid that there was foul play there. Our shells burst at the mouth of the gun or do not burst at all. The metal of which the new guns are made is of the most flimsy and brittle character and the casting is very bad. . . ."
Randolph replied 25 April 1862, p. 464: "I regret extremely the bursting of the rifle guns, but do not attribute it to foul play as they were cast by Southern foundries. The scarcity of metal has caused the use of inferior qualities and hence these accidents. . . . We have sent you a smooth 10-inch and will send immediately a smooth 8-inch gun. These are safe and in my judgment are better guns than the rifled guns. We cannot rely upon the latter and for the present have ceased to make them. . . ."
28. *Official Records,* Series I, Vol. 46, Part 3, pp. 1007–1010, report of Capt. Daniel W. Flagler, 28 April 1865.
29. Henry L. Abbot, "Siege Artillery in The Campaigns Against Richmond With Notes on The 15-Inch Gun," *Professional Papers No. 14, Corps of Engineers,* 1867, p. 182.
30. Josiah Gorgas, "Contributions to The History of The Confederate Ordnance Department," *Southern Historical Society Papers,* Vol. XII, 1884, p. 94.

Chapter 5

The Dahlgren

ADMIRAL JOHN A. DAHLGREN, COMMANDER of the South Atlantic Blockading Squadron 1863-65 and chief of Naval Ordnance 23 July 1862-25 June 1863, invented many of the Navy's weapons. They consisted of varied rifles and smoothbores ranging in caliber from 12-pounder to 20-inch and in weight from 300 to 100,000 pounds. Some, experimental, comprised only a few pieces; others, unsuccessful, were gradually phased out of service. But many gave excellent performance both before and during the war and a few even continued into peacetime armament.

Broadly speaking, the Dahlgrens fall into three categories—bronze boat howitzers and rifles, iron smoothbores, and iron rifles. The pieces in each group, although varied in caliber, are usually similar in appearance and in most cases easy to identify. Experimental models are considerably tougher since few were made and little statistical data is available.

The admiral (1809-1870) entered service as a midshipman in 1826 and rose to lieutenant by 1837 when he dropped out of service due to failing eyesight. After about five years, his sight improved to the extent that he returned to the Navy and served afloat and ashore until January, 1847 when he began his ordnance career at the Washington Navy Yard and which, with minor interruptions, lasted throughout the remainder of his life.

The Mexican War had broken out the previous year and caught the Navy woefully unprepared. Navy commanders, willing and able to fight ship to ship, found themselves engaged with a nation which had no fleet. Instead, the Americans were faced with miles of coast line protected by shallow waters which kept our vessels beyond range of their heavy guns.

We needed light artillery suitable for inshore work aboard small boats and it simply wasn't available. As a makeshift, Army 6- and 12-pounders, even the little 12-pounder mountain howitzers, were pressed into a service for which they were never intended and in which they proved totally inadequate.

Against this background, Dahlgren set to work to turn out not a single weapon, but a system of boat armament that would remedy the faults brought so glaringly to light under wartime conditions. His success provoked envy in ordnance circles throughout the world and the tacit acknowledgment that in this department, the United States Navy was second to none.

The weapons completed in 1849 and adopted

for Navy use the following year[1] consisted of three smoothbore howitzers—a 24-pounder weighing 1,310 pounds, a 12-pounder (light) of 430 pounds, and a 12-pounder (medium) of 750 pounds. To these were later added a 12-pounder (small) of 300 pounds and two rifles. All were bronze and, with exception of one rifle, similar in appearance.

Although a great many 24-pounders were manufactured—Dahlgren's widow compiled a total of 1,009 from official records[2]—the piece is far from common today. The weapon (Fig. V-1) in the Petersburg National Military Park was made by Ames in 1863. Only 456 medium 12-pounders were cast, according to Mrs. Dahlgren, but this is the model usually encountered today. The Portsmouth Naval Shipyard Museum piece (Fig. V-2) is mounted on a standard field carriage and is one of several in the Portsmouth-Norfolk area. It was made at Washington Navy Yard in 1854. Light 12-pounders are quite rare since only 177 were fabricated, but an excellent specimen (Fig. V-3) has been preserved in the U.S. Army Artillery and Missile Center Museum at Fort Sill, Oaklahoma. The piece was made in 1860 at the Washington Navy Yard. Twenty-three small 12-pounders were made, Mrs. Dahlgren states, and these weapons today are scarce as hen's teeth. Thus far neither specimens nor specifications, other than caliber and weight, have been found.

Of the four howitzers, the light and small 12-pounders seem to have gained relatively little favor, and the 24, although designed as boat armament, apparently was used primarily aboard ship. The medium 12-pounder, however, was the heart of the admiral's system and proved an extremely efficient and versatile weapon.

There is, unfortunately, a certain amount of confusion regarding the weapon's name. During the war, the Official Navy Records list 12-pounder boat howitzers again and again as "light" and "heavy." Very few instances have been found where the term "medium" is used although it is obvious that numbers of the old weapons must have been pressed into service. Moreover, contemporary photographs show the "medium" and "heavy" to be identical in appearance and Mrs. Dahlgren's list of the admiral's weapons notes the "12-pounder heavy" at the same 750-pound weight as the "medium" and omits all mention of the latter weapon.

Consequently, it is the writer's belief that the change from "medium" in Dahlgren's books and correspondence of the 1850s to "heavy" during the war was one of semantics rather than model and was due to a logical association of the word "light" with

FIGURE: V-1 LOCATION: Petersburg, Va. IDENTIFICATION: Dahlgren, Howitzer, Boat, 24-Pounder, Bronze. BORE: Diameter — 5.82. Smoothbore. Length — 58.2 LENGTH O/A: 68. MARKINGS: Tube — Dahlgren, 24-Pdr., 1863, J.A.D. Breech — 1314 lbs., 90 Pre., No. 388. REMARKS: Normally used as deck howitzer. COMMON NAME: 24-Pounder Dahlgren Boat Howitzer.

FIGURE: V-2 LOCATION: Portsmouth Naval Shipyard Museum, Portsmouth, Va. IDENTIFICATION: Dahlgren, Howitzer, Boat, 12-Pounder, Medium, Bronze. BORE: Diameter — 4.62. Smoothbore. Length — 55. LENGTH O/A: 63. MARKINGS: Tube — Anchor, 12-Pdr. Boat Howitzer, 1854, J.A.D. Breech — U.S.N.Y. Washington, 754 lbs., 55 Pre. REMARKS: Also called "Heavy" (see text). Standard iron field carriage for this weapon. COMMON NAME: 12-Pounder Dahlgren Boat Howitzer, Medium.

FIGURE: V-3 LOCATION: Fort Sill, Okla. IDENTIFICATION: Dahlgren, Howitzer, Boat, 12-Pounder, Light, Bronze. BORE: Diameter — 4.62. Smoothbore. Length — 44. LENGTH O/A: 51. MARKINGS: Tube — Anchor, 12-Pdr. Boat Howitzer, 1860, J.A.D., Dahlgren. Breech — U.S.N.Y. Washington, 428 lbs., 27 Pre. REMARKS: Note "Loop" used in lieu of trunnions. COMMON NAME: 12-Pounder Dahlgren Boat Howitzer, Light.

"heavy" rather than "light" and "medium." So in view of Dahlgren's initial nomenclature and as a matter of convenience, the howitzer will be referred to herein as 12-pounder medium instead of the later term. Regardless of name, the piece was much admired by Navy men and generally considered the world's most efficient boat weapon of the day.

Mounted in the bow of a launch, it could be employed against enemy small boats or even light vessels and was capable of sustained fire through a wide angle of traverse without altering the direction of the launch—a tremendous advantage compared to former weapons which had very limited traverse necessitating continued shifting of the boat's course. The piece starred in amphibious assault for it could keep up covering fire as the launch approached shore, then in unbelievably short time shift to a field carriage, be hauled ashore, and resume fire support as field artillery.

Handles on the wood boat carriage (Fig. V-4) compressed the bed, which carried the piece, against the slide to limit recoil by friction between the two. When mounted in the bow of a frigate's launch (Fig. V-5) the carriage could be pivoted between three points to give 360° traverse although it is doubtful if the piece was ever fired astern.

Figure V-6 depicts the howitzer mounted on a boat carriage in the bow of a launch with the field carriage astern. As soon as the craft neared shore, the field carriage, which weighed about 500 pounds, was run to the bow over planks laid fore and aft, the trail wheel running along the center track. The piece was then lifted from one carriage to the other, wood skids were run out from the bow, and the weapon hauled ashore by crewmen in the water or who had waded to the beach.

Although time of the transfer depended on conditions—the howitzer could even be dropped into deep water and dragged ashore by long ropes—practice under good conditions showed the piece could fire from the boat carriage, be transferred, landed and fired ashore in the incredibly short time of one minute, forty-two seconds. Re-embarking, with the maneuvers reversed, took some ten seconds longer.[3]

The iron field carriage had no limber since the Navy was not expected to engage in prolonged or extensive land warfare and the limber would take up badly needed space aboard boat and ship. However, the carriage did have a small trail wheel which was an aid to men dragging the piece yet could be folded out of the way to permit the trail to rest on the ground for increased friction during firing. Two am-

munition boxes could be lashed to the carriage and each crew member carried two rounds in leather pouches.[4] This gave the piece seventy-two rounds of "fixed" ammunition in which each projectile—shell, shrapnel, case, or canister—was tied or "fixed" to its charge.

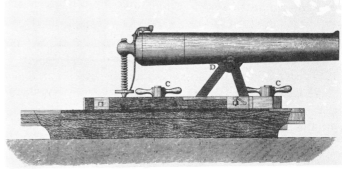

FIGURE: V-4 IDENTIFICATION: Boat Carriage for 12-Pounder Boat Howitzer. SOURCE: *Ordnance Instructions for the United States Navy*, 1866. REMARKS: A — Bed. B — Slide. Compressor Plate and Compressor Bolts beneath slide and not shown. C — Handles for Compressors. D — Lugs for Loop.

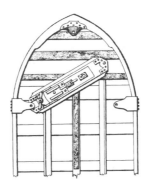

FIGURE: V-5 IDENTIFICATION: Boat Carriage in Bow of Frigate's Launch. SOURCE: Dahlgren. *Boat Armament.* REMARKS: By using different pivot points, piece could be traversed 360°.

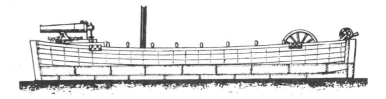

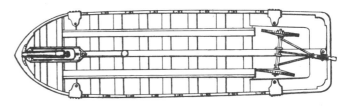

FIGURE: V-6 IDENTIFICATION: 12-Pounder Dahlgren Boat Howitzer, Medium, on Boat Carriage in Bow of Frigate's Launch. Field Carriage astern. SOURCE: Dahlgren. *Boat Armament.* REMARKS: Note tracks to run field carriage forward for transfer of howitzer and landing.

A Civil War photograph (Fig. V-7) shows the howitzer on field carriage aboard an unidentified monitor. Instead of trunnions, boat howitzers were mounted by means of a "loop" beneath the tube after the fashion of carronades. In a relatively light weapon, this method was sufficiently strong to withstand the shock of firing and, since only a single pin had to be removed, facilitated transfer between carriages.

The first of these pieces were made with a horizontal hole in the cascabel immediately in rear of the breech plate to permit reeving a breeching.[5] However, it was soon discovered that the boat carriage was able to absorb the shock of recoil and the hole was omitted in later weapons thereby strengthening the cascabel.

Range of the 12-pounder medium with a pound of powder and 5° elevation was 1,150 yards with case and 1,085 with shell. The 24-pounder gave 1,308 and 1,270 yards respectively using 2 pounds of powder and the same elevation.[6] No ranges are available for the light or small 12-pounders.

Recognizing the advent of rifled cannon, Admiral Dahlgren shortly before the war added a rifled 12-pounder to the boat armament and followed it later with a 20-pounder bronze howitzer. In addition, although specified neither by the admiral, his widow, nor naval ordnance texts, there is evidence that a few 24-pounder Dahlgren boat howitzers were rifled. Records of vessel armament list what appears to be sixteen such weapons aboard seven warships. Most, unfortunately, call the piece a 24-pounder rifled, or 24-pounder howitzer rifled. However, one, the U.S.S. Mendota,[7] had on 1 July 1864 two "24-pounder Dahlgren rifles" in addition to other armament which included two "20-pounder Dahlgren rifles."

This fortunate coincidence of two types of Dahlgren rifles aboard a single ship would tend to eliminate chances of the 20-pounder being erroneously called a 24. Moreover, the number of references to a 24-pounder rifle or rifled howitzer certainly substantiates the belief that such a piece existed while lack of mention in ordnance tables indicates that it was a case of rifling existing or new weapons in the same bore diameter as the Army did many smoothbores, thus not creating another model.

Such was not the case with the 12-pounder rifled howitzer. This piece (Fig. V-8) was changed into a new model for although the exterior form of the 12-pounder medium was followed exactly, the piece was bored to 3.4-inch diameter and rifled with 12 lands and grooves which increased the weight to 880 pounds. With a single pound of powder and 5°, it

could propel an 11-pound shell 1,770 yards. According to Mrs. Dahlgren, 428 were made.[8]

The photograph illustrates one of the pieces on the deck of the Agawam, a wood sidewheeler of 974 tons. She was 205 feet long and mounted two 100-pounder Parrots, four 9-inch Dahlgrens, two 24- and two 12-pounder smoothbores and the single 12-pounder rifle. Although Dahlgren's 12-pounder rifled boat howitzers were bronze, similar pieces were made by others in iron and steel and several of these weapons will be discussed in Chapter IX.

The 20-pounder rifle differs considerably from the previous weapons, but is listed with them since Dahlgren apparently considered it light artillery, although not boat armament.[9] The piece had a 4-inch bore and weighed 1,340 pounds. With 2 pounds of powder and 5° elevation, it hurled an 18-pound shell 1,960 yards.[10] An even hundred were made.

The author believes the piece shown in Figure V-9 is one of these rifles. The man is Admiral David D. Porter. Note the weapon has trunnions instead of a loop and the tube tapers noticeably. It is mounted on a deck carriage which is quite similar to the boat carriage. The admiral's own projectiles, known as "Dahlgrens" or "JAD" shells, were specified for the rifles along with Hotchkiss and Schenkl shells.[11] (See Chapter XIII.)

Dahlgren submitted plans for the first of a long line of iron weapons 19 January 1850. The piece, a 9-inch, smoothbore shellgun of 9,000 pounds, was cast at West Point Foundry and arrived for testing at Washington Navy Yard four months later.[12] This was the forerunner of a type weapon which in 9- and 11-inch calibers, and to a lesser extent 10, proved highly successful throughout the war. The Dahlgrens were designed to fire shells at wooden vessels of the 1850s, but were strong enough to switch to shot when the increasing use of ironclads during the following decade made heavier striking power imperative.

After practice with the 9-inch, Dahlgren submitted plans for an 11-inch of similar design 24 March 1851, and the first of this caliber was cast by Cyrus Alger in July. Acceptance of the two weapons was far from general or immediate. The 11-inch in particular struck heavy opposition from those who considered its 15,700-pound weight entirely too heavy for naval service.

In an effort to meet the objections, Dahlgren was permitted to arm the Plymouth with an 11-inch in 1857. Sea tests proved the merit of his theories and the next few years saw increasing use of the 9-inch in broadside batteries and the 11-inch for pivots.

FIGURE: V-7 IDENTIFICATION: Civil War view, deck of unidentified monitor with 12-Pounder Dahlgren Boat Howitzer, Medium, on Field Carriage.

FIGURE: V-8 IDENTIFICATION: Dahlgren, Howitzer, Boat, 12-Pounder, Rifle, Bronze. BORE: Diameter — 3.4. Rifling — 12 x 12. Length — 55.23. LENGTH O/A: 63.5. REMARKS: Men unidentified. Civil War view of piece on deck of *U.S.S. Agawam*. Weapon statistics from appendix tables.

FIGURE: V-9 IDENTIFICATION: Dahlgren, Howitzer, 20-Pounder, Rifle, Bronze. REMARKS: Admiral David D. Porter aboard the *U.S.S. Malvern* with weapon believed to be this 4-inch rifle. Note trunnions and deck carriage.

Mounted in conjunction with traditional, smaller weapons, they gave American ships the ability to throw 70-pound shells from broadside and 127-pounders from pivot. Shot increased the weight to 90-pounders from the 9-inch and formidable 170-pounders from the 11-inch.

On occasion, the 11-inch was also used in broadside. During the war the *New Ironsides,* for instance, had sixteen of these weapons and when she steamed into position and unlimbered her port or starboard battery, the rapidity with which shot and shell came whistling into forts ashore sent Confederate cannoneers scurrying for the bombproofs. This speed of fire made her a valuable asset to the South Atlantic Squadron and led its commander, Admiral Samuel F. DuPont, to prefer her over a similar number of larger caliber weapons buttoned up in monitors where speed was a non-existent factor.

A 10-inch Dahlgren was designed somewhat later and although listed with the others, only a few served at sea during the war and it never acquired their popularity. It weighed 12,000 pounds and fired a 97-pound shell and a shot of roughly 125 pounds.

An excellent 9-inch Dahlgren (Fig. V-10) is in the Portsmouth Naval Shipyard Museum collection and a Civil War photograph (Fig. V-11) shows one of these pieces with a 100-pounder Parrott aboard

FIGURE: V-10 LOCATION: Portsmouth Naval Shipyard Museum, Portsmouth, Va. IDENTIFICATION: Dahlgren, Shellgun, 9-Inch, Iron. BORE: Diameter — 9. Smoothbore. Length — 107. LENGTH O/A: 131.5. TRUNNIONS: Diameter — 7.25. Length — 7.25. MARKINGS: Left Trunnion — P. W.R.T. Right Trunnion — IX-In., 1859. Breech — C.A. & Co., No. 242, 9045 Lbs. Cascabel — 732. COMMON NAME: 9-Inch Dahlgren.

the *U.S.S. Commodore Perry*. The *Perry,* 143-foot sidewheeler of 512 tons, in July 1864 mounted the Dahlgren and Parrott at one end and two more 9-inch Dahlgrens at the other. However, since the vessel was a converted ferryboat, determination of which were bow guns and which stern depended largely on the whim of her skipper.

FIGURE: V-11 IDENTIFICATION: Dahlgren, Shellgun, 9-Inch, Iron. REMARKS: 9-Inch Dahlgren (left) and 100-Pounder Parrott aboard the *U.S.S. Commodore Perry*.

All Dahlgren iron smoothbores had a characteristic shape which led critics in England to dub them "soda-water bottles," a term which later was rammed down British throats when the 11-inch pivot of the *Kearsarge* played havoc with the inside of the *Alabama* despite the Confederate vessel's vaunted and beloved British-made 68-pounder and Blakely rifle. In all fairness, however, it should be pointed out that had the shell from the Blakely—which lodged harmlessly in the federal ship's rudder post—exploded as it should have, the outcome might have been somewhat different. Rudder post and shell, incidentally, are now on display at the Washington Navy Yard and a sketch is in Chapter XIII.

If the *Kearsarge-Alabama* engagement fixed the 11-inch in the eyes of the world, the weapon's baptism of fire was no less spectacular. Two of these pieces were the sole armament in the turret of the *Monitor* when she crept into Hampton Roads to hammer it out with the *Virginia* 9 March 1862, an engagement too well known to recount here.

The *Monitor's* guns, if ever salvaged from her watery grave off Cape Hatteras doubtless will be among the most valuable pieces of antique ordnance in the country—certainly the most historic Dahlgrens. Until then, the 11-inch (Fig. V-12) is a leading candidate for the honor. This weapon is the survivor of a pair that served on both sides during the conflict and figured in one of the most daring salvage operations of any war. The Dahlgren now rests peacefully on Charleston's Battery, a harmless iron monster, its top worn smooth by generations of climbing children. Its muzzle is plugged, its vent spiked. Yet the piece is sighted on Fort Sumter and the harbor entrance where sweating men once fed its maw and the waters echoed to its thunder.

FIGURE: V-12 LOCATION: Charleston, S.C. IDENTIFICATION: Dahlgren, Shellgun, 11-Inch, Iron. BORE: Diameter — 11. Smoothbore. Length — 132. LENGTH O/A: 161. TRUNNIONS: Diameter — 10. Length — 9. MARKINGS: Left Trunnion — P. T.A.H. Right Trunnion — 1862. Breech — C.A. & Co., No. 235, 15960 Lbs. Cascabel — 969. REMARKS: Salvaged by Confederates from the *U.S.S. Keokuk*. COMMON NAME: 11-Inch Dahlgren.

The weapon—and presumably its mate—was made by Cyrus Alger in 1862. They were mounted aboard the *U.S.S. Keokuk* (Fig. V-13), an experimental ironclad of 677 tons launched at New York December 6 of that year. The twin-screw vessel was 159 feet long and had two turrets with a Dahlgren in each. Unlike the monitor turrets—which revolved to traverse cannon mounted on fixed carriages—the *Keokuk's* turrets were stationary. Each had six ports through any one of which that turret's Dahlgren could be trained by shifting the carriage.

The *Keokuk* had her date with destiny 7 April 1863. On that day Admiral DuPont sent his ironclads against Fort Sumter in an all-out effort to smash the stubborn bastion guarding the way to Charleston. But the Fort, armed with 10-inch smoothbores and 7-inch rifles to contest the issue

FIGURE: V-13 IDENTIFICATION: *U.S.S. Keokuk*. SOURCE: *Official Records, Navy*, Vol. 14. REMARKS: Twin screw, double turret monitor of 677 tons. Length 159′6″, beam 36′. Armament, two 11-inch Dahlgrens. Launched 6 Dec. 1862 at New York. Sank 8 April 1863 off Morris Island, S.C., after engagement with Fort Sumter the previous day.

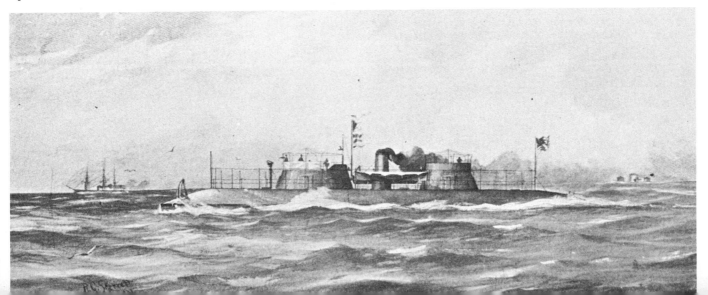

with 11-and 15-inch Dahlgrens and 8-inch Parrott rifles, gave as good as it took and perhaps better. Since the *Keokuk* was an untried vessel, her skipper, Commander A.C. Rhind, an especially courageous officer, took her in closer than any of the monitors, variously estimated from 550 to 900 yards, and stayed there thirty minutes in an effort to find out her capabilities.

He discovered they weren't much. The relatively thin-skinned *Keokuk* was hulled over and over again and limped out of battle to her anchorage off nearby Morris Island with holes and dents attesting to ninety hits. Many round shot and rifle bolts had gone completely through her, yet casualties were surprisingly light, ". . .four wounded dangerously or severely, one painfully, and 11 slightly," as the skipper put it.

Rhind and his crew worked through the night to keep her afloat, but with a rising sea in the morning, the *Keokuk* began taking in water faster than the pumps could handle it. A rescue vessel was flagged along side, the crew transferred without loss of life, and the *Keokuk* settled gently in 15 feet of water leaving the top of her stack visible at high tide and her turrets barely awash at low.

During the ensuing days, the wreck became a leading tourist attraction with U.S. Navy officers sloshing aboard each day figuring ways to raise or destroy her, and Confederates poking around after dark hunting souvenirs, mainly smallarms, flags, and clothing which were exhibited in the city as trophies of war. Several Union attempts were made to blow up the wreck, but for one reason or another they ended

FIGURE: V-14 IDENTIFICATION: Charleston Harbor, 1865. SOURCE: U.S. Department of Commerce, Coast & Geodetic Survey, Selected Civil War Maps. REMARKS: Arrow points to wreck of *U.S.S. Keokuk*. Fort armament statistics not accurate.

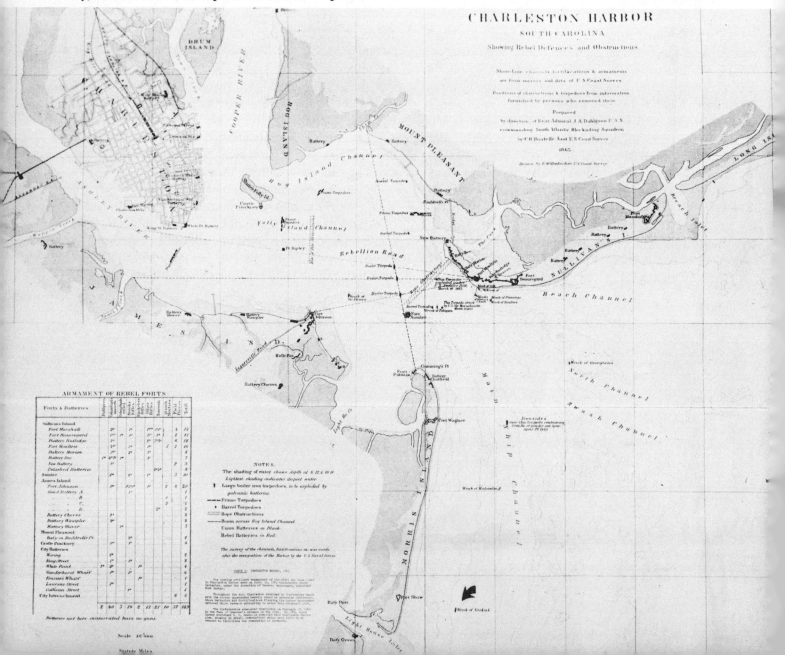

in failure while plans to raise her proved equally unsuccessful.

Finally the federals washed their hands of the *Keokuk* and a newspaper correspondent with the fleet informed readers back home: "At all events she is useless to the Rebels. She is filled with sand and will be broken up or buried after the first gale. The Rebels cannot raise her as she is covered by the guns of the blockading fleet, and will ever be beyond their reach."

C.S. Navy officers, after a nighttime tour, pronounced recovery of the guns "positively impossible." Confederate Army officers, however, had a different opinion. Spurred on by versatile General Beauregard, who excelled in unorthodox operations and had a keen appreciation of heavy-caliber ordnance, they decided recovery was feasible and began looking for a man who could handle the job. Their eyes fell on Adolphus W. LaCoste, a civilian shiprigger working for the Ordnance Department mounting heavy guns, a Jack-of-all-trades with a reputation for accomplishing what others deemed impossible.

An appreciation of LaCoste's problem may be gathered by a glance at the chart (Fig. V-14). Fort Sumter is at the harbor throat flanked by Sullivan's Island and Morris Island stretching like open arms north and south with the wreck of the *Keokuk* (arrow) some 1,400 yards off the southern tip of the latter. Not shown on this 1865 chart, but ever present in 1863, was the blockading fleet strung out like a rope between the "arms" made by the Confederate-held islands.

LaCoste gathered a picked crew, mainly civilians, and with volunteer guards from Fort Sumter set out in small boats one night during the latter third of April for the long row to the wreck. Preferably the salvors hoped for a calm, dark night, but this was secondary to the stage of the tide. Since the turrets were awash at the low, LaCoste found it possible to work only two hours each night, the last hour of the ebb and the first of the flood. This limited the amount of work accomplished each trip, but did have one redeeming feature—the boats could ride the outgoing tide down to the wreck, and catch the flood on the way home.

Arriving at the wreck, workmen and tools were unloaded and the boats pulled off for sentry duty. Work on the turrets was a hard, lonely job which called for tough men with more than a fair share of courage. They stood on the turret tops, circular iron platforms 14-feet in diameter sloping to 20 at the deck below, awash at low tide and covered by several feet of water at the high. With any sea running—and it generally was—the men were constantly drenched and in imminent danger of being washed from their slippery perch into the fast-running current where rescue in the dark would be a matter of luck. Just to stand there was hard enough. But these men had to work, work within less than a mile of the enemy, without lights, and in silence—for sound carries at night. Death was ever present from the sea and had a good chance of showing up at any moment in the form of a prowling gunboat. The blockaders usually anchored at night, but they could, and did, cross the bar at any time and the chances of one steaming over to check on the *Keokuk* were excellent and far from comforting. The guard boats could be counted on to give a few minutes warning, but they were no match for a large vessel and rowing 1,400 yards to Morris Island through a barrage of heavy shells was no cheerful prospect.

Yet LaCoste was never at a loss for workmen. Night after night men went back to the wreck. With wrenches and crowbars they battled the heavy turret tops consisting of two thicknesses of inch or inch and a half iron plate over 10-inch girders ceiled below with another layer of plate. Piece by piece the top layers were removed and dropped over the side, the beams cut through and the ceiling ripped out to leave a forbidding inky well with the guns below. Then a deep breath and a man slipped into the well, dropping straight down into the blackness dragged by a heavy wrench to attack the nuts holding the huge bronze cap squares over the trunnions, fighting weightlessness, straining to push the wrench a fraction of a turn. Then up again, lungs bursting, eyes protruding, praying not to miss the hole above to the surface, to clutch the ragged metal of the turret edge, gasping in the chill April air, and await another turn into the silent blackness. Finally, the last nut fell to the deck below. The guns were free, but a long way from the surface—in effort if not in feet.

LaCoste, however, was ready for the next step. While work went on at the wreck each night, another crew in the city had spent the days mounting heavy shears and tackle over the bow of an ancient hulk which in better days had seen service as a lightship. In addition, since the piece was more than 13 feet long and the shears, in order to carry the weight, couldn't be made very tall, LaCoste ordered aboard some 1,500 sandbags. These were piled on the deck at the bow until the hulk was noticeably out of trim with the bow sunk well below the waterline.

The next dark night with the proper tide found the hulk, loaded with LaCoste and his crew, augmented by Army personnel, under tow of the steamer

Etiwan headed for the wreck. This was a major operation and in view of the amount at stake, the Navy sent along its ironclads *Chicora* and *Palmetto State* to put up a fight in case the federals interfered. The hulk was made fast to the *Keokuk,* and the *Etiwan* steamed off to take up guard duty. The falls were lowered and men swam down into the turret to hook on to the Dahlgren's cascabel. Civilians and soldiers strained at the line and the huge piece, weighing nearly 16,000 pounds, rose smoothly, breech first, from the turret while the hulk bobbed sluggishly in a rising sea.

Then movement stopped. The blocks had met near the top of the shears. Tackle could lift no farther although the muzzle was still far down in the turret. Now the reason for the sandbags became apparent. LaCoste's muted order: "Belay. Move the bags," was whispered from man to man. Lines were formed port and starboard and the sandbags passed from bow to stern. Slowly the bow lifted and with it the gun. Then the last bag dropped on the deck astern. The last man moved aft. LaCoste, peering over the bow, could tell the muzzle was still locked within the turret, banging against the iron sides like the clapper of some huge underwater gong.

Now came a new sound, a muffled hail from the *Etiwan,* her skipper pointing frantically to the lightening sky in the east. Dawn was only minutes away and with it death from the guns of the blockaders. LaCoste knew man could do no more. Only a few inches of the weapon's muzzle remained in the turret, but those inches spelled defeat. There was nothing to do but lower away and hope a future attempt might meet with better success.

Then fate took a hand. Tide and sea had continued to rise and as the old ship rose and fell, a wave a little larger than the rest passed beneath her. The bow lifted, fell again with the gun slamming against the turret, this time on the outside, free. Lines were cast loose from the *Keokuk* and passed to the *Etiwan.* The expedition headed back to harbor, the Dahlgren dangling from the shears, its chase lashed securely to prevent pounding in the bow wave.

It was a triumphant procession that arrived back in the city. One that was repeated when the second piece was salvaged a few nights later. This time LaCoste didn't make the trip. He was temporarily laid up from exhaustion and exposure. Instead his brother, James, took out the expedition which went like clockwork with none of the suspense of the first.

Charleston papers on 6 May announced recovery of the guns which sets a time of roughly two and a half weeks for the entire operation. The weapons, after cleaning at Charleston, were mounted one at Fort Sumter and the other in Battery Bee on Sullivan's Island. Both pieces later fired on the ironclads

FIGURE: V-15 IDENTIFICATION: 1865 view of Charleston's White Point Gardens, better known today as The Battery. REMARKS: 11-Inch Dahlgren from *Keokuk* (left). Center and right are 10-Inch Confederate Columbiads, Model 1861. Remains of 12.75-Inch Blakely Rifle, blown at evacuation of the city (Chapter VIII), lie behind huge mound at right.

FIGURE: **V-16** LOCATION: Charleston Naval Shipyard, S.C. IDENTIFICATION: Dahlgren, Shellgun, 11-Inch, Sleeved to 8-Inch Rifle, Iron. BORE: Diameter — 8. Rifling 15 x 15, straight. Length — 125v. LENGTH O/A: 159.5. TRUNNIONS: Diameter — 12. Length — 5. MARKINGS: Left Trunnion — P. H.W.L. 1879. Right Trunnion — 8-In. Rifle, 17430 lbs. No. 44. Tube — anchor Breech — B.F. No. 63 15805 lbs. (original marks). REMARKS: One of four identical pieces converted 1879–80. COMMON NAME: Dahlgren 8-Inch M.L.R. (Muzzle-Loading Rifle).

and, with exception of two unused Blakely rifles in the city, were the heaviest caliber in the Charleston defenses.

The Fort Sumter Dahlgren was later returned to the city and mounted on The Battery (Fig. V-15) not far from the spot where its mate stands today. The piece is accompanied by a pair of 10-inch "Confederate Rodmans" and out of sight behind the mound—which served as bombproof and ammunition storage—was one of the aforementioned Blakelys, described in Chapter VIII. Although the Blakely was blown at the evacuation of the city during the night and early morning of 17-18 February 1865, the photograph shows other pieces were left intact on damaged carriages (note brace is cut near trunnions). Future history of this Dahlgren is unknown, but it is thought to have been sold as scrap.

The Battery Bee Dahlgren also was left in position on its carriage which eventually rotted, dumping the piece in the island sand that soon drifted over it. Years later it was found and mounted in its present position. Vandals long ago removed a bronze plaque which told its story, so the historic value of the piece is lost to thousands of visitors who seldom give it a second glance. Unmarked and generally unnoticed, it remains a monument to a group of Americans who proved that courage, ingenuity, and hard work can accomplish what sometimes seems impossible. The feat even drew praise from former enemies[13] for in 1893 Rhind, now an admiral, told a *New York Times* reporter he considered the accomplishment

"one of the most daring of the war, and in point of skill had probably no counterpart."

Success of the Dahlgrens in war led the government, during the conversion fad of the 1870s, to change a number of 11-inchers to 8-inch rifles. The alteration consisted in reaming out the bore to 13 inches or so, then sleeving it down to 8-inch caliber rifled with 15 lands and grooves. At the same time the muzzle was cut back about three inches and the swell turned off. Diminishing the size of the bore, of course, changed the balance of the piece, so the trunnions were shaved an inch at the rear, then increased to 12-inch diameter with an eccentric ring built up mainly in front. This moved the axis forward 1.5 inches and counteracted the tendency of the rifle to be muzzle heavy. Lock pieces were removed since firing was by friction primer. The converted piece weighed roughly 17,330 pounds.[14]

Figure V-16 is of one of four converted Dahlgrens almost concealed by shrubbery at the entrance to the Charleston Navy Yard. They bear conversion dates of 1879 or 1880 and are mounted on broadside carriages of later vintage than the Civil War. They were installed aboard the *U.S.S. Lancaster* in 1881 and set ashore in 1895 as ornaments when the Dahlgrens proved no better converted to rifles than the 10-inch Rodmans.

Since Dahlgren was the acknowledged expert of naval ordnance, he was asked in March, 1862, to design a 15-inch smoothbore for one class of monitors and 20-inchers for another. This led to production of two new weapons and eventually brought into the open a smoldering resentment over credit for weapons development that confused many officers of both services during the war and has plagued researchers ever since. It is not the purpose of this book to delve into the merits of either side of the argument, but a brief synopsis is necessary to understand why one writer refers to the 15- and 20-inch naval shellguns as "Rodmans" yet another calls the same weapons "Dahlgrens."

Rodman, it will be remembered from the chapter on columbiads, was an exponent of the theory of interior cooling for large calibers. In contrast, Dahlgren believed this had nothing to do with the strength of the piece which he felt was due solely to form. Hence the admiral's 9-, 10-, and 11-inchers— although the 11 later was made according to Rodman's principles—were poured in the form of a huge cylinder and cooled from the exterior in the traditional manner. The excess metal was then turned off in a lathe to give the piece the required form.

The argument between the two inventors seems to have started when Rodman was about to cast his first 15-inch in 1860. Dahlgren saw the plans and immediately charged plagiarism of design from the naval shellgun. A verbal and written battle ensued with Rodman trying to prove his design went back to older columbiads and Dahlgren claiming hollow and solid cast guns broke with equal facility until the form was changed to roughly that of the Dahlgren.

With this as a background, the admiral was suddenly put on the spot when the Navy asked him to turn out 15-and 20-inch pieces. The Navy insisted on having the guns immediately, leaving no time for an orderly, and time consuming, process of experiment and testing. Dahlgren pointed out the necessity of testing, even advocated arming the monitors with 11-inchers pending systematic development of a heavier weapon. But the Navy was adamant, so he submitted a design for a 15-inch smoothbore. It was generally in the form of his other iron smoothbores, but shortened to fit the monitor turrets, and since the only successful 15-inch ever made was Rodman's, the admiral swallowed his pride for the good of the service and urged that the weapon be cast by the hollow-core method. He submitted the final design to Fort Pitt Foundry 7 April 1862, and presumably the piece was cast not long thereafter although due to delays in boring the vent, the weapons were not delivered for introduction into monitor turrets until September.[15]

The original piece was tested on the range and stood well. However, since the gun ports of the monitors had been built to accommodate 13-inch, rather than 15-inch guns, the chase and muzzle of this and a number of subsequent pieces were turned down to fit and a teat chamber, which Dahlgren had designed, was reamed out to leave the bottom of the bore hemispherical.

These "hybrids," as Dahlgren called them, were placed in the monitors much to the dismay of the admiral, whose nightmares envisioned one exploding in a turret with death to the gun crew and probably destruction of the vessel. In an effort to ensure safety, he issued on 5 January 1863, what is probably one of the most amazing orders ever to come from a chief of naval ordnance.[16] It prohibited the firing of shot from the 15-inchers except against other ironclads, urged accuracy to limit the number of rounds that would be fired in action and instructed that the lowest possible charge be used that would serve the purpose, forbid firing out of action except occasionally to test the workings of the machinery, advocated use of the companion turret gun, generally an 11-inch, if possible, required examination of the vent at frequent intervals for signs of weakness, limited the charge with shells to 35 pounds of powder, and, finally, suggested that they be used "with utmost prudence." Fortunately, the monitor skippers were a tough breed who seem to have winked at both the admiral's fears and his orders which could have seriously limited their combat efficiency.

Not long after their introduction into service, articles began appearing in newspapers condemning the new shellguns and censuring the Bureau of Ordnance. Consequently, in an effort to be fair to Dahlgren, G.V. Fox, assistant secretary of the Navy, issued a statement pointing out that the weapons had been adopted despite Dahlgren's protests and accepting upon himself full responsibility for them.[17]

The gesture cleared Dahlgren temporarily, but relief turned to gall 17 June 1863 when the monitor *Weehawken* unlimbered her ponderous 15-inch against the iron plating of the Confederate ram *Atlanta*. The *Atlanta* had been converted the previous year from the British Steamer *Fingal* and when she swept down the Savannah River with her four 6.4- and 7-inch rifles, there was little doubt she would knock out the *Weehawken* and her companion monitor, the *Nahant*, it they should be so bold as to challenge her.[18] Unfortunately for the *Atlanta*, she went aground and although she began the fight at a distance with a 7-inch, the *Weehawken* came slowly on until only about 300 yards separated the vessels.

There are a few minor discrepancies between the account of W.A. Webb, commander of the *Atlanta*, and the *Weehawken's* skipper, Captain John

Rodgers, due no doubt to the heat of battle.[19] However, both agree the *Weehawken* fired five rounds, 15- and 11-inch, and connected with four. They were enough to bring down the *Atlanta's* colors and reveal to the world the awesome power of 400-pound cored shot crashing through armor and wood backing, filling the casemates with splinters, flying iron, and the groans of wounded men. The *Atlanta* struck within fifteen minutes despite light casualties—she had only one dead and sixteen wounded out of a complement of one hundred and forty-five. But she was aground, could not bring her guns to bear on the monitors, and the punishment from the 15-inch was too intense to long endure. In all, the *Atlanta* seems to have gotten off seven shots, none apparently taking effect.

Dahlgren was happy to take credit for the piece now. But the Navy Department followed the line of its assistant secretary—the congratulatory message to Captain Rodgers praised the "15-inch gun of Rodman." This was bitter indeed and the admiral sent off an immediate protest claiming design of the piece and that only the cooling process of Rodman had been used. This brought the following reply[20] 9 July 1863 from the Secretary of the Navy:

"Sir: I have your letter of the 29th ultimo relative to the 15-inch guns in the turret of the *Weehawken* and other ironclads alluded to in the letter to Capt. Rodgers and therein styled the 'gun of Rodman'.

"I had supposed you were unwilling to take the paternity of the 15-inch gun from all the conversations we have had, and there was subsequently some embarrassment in defining the piece and relieving you of responsibility. It was part of the original plan of Mr. Ericsson [who designed the monitors] as you are aware, to have guns of large caliber in the turrets, but your opinion was against it, and you were unwilling to take the responsibility of recommending the 15-inch gun. But others, particularly the assistant secretary, adopting Mr. Ericsson's suggestion, earnestly advocated it and it was decided that the experiment should be made. Under this decision, the Ordnance Bureau took the necessary measures to have them built and you, as stated in your letter, designed the pattern, making it conform to the diameter of the turret. I supposed you wished it distinctly understood that you were acting under orders and that this turret 15-inch gun was not a Dahlgren and that you were in no way responsible for its success or failure.

"The form of the gun is after your design, but you had made no guns of that caliber. Rodman had and, as you observe, when the gun was manufactured, the cooling process invented by Capt. Rodman was used by the founder. Strictly, perhaps, it is neither a Dahlgren nor Rodman. As, however, you had never identified your name

with the 15-inch gun, but had expressly disclaimed it, while Rodman had designed them, it seemed proper that allusion to him should be made, to relieve you quite as much as to identify him. The particular gun had its origin in Mr. Ericsson's invention which made it a necessity and was ordered by the department irrespective of inventors. There was no intention to do injustice to either, I assure you, in the allusion made to the gun in the letter to Captain Rodgers."

The secretary's letter seems to have been the last word in the argument, officially at any rate. But most officers in both services preferred to call the Army 15-inch a Rodman and the Navy piece Dahlgren, terminology which seems logical to continue since the weapons differ considerably in appearance, and admittedly were designed separately by the two individuals.

Early 15-inch Dahlgrens fired entirely within the turret, only the ball going through the port. This necessitated a "smoke box" of iron plating around the muzzle to prevent the crew from being wiped out by the blast. The box was later eliminated in the *Tecumseh* class of monitors by widening the port, lengthening the piece 16 inches and turning it slim enough to enter the opening. Both pieces are illustrated in the hypothetical turret (Fig. V-17). Note sight bracket at rear of each piece and off-center lock piece for single vent. Smaller caliber Dahlgrens, expected to last for many rounds, had twin lock pieces and vents. One vent, generally the left, was closed with zinc at the foundry and the lock attached to the right. When this vent became worn through continued firing, it was blocked and the other drilled open for further use. The 15-inch wasn't expected to last that long—not a comforting thought for the gunners.

No 15-inch Dahlgren has been found thus far and Figure V-18 is probably one of the few photographs made of the piece. Whether it was the long or short model is a matter of guess, although based on the thinness of metal at the muzzle, the former seems preferable.

Statistics are meager:[21] weight 42,000 pounds, compared to roughly 50,000 for the Rodman; maximum diameter 48 inches, bore length 130 inches. The bore length could refer to either model, but the author believes it more applicable to the early type. If so, bore length for the *Tecumseh* class would be 146 inches. No statement of overall length has been found, but approximations of 162 and 178 may be obtained by averaging figures in several drawings.

Projectiles were solid shot of 440 pounds for use against ironclads, cored shot of 400, shell of 330, grape, and canister. Cored shot, although fired against

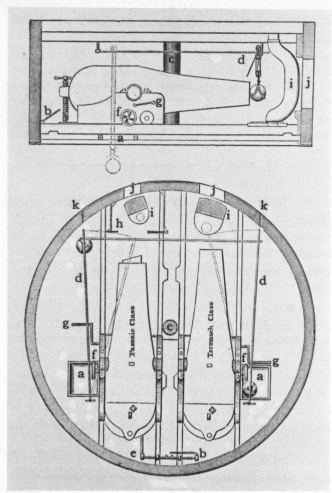

FIGURE: V-17 IDENTIFICATION: Dahlgren, Shellgun, 15-Inch, Iron. SOURCE: Cooke. REMARKS: *Passaic* and *Tecumseh* Class weapons in hypothetical monitor turret. Note smokebox (h) used with *Passaic* Class.

   a. Ammunition Scuttle.
   b. Starting Bar for revolving turret and training weapon.
   c. Shaft on which turret revolved.
   d. Traveling Bar on which shell whip moved.
   e. Position of engineer stationed at Starting Bar to revolve turret and train piece.
   f. Compressor Wheel to check recoil — hove taut before firing.
   g. Crank for running weapon in and out.
   h. Smoke Box (*Passaic* Class).
   i. Port Stopper.
   j. Porthole.
   k. Sighthole.

the *Atlanta,* were designed to bombard masonry forts. Shell carried three fuses of 3.5, 5, and 7 seconds for use at various ranges. Charges, despite Dahlgren's order, were later set at 35 pounds service with shell and never more than 50, 50 pounds maximum with cored shot, and 60 pounds maximum for not more than twenty rounds when firing solid shot at close quarters, say 50 to 150 yards.

Ricochet was especially successful with these weapons, the shell bounding low and rolling for a considerable distance if the sea was calm. This is attested in the *Letter Book of Fort Sumter*[22] under the date of 4 February 1864: . . . "one monitor is firing 11- and 15-inch shells at [two words illegible, but presumably 'the fort'] this morning. The sea being smooth, their ricochet fire is effective."

No record has been found of a 20-inch Dahlgren being used during the war although Dahlgren submitted a design for the piece 13 May 1862, only a short time after his draft of the 15-inch was forwarded. However, Captain H.A. Wise, who succeeded Dahlgren in June, 1863, as Chief of Naval Ordnance, testified 28 January 1864 before a U.S. Senate committee when asked if it would be desirable to cast a gun larger than the 15-inch: "That is a question yet to be solved. We are going to try the experiment at all events. We are about to cast a 20-inch gun—to be cast on Rodman's method of the Navy form. . ."

Apparently the piece was poured during the year for in a note to the chief's annual report as quoted in Dahlgren's Memoir[23] Wise said: " . . . and in the target experiments, the XX-inch gun has broken up and shattered plates exceeding in thickness anything hitherto proposed as defensive armor. . . ." The 20-inch, according to Holley,[24] was 204 inches long with a bore length of 163 inches. Maximum diameter was 64 inches, trunnion diameter 16, and total weight about 100,000 pounds. It was expected to fire 1,000-pound cored shot with a 100-pound service charge.

Two other iron Dahlgren smoothbores which apparently saw no service were a 13-inch and a 130-pounder 10-inch which, to follow modern terminology, might be called a "Super 10."

Writing on 15 April 1864,[25] the admiral explained that he had designed three weapons as a possible solution to the ironclad problem:

First, the 15-inch which was already seeing service in monitor turrets.

Second, a 13-inch of 34,000 pounds to throw a 280-pound shot with 50 pounds of powder. ". . . it has not been in action yet, but one of them has been proved to 500 fires which I look on as very satisfactory."

Third, a 130-pounder (10-inch) throwing a shot ". . . with thirty pounds and even 40 pounds of powder. It has pierced six inches of iron at 200 yards."

The theory behind the three cannon was to embrace all powers of ordnance as advanced by vari-

FIGURE: V-18 IDENTIFICATION: Dahlgren, Shellgun, 15-Inch, Iron. REMARKS: Believed to be at Washington about 1864.

ous experts of the day. Thus the first produced momentum by maximum weight and minimum velocity, the third by minimum weight and maximum velocity, and the second by a combination of the two.

These were the 13-inch weapons designed for the Ericsson monitors[26] and for which the ports already had been cut only to have orders changed virtually at the last moment and 15s substituted.

It seems that a number of trial 13-inch had been cast solid by both Fort Pitt Foundry and the Builders Iron Works of Providence, Rhode Island. At the same time, others were cast hollow at Scott Foundry, Reading, Pennsylvania. Unfortunately for Dahlgren, the solid cast weapons went up in pieces after a few rounds while the hollow cast survived more than 500 rounds.[27] This apparently tossed a hitch into his theories and rather than await more experimental results with the 13, the 15 was designed.

Why a partially successful weapon intended for a particular job should have been discarded in favor of a new, untried piece of similar form that had to be tailored to fit is difficult to understand. It may have been a face-saving gesture enabling Dahlgren to use a casting method indicated by the 13-inch trials as superior to his own theories. He could do this with impunity by changing caliber on the basis that the only successful 15-inch made thus far, Rodman's, had, of course, been cast by this method and any new attempt should follow identical procedure—but using the admiral's design.

The 13-inch had a 130-inch bore length and 44.7-inch maximum diameter. Benton,[28] in contrast to Dahlgren, lists the weight as 36,000 pounds and service charge at 40 pounds. He also gives the piece a shell weighing 224 pounds.

Statistics show the "Super 10"—which Holley calls a 125-pounder in contrast to Dahlgren's 130—differed from the standard 10-inch in having a shorter bore, 117.75 inches compared to 119.5, a larger maximum diameter, 33.25 to 29.1 inches, and a much heavier weight, 16,500 to 12,000 pounds. Weights of shot and shell were the same for both, roughly 125 and 97 pounds respectively, but the service charge initially differed materially—12.5 pounds for the standard and 40 for the "Super 10"[29] By 1866, the gap had narrowed with maximum charge for the "Super 10" reduced to 30 and service charge to 18 pounds.

The "Super 10" had no chamber and was classified in 1866 ordnance tables[30] as a gun with solid shot as its primary projectile although shells could be used on occasion. Mrs. Dahlgren[31] catalogued production of various types as follows: 15-inch, 113; 13-inch, 11; 11-inch, 465; 10-inch (standard) 10; 10-inch (Super 10) 34, and 9-inch, 1,185. She fails to mention the 20-inch of which at least one was made.

The admiral may have experimented with 8-inch caliber, but made no such service piece prior to 1864 (probably 1865), for although he often refers to his 9-, 10-, 11-, and 15-inch, and occasionally 20-inch, he makes no mention of a service 8-inch. Admiral DuPont, when asked 5 February 1864 what size guns were used on shipboard prior to the war stated:[32] ". . .of the improved guns, what were known as the 8-inch, 9-inch and 10-inch guns. The 9-and 10-inch

FIGURE: V-19 LOCATION: West Point, N.Y. IDENTIFICATION: (Second from front) Shellgun, 8-Inch, 63 cwt., Model 1841, Iron. BORE: Diameter — 8 (flared to 8.25 at muzzle). Smoothbore. Length — 101.5. LENGTH O/A: 117.5. TRUNNIONS: Diameter — 8.5. Length — 6.5. MARKINGS: Left Trunnion — 8, A.S.W. Breech — W.P.F.A., No. 264, 62-2-12. REMARKS: Right trunnion, which probably held date, is broken. Piece in foreground is a 42-Pounder Carronade (Chapter IX). Bore diameter — 7 (flared at muzzle to 7.9). Smoothbore. Bore Length — 57. Length O/A — 71.5. Markings: Tube at breech — 42, 1822, No. 98. Base of breech — I.C. & Co., B.F. Vᵃ.

were Dahlgren guns, the 8-inch was of different form, but a very effective gun. . . ." In addition, Captain Wise, in testimony[33] corrected 8 February 1864, on the number of smoothbores made for the

FIGURE: V-20 LOCATION: Vicksburg, Miss. IDENTIFICATION: Shellgun, 8-Inch, 63 cwt., Model 1845, Iron. BORE: Diameter — 8. Smoothbore. Length — 102v. LENGTH O/A: 119. TRUNNIONS: Diameter — 7. Length — 6.4. MARKINGS: Left Trunnion — P. G.A.M. Right Trunnion — 8-In., 1845. Base Ring — F.P.F., No. 368, 64-0-26. REMARKS: Salvaged from *U.S.S. Cairo*. COMMON NAME: 8-Inch Shellgun, 63 cwt. Model 1845.

FIGURE: V-21 LOCATION: Oakland, N. J. IDENTIFICATION: Dahlgren, Shellgun, 8-Inch of 6,500 lbs., Model 1864, Iron. BORE: Diameter — 8. Smoothbore. Length — 98v. LENGTH O/A: 115.5. TRUNNIONS: Diameter — 7.1. Length — 3. MARKINGS: Left Trunnion — P. T.A.H. Right Trunnion — VIII-In., 1866. Breech — C.A. & Co., No. 172, 6460. Cascabel, rear — 2146. Cascabel Block — 2146. COMMON NAME: 8-Inch of 6,500 lbs.

Navy since the war began, failed to list a single 8-inch.

Judging from this, it seems a relatively safe bet that at least until February, 1864, 8-inch shellguns used by the Navy were not Dahlgrens. But if not, what were these weapons? The answer lies, at least partially, in Dahlgren's book *Shells and Shellguns,* published in 1856.[34]

The first shellgun mentioned by the admiral is the Model 1841. Limited numbers of this weapon were made in both 8- and 10-inch caliber—63 cwt. (7,056 lbs.) and 86 cwt. (9,632 lbs.) respectively. One of these rare 1841 models (Fig. V-19) is in the West Point collection. The piece, partially blocked by a 42-pounder carronade, is an 8-inch made by West Point Foundry. Unfortunately, the right trunnion is broken and the date unavailable, but it is of the same general form as the 32-pounder gun cast in 1842 (Figs. I-42, 43) and presumably of the same vintage. The muzzle interior of the 8-inch is flared to 8.25 inches in similar fashion to the Pulaski 24-pounder (Fig. I-36).

No 10-inch has been found, but the weapon was identical to the 8-inch except for size. Its length from muzzle face to rear of the base plate was 117 inches as compared to 111.5 for the 8-inch. This, of course, is the length less cascabel which, in the case of the West Point piece is 6.25 inches. The 10-inch cascabel probably was only slightly longer thus giving an estimated length overall of 123.5. The 10-inch seems to have survived into the 1850s when it was superseded by the 10- and 11-inch Dahlgrens. Not so the 8-inch. This weapon went the way of the straight-muzzle 32-pounders during the extensive naval armament revision of 1845 which resulted in the 32-pounder gun Models 1845-47.

Two Model 1845 8-inch were adopted—55 and 63 cwt. (6,160 and 7,056 lbs.) No specimen of the lighter weapon has been found, but in external appearance it seems to have resembled the guns of that era including muzzle swell, greater thickness around the chamber, sight mass forward of the trunnions, and, as Dahlgren put it, "a stouter knob (cascabel)." Specifications listed in the Army Ordnance Manual of 1861[35] are 95.4-inch bore length and 114.5 overall. Charge was 7 pounds of powder with a 51-pound shell. Manual specifications[36] of the 8-inch of 63 cwt. are bore length 100.3 inches and overall 119.31. It burned an 8-pound charge to project the same shell.

Salvage of the *Cairo* brought to light three of these weapons of which one is shown in Figure V-20. All are dated 1845 and have similar measurements conforming closely to manual specifications. They are listed in the Official Navy Records[37] as "3 VIII-inch 63 cwt." although two are stamped a few pounds over 64 cwt.

Even though Wise in February, 1864, recalled no 8-inchers made thus far during the war, the captain reported[38] in October, 1865: "At present no change is contemplated in the distinctive features of our naval armaments for there does not appear any good reason for departing from the established system of a mixed battery of broadside and pivot guns, 9-inch being the principal of the former, and the 11-inch of the latter, wherever it can be carried and in the lighter vessels the new 8-inch of 6,500 pounds, or 32-pounders of 4,500 pounds, with one or two 100-pounder rifles in pivot. . . ."

This introduces a new model, the 8-inch Dahlgren of 6,500 pounds, which could have gone to sea any time after February, 1864. In fact, the Official Records mention two or three ships armed with "VIII-In. Dahlgren smoothbores" during the year. However, the theory that these were the new shellguns immediately falls apart since the same weapons are also listed aboard the ships early in the war. Here is a case where the author feels the Official Records are definitely in error.

Dahlgren claimed no 8-inch. DuPont said the pre-war 8s were not Dahlgrens, and Wise testified none were manufactured during the war up to February, 1864. Consequently, these pieces must have been one of the 1845 models, probably the 63 cwt., erroneously attributed to Dahlgren—an opinion substantiated by the reported[39] October, 1861 battery of the *U.S.S. Isaac Smith*: ". . . 8 VIII-In Dahlgren S.B. [smoothbore] of 63 cwt." This is obviously the 1845 model not claimed by Dahlgren.

Only mention found in wartime ship armament of the "new" 8-inch is that of the *U.S.S. Conemaugh*[40] where "4 VIII-In of 65 cwt." are recorded for 29 December 1865. If this is the piece, the report is technically in error since 65 cwt. (7,280 lbs.) is a much heavier cannon than 6,500 pounds. However, since no other 8-inch falls into this category, it probably was a mistake based on the previous way of stating weight and first acquaintance with the new piece.

One of these "new" 8-inchers (Fig. V-21) is at Oakland, New Jersey. It was made by Cyrus Alger & Co. of Boston in 1866 and is marked 6,460 pounds. Although the piece has certain minor characteristics unlike traditional Dahlgrens, particularly the cascabel which is more like the 32-pounder guns of 1845-47 and the 1845 8-inch, overall appearance is generally similar. The model is included in Mrs. Dahlgren's list[41] of the admiral's weapons with 355 having been produced. Moreover, in February, 1867, Cyrus Alger paid a royalty on the Dahlgren patent for ten "8-inch guns weighing 64,270, $642.70."

Along with the 8-inch, the admiral designed a 32-pounder. This piece, known as the 32-pounder of 4,500 pounds, was mentioned in Chapter I, but is listed here since it was definitely the admiral's design and, despite caliber, was a shellgun rather than a gun. The weapon was chambered and was classified with other shellguns in Ordnance Instructions for the U.S. Navy, 1866.[42] Specimens such as the Belfast, Maine, 32-pounder (Fig. V-22) have all been dated 1865-66. Total production was 383, according to the admiral's widow.[43]

In the course of experimentation, the admiral doubtless made iron smoothbores in various calibers including a 50-pounder for which he submitted a

FIGURE: V-22 LOCATION: Belfast, Me. IDENTIFICATION: Dahlgren, Shellgun, 32-Pounder of 4,500 lbs., Model 1864, Iron. BORE: Diameter — 6.4. Smoothbore. Length — 92.25v. LENGTH O/A: 107.5. TRUNNIONS: Diameter — 6.4. Length — 3. MARKINGS: Left Trunnion — P. T.A.H. Right Trunnion — 32-Pdr., 1865. Tube — Anchor, s, J.F.G. Breech — C.A. & Co., No. 169, 4495 lbs. Cascabel — 381. Cascabel Pin — 2026. Hammer — N.O.Y.W., 1866, Anchor, W.R.T. REMARKS: (See text). COMMON NAME: 32-Pounder of 4,500 lbs.

draft 14 July 1850. The 8,000-pound piece, which probably had a bore diameter of roughly 7.5 inches, was ordered cast at the West Point Foundry 19 January 1851 and was received 21 May at Washington Navy Yard for testing.[44] Since it was not adopted into service, presumably the tests were unsuccessful and such one-of-a-kind weapons as this were junked, returned to the melting pot, or may still be resting in some out-of-the-way park.

Before leaving the smoothbores, a Confederate shellgun at Vicksburg National Military Park, although not a true Dahlgren, should be included. This (Fig. V-23) is a 9-inch cast in 1862 by Bellona Foundry. It has the general form of the Dahlgren and was apparently copied from the admiral's design, but close examination reveals minor differences at muzzle and cascabel and in elimination of breech and tube sight brackets as well as lock pieces. However, based on appearance, it has as much right to the title "Confederate Dahlgren" as the previously discussed "Confederate Rodmans."

Dahlgren tried to begin work with iron rifled cannon as early as 1856 and in that year submitted to the Bureau of Ordnance preliminary sketches of a 10-inch rifle, but it wasn't until about 1859, after Sir William Armstrong's experiments in England had come to public notice, that he was permitted to proceed. Apparently he scrapped earlier work on the 10-inch and began experiment in rifling by casting a number of small calibers — including two 10.5-pounder rifles — and then a pair of iron 40-pounders in an effort to determine the proper twist. Commenting on this the admiral remarked:[45] "I am far from

abandoning the idea of getting cast iron to withstand the strain of heavy rifle cannon, having already attained sufficient results to encourage the hope, though very much short of anything like absolute proof. . . . The samples of cannon I cast here myself, with some variation in form from the smoothbore. The trial gun weighing 600 pounds and bored smooth, stood 1,000

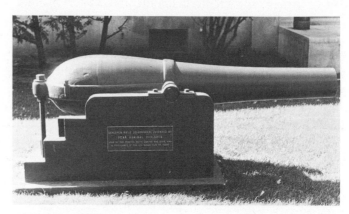

FIGURE: V-24 LOCATION: U.S. Naval Academy, Annapolis, Md. IDENTIFICATION: Dahlgren, 30-Pounder, Rifle, Iron. BORE: Diameter — 4.2. Rifling — 10 x 10, Straight. LENGTH O/A: 92. TRUNNIONS: Diameter — 4. Length — 3.5. MARKINGS: Breech — 30-Pdr., No. 21, USN, Washington. REMARKS: Trunnions and Trunnion Band made of bronze. COMMON NAME: 30-Pounder Dahlgren Rifle.

FIGURE: V-25 IDENTIFICATION: Dahlgren, 50-Pounder, Rifle, Iron. REMARKS: Rear Admiral John A. Dahlgren aboard the *U.S.S. Pawnee* in Charleston Harbor.

FIGURE: V-23 LOCATION: Vicksburg, Miss. IDENTIFICATION: Shellgun, 9-Inch, Confederate, Iron. BORE: Diameter — 9. Smoothbore. LENGTH O/A: 131.5. TRUNNIONS: Diameter — 7. Length — 7.1. MARKINGS: Left Trunnion — 1862. Right Trunnion — J.L.A., B.F. Tube — C.S. Breech — 9480. REMARKS: Apparently made on Dahlgren pattern. COMMON NAME: 9-Inch Confederate Dahlgren.

FIGURE: V-26 LOCATION: West Point, N.Y. IDENTIFICATION: (Second from front) Dahlgren, 50-Pounder, Rifle, Iron. BORE: Diameter — 5.1. Rifling — 12 x 12, Straight. Length — 88.5. LENGTH O/A: 107. TRUNNIONS: Diameter — 5.25. Length — 5.25. MARKINGS: Left Trunnion — F.P.F. REMARKS: Trunnions and Trunnion Band are bronze. First five weapons, front to rear, are: Improvised Confederate Cannon (Chapter IX); the Dahlgren; 8-Inch Seacoast Howitzer, Model 1841 (Chapter II); foreign 24-pounder believed used in War of 1812, and 8-Inch Blakely Rifle (Chapter VIII).

fires with 12-pounder shot and 12½ pounds charge. The last, a rifled 40-pounder (5,700 pounds) has been fired to a moderate extent with projectiles varying from 35 to 42 pounds and four pounds charge. . . ."

By December, 1860, Dahlgren had completed most of the design of three of his rifles, the 50-pounder of roughly 5-inch bore, 80-pounder of 6, and 150-pounder of 7.5.[46] Experimental models of these had been cast at the Washington Navy Yard, but it wasn't until after the firing on Sumter in April, 1861, that work really started on the rifles. In final form these pieces—and a 30-pounder developed somewhat later—were made without trunnions or protuberances of any sort. Trunnions were cast separately on a two-piece band attached as illustrated by the U.S. Naval Academy 30-pounder (Fig. V-24) which has a 4.2-inch bore rifled with 10 lands and grooves.

Plans for the first 30-pounder were sent to the Bureau of Ordnance about the end of August, 1861. No date of the initial casting is available, but 1 February 1862 the admiral recommended[47] withdrawing from service the first dozen 4.2-inch cast at Fort Pitt on the grounds that the iron was inferior. A week later he reported one of the weapons had been mounted on the *U.S.S. Harriet Lane* and 8 July remarked that forty-two of the rifles had been constructed either at the Washington Navy Yard or by private founders. The Annapolis weapon, which is undated, is No. 21 made at the yard and could have been within this group.

In the July statement,[48] he also mentioned that thirty-four 50-pounders had been turned out, fourteen 80-pounders and five 150. Figure V-25 shows Admiral Dahlgren with one of his 50-pounders aboard the *U.S.S. Pawnee*. This caliber seems to have been the best of the lot and saw service aboard various vessels throughout the war although toward the end it was beginning to be supplanted by the 60-pounder Parrott.

During the early part of 1862, a Dahlgren 50-pounder stood well in firing tests[49] beside a captured 7.5-inch Blakely and a 4.62-inch Sawyer. Few statistics have been found, but one of the weapons (Fig. V-26) in a line of tubes at West Point has a 5.1-inch bore rifled with 12 lands and grooves. Although Dahlgren called the piece a 5-inch, he

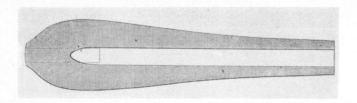

FIGURE: V-27 IDENTIFICATION: Dahlgren, 150-Pounder, Rifle, Iron. BORE: Diameter — 7.5. Length — 119 (Estimated). LENGTH O/A: 140 (Estimated). SOURCE: Holley. REMARKS: Had bronze trunnions and trunnion band, not shown.

FIGURE: V-28 LOCATION: U.S. Naval Academy, Annapolis, Md. IDENTIFICATION: Dahlgren (Type Undetermined). BORE: Diameter — 5 (estimated, bore is plugged with tampion). LENGTH O/A: 94.5. TRUNNIONS: Diameter — 5.8. Length — 5. MARKINGS: Left Trunnion — VIII, 18 1 (missing digit not readable due to paint). Right Trunnion — C.A. & Co., Boston. Breech — 3596. REMARKS: Left trunnion markings difficult to read and may be in error. Piece is obviously too small for an 8-Inch. Whether rifle or smoothbore is undetermined and weapon appears to be an experimental model. Plaque identification is doubtful.

spoke in general terms and the West Point rifle as well as recovered ammunition establish 5.1 inches as the correct bore diameter. The piece is 107 inches overall and trunnions and trunnion band, as in the 30-pounder, are made of bronze.

The first 80-pounder was completed at the West Point Foundry in August, 1861 and sent aboard ship. This piece was cast with trunnions, but the following month the admiral recommended that future 80-pounders be made without, and the weapon assumed the traditional form of Dahlgren iron rifles. They were mounted on a number of vessels during the early part of the war, but after exhibiting a discouraging tendency to burst, were generally replaced by other weapons. The log[50] of the *U.S.S. Hetzel* 7 February 1862, for instance, states: "At 5:15, rifled 80-pounder aft, loaded with 6 pounds powder and solid Dahlgren shot, 80 pounds, burst in the act of firing into four principal pieces. The gun forward of the trunnions fell on deck. One third of the breech passed over the mastheads and fell clear of the ship on the starboard bow. One struck on port quarter. And the fourth piece, weighing about 1,000 pounds, driving through the deck and magazine, bringing up on the keelson, set fire to the ship. Fire promptly extinguished. . . ."

Only a handful of 150-pounders (Fig. V-27) were produced. These were test-fired from 20 to 75 rounds with excellent accuracy, but although they remained unbroken, the quality of their iron was distrusted by the admiral and they were never placed in service.

A fascinating little Dahlgren (Fig. V-28) at Annapolis seems to be an experimental model despite identification on the plaque. The piece has the traditional form of the Dahlgren smoothbore, but is too

small for a service shellgun. It could have been a small-scale test model of a service smoothbore or, if rifled, an experimental form which, like the first 80-pounders, was cast with trunnions. When examined, the bore was plugged and the date obscured by paint. However, bore diameter appeared to be approximately 5 inches and visible marks showed the piece was made by Cyrus Alger of Boston and weighs 3,596 pounds.

Early in 1864,[51] Fort Pitt Foundry was busy rifling three huge cannon produced by boring standard Navy 15-inchers—probably in light of the date, the long model—to 12-inch diameter. The pieces were identical in all respects except rifling which was purposely of three different forms—Parrott, Rodman, and Atwater—to test their respective merits in rifles of this size. Each weighed as close to 45,500 pounds as the foundry could produce and was intended to throw a 600-pound bolt. Tests conducted at Fort Monroe in 1867[52] resulted in the Parrott rifling bursting at the twenty-seventh round, the Rodman cracking at the sixteenth and Atwater's going to pieces at thirty. Charges were 35 to 50 pounds for the Parrott and Rodman and mainly 55 for the Atwater. Weight of the Parrott projectiles was not recorded, but Rodman shot varied from 618 to 619 pounds and that used with Atwater's rifling from 416 to 535. Apparently no others of these types were made.

NOTES

1. Madeleine Vinton Dahlgren, *Memoir of John A. Dahlgren, Rear Admiral, U.S.N.*, 1882, p. 318; J. A. Dahlgren, *Boat Armament of The U. S. Navy*, 1856, p. 21 (Regulations Navy Department, 17 December 1850) and pp. 36–37.

2. Madeleine Vinton Dahlgren, *The Petition to The National Government of Madeleine Vinton Dahlgren, Widow of The Late Rear Admiral Dahlgren, Submitting Her Claim Asking for Compensation for The Adoption and Use by The United States Navy of Certain Inventions of The Late Rear Admiral Dahlgren Relating to Ordnance*, 1872, Appendix A, p. 5, list of Dahlgren weapons made for the Navy. Total numbers of the admiral's other weapons mentioned in the text are taken from this list.

3. Dahlgren, *Boat Armament, op. cit.*, p. 121.

4. *Ibid.*, p. 43.

5. *Ibid.*, p. 38.

6. *Ordnance Instructions for The United States Navy*, 1866, Part II, "The Equipment and Manoeuvre of Boats and Exercise of Boat Howitzers," Addenda, pp. 16–17.

7. *Official Navy Records*, Series II, Vol. 1, vessel statistics, p. 140, *U.S.S. Mendota*; p. 51, *U.S.S. Canandaigua*; p. 91, *U.S.S. Gazelle*; p. 197, *U.S.S. Saginaw*; p. 202, *U.S.S. Sassacus*; p. 209, *U.S.S. Silver Cloud*; p. 237, *U.S.S. Watch*.

8. *Ordnance Instructions* (Navy), *op. cit.*, p. 101, Table XVII. Mrs. Dahlgren, *Petition, loc. cit.* Appendix A, p. 5.

9. Mrs. Dahlgren, *Memoir, loc. cit.*, p. 318.

10. *Ordnance Instructions* (Navy), *op. cit.*, p. 101, Table XVII.

11. *Ibid.*, p. 109.

12. Mrs. Dahlgren, *Memoir, op. cit.*, p. 136.

13. *The News and Courier*, Charleston, S.C. daily newspaper, 3 March 1893 quoting *The New York Times* of 5 February 1893.

14. Auguste Paul Cooke, *A Text-Book of Naval Ordnance and Gunnery, Prepared for Use of The Cadet Midshipmen of The United States Naval Academy*, 1880, p. 234.

15. Reports of committees of the U.S. Senate, 2nd session, 38th Congress, "Heavy Ordnance," p. 126. Mrs. Dahlgren, *Memoir, op. cit.*, p. 275.

16. *Ibid.*, "Memorandum No. 6, Bureau of Ordnance, Navy Department, Washington City," 5 January 1863, pp. 126–127.

17. *Ibid.*, quoting *The New York Times* of 28 May 1862, p. 127.

18. *Official Navy Records*, Series II, Vol. 1, p. 248.

19. *Ibid.*, Series I, Vol. 1, pp. 290–291 (Webb), 265–266 (Rodgers).

20. Reports of committees of the U.S. Senate, *op. cit.*, pp. 127–128.

21. Alexander L. Holley, *A Treatise on Ordnance and Armor*, 1865, p. 120; J. G. Benton, *A Course of Instruction in Ordnance and Gunnery Composed and Compiled for Cadets of The United States Military Academy*, 1875, p. 550.

22. John Johnson, "Collected Papers 1862–1906," *South Carolina Historical Society Collections*.

23. Mrs. Dahlgren, *Memoir, op. cit.*, pp. 302–303.

24. Holley, *loc. cit.*, pp. 120–121.

25. Reports of committees of the U.S. Senate, *op. cit.*, p. 123, statement by Rear Admiral Dahlgren, 15 April 1864.

26. *Ibid.*, p. 168, testimony 21 January 1865 by Capt. G. V. Fox, assistant secretary of the Navy to the effect that Ericsson also made a 13-inch for the monitors, a wrought iron piece, but it developed a crack and was not accepted by the Navy.

27. *Ibid.*, p. 129.

28. Benton, 1875, *loc. cit.*, p. 550. Holley, *loc. cit.*, p. 120, Table XXIII.

29. Ibid.

30. *Ordnance Instructions for The United States Navy*, 1866, Part III, "Ordnance and Ordnance Stores," p. 53, table of service charges for naval guns.

31. Mrs. Dahlgren, *Petition, loc. cit.*, Appendix A, p. 5.

32. Reports of committees of the U.S. Senate, *op. cit.*, p. 93, testimony of Rear Admiral Samuel F. DuPont, 5 February 1864.

33. *Ibid.*, pp. 33–35, appendix accompanying testimony of Capt. Henry A. Wise, corrected 8 February 1864, "Number of Navy Guns Made Since The Beginning of The Rebellion."

34. J. A. Dahlgren, *Shells and Shellguns*, 1856, numerous references especially pp. 23, 26, 220, 252.

35. *Ordnance Manual for The Use of Officers of The United States Army*, 1861, p. 492.

36. Ibid.

37. *Official Navy Records*, Series II, Vol. 1, p. 49, battery of *U.S.S. Cairo* as of January, 30 September, and December 1862.

38. Mrs. Dahlgren, *Memoir, op. cit.*, p. 295, report to Navy Department by Bureau of Ordnance Chief H. A. Wise, October 1865.

39. *Official Navy Records*, Series II, Vol. 1, p. 109, *U.S.S. Isaac Smith*, 18 October 1861; p. 109, *U.S.S. Iron Age*, January 1863, "6 VIII-In. Dahlgren SB;" p. 120, *U.S.S. Keystone State*, 4 May 1863, "3 VIII-In. Dahlgren SB," and p. 122, *U.S.S. Kingfisher*, 8 October 1861, "4 VIII-In. Dahlgren SB."

40. *Ibid.*, p. 65, *U.S.S. Conemaugh*.

41. Mrs. Dahlgren, *Petition, op. cit.*, Appendix A, p. 6, Table p. 5.

42. *Ordnance Instructions* (Navy), Part III, *op. cit.*, p. 53.

43. Mrs. Dahlgren, *Petition, loc. cit.*, Appendix A, p. 5.

44. Mrs. Dahlgren, *Memoir, op. cit.*, p. 136.

45. *Ibid.*, p. 226.

46. *Ibid.*, pp. 271–274.

47. *Ibid.*, pp. 272–273.

48. *Ibid.*, p. 274.

49. *Ibid.*, p. 273.

50. *Official Navy Records*, Series I, Vol. 6, p. 561.

51. Reports of committees of the U.S. Senate, *op. cit.*, pp. 24, 31, testimony of Capt. H. A. Wise, 28 January 1864. Also, p. 87, testimony of Charles Knap, proprietor of Fort Pitt Foundry, 4 February 1864.

52. Reports of committees of the U.S. Senate, 3rd. session, 40th Congress, "Heavy Ordnance," pp. 143, report of Admiral J. A. Dahlgren, 11 February 1869.

Chapter 6

The Parrott

JULY 1, 1824 SAW GRADUATE from the United States Military Academy a cadet who many years later would produce the most controversial rifles of the Civil War. Robert Parker Parrott (1804-1877), entered the artillery upon graduation and after a spell of teaching at the Academy and a tour of garrison duty, changed his branch to ordnance. He served as inspector of cannon 1834-35, and resigned in 1836 with the rank of captain. From that time until 1867 he was superintendent of the West Point Foundry which became such a leading producer of ordnance for both Army and Navy that the initials WPF and RPP were well-known throughout both services. In fact, the Parrott rifle became so renowned during the war that one wag suggested[1] the parrot should replace the eagle as the emblematic bird of state.

Being a private founder, unhampered by government regulation and budgets, Parrott was able to begin experiment fairly early on rifled cannon. He turned out his first piece, a 10-pounder, in 1860 and by the outbreak of war had developed 20- and 30-pounder rifles. These were snapped up by various states, including Virginia, before the start of hostilities and by the Army not long after the first shots were fired. He continued full-scale production of these weapons, and in the summer of 1861 developed a 100-pounder and turned out a 200-pounder that winter. Roughly a year later, the 300-pounder was produced and finally, toward the end of the war, a 60-pounder.

These were the basic calibers of the Parrott rifles which saw continued use in field and siege as well as aboard ship throughout the war. They were praised. They were cursed. Some of the smaller calibers weren't up to the standard of competing rifles and the larger models had an unfortunate tendency to burst. But considered collectively, as a rifled weapons system, the Parrott was hard to beat.

Civil War officers and today's buffs may have their pets—the federal 3-inch Ordnance Rifle, the Confederate Brooke, or the English Whitworths, Blakelys, and Armstrongs. Gun for gun and caliber for caliber, maybe the Parrott couldn't hold its own. But the Parrott was easy to operate by inexperienced cannoneers. It was tough: break off a piece of the muzzle, chip it back, and keep on firing. It was cheap to manufacture costing not much more than a comparable smoothbore. Best of all, it could be produced quickly and in quantity when the crying need was for rifles—not necessarily the best rifles—but rifles. The Parrott wasn't the best, but it was good enough. If heavy rifles burst killing their cannoneers on the platforms, far more of the enemy died on target. And few were the Southern commanders who wouldn't have cheered had the North concentrated on making more expensive and better rifles—and fewer of them.

Parrott was under no delusion that his rifles were perfect, for he said of them:[2] "I do not profess to think that they are the best gun in the world, but I think they were the best practical thing that could be got at the time, and I suppose that was the reason for getting them . . . ." The simple statement carries the reminder that wars are fought with what you have at hand and can get immediately—not what you'd like to have. It's a sobering thought even today.

So here's the Parrott, good and bad. They are scattered through many of the nation's parks and like them or not, they are a boon to the ordnance buff since recognition is easy and pitfalls are few.

Parrotts of all calibers are basically the same, differing within caliber only in such minor details as muzzle swell and cascabel, which will be discussed later. It is a long-tube, cast iron piece with a wrought iron reinforcing band over the breech. The band was made by coiling a wedge-shaped bar around a mandrel, then upsetting the coil and pounding the joints together until welded solid. The wedge shape was used to permit escape of slag or dirt during the process. Parrott made no claim to being the first person to band a rifle. His patent, and the distinctive feature of the Parrott, although no aid to identification, was the method of attaching the band.

In most banding, American and European, the ring of metal was heated, slipped on the tube and allowed to cool. Sometimes it was threaded and screwed on, often tube and band were tapered. But in all cases, the tube was stationary.

Not so in the Parrott.[3] The tube was rotated horizontally on rollers and a stream of water played inside to keep it cool. The hot band was slipped on and because of the tube rotation, cooled and clamped itself uniformly to the breech instead of hanging from one spot and cooling there first as it would if the tube were stationary. This, Parrott felt, was the major reason for the strength of his rifles and it was on this that his patent hinged.

Although traditionally called by numerical designation and the word "pounder," there is so much confusion in the term that the author feels Parrotts should be more accurately designated by bore diameter. This would eliminate the difficulty whereby the 8-inch Parrott is called a "150-pounder" in the Navy and a "200-pounder" in the Army, although exactly the same gun. The confusion arose because the shell originally designed for the 8-inch weighed 200

pounds, but was later shortened cutting the weight to roughly 150. Similarly, the 10-inch Parrott was known as a "300-pounder" from its designed shell, but actually fired a projectile weighing about 250. Shells of varying weights were used in the "100-pounder" which had a 6.4-inch bore, and the bolts, the solid projectiles, of all three differed from shell weight.

The problem becomes even more acute when the so-called "10-pounder" is examined. It had two standard bore diameters in the U.S. model and one, possibly more, in those produced prior to and shortly after the outbreak of war when Parrott seems to have been experimenting with bore diameter and form of rifling. Most, if not all, of these were casually referred to as "10-pounders," sometimes "12-pounders," although shell weights must have varied considerably.

The first U.S. model of the "10-pounder" (Fig. VI-1) had a 2.9-inch bore rifled with 3 approximately equal size lands and grooves. The two illustrated rifles are in a park at Orangeburg, South Carolina. They are dated 1861 and bear the initials WPF and RPP. U.S. is on the tubes. Note the slight muzzle swell which, along with bore diameter, is an identifying mark of this model Parrott. Brady photographed a battery of 2.9-inch Parrotts at drill (Fig. VI-2). Limbers are behind each section and caissons on the hill crest at rear.

The second form of U.S. "10-pounder" (Fig. VI-3) came out in 1863 and remained standard throughout the rest of the war. It is characterized by 3-inch bore with 3 lands and grooves and no muzzle swell. The illustrated piece is in Kennesaw National Military Park near Atlanta, Georgia, and was made in 1864. It bears the initials RPP, but does not carry the foundry designation.

In addition to standard models, cannon enthusiasts may run into "10-pounders" which bear no U.S.

FIGURE: VI-1 LOCATION: Orangeburg, S.C. IDENTIFICATION: Parrott, Field, 2.9-Inch, Rifle, Model 1861, Iron. BORE: Diameter — 2.9. Rifling — 3 x 3, Straight. Length — 70. LENGTH O/A: 78. TRUNNIONS: Diameter — 3.67. Length — 2.75. MARKINGS: Muzzle Face — (Front) No. 72, 10-Pdr., 2.9; (Rear) No. 78, 10-Pdr., 2.9. Left Trunnion — (Front) 1861; (Rear) 1861. Right Trunnion — (Front) R.P.P., W.P.F.; (Rear) R.P.P., W.P.F. Tube — (Front) U.S.; (Rear) U.S. COMMON NAME: 10-Pounder Parrott, Old Type. Or, 2.9-Inch Parrott.

FIGURE: VI-2 IDENTIFICATION: Parrott, Field, 2.9-Inch, Rifle. Model 1861, Iron. REMARKS: Ringgold Battery at Drill. Note limbers behind pieces and caissons on crest of hill. Estimated date, 1861. COMMON NAME: 10-Pounder Parrott, Old Type. Or, 2.9-Inch Parrott.

marking and presumably were turned out during the early days of production. Two identical weapons, the only ones discovered thus far, are in South Carolina. One (Fig. VI-4) graces the Williamsburg County Courthouse grounds at Kingstree and, within memory of the town's old-timers, was fired with blanks during various celebrations. It was placed on a concrete pedestal when the carriage began to rot and, like many other such municipal ornaments, receives sever-

al surreptitious and gaudy coats of paint each football season. The other is on the campus of The Citadel, the state military college at Charleston. This piece was found during excavation for the Spartanburg, South Carolina, City Hall some years ago about 20 feet down in a dry well where it doubtless had been dumped by retreating Confederates.

With exception of bore, both rifles have statistics of the 2.9-inch model. WPF is stamped on the right

FIGURE: VI-3 LOCATION: Kennesaw, Ga. IDENTIFICATION: Parrott, Field, 3-Inch, Rifle, Model 1863, Iron. BORE: Diameter — 3. Rifling — 3 x 3, Straight. Length — 70. LENGTH O/A: 78. TRUNNIONS: Diameter — 3.67. Length — 2.75. MARKINGS: Muzzle Face — No. 33, 1864, PFNI, 895, D.W.F., 3. Right Trunnion — R.P.P. Breech — 3-In. Bore. Tube — U.S. COMMON NAME: 10-Pounder Parrott, New Type. Or, 3-Inch Parrott.

FIGURE: VI-4 LOCATION: Kingstree, S.C. IDENTIFICATION: Parrott, Field, 3.3-Inch, Rifle, Model 1861*, Iron. BORE: Diameter — 3.3 Rifling — 12 x 12, hook-slant, or "Brooke" type. Length — 70. LENGTH O/A: 78. TRUNNIONS: Diameter — 3.67. Length — 2.75. MARKINGS: Muzzle Face — 3.3. Left Trunnion — 1861. Right Trunnion — W.P.F. Right Rimbase — 235. Reinforcing Band, Rear — CAV. Base of Breech — 904. REMARKS: *Model may be 1860. Piece seems to have been made during formative stage of the Parrott Rifle and although measurements conform to the 2.9-Inch, bore diameter and form of rifling are non-standard. The piece carries no "U.S." and presumably was made for a state government. COMMON NAME: 14-Pounder Parrott. Or, 3.3-Inch Parrott.

trunnions and 1861 on the left, but the customary U.S. is absent from the tubes. Based on appearance, measurement, and markings, the weapons are obviously Parrotts. However, the bore is far from standard. It measures about 3 5/16 inches and the numerals "3.3" are stamped on each muzzle face. This, under the "pounder" system—if the 3-inch is considered a 10-pounder and the 3.67 a 20—would work out to roughly a 14-pounder. In addition to being oversize, the bore differs from standard Parrotts in having 12 lands and grooves instead of 3, and these, rather than conventional in form, are of the "hook" type generally associated with the Confederate Brooke.

The pieces could, of course, be standard 2.9-inch Parrotts which, becoming worn, might have been rebored by the Confederates and re-rifled. However, the fact that there are at least two of the weapons argues against this theory as does the 12 lands and grooves since the Confederates habitually used 7. Furthermore, the 3.3 is cut on the muzzle faces in clear, sharp numerals more indicative of initial foundry marks than a re-rifling job. Parrott no doubt was experimenting both with size of bore and rifling during the early 1860s and since the "hook" type of rifling was a well-known variety, it seems probable that the weapons were experimental and early models.

There is an intriguing possibility these cannon were part of a shipment ordered from Parrott by the State of Virginia prior to the start of war.[4] It is known that Virginia first ordered one piece which was tried in July, 1860, at Virginia Military Institute by the future General T. J. (Stonewall) Jackson. He was so impressed with the weapon he prevailed upon the state to order a dozen more.

However, it remains only a possibility that these rifles were part of the Virginia shipment, for other states also had Parrott batteries and the cannon may have been captured from Northern units. The Official Records,[5] for instance, list correspondence of New York Governor E. D. Morgan offering half a dozen 10-pounder Parrotts to the government 24 July 1861 and mentioning delivery the following month.

The 3.67-inch, U.S. "20-pounder" Parrott like its smaller cousin went through a model change. Both types are shown in Figure VI-5, the later model in the foreground and two earlier pieces at rear. The weapons, in the Kennesaw collection, are rifled with 5 lands and grooves. The late model is dated 1865 and the others 1861 and 1862. All are marked "20-Pdr." on the left trunnion. The right trunnions of the old models are stamped with Parrott's initials, that of the

new weapon could not be checked, but similar rifles are so marked.

Navy-type cascabel makes these pieces a little longer overall, 91.5 inches, than the 3.67-inch at Newport, Rhode Island (Fig. VI-6) which has an Army knob and measures 89.5 inches. It also is rifled 5 x 5 and, while obviously a Parrott, is one that escaped the foundry with practically no markings. At the time it was photographed in 1964, the rifle was covered with layers of paint and no marks were visible. However, after correspondence with the Newport Artillery Company Museum, parts of the piece were scraped by this organization and the author notified that nothing was found on the muzzle face or right trunnion and only "20-Pdr." on the left. It is mounted on a field carriage which is said to be of Civil War vintage.

Use aboard ship no doubt resulted in the unusual cascabel conversion (Fig. VI-7) of an Army 3.67-inch now in the Gettysburg collection. The knob was slotted top and bottom, bored for a bolt, and the U-shaped, iron strap installed to hold breeching tackle. In other respects, the piece appears standard.

A Brady photograph (Fig. VI-8) shows an unidentified gun squad drilling with a 3.67-inch (the designation is barely discernible at the bottom of the muzzle). However, this caliber, although well represented in the fleet, doesn't seem to have been too popular ashore for in a discussion of rifled artillery, Abbot observed:[6] "The 20-pdr. Parrott . . . proved to be too small to give the precision of fire demanded of

FIGURE: VI-5 LOCATION: Kennesaw, Ga. IDENTIFICATION: (Front) Parrott. Navy, 3.67-Inch, Rifle, Model 1863, Iron. (Center and Rear) Parrott, Navy, 3.67-Inch, Rifle, Model 1861, Iron. BORE (All): Diameter — 3.67. Rifling — 5 x 5, Straight. Length — 79. LENGTH O/A (All): 91.5. MARKINGS: Left Trunnion — (Front) 1865, 20-Pdr., 3.67; (Center) 1861, 20-Pdr. 3.67; (Rear) 1862, 20-Pdr., 3.67. Right Trunnion — (Front) Not Available; (Center) R.P.P., No. 84, 1695 Lbs.; (Rear) R.P.P., No. 82, 1860 Lbs. REMARKS: Note muzzle swell on older model. COMMON NAME: (Front) 20-Pounder Parrott, Navy, New Type. Or, 3.67-Inch Navy Parrott, Model 1863. (Center and Rear) 20-Pounder Parrott, Navy, Old Type. Or, 3.67-Inch Navy Parrott, Model 1861.

FIGURE: VI-6 LOCATION: Newport, R.I. IDENTIFICATION: Parrott, Field*, 3.67-Inch, Rifle, Model 1863, Iron. BORE: Diameter — 3.67. Rifling — 5 x 5, Straight. Length — 79. LENGTH O/A: 89.5. TRUNNIONS: Diameter — 4.62. Length — 3.5 MARKINGS: Left Trunnion — 20-Pdr. REMARKS: *Also employed as Siege and Garrison. Usual marks apparently omitted on this piece. COMMON NAME: 20-Pounder Parrott, New Type. Or, 3.67-Inch Parrott, Model 1863.

FIGURE: VI-7 LOCATION: Gettysburg, Pa. IDENTIFICATION: Parrott, Field*, 3.67-Inch Rifle, Model 1861, Iron. BORE: Diameter — 3.67. Rifling — 5 x 5, Straight. Length — 79. LENGTH O/A: 89.5 (Excluding breeching loop). TRUNNIONS: Diameter — 4.62. Length — 3.5. REMARKS: *Piece has been converted for naval use by bolting iron "U" to cascabel knob, probably a Confederate innovation. Marks covered by paint. COMMON NAME: 20-Pounder Parrott, Old Type. Or, 3.67-Inch Parrott, Model 1861.

FIGURE: VI-8 IDENTIFICATION: Parrott, Field, 3.67-Inch, Rifle, Model 1861, Iron. REMARKS: Gun crew at drill, location and date not recorded.

a siege gun and to be too heavy for convenient use as a field gun. Moreover, its projectiles did not seem to take the grooves as well as those of either smaller or larger calibers. The gun was accordingly not regarded with favor . . . ."

The 4.2-inch (30-pounder), like the 10s and 20s, came in two models for the Army, differing primarily in the muzzle swell and a doorknob-shaped cascabel for the old model (Fig. VI-9) compared to straight muzzle with more elongated cascabel—bored horizontally for elevating mechanism—for the new (Fig. VI-10).

The old model, at Vicksburg, is marked "WPF, RPP" on the right trunnion and "1861" on the left. The other, a Fort Sill specimen, is similarly marked on the right trunnion, but dated 1862 on the left denoting an earlier change to straight muzzle in this caliber. Bore of each is 4.2 inches rifled with 5 lands and grooves.

All 4.2-inch Parrotts checked thus far have had 5 lands and grooves of the straight type. In addition, 30-pounder Parrott shells recovered in the field bear the imprint of 5 lands. However, two writers of the Civil War era[7] have listed the number for this weapon as 7, and while the author believes 5 is correct, the reader is warned Army 4.2 Parrotts with 7 lands may exist.

Despite a tendency to break elevating screws—which could be removed and the piece used with equal facility—the 4.2 was well liked in service.[8] It was ranked in the siege category, but Abbot[9] considered it valuable as a sniping rifle. In Virginia, for instance, a few 30-pounders placed in batteries with heavy caliber Parrotts were able, by their accuracy and rapidity of fire, to play against Confederate gun embrasures, making the Southern fire wild and spasmodic and permitting carefully aimed practice by the heavy federal artillery.

The piece also was admired by General Quincy A. Gillmore whose experience with one during the siege of Charleston follows.[10] His comments are quoted in detail since they convey considerable miscellaneous information on firing under combat conditions:

"Perhaps the most remarkable example of endurance furnished by any of our guns, and perhaps the most remarkable on record, was that of a 30-pdr. Parrott rifle. The following story of the piece is furnished by Capt. [Alfred] Mordecai, chief of ordnance of this department.[11]

"The gun was cast at the West Point Foundry in 1863; its ordnance number is 193; it was mounted on Cummings Point [Morris Island] in December, 1863, for

FIGURE: VI-9 LOCATION: Vicksburg, Miss. IDENTIFICATION: Parrott, Siege & Garrison, 4.2-Inch, Rifle, Model 1861, Iron. BORE: Diameter — 4.2. Rifling — 5 x 5, Straight. Length — 120. LENGTH O/A: 133.5. TRUNNIONS: Diameter — 5.25. Length — 2.75. MARKINGS: Muzzle Face — No. 29. Left Trunnion — 1861. Right Trunnion — R.P.P., W.P.F. COMMON NAME: 30-Pounder Parrott, Old Type. Or, 4.2-Inch Parrott, Model 1861.

FIGURE: VI-10 LOCATION: Fort Sill, Okla. IDENTIFICATION: Parrott, Siege & Garrison, 4.2-Inch, Rifle, Model 1862, Iron. BORE: Diameter — 4.2. Rifling — 5 x 5, Straight. Length — 120. LENGTH O/A: 132.5. TRUNNIONS: Diameter — 5.25. Length — 2.75. MARKINGS: Muzzle Face — No. 94, 30-Pdr., 4.2. Left Trunnion — 1862. Right Trunnion — R.P.P., W.P.F. COMMON NAME: 30-Pounder Parrott, New Type. Or, 4.2-Inch Parrott, Model 1862.

the purpose of throwing shells into the City of Charleston. It was placed on a plain wooden carriage manufactured on Morris Island.

"Sixty-nine days elapsed between the first and last discharge of the gun. It was being fired the 4,606th round when it burst.

"There were fired 4,594 rounds with 3¾ pounds of powder and percussion shells of 29 pounds charged with 1½ pounds of powder with elevation of 40 degrees. One round . . . elevation . . . 49 degrees 45 minutes; seven . . . time fuse . . . 40 degrees elevation, [and] four rounds . . . time fuse . . . elevation 2 degrees 50 minutes.

"Of these rounds, 4,253 reached the city; 259 tripped and fell short; 10 took the rifling and fell short; 80 exploded prematurely, but none in the gun, and four were fired at Fort Sumter and reached it, the distance being 1,390 yards.

"The first 2,164 rounds were fired at intervals of five minutes, but the firing was not continuous, 237 being the greatest number fired in any one twenty-four hours and two rounds the least. The average per day was 127 rounds. The last 2,442 rounds were fired at intervals of 15 minutes, not continuously, 157 rounds being the greatest number fired in any one day and 7 the least; the daily average being 97 rounds.

"All the shells were swedged and greased. The gun cleaned after each discharge, first with a dry sponge and then with an oiled one. It was washed out with water and cooled after every ten fires. After the gun was loaded and waiting to be fired, a canvas cap was placed over the muzzle to keep out drifting sand and every care was taken that the gun should be clear from sand and dirt when fired. The vent of the gun was bushed twice during the time used. The bushing in use when the gun gave out was somewhat eaten, but very regularly and not badly. The diameter of the vent at the exterior being .25 inch and at the interior .375.

"The gun when it burst went into seven pieces, the muzzle and chase back to the axis of the trunnions being one piece; that part of the cast iron reinforce from six inches in rear of the front of the wrought iron band with the band, breech and cascabel being the second. The metal between these two went into five fragments. . . ."

The general neglected to mention that the range from Cummings Point to the nearest part of the city is 6,600 yards.

Colonel J. G. Benton also had a high opinion of the 4.2-inch Parrott stating:[12] ". . . its weight is 4,200 pounds and it is carried on the 18-pounder siege carriage . . . it has no preponderance and has been found to be a very accurate and reliable gun in service. . . ."

The Navy also had a 4.2 Parrott. It measured roughly 112 inches overall, weighed 3,550 pounds—compared to 132.5 and 4,200 for the Army—and is easily distinguished by the Navy-type cascabel. Charge was 3.25 pounds of powder and projectile weights ranged from 25 to 30 pounds.[13] A Navy 4.2-inch (Fig. VI-11) in the Portsmouth Naval Shipyard Museum is dated 1864 which indicates that muzzle swell continued in the Navy model although dropped by the Army. Five similar pieces are in the towns of Waterville and Winston, Maine, but ornamental cap squares prevent examination of trunnions to determine the dates. After the war, some of the Navy 4.2-inch, like certain heavier models, were converted to breechloaders.[14]

Toward the end of the war, Parrott turned out a 60-pounder rifle for the Navy. No record of the date of the first one has been found, but the inventor told the Senate Committee on Ordnance[15] 18 January 1865: "I now make a 60-pounder for the Navy. That is a gun quite recently made, and not yet much introduced into the service." The Official Navy Records of ship statistics, however, list a fair number of these weapons in use during 1864-65, and Holley mentions that by 1 April 1864 Parrott had made ten of the new rifles which would indicate start of production only a short time before.[16]

One of these rare weapons (Fig. VI-12) is in the Norfolk Naval Shipyard collection of ancient cannon. It has a bore diameter of 5.3 inches rifled with 7 lands and grooves, bore length 105 inches, length overall 124 inches, and weighs 5,430 pounds, although Holley[17] listed the "standard" as 5,360 pounds. It has the type cascabel used in heavy Parrott rifles, and burned a 6-pound charge with a 55-pound projectile.

FIGURE: VI-11 LOCATION: Portsmouth Naval Shipyard Museum, Portsmouth, Va. IDENTIFICATION: Parrott, Navy, 4.2-Inch, Rifle, Model 1861, Iron. BORE: Diameter — 4.2. Rifling — 5 x 5, Straight. Length — 96.8. LENGTH O/A: 112. TRUNNIONS: Diameter — 5.6. Length — 5. MARKINGS: Right Trunnion — 1864. Breech — R.P.P., No. 303, 3500. COMMON NAME: 30-Pounder Parrott, Navy, Or, 4.2-Inch Navy Parrott.

FIGURE: VI-12 LOCATION: Norfolk Naval Shipyard, Norfolk, Va. IDENTIFICATION: Parrott, Navy, 5.3-Inch, Rifle, Model 1864, Iron. BORE: Diameter — 5.3. Rifling — 7 x 7, Straight. Length — 106.75v. LENGTH O/A: 124. TRUNNIONS: Diameter — 6. Length — 4. MARKINGS: Right Trunnion — 1865, 60-Pdr. REMARKS: Navy Yard records list other marks as: 5430 (weight), R.P.P., No. 56. COMMON NAME: 60-Pounder Parrott. Or, 5.3-Inch Parrott.

Manufacture of the 5.3-inch lasted only two years, for Cooke, writing in 1880, stated[18] that no Parrotts were fabricated after 1865. However, a number of existing rifles were converted to breechloaders and the Norfolk Yard also has a specimen of the converted 5.3-inch (Fig. VI-13) which was known as the "60-pdr. B.L.R. (Breech-Loading Rifle)." The breechblock is missing, but was attached to the lug affixed to the reinforcing band. The piece retained the same bore diameter, but was shortened to 112 inches overall in the conversion process which will be described in more detail in connection with similar alteration of the 6.4-inch.

Parrott's heavy rifles—the 6.4-inch 100-pounder, 8-inch 200-pounder, and 10-inch 300-pounder—all had the same general form with straight muzzle and the type cascabel used by the 5.3-inch. The pieces were designed to be used indiscriminately on land or sea, although there is no record of the 10-inch being used aboard ship during the war. Weapons made expressly for the Navy have an anchor instead of U.S. on the tube approximately between the trunnions and are marked on the reinforcing band rather than the muzzle face.

Two excellent specimens of the 6.4-inch are at Greenville, South Carolina (Fig. VI-14). Both carry the WPF, RPP initials as well as 6.4 on the muzzle face and 100-pdr. on the left trunnion. The piece in foreground was made in 1864 and the other in 1862. Weights are 9,782 and 9,827 pounds respectively. They are rifled with 9 lands and grooves.

Figure VI-15 shows one of eleven 6.4-inch rifles on iron casemate carriages uncovered several years ago during excavations at Fort Sumter. The weapons, mounted in the fort by federal forces after the war, were buried deliberately during repairs and alterations to the fort after the hurricane of 1893. By this time they were obsolete and, fortunately, left as fill

FIGURE: VI-14 LOCATION: Greenville, S.C. IDENTIFICATION: Parrott, Seacoast or Navy, 6.4-Inch, Rifle, Model 1861, Iron. BORE (Both): Diameter — 6.4. Rifling — 9 x 9, Straight. Length — 130. LENGTH O/A (Both): 155. TRUNNIONS (Both): Diameter — 8. Length — 5. MARKINGS: Muzzle Face — (Front) No. 181, 1864, W.P.F., R.M.H., 6.4, 9782. (Rear) No. 54, 1862, W.P.F., 6.4, 9827, A.M. Left Trunnion — (Front) 100-Pdr.; (Rear) 100-Pdr. Right Trunnion — (Front) R.P.P.; (Rear) R.P.P. REMARKS: Weapon used interchangeably between Army and Navy. COMMON NAME: 100-Pounder Parrott. Or, 6.4-Inch Parrott.

FIGURE: VI-15 LOCATION: Fort Sumter, S.C. IDENTIFICATION: Parrott, Seacoast or Navy, 6.4-Inch, Rifle, Model 1861, Iron. BORE: Diameter — 6.4. Rifling — 9 x 9, Straight. Length — 130. LENGTH O/A: 155. TRUNNIONS: Diameter — 8. Length — 5. REMARKS: One of eleven such weapons excavated from filled casemates at Fort Sumter. Piece was deliberately left in uncleaned state. Marks not readable. COMMON NAME: 100-Pounder Parrott. Or, 6.4-Inch Parrott.

in the fort's casemates which were packed with sand. The piece illustrated was left caked with rust to demonstrate the condition of all when excavated. The other weapons have been cleaned and painted, but markings have been largely obliterated by rust. Sufficient are left, however, to establish that the rifles were made during the war years.

After fighting ended, there was an attempt to turn the 6.4-inch Parrott into a breechloader.[19] Converted, it was known as an "80-pdr. B.L.R."

FIGURE: VI-13 LOCATION: Norfolk Naval Shipyard, Norfolk, Va. IDENTIFICATION: Parrott, Navy, 5.3-Inch, Rifle, Model 1864, Iron, Converted to 5.3-Inch Breech-Loading Rifle (B.L.R.). BORE: Diameter — 5.3. Rifling — 7 x 7, Straight. Length — 112. LENGTH O/A: 112 (Excluding breechblock). TRUNNIONS: Diameter — 5.75. Length — 4. MARKINGS: Right Trunnion — 1865, 60-Pdr. Breech — R.P.P., No. 61, 5400. REMARKS: Breechblock missing. COMMON NAME: 60-Pounder Parrott B.L.R. Or, 5.3-Inch Parrott B.L.R.

Bore diameter was still the same, but the "pounder" designation was now more in line with the commonly used "short" shell in contrast to the "long," which weighed in the neighborhood of 100 pounds.

The conversion (Fig. VI-16) was accomplished[20] by cutting off the breech immediately in rear of the reinforcing band, reaming out the bore to a point a little past the trunnions and cutting rough threads into the rear part. Into this was inserted a steel sleeve threaded at the base to receive the breech plug (today known as the breechblock) which, in modern terminology, would be designated as the interrupted-screw type. It was closed (Fig. VI-17) by a gear arrangement which was omitted in the similar breech apparatus of the 60-pdr. B.L.R. The original reinforcing band, which had been removed at the beginning of the process, was lengthened from 27 to 39 inches and replaced in the 6.4 although it remained unchanged in the 5.3-inch.

Although Cooke described the procedure, he failed to relate success or failure of the experiment. Judging from the prevalence of 6.4-inch Parrots in their original form, however, indications are that the attempt met with little success. One of the altered weapons (Fig. VI-18) is at the Norfolk Naval Shipyard and measures, minus breechblock, 139.25 inches overall, compared to 155 for the original piece.

Both the 6.4- and the 8-inch, which, as previously mentioned, was known as a 200-pounder to the Army and 150 to the Navy, were used extensively at sea, but fell into disfavor with many officers toward the end of the war due to bursting. Captain Fox

FIGURE: VI-17 IDENTIFICATION: Parrott, Seacoast or Navy, 6.4-Inch, Rifle, Model 1861, Iron, Converted to 6.4-Inch Breech-Loading Rifle (B.L.R.). SOURCE: Cooke. REMARKS: Breech of converted 6.4-Inch Parrott.

FIGURE: VI-18 LOCATION: Norfolk Naval Shipyard, Norfolk, Va. IDENTIFICATION: Parrott, Navy, 6.4-Inch, Rifle, Model 1861, Iron, Converted to 6.4-Inch Breech-Loading Rifle (B.L.R.). BORE: Diameter — 6.4. Rifling — 9 x 9, Straight. Length — 139.25. LENGTH O/A: 139.25 (Excluding Breechblock). TRUNNIONS: Diameter — 8. Length — 5. MARKINGS: Right Trunnion — 100-Pdr. Top of Band, Rear — W.P.F. REMARKS: Navy Yard records list the following additional marks, now concealed by paint: 1862, 9850, R.P.P., No. 75. COMMON NAME: Parrott 80-Pounder B.L.R. Or, Parrott 6.4-Inch B.L.R.

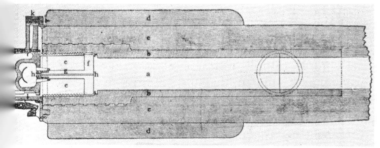

FIGURE: VI-16 IDENTIFICATION: Parrott, Seacoast or Navy, 6.4-Inch, Rifle, Model 1861, Iron, Converted to 6.4-Inch Breech-Loading Rifle (B.L.R.). SOURCE: Cooke. REMARKS: (a) Bore; (b) Steel Tube; (c) Cast Iron Gun; (d) Wrought Iron Coil or Band; (e) Breech Plug (Breechblock in modern parlance); (f) Nose Plate; (g) Stem of Nose Plate; (h) Vent; (i) Handle; (k) Gearing for Turning Plug; (l) Bearer for Plug (m) Spring Catch for Locking Bearer. COMMON NAME: Parrott 80-Pounder B.L.R. Or, Parrott 6.4-Inch B.L.R.

testified[21] before the Senate committee 21 January 1865 that nineteen out of three hundred 6.4-inch Parrotts in the service afloat had burst and advised that the Navy give up cast iron rifles in favor of wrought iron or steel.

Two days later, Captain James Alden of the *U.S.S. Brooklyn* stated[22] before the committee that during the attack on Fort Fisher, after hearing that several Parrotts had burst, he placed his pair of 6.4-inch on the opposite side of the ship from that firing and never used them again. Dissatisfaction with the Parrotts was amplified in the Navy since the elementary state of fire control during the Civil War prevented utilization of heavy rifles to their full potential.

The 6.4-inch rifles scattered extensively through the fleet and the 8-inchers aboard large vessels and paired with Dahlgrens in several monitors were capable of 4 and 5 mile ranges. But even from the best of land platforms, accuracy at this distance was restricted to hitting somewhere within a several block area of a city. Fired from the rolling deck of a ship, chances of even hitting the city would have been slight.

Yet the Navy needed sufficient precision to hit another ship, and this was realized only at relatively short distances where smoothbores were just as accurate. In fact, they were even more so for roundshot falling short of the target skipped along the water in a straight line and eventually hit with little loss of effect. Yet rifle projectiles would ricochet at unpredictable angles necessitating a direct hit from the air. Consequently, the rifle's accuracy was largely wasted in the Navy except under the very best conditions and in most cases heavy-caliber smoothbores could do an equal or better job. This perhaps explains to a certain extent why bursting Parrotts discouraged Army officers somewhat less than their Navy brethren.

The rifles went to pieces on land too, perhaps even more than afloat. But operating from stable platforms, the Army could utilize the long range to bombard cities and at medium ranges, up to 4,000 yards or so, the heavy Parrotts were deadly.

Consequently, although Gillmore lost twenty four Parrotts on Morris Island, he was prompted to write:[23]"

"There is perhaps no better system of rifled cannon than Parrott's; certainly none more simple in construction, more easily understood or that can, with more safety, be placed in the hands of inexperienced men for use . . . the Parrott guns are not without defects, the most serious of which we found to be the very unequal endurance. Some of our most valuable batteries were disabled at a very early stage in the operations. The 8-inch rifle in the Marsh Battery burst at the 36th discharge . . . two 100-pounders . . . burst as follows: One of them at the 122nd round . . . the other burst at the 1,151st round."

Benton, even in 1875, still had a high opinion of these weapons for he states:[24] "A large number of these guns were used in the late war, both on sea and on land, and the amount of work done by them, especially in breaching masonry, is probably not ex-

ceeded by rifled guns of any other system. While a few of them have failed in the service, others have shown great endurance. . . ."

Benton seems to have touched the heart of the matter. From the point of view of the Army, the accomplishments of the Parrott were worth the risk. This was borne out particularly by an 8-inch that failed very early in its career—the thirty-sixth round. Yet the preceding thirty-five made it beyond shadow of a doubt the most famous of all Parrotts and probably of all Civil War cannon.

The piece earned its niche in history about 1:30 A.M. 22 August 1863 when it lofted a 150-pound shell into the heart of the City of Charleston at the unprecedented range of 8,000 yards.[25] The first shell was soon followed by fourteen more that whistled out of the early morning darkness routing men, women, and children from their beds amid the clanging of church bells and the shouts of firemen dragging heavy equipment from one danger point to the next.[26] Damage was slight, no casualties, a minor fire or two, some vacant lots plowed up. But it was a foretaste of the future—shattering evidence that death could come from miles away to claim its victims without regard to age or sex. This was no longer a conflict fought by men on battlefields. It was total war where noncombatants took their chances and rear lines ceased to exist.

Technically, General Gillmore had given warning, required by convention, that the city would be brought under fire. But instead of the customary two or three days, the message arrived only four hours before the first shell. Moreover, since the letter was unsigned, it was returned for authentication and by the time it was again received, the first morning's shelling was history. In his message, Gillmore demanded surrender of Battery Wagner on Morris Island and Fort Sumter or he would shell the city. Beauregard, in return, refused to give up the forts and bitterly rebuked his opponent for ". . . the novel measure of turning your guns against the old men, women and children, and the hospitals of a sleeping city, an act of inexcusable barbarity. . . ."

After this exchange, Gillmore did suspend fire for about a day, but the delay gave little aid to the Confederates since a mixup in delivery cut the time to a few hours. More shells fell starting about midnight of the 23rd, including a number loaded with "Greek Fire," an incendiary composition, but again seem to have created more excitement than damage.

The Confederates, although puzzled at first by the location of the gun, soon spotted it in the marsh, but their efforts to bring it under fire were largely ineffective. So the "Swamp Angel" as it has become known through history, or the "Marsh Battery" as it was officially designated, continued its work until about 1 A.M. of the 24th when the piece burst near the vent (Fig. VI-19) throwing off the breech from under the reinforce and tossing the rest of the tube onto the sand-bagged parapet (Fig. VI-20).

The Marsh Battery originated 16 July 1863 with orders for a reconnaissance to find a suitable site. The area, which stretches behind Morris Island, consists almost entirely of marsh growing out of a jelly-like substance known locally as "pluff mud." Through it meander a few small creeks, almost dry at low tide, but navigable by light boats at high tide, when the mud is generally covered and only the top of the marsh grass is exposed. At low tide, a light man, being careful to bend over and step on the marsh grass, can often traverse a few yards of the mud in safety, but a prolonged trip will likely end in sinking to knees or hips, a trap from which assistance is needed before incoming tide makes the position dangerous.

Surprisingly, the reconnaissance turned up a small spot of relatively hard ground ranging from a few inches above to a few inches below high water mark and covering an area from 25 to 30 feet long and about 15 to 18 wide. It was located on one of the larger creeks which has 3 or 4 feet of water even at low tide and enough at high to float a barge.

In addition to the reconnaissance, the federal engineers began experiments with the mud which they found to be a formidable obstacle. Their reports mention: ". . . a couple of men on a plank resting on the surface can shake it [the mud] by surging themselves about. The vibrations extend over many hundreds of square yards as if they were on jelly. . . ." On this "jelly" the engineers were expected to build a platform stable enough to hold a 16,000-pound gun, not only at rest, but during the shock of firing.

Artillery platforms even on hard ground were no flimsy structures. They were built to definite specifications of heavy stringers and planks to form a level, hard base from which the piece could be fired. Platforms were advisable, although seldom used, even with field pieces since by being level they made aiming easier and prevented errors in deflection caused by one wheel being higher than the other. In the case of siege pieces, they were even more necessary, and when it came to artillery in the seacoast category, such as the 8-inch Parrott, they were mandatory.

Consequently, the first problem that had to be solved before a platform could be built for the "Swamp Angel" was how much weight the mud would support. This, by piling sandbags on a 4-foot square wood platform until it toppled over, the engineers determined to be 600 pounds per square foot.

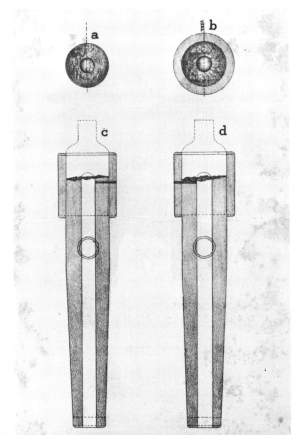

FIGURE: VI-20 IDENTIFICATION: "Swamp Angel" thrown forward on parapet after bursting while firing on Charleston, S.C.

FIGURE: VI-19 IDENTIFICATION: Parrott, Seacoast or Navy, 8-Inch, Rifle, Model 1861, Iron. SOURCE: Gillmore. REMARKS: The "Swamp Angel" which fired from the marsh near Morris Island into Charleston. Piece burst at 36th round, charge 16 pounds, elevation 31°30′, projectile weight 150 lbs. (a) Breech thrown off; (b) Rear view of piece; (c) Left side; (d) Right side.

Next they had to figure out a way to drive piling since obviously they couldn't set up a pile driver within range of Confederate guns. They tried various methods of forcing pointed plank piles into the mud by leverage (Fig. VI-21) and eventually discovered that a number of men putting their weight on a pole lashed horizontally across the plank could push it effectively to the sand bottom roughly 20 feet below and into which the point could be driven a short distance by a few blows of a maul.

With site selected and experiments completed, orders were given 2 August to start work. A rumor, that has been published in several accounts of the "Swamp Angel," has it that the lieutenant in charge, inclined to abandon the job as hopeless, was told he could have anything he needed to accomplish the mission. With tongue in cheek, he forwarded a requisition for "100 men 18-feet high to wade through mud 16-feet deep." He also requested that the surgeon stand by to "spice them" when needed. This facetiousness, so the story goes, landed the lieutenant in the guardhouse. Unfortunately for a good story, the tale is entirely apocryphal and while Colonel E. W. Serrell, who directed construction of the Marsh Battery, and his junior officers who supervised the work, may have felt that way, they were far too experienced to say so officially.

The battery was built on the principle of counterbalance (Fig. VI-22). Plank pilings were driven through the mud and into the sand until a box, open top and bottom, was formed the size of the gun platform. The "box" contained mud inside roughly up to the top of the piling. On top of this mud was laid a thick layer of marsh grass which was thoroughly trampled down. On that went two thicknesses of tarpaulin overlaid with about 15 inches of well-rammed sand. This served as a base for the platform which consisted of three layers of 3-inch thick, yellow pine planks. The top layer was parallel to the direction of fire while the bottom two were alternately diagonal to it. The platform was in no way attached to the piling, but instead "floated" inside the piling box.

Now, since the weight of the piece would force the platform down and like a huge hydraulic ram drive the mud between the planks, or, more likely, tear them apart, some method of counterbalance had to be devised. This was accomplished by laying marsh grass, tarpaulins, and sand in a square on the mud outside the platform as foundation for a grillage of logs. On top of the logs were laid thousands of sandbags until, when the weapon was mounted, pressure on the exterior balanced that of the platform.

Later, if the platform began to sink from firing, it was a simple matter of adding more sandbags to the log grillage until it was forced back up again.

Finally, the Parrott was brought in, either by barge or by rolling it across the marsh on planks after the chase had been built up with wood, barrel-like to match the diameter of the reinforcing band. It was mounted on a barbette carriage and well protected from enemy fire by the sandbags surrounding it on the grillage. Engineer records show the Marsh Battery required 13,000 sandbags, 123 pieces of 15- to 18-inch timber (for the grillage), 9,156 feet of 3-inch plank for the pile "box" and platform, some 600 pounds of nails and numerous other items. It took 91 man-days labor of engineer officers, 1,384 days of engineer troops, and 7,390 of infantry.

In 1957, the author and a number of local businessmen dug into the site and although the labor wasn't quite so impressive, it did require going down 3 feet or so through sand to the platform which was still in excellent condition and proved the accuracy of the official reports. Today the site has filled in again and the Marsh Battery is only a slight rise with a few scrub bushes above the general level of the marsh.

Although supply of the battery seems to have been largely by boat, the engineers also connected the site to Morris Island by a long, plank causeway which resembled a flimsy dock. This was accurately plotted on Civil War charts and certain sections of the marsh have changed so little during the hundred years or so that the plank piling of the causeway may still be found, well preserved in a coating of mud. Construction of the work even drew praise from Europe for one author[27] quotes the English journal "Engineering," in its review at the close of the war of the operations of Union and Confederate armies, as considering the Marsh Battery one of the most important engineering accomplishments done by either army.

After the Parrott burst—it had been fired with charges of 16 pounds at elevations ranging from 31° 30' to 35°—it apparently was removed from the site and presumably returned to Morris Island.[28] The battery was later occupied[29] by two mortars (10-inch, Model 1861, probably seacoast) for firing on Fort Sumter (Fig. VI-23), then in August, 1864, by a 4.2-inch Parrott on siege carriage (Fig. VI-24) which also played against Sumter.[30]

The original "Swamp Angel" has long been assumed to be located at Trenton, N.J. In fact, the author recalls this was so stated in a history book studied in elementary school. That the weapon, now in Cadwallader Park in Trenton (Fig. VI-25) and formerly at Clinton Avenue and Perry Street in that

FIGURE: VI-23 IDENTIFICATION: Marsh Battery armed with mortars after bursting of "Swamp Angel." SOURCE: *Battles and Leaders,* Vol. 4. REMARKS: Probably 10-Inch Seacoast Mortars, Model 1861.

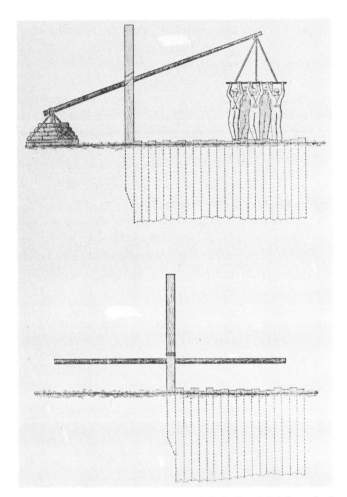

FIGURE: VI-21 IDENTIFICATION: Methods of driving planks for Marsh Battery (Swamp Angel) platform. Initial method (top) was successful, but not used since easier way (bottom) was discovered. Men leaning on horizontal pole strapped to plank drove it through mud to sand below. SOURCE: Gillmore.

FIGURE: VI-24 IDENTIFICATION: Marsh Battery armed during later period with 4.2-Inch Parrott on Siege Carriage. REMARKS: Marsh in foreground grows on top of mud.

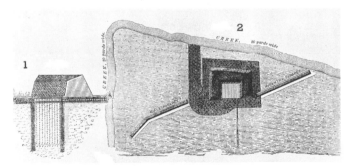

FIGURE: VI-22 IDENTIFICATION: The Marsh Battery (Swamp Angel). SOURCE: Gillmore. REMARKS: (1) Profile; (2) General Plan.

FIGURE: VI-25 LOCATION: Trenton, N.J. IDENTIFICATION: Parrott, Seacoast or Navy, 8-Inch, Rifle, Model 1861, Iron. (Reinforcing Band missing). BORE: Diameter — 8. Rifling — 11 x 11, Straight. Length — 136. LENGTH O/A: 162. TRUNNIONS: Diameter — 10. Length — 5. MARKINGS: Muzzle Face — W.P.F., 1 (rest obliterated). Right Trunnion — R.P.P. REMARKS: Reported to be the "Swamp Angel." COMMON NAME: 200-Pounder Parrott (Army designation). 150-Pounder Parrott (Navy designation). 8-Inch Parrott (Preferred).

city, is an 8-inch Parrott minus its reinforcing band cannot be denied. But that the piece is the "Swamp Angel" is open to serious doubt.

At the time the Marsh Battery site was excavated, the author engaged in considerable correspondence with the Trenton Chamber of Commerce and various individuals in New Jersey and elsewhere in an effort to establish the authenticity of the piece, but without receiving anything in the way of proof. Apparently the rifle arrived at Trenton with a shipment of cannon destined for the melting pot, was recognized, and mounted by public spirited citizens.[31] Even at that time there were doubts that it was the "Swamp Angel," but these seem to have been dispelled some years later when a former officer, who had served on Morris Island, identified the piece by the crack in it.

The claim at first glance seems reasonable, but further inquiry into history makes it subject to question. Major source of information on the "Swamp Angel," other than the Official Records, is General Gillmore's book which not only goes into construction of the battery and firing of the piece, but also discusses the bursting of other Parrotts on Morris Island. The general had no less than twenty-four Parrotts burst on Morris and his successor lost twenty-seven. Taking Gillmore's alone, six of this number were 8-inch and four of these broke at the vent, three so close to the same spot and with the same type fracture that unless they were side by side, it would be almost impossible to distinguish one from the others and even together would be a difficult job. No doubt there were 8s among the additional twenty-seven destroyed on Morris and since this caliber had a tendency to break at the vent, it is likely a few more would have been added to the heap. Unfortunately, no records were kept on these later weapons and there is no way of knowing.

Now, out of this pile of rifles, of which at least three and possibly more had almost identical fractures, one was picked as the "Swamp Angel." Moreover, it was one of which broken fragment and tube had remained together despite several handlings as junk iron with presumably no studied attempt to keep them together, for the Trenton newspaper article, previously mentioned in footnote 31, states the weapon was recognized after arrival, not brought from Morris Island as an historic relic. In addition, although fragment and tube remained together, a section so firmly attached it survived firing and explosion, the reinforcing band (Figs. VI-19 and 20), apparently was lost along the way.

Normally it would be a simple matter to check the weapon's number, but the muzzle face is so badly pitted that only a single numeral, "1," can be seen and while that could be part of the number, it also may be a digit of date or weight and, consequently, is useless. Another identification method, foundry numbers, which in large Parrotts coincided with gun numbers and were placed on the sight bracket, also fails in this case—the bracket has been destroyed.

As a result, the Trenton cannon has been neither authenticated nor disproved although on the basis of similarly damaged Morris Island 8-inchers, the weight of evidence is three to one, and probably higher, against its being the "Swamp Angel." On the other hand, 8-inch Parrotts are quite rare and on these grounds alone it is well worth preserving.

A complete 8-inch (Fig. VI-26) is displayed at Fort Sumter. It has the standard 11 lands and grooves of this caliber and was made in 1864. The weight is 16,537 pounds. Forts Sumter and Moultrie, which never mounted Parrotts during the war, yet took as much pounding as any installations in the country from these rifles, today have probably the world's best collection of heavy Parrotts. Fort Sumter's impressive display of eleven 6.4-inch on carriages plus the single 8-inch when added to an extremely rare 10-inch at Fort Moultrie, makes a visit to the forts imperative for anyone interested in a study of these calibers. The Moultrie 10-inch (Fig. VI-27) was cast in 1864, No. 5 of this caliber. It weighs 26,900 pounds and is rifled with 15 lands and grooves. History of the piece is not known, but there is a possibility it may have been used on Morris Island.

FIGURE: VI-26 Location: Fort Sumter, S.C. Identification: Parrott, Seacoast or Navy, 8-Inch, Rifle, Model 1861, Iron. Bore: Diameter — 8. Rifling — 11 x 11, Straight. Length — 136. Length O/A: 162. Trunnions: Diameter — 10. Length — 5. Markings: Muzzle Face — No. 58, 1864, W.P.F., 8, 16537, R.M.H. Right Trunnion — R.P.P. Common Name: 200-Pounder Parrott (Army designation). 150-Pounder Parrott (Navy designation). 8-Inch Parrott (Preferred).

FIGURE: VI-27 LOCATION: Fort Moultrie, S.C. IDENTIFICATION: Parrott, Seacoast, 10-Inch, Rifle, Model 1862, Iron. BORE: Diameter — 10. Rifling — 15 x 15, Straight. Length — 138.75v. LENGTH O/A: 177. TRUNNIONS: Diameter — 10. Length — 4.5. MARKINGS: Muzzle Face — No. 5, 1864, W.P.F., R.M.H., 26900. Right Trunnion — R.P.P. Tube — U.S. COMMON NAME: 300-Pounder Parrott (Army designation). 250-Pounder Parrott (Seldom used). 10-Inch Parrott (Preferred).

Only three 10-inch Parrotts saw service during the war, all on Morris. The number of the first we know since Capt. Parrott testified[32] before the Senate committee 18 January 1865: ". . . the first of my largest guns—300-pounder—was made in the winter of 1862-63. That is a 10-inch gun. The government took that for the purpose of an experiment in the service and sent it down to Morris's (sic) Island. . . ."

Similarly, General Gillmore in reference to the piece shows a drawing of the muzzle face[33] which bears the data: "No. 1, 1863, WPF, AM (initials of Alfred Mordecai, the inspector), and 27,030 (the weight)." Mounted on a center-pintal, iron barbette carriage in Battery Strong, the piece bore on Fort Sumter at 4,290 yards. It was fired a few times and then the premature burst of a shell took off 18 inches of the muzzle (Fig. VI-28). However, the ragged edges of the break were chipped smooth, the rifling removed for a short distance and the piece returned to action. It subsequently fired 370 times with no appreciable change in range or accuracy until it was completely disabled by continued muzzle bursts.[34] "No one," Gillmore said, "could witness its performance during the bombardment of Sumter and notice the terrible crushing effect of its huge projectiles upon the masonry of that place, the ease with which it was worked, and its remarkable accuracy at a distance of two miles and a half, without being filled with admiration and wonder. . . ."

No record has been found of the other two 10-inch used later on Morris. These may have been guns No. 2 and 3. On the other hand, this cannot be assumed, and it is perfectly conceivable that No. 5 or any other low number may have been picked up at the foundry and forwarded south.

Thus there is a possibility that the Fort Moultrie piece saw service on Morris, a view that is strengthened a bit by location of the weapon in the area which presumes either use of the piece during the war, or its being brought to Charleston after the end of hostilities. Unfortunately, the 10-inch was not tried for range, so we have no idea of its extreme capabilities. It no doubt was a formidable weapon and a valuable addition to United States armament.

FIGURE: VI-28 IDENTIFICATION: Parrott, Seacoast, 10-Inch, Rifle, Model 1862, Iron. REMARKS: Weapon damaged on Morris Island. Muzzle was trimmed smooth and firing continued. Piece is documented (Gillmore) as No. 1, 1863, W.P.F., A.M., 27030, all on the muzzle face. Streaks are in the glass-plate negative which has been damaged since it was taken in 1863.

Although Parrotts are easy to recognize, there is one pitfall to be avoided—the Confederate Parrott. These weapons will be found in 10-, 20-, and 30-pounder calibers and although often called "Brooke rifles" in modern as well as Civil War identification, the author feels they should be properly catalogued as "Confederate Parrotts."

For instance, U.S. Ordnance Captain Daniel W. Flagler, in his report of 28 April 1865, of weapons captured at Tredegar Foundry in Richmond[35] lists: ". . . three unfinished rifled field guns, 2.9-inch, of Parrott pattern, but heavier than the old Parrott 10-pdr., weighing 1,500 pounds. . ." Further in the report he states: ". . . also some Brooke banded and rifled Navy guns—three 6.4-inch, one 8-inch and one 7-inch. . . ." Presumably, as an ordnance officer, Captain Flagler knew his business and if the small rifles had been "Brooke guns" would have listed them as such. Similarly we find an Army of Northern Virginia Special Order dated 23 April 1863[36] ordering a board to examine a "Tredegar-made 20-pounder Parrott," and a 13 November 1862 Confederate Ordnance Circular[37] authorizing the types of artillery to be made including 10-, 20-, and 30-pounder Parrotts. Finally, from the point of view of identification, the Confederate Parrotts have a long tube like the U.S. Parrotts banded at the breech by what appears to be a single band (although made up of several small rings). The Brooke (q.v.) has a heavier, sharper tapering tube with one, two, or three layers of bands.

A 10-pounder Confederate Parrott (Fig. VI-29) is one of four surrounding a statue at Hightstown, New Jersey. Bores of all are badly rusted and measure 3 to 3.1 inches, but originally were the 2.9

mentioned by Flagler. Rifling consists of 7 lands and grooves of the "hook" form used in Brooke rifles, a characteristic which no doubt helped hang the identification "Brooke" on these weapons. They are about 3 inches longer than the old U.S. Parrott—81 compared to 78. However, the main point of identification is the reinforcing band. The U.S. Parrott band drops off sharply, while that of the Confederate model is a bit longer and tapers on the end toward the trunnions.

A particularly interesting Confederate Parrott (Fig. VI-30) came from the tug *Teazer* which charged into Hampton Roads along with the *Virginia* on the first outing of the Southern ironclad 8 March 1862. Then mounting only this rifle, the tug brazenly used it against Union shore batteries. July 4, after another piece, a 32-pounder, had been installed, the *Teazer* tangled in the James River with the *Maratanza* and the *Monitor* and a shot pierced her boiler. Her crew went over the side leaving her to the federals.

The piece, now at the Washington Navy Yard, is the same 81 inches overall of other Confederate Parrotts and the bore, which is plugged, measures 2.9 inches. Main difference is the substitution of a loop for trunnions after the manner of the Dahlgren boat howitzer, an arrangement which shows clearly in the Civil War photograph (Fig. VI-31) of the piece mounted on an improvised pivot carriage aboard the tug which is spelled *"Teazer"* in the OR's and *"Teaser"* in the ONR's. In his report of the engagement,[38] the *Maratanza's* skipper called the weapon a 12-pounder, but in view of similar bore to the U.S. 2.9 Parrott, the designation probably should have been 10-pounder.

FIGURE: VI-29 LOCATION: Hightstown, N.J. IDENTIFICATION: Parrott, Confederate, Field, 2.9-Inch, Rifle, Iron. BORE: Diameter — 2.9. Rifling — 7 x 7, Hook-Slant or "Brooke" type. LENGTH O/A: 81. TRUNNIONS: Diameter — 3.6. Length — 2.9. REMARKS: Marking obscured by paint. Note taper of Reinforcing Band. COMMON NAME: 10-Pounder Confederate Parrott. Or, 2.9-Inch Confederate Parrott.

FIGURE: VI-30 LOCATION: Washington Navy Yard, D.C. IDENTIFICATION: Parrott, Confederate, Navy, 2.9-Inch, Rifle, Iron. BORE: Diameter — 2.9. Rifling 7 x 7, Hook-Slant or "Brooke" type. Length — 72.5v. LENGTH O/A: 81. REMARKS: Note loop in place of trunnions. Foundry marks, if any, obscured by paint. Piece was captured aboard the Tug *Teazer* — See Fig. VI-31. COMMON NAME: 10-Pounder Confederate Navy Parrott. Or, 2.9-Inch Confederate Navy Parrott.

No 20-pounder Confederate Parrotts have been found other than two badly damaged tubes at West Point, and no statistics are available. However, it resembled the 10- and 30-pounders and with a 3.67-inch bore rifled with 7 hook-type lands and grooves should not be difficult to identify.

Fort Morgan, some 65 miles from Mobile, Alabama, displays the 30-pounder Confederate Parrott (Fig. VI-32). The breech has been blown out beneath the reinforcing band, but the remainder of the rifle is in excellent condition. The bore measures 4.2 inches and has 5 lands and grooves of a straight type similar to the U.S. Parrott rather than the hook-type which would be expected. Total length, of course, is not available, but a similar Confederate 4.2 at West Point, which also has 5 straight-type lands and grooves, is 132 inches from muzzle face to end of its knob-type cascabel.

Markings on the Fort Morgan piece are 1862 on the left trunnion and JRA (J. R. Anderson) and TF (Tredegar Foundry) on the right. It has the number 2,154 on the muzzle face and the weight, 4,730, on the reinforce. Lines on the band show it is composed of four rings instead of a single piece as in Northern Parrotts. This type construction is typical of Southern weapons and is found in Brookes as well as the Confederate Parrotts. However, it was also used by the British and while its presence may be considered strong evidence of a "Made in Dixie" label, other factors must be considered for positive identification. The converse does not hold true and single piece construction cannot be construed as a guarantee of Northern manufacture.

FIGURE: VI-32 LOCATION: Fort Morgan, Ala. IDENTIFICATION: Parrott, Confederate, Siege & Garrison, 4.2-Inch, Rifle, Iron. BORE: Diameter — 4.2. Rifling — 5 x 5, Straight. LENGTH O/A (Muzzle face to rear of band): 121. TRUNNIONS: Diameter — 5.25. Length — 4.75. MARKINGS: Left Trunnion — 1862. Right Trunnion — J.R.A., T.F. REMARKS: Face of broken breech shows the boring machine wandered a full inch off center. COMMON NAME: 30-Pounder Confederate Parrott. Or, 4.2-Inch Confederate Parrott.

NOTES

1. J. N. Paulding, *The Cannon and Projectiles Invented by Robert Parker Parrott*, 1879, p. 14.
2. Reports of committees of the U.S. Senate, 2nd session, 38th Congress, "Heavy Ordnance," p. 135–144, testimony of Robert P. Parrott, 18 January 1865.
3. Alexander L. Holley, *A Treatise on Ordnance and Armor*, 1865, pp. 871–873.
4. Jennings Cropper Wise, *The Long Arm of Lee*, 1915, Vol. 1, p. 63.
5. *Official Records*, Series III, Vol. 1, pp. 347, 356, 379, 386, 391.
6. Henry L. Abbot, "Siege Artillery in The Campaigns Against Richmond With Notes on the 15-Inch Gun," *Professional Papers No. 14, Corps of Engineers*, 1867, pp. 124–126.
7. Holley, *op. cit.*, p. 55; J. G. Benton, *A Course of Instruction in Ordnance and Gunnery Composed and Compiled for Cadets of The United States Military Academy*, 1875, p. 548.
8. Abbot, *op. cit.*, p. 171.
9. *Ibid.*, pp. 124–126.
10. Q. A. Gillmore, *Engineer and Artillery Operations Against The Defenses of Charleston Harbor, 1863*, pp. 85–88, Plates IX, X, XI. *Official Records*, Series I, Vol. 28, Part 1, pp. 31–32.
11. Mordecai, class of 1861 at West Point, served as ordnance inspector 28 June 1862 to 1 June 1863 and in ordnance with the Department of The South, primarily on Morris Island 11 June 1863—22 April 1864. He was a son of Major Alfred Mordecai, West Point 1823, who was a leading developer of United States ordnance and compiled the *Ordnance Manual for The Use of Officers of The United States Army*, 1841.
12. Benton, 1875, *op. cit.*, p. 184.
13. Holley, *op. cit.*, p. 55, Table XII.
14. Auguste Paul Cooke, *A Text-Book of Naval Ordnance and Gunnery Prepared for Use of The Cadet Midshipmen of the United States Naval Academy*, 1880, p. 286.
15. Reports of committees of the U.S. Senate, *loc. cit.*, p. 138.
16. Holley, *op. cit.*, p. 54.
17. *Ibid.*, p. 55, Table XII.
18. Cooke, *op. cit.*, p. 235.
19. *Ibid.*, pp. 235–238.
20. *Ibid.*, p. 81.
21. Reports of committees of the U.S. Senate, *op. cit.*, p. 169, testimony of Assistant Secretary of The Navy, Capt. G. V. Fox.
22. *Ibid.*, p. 170.
23. *Official Records*, Series I, Vol. 28, Part 1, pp. 31–32.
24. Benton, 1875, *loc. cit.*, p. 548.
25. Range to St. Michael's Church, an aiming point in the city, was 7,900 yards and shells seem to have fallen both short and beyond; the author has arbitrarily picked 8,000.
26. Specific references regarding the firing of the Swamp Angel and construction of the battery are numerous and lengthy. Consequently, readers desiring further information are advised to consult Gillmore's *Engineer and Artillery Operations Against the Defenses of Charleston Harbor, 1863*, *Official Records*, Series I, Vols. 28 and 35, Parts 1 and 2, as well as issues of the city's newspapers, *The Charleston Daily Courier*, and *The Charleston Mercury*, during the period August 24–26 and the *Mercury* of 7 September 1863.
27. John Johnson, *The Defense of Charleston Harbor 1863–65*, 1890, p. 132.
28. *Official Records*, Series I, Vol. 35, Part 2, p. 43.
29. *Ibid.*
30. *Ibid.*, Part 1, p. 235.
31. Undated newspaper clipping in the author's possession believed to be from a Trenton, N. J. newspaper.
32. Reports of committees of the U.S. Senate, *loc. cit.*, p. 138.
33. Gillmore, *op. cit.*, Plate XVIII.
34. *Ibid.*, pp. 152–153; *Official Records*, Series I, Vol. 28, Part 1, pp. 219–224.
35. *Official Records*, Series I, Vol. 46, Part 3, p. 1009.
36. Special Order No. 113, paragraph XI, 23 April 1863, Headquarters Department of Northern Virginia, *A Calendar of Confederate Papers*, 1908, p. 323.
37. Circular, 13 November 1862, signed by J. Gorgas, Colonel, Chief of Ordnance, Richmond, Va., *General Orders from Adjutant and Inspector General's Office, C. S. Army from January 1862 to December 1863*, pp. 234–235.
38. *Official Navy Records*, Series I, Vol. 7, p. 543.

Chapter 7

The Brooke

A FORMER UNITED STATES NAVY OFFICER developed the Confederate answer to Captain Parrott's heavy rifles. John Mercer Brooke (1820-1906) was born near Tampa, Florida, and joined the Navy as a midshipman in 1841, serving on sea duty until 1845 when he entered the recently established Naval Academy at Annapolis. Following graduation, Brooke spent several years in coastal survey work and at the Naval Observatory in Washington where he developed a device to take deep sea soundings by which specimens from the depths were first brought to light. He resigned at the outbreak of war joining the Virginia State Navy and later the Confederate Navy. During the initial phase of the conflict, he worked on development of his gun and plans for raising and converting the sunken *U.S.S. Merrimac* into the ironclad *Virginia,* a vessel which carried four of his rifles as well as standard smoothbores. From March, 1863, until the close of the war he was chief of the Bureau of Ordnance and Hydrography. After Appomattox, Brooke settled into civilian life as professor of physics and astronomy at Virginia Military Institute, retiring in 1899. His gun was produced at two locations, Tredegar Foundry in Richmond, which was owned by Joseph Reid Anderson, and the Confederate Naval Ordnance Works at Selma, Alabama, operated by Commander Catesby ap Roger Jones.

Anderson (1813-1892) has been mentioned previously in connection with other ordnance. He graduated from West Point in 1836, but returned to civilian life after a year in the Army and in January, 1848, became owner of Tredegar Iron Works, later better known as Tredegar Foundry. Under his management the firm became a leading manufacturer of locomotives for Southern railroads and a well-known supplier of cannon for the federal government, furnishing a reported 1,200 during the years prior to the war.

Shortly after the firing on Sumter, Anderson was commissioned a brigadier general and went on active duty with the understanding that he would return to the foundry should his presence be needed. He participated in various engagements and finally wound up this phase of his career 30 June 1862 at Frayser's Farm where he was wounded. He tendered his resignation two weeks later and returned to Tredegar which during the war became the major supplier of munitions for the Confederacy and from 1861 to 1863 was almost the sole source of heavy weapons, including the Brooke. Confiscated at the close of the war, the company was soon released and back in business by 1867 with Anderson as president, a post he retained until his death with exception of the period 1876-78 when the firm was in receivership.

Like Brooke and Anderson, Jones also began his career in the service of the United States. Born at Fairfield, Virginia in April, 1821, he was appointed midshipman in June, 1836, and served at sea and in Washington until 28 February 1853, when, as a lieutenant, he was ordered to ordnance duty at the Washington Navy Yard. Here Jones assisted Dahlgren in perfection of the inventor's shellgun and later went to sea as ordnance officer aboard the *Merrimac* and other vessels on which the new Dahlgrens were installed.

After his state seceded, Jones resigned his commission and was appointed a captain in the Virginia Navy, a post he later relinquished to transfer to the Confederate Navy as a lieutenant. March 8, 1862 found him executive officer of his former vessel, now the *Virginia,* in her first incursion into Hampton Roads. During this action, the vessel's commander, Captain Franklin Buchanan, was wounded, so Jones succeeded to command and took her out the following day for the celebrated fight with the *Monitor,* a battle in which the *Virginia's* Brooke rifles traded shot with the *Monitor's* Dahlgrens.

In May, 1863, he became commander of the Naval Ordnance Works—also called "Naval Gun Foundry and Ordnance Works" and "Selma Cannon Foundry"[1]—a post he held throughout the remainder of the war. After the surrender, he joined Brooke and another ex-Confederate naval ordnance officer, Robert D. Minor, in a venture to purchase surplus United States war materials for foreign governments, but the partnership dissolved after a year or two. Jones then settled at Selma where in 1877 he was fatally shot during an argument with a neighbor.

These then were the men—Brooke, the inventor, Anderson, and Jones the producers—whose names are intertwined with the weapon which, as a Southern piece from start to finish, was a source of pride to the hard-pressed Confederacy.

Basically, like the Parrott, the Brooke is a cast iron weapon with a wrought-iron reinforce. But there the resemblance ends. The Brooke has a heavier, sharper tapered tube and it may be single, double, or even triple banded. The band itself, instead of a single piece like the Parrott, consists of several rings, approximately 6 inches wide, in the manner of the Confederate Parrott. These were not welded together[2]

and the joints are often apparent if the band is examined closely. The Brooke was rifled with 7 lands and grooves in the hook-slant fashion illustrated in Figure VII-1. This apparently was not invented by Brooke for the same type is used in the little 3.3-inch Parrotts, although with 12 lands and grooves rather than 7. It appears to be merely a simplified form of the hook-slant rifling used in the English Blakely (Fig. VII-2) and described in Chapter VIII. However, since this form of rifling is used often in Southern weapons and appears standard for Brookes, it will be referred to hereafter as "Brooke" rifling.

Brookes today are harder to find than identify for, with three fortunate exceptions, surviving specimens are few and far between. Best collection, with nine weapons, is at Washington Navy Yard, followed by four at Columbus, Georgia, three at Charleston, four at various locations in Alabama, and one each at West Point and Fort Pulaski. No doubt there are others, but these are all judicious search has thus far brought to light.

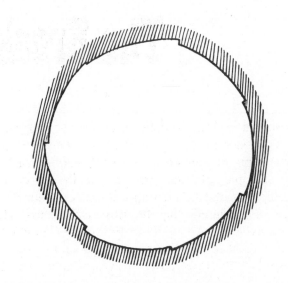

FIGURE: VII-1 IDENTIFICATION: Brooke Rifling. SOURCE: Holley. REMARKS: Typical hook-slant rifling used in Brooke and many other Confederate rifles.

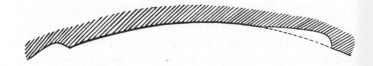

FIGURE: VII-2 IDENTIFICATION: Rifling of 9-Inch Blakely. SOURCE: Holley. REMARKS: Typical hook-slant rifling used in many Blakely Rifles. Compare with Brooke Rifling, Fig. VII-1.

FIGURE: **VII-3** LOCATION: Washington Navy Yard, D.C. IDENTIFICATION: Brooke, Seacoast and Navy, 6.4 and 7-Inch, Rifles, Double and Single-Banded, Iron. Measurements and Marking, front to rear, as follows:

	Double Band	Double Band	Single Band	Double Band
BORE:				
Diameter	6.4	6.4	7	7
Rifling	7 x 7, Brooke.	7 x 7, Brooke.	7 x 7, Brooke.	7 x 7, Brooke.
Length	115.5v.	115.5v.	117.75v	117.5v
LENGTH O/A:	144	141	145	147
TRUNNIONS:				
Diameter	7	7	8.1	8
Length	6.5	6.5	8.25	7.25
MARKINGS:				
Muzzle Face	—	—	1842	—
Left Trunnion	P. A.D.B.	P. A.D.B.	P. A.D.B.	—
Right Trunnion	1864	6.4, 1863	—	—
Breech	T.F., 10799	T.F., 10675	T.F., 15162	S-5

COMMON NAME: 6.4-Inch Double-Banded Brooke Rifle. 7-Inch Double-Banded Brooke Rifle. 7-Inch Single-Banded Brooke Rifle.

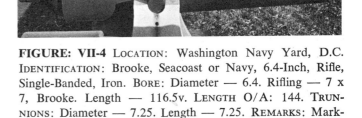

FIGURE: **VII-4** LOCATION: Washington Navy Yard, D.C. IDENTIFICATION: Brooke, Seacoast or Navy, 6.4-Inch, Rifle, Single-Banded, Iron. BORE: Diameter — 6.4. Rifling — 7 x 7, Brooke. Length — 116.5v. LENGTH O/A: 144. TRUNNIONS: Diameter — 7.25. Length — 7.25. REMARKS: Marking obscured by paint. Navy Yard records list weight as 9,110 lbs. and state piece was captured aboard the *C.S.S. Atlanta.* COMMON NAME: 6.4-Inch Single-Banded Brooke Rifle.

The Washington Brookes are all close together and four (Fig. VII-3) fortuitously grouped in line where minor variations, such as the form of tube sight masses, may be observed. The near two are 6.4-inch caliber and the last pair 7-inch, one of the latter being a relatively rare single-banded weapon. The first three were made at Tredegar, the last, although captured aboard the Confederate ironclad *Tennessee* with the other double-banded Richmond pieces, was produced at the Selma works. History of the single-banded rifle is not available.

Lengths of Brookes vary considerably, even within the same caliber, a discrepancy probably due more to foundry inconsistency than to model change. Seven-inchers range from 143 to 147.5 inches for single or double-banded weapons. Standard length, according to Holley,[3] was 146.05 inches, but Jones mentions making one at Selma 5 inches longer than usual for use in the *Nashville.*[4] The only triple-banded rifle believed still in existence measures 153 inches. The 6.4-inch model, both single (Fig. VII-4) and double-banded, ranges from 141 to 144 inches. The difference in length is noted in rifles of each foundry as well as between foundries with perhaps greater fluctuation in the Richmond pieces. Trunnion diameters vary from 7 to 7.25 inches for the 6.4 and 8 to 8.5 for the 7. The rifle was made in a variety of calibers with 6.4 and 7 inches being the most popular. An 8-inch was made, however, for Abbot mentions[5] its use on the James River and lists two such pieces among captured artillery, and an 11-inch is also reported.

The 4.62-inch siege and garrison rifle (Fig. VII-5) has the general appearance of a Brooke other than cascabel knob and apparent one-piece, rather than ring, construction of the reinforcing band. Abbot records a "4.62-inch Brooke" in his list of captured weapons although the drawing from his book[6] calls it a "4.62-inch Siege Rifle." Unfortunately, statistics are lacking and although a 4.62-inch siege rifle is mentioned in the 1863 Confederate Ordnance Manual (See Chapter IX), it seems to have been an entirely different model. Consequently, despite resemblance to other Brookes, the rifle can be given only a tentative identification pending discovery of additional information.

Based on Abbot's drawing, the piece was roughly 111 inches overall with a bore length of 95 inches or so. Trunnions, to fit the same carriage as the other siege rifle of similar caliber, would have been 5.82 inches which seems to conform to the drawing. Trunnion length, based on estimated diameter and the drawing, would have been a shade under 3 inches.

Although the Brooke is normally considered a rifle, smoothbore varieties also will be found. E. P. Alexander in an 1883 article stated:[7] "In addition to the rifles, Capt. Brooke also furnished some heavily banded smoothbores of 10 and 11-inch caliber to fire wrought iron balls with very high charges against the ironclads which doubtless would have been extremely effective at short range. . . ."

A Tredegar 10-inch, made in 1865, is now in the Washington Navy Yard collection (Fig. VII-6). It measures 150.5 overall and weighs 21,140 pounds. Records at the Navy Yard state it was made for the Confederate ironclad *Columbia*. This vessel was built at Charleston near the end of the war, but was bilged after grounding on a bar. There is some argument whether or not her armament was aboard at the time, so this particular weapon may have been captured at Richmond before being sent to Charleston, or taken over in the latter city. In either case, in view of its designed use, which would have been to fight other ironclads, probabilities are it is one of the weapons to which General Alexander referred.

Selma also cast 10-inch smoothbores, for a letter from Commander Jones, dated 11 May 1864,[8] mentions his problems in handling such heavy weapons. A double-banded piece, which weighed approximately 24,000 pounds in rough form and 22,000 finished, played havoc with his hoisting equipment and elicited the comment that he would make no more of this caliber until the foundry obtained another crane. A Selma 10-inch (Fig. VII-7) is now at Columbus, Georgia, where it has been delayed a

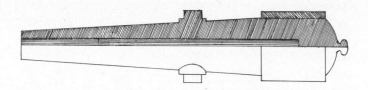

FIGURE: VII-5 IDENTIFICATION: Brooke*, Siege & Garrison, 4.62-Inch, Rifle, Single-Banded, Iron. BORE: Diameter — 4.62. Length — 95 (estimated). LENGTH O/A: 111.5 (estimated). TRUNNIONS: Diameter — 5.85 (estimated). Length — 3 (estimated). SOURCE: Abbot. REMARKS: *Tentatively identified as Brooke. Abbot calls it "Confederate 4.62-Inch Siege Rifle". Note knob-type cascabel. COMMON NAME: 4.62-Inch Brooke Rifle.

FIGURE: VII-6 LOCATION: Washington Navy Yard, D.C. IDENTIFICATION: Brooke, Seacoast or Navy, 10-Inch, Smoothbore, Double-Banded, Iron. BORE: Diameter — 10. Smoothbore. Length — 125v. LENGTH O/A: 150.5. TRUNNIONS: Diameter — 10. Length — 6.5. MARKINGS: Left Trunnion — A.D.B., 57. Right Trunnion — 10-In., 1865. Breech — T.F., 21140 Lbs. REMARKS: Made for the Confederate Ram, *Columbia*. Other weapons, front to rear, are: 5-Inch Whitworth (Chapter VIII); 32-Pounder, 57 cwt. Model 1846 (Chapter I), and 6.4-Inch Single-Banded Brooke Rifle (Fig. VII-4). COMMON NAME: 10-Inch Brooke Smoothbore.

FIGURE: VII-7 LOCATION: Columbus, Ga. IDENTIFICATION: Brooke, Seacoast or Navy, 10-Inch, Smoothbore, Double-Banded, Iron. BORE: Diameter — 10. Smoothbore. Length — 126v. LENGTH O/A: 158.5. TRUNNIONS: Diameter — 10. Length — 6.5. MARKINGS: Left Trunnion — X-In., 21562. Right Trunnion — X-In, C. ap R.J., 1864. REMARKS: Piece is reported to be No. S-87, but the marks, if present, are obscured by paint. COMMON NAME: 10-Inch Brooke Smoothbore.

hundred years or so while enroute to Charleston, probably also destined for the Columbia. It measures 158.5 overall, 8 inches more than the Tredegar specimen, and weighs 21,562 pounds. It is dated 1864. Another smoothbore "delayed" indefinitely at Columbus is a very rare 11-inch, also shipped from Selma for Charleston. The piece (Fig. VII-8) is 170 inches overall and weighs 23,612 pounds. Jordan Vocational High School in Columbus boasts two fine, double-banded 7-inch rifles, both made at Selma, which were on the gunboat *Chattahoochee*.[9] Cascabels of both are broken, but extension of existing metal indicates an extreme length of 148 inches.

In addition to casting smoothbores, the Confederates converted some of the 8-inch rifles to smoothbores by reaming them to 10 inches for Abbot records:[10] ". . . two 8-inch Brooke guns bored to 10-inch smooth. . ." in his list of ordnance captured in the Water Battery at Drewry's Bluff. Civil War photographs (Figs. X-61 and 62) show two Brookes captured in the Drewry's Bluff defenses. They are of undetermined caliber and could be rifled or smooth.

Other Brooke rifles also were converted. In the previously mentioned Jones' letter of 11 May, he said: "We have reamed out a number of guns to 8-inch smoothbore that were cast for 6.4-inch rifles. No change in the exterior. . . ." One of these weapons is today at Gainesville, Alabama. The double-banded piece measures 142 inches overall and has trunnions 7.25 inches in diameter. The bore, is, of course, 8 inches, smooth. Markings are: Right trunnion, "1864," Left trunnion, "C. ap. R.J., 10,370 (the weight), S-26." "S-26" also is stamped on both breech and tube sight masses.[11]

Alabama's other three Brookes, all Selma rifles and double-banded, are believed to have been used at Chocktaw Bluff (also known as Fort Stoneman)[12] not far from Jackson where one of the pieces is mounted in front of the town police station. This is a particularly fine 6.4-inch rifle (Fig. VII-9) which measures 143 inches overall and has 7.25-inch trunnions. It is marked on the right trunnion "VI-In., C. ap R.J.," and has "S-96" on the breech and "S" on the top of the first band. The left trunnion is stamped "VI-In," as close as Roman numerals could get to 6.4.

In private hands at Chocktaw Bluff is a 7-inch and another of this caliber is now at Fort Morgan. The latter weapon formerly was at Montgomery and measures 146.5 inches overall and has trunnions 8.25 inches in diameter. The left trunnion is stamped "VII, 14,800 lbs., S-89." The top of the second reinforcing band at the rear has an "S."

FIGURE: VII-8 LOCATION: Columbus, Ga. IDENTIFICATION: Brooke, Seacoast or Navy, 11-Inch, Smoothbore, Double-Banded, Iron. BORE: Diameter — 11. Smoothbore. Length — (2 vents, 136 to one, 139 to the other). LENGTH O/A: 170. TRUNNIONS: Diameter — 10.5. Length — 7. MARKINGS: Left Trunnion — 23612. Right Trunnion — XI-In., C.ap.R.J., 1864. Inner Band, top, rear — S-97. Outer Band, top, rear — S-97. Cascabel, top — S-97. Cascabel Block, top — S-97. COMMON NAME: 11-Inch Brooke Smoothbore.

FIGURE: VII-9 LOCATION: Jackson, Ala. IDENTIFICATION: Brooke, Seacoast or Navy, 6.4-Inch, Rifle, Double-Banded, Iron. BORE: Diameter — 6.4. Rifling — 7 x 7, Brooke. LENGTH O/A: 143. TRUNNIONS: Diameter — 7.25. Length — 6.5. MARKINGS: Left Trunnion — VI-In. Right Trunnion — VI-In., C.ap.R.J. Breech — S-96. Inner Band, top rear — S. COMMON NAME: 6.4-Inch Double-Banded Brooke Rifle.

Markings of Brooke guns appear to have followed the whim of the marker more than any formal practice and those examined have ranged from excellent to zero. Even the weapons in the former category often have marks that are difficult to detect. Consequently, the following are suggested locations where a bit of paint scraping may prove fruitful and perhaps narrow the search. They should be used solely as a guide and failure in these areas merely indicates that the hunt should be extended to other sections. Incidentally, since weapons are often covered with many coats of paint, be sure to scrape down to metal—many a mark has been overlooked through failure to do this. Best place to start is the left trunnion face.

FIGURE: VII-10 LOCATION: Charleston, S.C. IDENTIFICATION: Brooke, Seacoast or Navy, 7-Inch, Rifle, Double-Banded, Iron. BORE: Diameter — 7. Rifling — 7 x 7, Brooke. Length — 117.5v. LENGTH O/A: 147. TRUNNIONS: Diameter — 8.1. Length — 7.25. MARKINGS: Muzzle Face — 76. Left Trunnion — VII-In. Right Trunnion — VII-In., C.ap.R.J., 1864. Inner Band, top rear — S-76. Outer Band, top rear — S-76. Breech Sight Bracket — S-76. Tube Sight Piece — S-76. Cascabel, rear — S-76. Cascabel Block — S-76. COMMON NAME: 7-Inch Double-Banded Brooke Rifle.

FIGURE: VII-11 LOCATION: Fort Moultrie, S.C. IDENTIFICATION: Brooke, Seacoast or Navy, 7-Inch, Rifle, Triple-Banded, Iron. BORE: Diameter — 7. Rifling — 7 x 7, Brooke. Length — 126v. LENGTH O/A: 153. REMARKS: Trunnions were attached by Trunnion Band, now missing. See Fig. VII-12. Piece apparently is unmarked. COMMON NAME: 7-Inch Triple-Banded Brooke Rifle.

Most Tredegar and Selma weapons have markings here and anything found may well indicate the next move.

Tredegar weapons thus far examined, if marked, have had the initials ADB, generally written together, but sometimes "A DB." They are believed to be the initials of Lieutenant A.M. DeBree who presumably dropped the "M." If these letters are found, check the top of the breech between cascabel and reinforcing band and the initials of Tredegar Foundry and the weight of the piece may be discovered. The right trunnion face should also be examined since the date, if present, is generally placed here. Should the left trunnion face have only a Roman numeral, check the right trunnion where a similar numeral and the initials C. ap R.J. may be found. In this case, the piece was made at Selma. The entire face of the right trunnion should be closely examined since sometimes additional information is stamped here, especially the date.

If Jones' initials are discovered, the breech sight mass, top and rear, should be checked for an "S" generally followed by the number of the piece. Similar marks may be found on the exact top of the reinforcing band, or bands, less than an inch from the rear edge, as well as the rear of the cascabel, tube sight mass, and, occasionally, the muzzle face. Unlike the Tredegar lettering which is an inch or more high, the Selma marks may be only a quarter inch or so and are easily concealed by paint.

One 7-inch Selma Brooke at Charleston (Fig. VII-10) is a mark hunter's delight. On the left trunnion is "VII-In." On the right, "VII-In., C. ap R.J., 1864." Top band, lower band, breech sight mass, tube sight mass, back of cascabel and cascabel block all have "S-76" and the muzzle face has the number without the "S". If both left and right trunnions are blank, chances are the piece is unmarked and while a check should be made of the other locations, the outlook is dim. If the piece has no trunnions, as is the case in the Charleston weapon to be described next, just figure it isn't your day and give up—or get set for a long job of intensive examination.

The rifle (Fig. VII-11) is a 7-inch, triple-banded Brooke believed made at Tredegar despite apparent lack of identifying marks. It is mounted at Fort Moultrie only 200 yards east of the wartime position from which within ten days it helped sink a friendly vessel and slammed wrought iron bolts into enemy ironclads. First mention of the piece in the Official Records[13] is a letter from Jefferson Davis to Governor M. L. Bonham of South Carolina in which the President remarked: "One large, triple-banded, 7-inch Brooke gun will . . . be completed this week when it can . . . be sent (to Charleston)." The letter is dated 21 July 1863 and Davis was referring to manufacture at Tredegar.

Apparently the rifle originally was to go into the ironclad *Charleston,* then under construction, but using the President's letter as a lever, General Beauregard obtained it for harbor defense.[14] The weapon arrived in Charleston and was mounted in Battery Marion on Sullivan's Island just in time to open on a troop-laden Confederate supply boat which blundered past the forts through a combination of circumstances which fortunately culminated in the loss of only two lives.[15]

The event occurred at the end of August, 1863, a particularly hectic period in the defense of Charleston. Early the preceding month, federal troops had stormed ashore on Morris Island and since that time had been inching their way toward Battery Wagner in some of the bitterest fighting of the war. During the day no head dared show above entrenchments of either side and the nights, lighted by the flash of heavy guns, were little better. Yet munitions had to be supplied, tired men relieved, and replacements slipped into the lines. So each night a Confederate steamer loaded with men and supplies left the city for Fort Johnson. There the normal procedure was to transfer to small boats for a 2-mile row across shallow water to Cummings Point at the harbor end of Morris Island (See chart, Fig. V-14). From the point, the men marched to Battery Wagner, and troops relieved returned to Johnson and then to the city.

Shortly after dark 30 August, Major Motte A. Pringle, quartermaster in charge of transportation, left for Fort Johnson anticipating a routine voyage. But at Johnson two events occurred which radically altered the complexion of the trip. First, there were no small boats since the Navy, which handled this chore, had heard Union ironclads might try to enter the harbor during the night and required the boat crews elsewhere. Second, the major's steamer picked this time to have engine trouble, a frequent and sometimes fatal habit of Southern vessels.

Pringle, however, was not to be balked. He commandeered the steamer *Sumter,* which luckily was moored at Fort Johnson, transferred the men and equipment, and set out for Cummings Point. Arriving safely, passengers and cargo were unloaded, but now a third problem arose to plague the major—the men he was supposed to take back were still on guard duty and by the time they were aboard, several hours had elapsed.

With small boats, the delay would have made little difference. But during this time, the tide had dropped too far for the steamer, with deeper draft, to return over several bars she had crossed in the direct line trip from Fort Johnson to Morris, behind Fort Sumter. This left two alternatives, wait for higher tide, which wouldn't occur until after daylight when federal batteries would make short work of the little steamer, or use the main channel between Fort Sumter and Sullivan's Island. The second choice ostensibly offered the risk of running past the entire Sullivan's Island defenses. However, communication existed between Morris and Sullivan's, and Pringle had merely to notify the forts to make the trip perfectly safe.

This, however, was not done and looking at it in retrospect, was obviously a stupid and dangerous oversight for an officer entrusted with a vessel and the lives of dozens of men. But from the view of a harried field officer trying to do a job, it seems a very human decision. Here was a man beset by problem after problem during a long, hot night—and none really his fault. But if he awakened the commanding general of Sullivan's Island at 1 A.M. telling him to alert all his forts for the little *Sumter,* odds were good a certain major would be on the carpet a few hours later.

Pringle's continued supply of Morris Island night after night proved he was both an intelligent officer and a courageous one. He probably figured no sentry spotting the *Sumter* would be fool enough to take her for anything but a harmless supply vessel. Moreover, he doubtless had a fair appreciation of how long it would take the forts to get into action. By the time the *Sumter* was seen, crews routed out, guns prepared for action and traversed to bear on the steamer, she would be far out of danger. With the odds apparently in his favor, Pringle took a chance. He ordered the *Sumter* under way—blacked out to make her an almost impossible target for anything but a close range, or lucky shot.

But the major was playing against loaded dice. Unknown to him, the same order that had alerted the Navy to the likelihood of an ironclad attack, also had been passed along to the Sullivan's Island forts. When the *Sumter* rounded to port for the run down the main channel, she was doomed. Every battery had sentries straining for a glimpse of the first ironclad. Crews were sleeping at their posts with the uneasy rest of men expecting momentary action. And here, blacked out, on the same course the monitor's invariably used, churned the *Sumter,* like a mouse creeping down a hall lined with cats.

Moultrie opened first. One over, another short, and the third right on target—good shooting in any league. Then the other batteries, including the Brooke, went into action. Firing, fortunately, was deliberate rather than intensive or casualties would have been much higher. When Moultrie's third round hit—under the "starboard water wheel," as Captain James R. Riley, the vessel's skipper, put it—he swung the helm over and rammed her against the beach. Then, at Pringle's suggestion, he rowed ashore and managed to stop the firing. But the damage was done. The survivors were taken off about daylight, but the *Sumter* filled with the rising tide and overturned, the victim of bad luck and good shooting.

The Brooke fired only two rounds in this action and the results were not recorded, but a week later she found tougher game under her sights.[16] During the early morning darkness of 7 September, the Confederates abandoned Morris Island, so after daylight the Brooke lobbed thirteen shells the mile and a half to Cummings Point—a greeting to federals taking over Southern positions where Major Pringle had not long before made his fateful decision.

That afternoon, the monitors came up for a bit of practice and the Brooke again went into action hitting one repeatedly with wrought iron bolts backed by 20-pound charges. The ironclads retired at dark and both sides secured for the night.

With dawn of the 8th, the Confederates were presented with an unexpected opportunity. One of the monitors was aground on a bar near Cummings Point and every foot drop in tide exposed more of the unprotected wooden hull beneath the overhang of her armored deck plating. As light increased, she was identified as the *Weehawken* with whom the Southerners had a score to settle for her treatment of the *Atlanta* not many months before. She had gone aground while maneuvering in shallow water and despite intensive effort, had been unable to get off during the night.

Seeing the vessel in trouble, the Brooke and other Sullivan's Island cannon as well as several at Fort Johnson opened a deliberate fire in an effort to cut up her hull so she would fill when the tide rose. But the *Weehawken* gave better than she took. She had settled sufficiently level to use her guns and trained her 15-inch Dahlgren on Moultrie. The fort had been hit by such weapons before with little damage other than displacement of the sand which gave effective protection to her brickwork. But this time the *Weehawken* was lucky. Her second shot struck the muzzle of an 8-inch columbiad, glanced off at an angle, and exploded in a pile of ammunition which was well protected from normal fire. The resulting blast left eighteen dead and twenty-eight wounded, almost the entire Southern casualties for the day. To add to Southern woes, the other ironclads steamed up to take the pressure off the *Weehawken* and initiated a first-class battle. If the Confederates had

concentrated on the *Weehawken* alone, they might have destroyed her. Instead, they shifted to closer targets which, although hit repeatedly, received no damage that couldn't be repaired. In the meantime, since firing at the stranded monitor had stopped, her skipper calmly ignored the battle and piped his men to breakfast.

That afternoon, at high tide, the *Weehawken* floated once more and steamed off to lick her wounds. She had been struck twenty-four times including one shell under the overhang, but damage was not considered serious. She had received three casualties, all wounded, and fired eighty-two rounds—thirty-six at Sullivan's Island and forty-six at Sumter. The shot under the overhang, which caused a temporary leak and probably was the most serious of her wounds, may well have come from the Brooke since it was a 7-inch hole. The gun's commander also reported that his last shot, fired with reduced charge, struck her deck and was believed to have penetrated since no ricochet was observed.

Although the *Weehawken* escaped this time, her luck played out three months later only a few hundred yards from the same bar. In the afternoon of 6 December, astonished Confederates saw the *Weehawken* suddenly lift her screw and dive bow first to the bottom. Immediately they claimed credit for the sinking believing a shot during the September battle must have caused a delayed leak. The truth, however, was even more humiliating for their enemy. It was finally determined that she had taken on a load of ammunition which was all stored at the bow making her ride a little deeper than usual. In addition, a hatch near her windlass had been left open. Weather did the rest. A rising sea splashed water down the hatch which, since she was down at the bow, failed to run aft where the bilge pumps could handle it. Pooling at the bow, it pushed her lower until the hawsepipes went under and torrents poured in to send her down within a matter of minutes. She's still there, under 20 feet or so of water and roughly the same of sand—an intact monitor with guns, gear, and part of the crew waiting for salvage, undamaged except by the action of one hundred years of salt water.

The parting shot at the *Weehawken* while she was still on the bar took the Brooke out of action. One of the bands had given way during the morning, and the final round reportedly cracked the breech. The remainder of the rifle's wartime career is somewhat vague, but apparently damage was not so serious as first supposed. The piece seems to have been repaired and again mounted on Sullivan's Island

FIGURE: VII-12 IDENTIFICATION: Brooke, Seacoast or Navy, 7-Inch, Rifle, Triple-Banded, Iron. REMARKS: Civil War view of 7-Inch Triple-Banded Brooke in Battery Marion near Fort Moultrie where the weapon reposes today (Fig. VII-11). Note Trunnion Band.

where it saw little additional action. The end of the war found it at the old U.S. Arsenal in the city which had been taken over by the Confederates for the duration and reverted to federal control at the evacuation of Charleston 18 February 1865. The property, after serving as a collection point for abandoned Confederate arms, was of little further use to the government and within a few years became Porter Military Academy, a private school for boys.

The Brooke, which weighs an estimated 8 to 10 tons, was left on the campus where it gradually worked its way far enough into the ground to become a half-hidden hazard for recess games. This led the 1913 graduating class, in the age-old search of all such classes for something to do for the alma mater, to dig out the piece, drag it across the drill field by sheer boy-power, and mount it on a concrete base. There it remained until 1964 when the school moved to a new location and donated the rifle to Fort Moultrie.

During the Brooke's stay on the Porter campus, little attempt was made to determine its wartime history and the piece became well-known locally as the "Gun Without Trunnions," a puzzle to generations of cadets who wondered how the weapon could have been fired. Pieces of the puzzle began to fall into place during the furor of the Civil War Centennial when the author ran across a wartime photograph (Fig. VII-12) of Battery Marion and. identified the weapon as the Porter-Fort Moultrie Brooke. Corroborative information then was obtained by digging into the Official Records.

The piece was mounted by means of trunnions cast on a band which wrapped around the tube and breech in similar fashion to that used with Dahlgren iron rifles. The Dahlgren band was bronze, but the copper-short Confederacy likely used wrought iron. The method, although unusual, was far from unique in the South for the banded, and presumably rifled, 32-pounder (Fig. I-50) mounted in Fort Moultrie had a trunnion band without breech strap. This expedient no doubt was used to return to action a piece with a damaged trunnion. The Brooke, however, was made originally for this type mounting as was the case with the Dahlgren rifles.

The triple-banded Brooke was highly regarded by the Confederates as a powerful weapon for S. R. Mallory, secretary of the Navy, in April, 1863, wrote:[17] "At a recent experimental trial of the triple-banded Brooke Navy gun, a wrought iron bolt was driven through 8 inches of iron and 18 inches of wood. The distance was 260 yards, 16 pounds of powder with a bolt of 140 pounds. . . ." In view of President Davis' letter, mentioned previously, this obviously was not the Fort Moultrie Brooke.

The Charleston weapon was fired many times with 20-pound charges and presumably with Army powder which was considered more powerful than that used by the Navy. This is mentioned by Brooke[18] in recommending that charges of Army powder be 8 or 10 pounds for firing shells and 10-13 for bolts in the 7-inch and 7-8 and 8-10, respectively, in the 6.4.

No table of ranges for Brooke rifles has been found, but they seem to have been quite good since

FIGURE: VII-13 LOCATION: Fort Pulaski, Ga. IDENTIFICATION: Brooke, Seacoast or Navy, 6.4-Inch, Rifle, Double-Banded, Iron. BORE: Diameter — 6.4. Rifling — 7 x 7, Brooke. Length — 116v. LENGTH O/A: 142.5. TRUNNIONS: Diameter — 7.1. Length — 7.25. REMARKS: Note wide spacing between rings of both reinforcing bands. COMMON NAME: 6.4-Inch Double-Banded Brooke Rifle.

General R. S. Ripley mentions[19] getting 4 miles out of a 7-inch with 20.5° elevation and a 100-pound shell and an estimated 4½ with 23°. The charge in both cases probably was 10 pounds.

Before leaving Brooke's rifles, a particularly interesting specimen at Fort Pulaski (Fig. VII-13) should not be overlooked. This 6.4-inch piece is an excellent example of "ring" banding, although reason for the wide spacing between bands is difficult to determine at this date. Markings, if any, are covered by paint.

NOTES

1. *Official Navy Records,* Series I, Vol. 21, pp. 898, 902.
2. J. G. Benton, *A Course of Instruction in Ordnance and Gunnery Composed and Compiled for Cadets of The United States Military Academy,* 1875, p. 550.
3. Alexander L. Holley, *A Treatise on Ordnance and Armor,* 1865, p. 76.
4. *Official Navy Records,* Series I, Vol. 21, p. 892.
5. Henry L. Abbot, "Siege Artillery in The Campaigns Against Richmond With Notes on The 15-Inch Gun," *Professional Papers No. 14, Corps of Engineers,* 1867, pp. 125, 181.
6. *Ibid.,* Plate I.
7. E. P. Alexander, "Confederate Artillery Service," *Southern Historical Society Papers,* Vol. XI, 1883, p. 110.
8. *Official Navy Records,* Series I, Vol. 21, pp. 898–899.
9. Walter W. Stephen, "The Brooke Guns of Selma, Alabama," *Alabama Historical Quarterly,* Vol. 20, No. 3, 1958, p. 2, notes on Brooke rifled and smoothbore guns

made at the Confederate Naval Foundry at Selma under Confederate Naval Cmdr. Catesby ap R. Jones July 1863 to March 1865.
10. Abbot, *loc. cit.,* p. 181.
11. The piece is at the Old Cemetery in Gainesville and the author is indebted to the town's mayor, Mr. Barnes A. Rogers, for measurements and markings.
12. Mr. O. C. Miller Jr. supplied the author with the history of these rifles.
13. *Official Records,* Series I, Vol. 28, Part 2, p. 236.
14. *Ibid.,* p. 248.
15. *Ibid.,* Part 1, pp. 687–709.
16. *Ibid.,* pp. 712–713; *Official Navy Records,* Series I, Vol. 14, pp. 549–557.
17. *Official Navy Records,* Series II, Vol. 2, p. 407.
18. *Official Navy Records,* Series I, Vol. 21, p. 885.
19. *Official Records,* Series I, Vol. 35, Part 1, pp. 513–516.

Chapter 8

British Rifles

ENGLAND, WHICH HAD BEEN EXPERIMENTING with rifles for several years prior to the American Civil War, was a natural shopping ground for North and South in their frantic search for weapons during the early stages of the conflict. Before many months passed, however, Northern industry had tooled up to the point where it could supply government needs and foreign weapons, in all but a few instances, were discarded as a needless complication of ammunition supply problems.

Not so the South. The Confederacy needed every gun it could get and English rifles were imported in a steady stream until perfection of the federal blockade narrowed the flow to a trickle. Four types seem to have been sold to Americans. Three—Armstrong, Blakely, and Whitworth—came in a wide variety of calibers, some of them exceedingly fine weapons, although others drew mixed reaction. The fourth, Clay, was a complete failure.

One of the best overall appraisals of the four came from General Alexander,[1] although it must be remembered that his views applied only to weapons used in the Army of Northern Virginia where the general was Chief of Artillery, First Corps, and considered one of the great artillerymen of the war. They

did not always conform to opinions of officers using other calibers, and praise or disparagement of an inventor's field gun did not necessarily hold true for siege or seacoast models.

"Clay," the general commented, "was a breechloader and was called an improvement on the breech-loading Armstrong which was manufactured for the English government and could not be obtained. Its grooving and projectiles were very similar to the breech-loading Armstrong and its breech-loading arrangements appeared simpler and of greater strength. On trial, however, it failed in every particular. Every projectile fired 'tumbled' and fell nearer the gun than the target and at the seventh round the solid breech piece was cracked through and the gun disabled.

"The muzzle-loading 6-pdr. and six breech-loading 12-pdr. Whitworths were distributed through the army and often rendered valuable service by their range and accuracy. They fired solid shot almost exclusively, but they were perfectly reliable and their projectiles never failed to fly in the most beautiful trajectory imaginable. Their breech-loading arrangements, however, often worked with difficulty and every one of the six was at some time disabled by breaking of some of its parts, but all were repaired and kept in service. As a general field piece, the efficiency was impaired by its weight and the very

137

cumbrous English carriage on which it was mounted. While a few with an army may often be valuable, the U.S. 3-inch Ordnance Rifle is much more generally serviceable with good ammunition.

"The Blakely guns were 12-pounder rifles, muzzle-loading, and fired very well with English ammunition (built-up shells with leaden bases) but with the Confederate substitute they experienced the same difficulties which attended this ammunition in all guns. The only advantage to be claimed for this gun is its lightness, but this was found to involve the very serious evil that no field carriage could be made to withstand its recoil. It was continually splitting the trails or racking to pieces the carriages though made of unusual strength and weight.

"Of the Armstrong shunt guns, six were obtained just before the close of the war and were never tried in the field. They were muzzle-loading and nothing could exceed their accuracy and the perfection of their ammunition. Their heavy English carriages were more unwieldy than those of the American rifles, but taking all things into consideration, the guns are probably the most effective field rifles made. . . ."

Alexander was not the only Southerner with a low opinion of the Clay, for Captain Caleb Huse, purchasing weapons in England for the Confederacy, in an 1861 letter[2] that reeks with self-satisfaction mentions hearing that the North had purchased some Clay breechloaders ". . . at enormous prices. From accounts I have heard of them and from a cursory inspection of one, I should think the men about the breech would stand a little better chance than the enemy, but the difference would be slight. I am told they were invoiced as Armstrong guns. The true Armstrong cannot be had. I think, however, that they can be manufactured from the drawing which I shall send. . . ."

Unfortunately, no report has been found of Northern opinion of the guns if and when they arrived. Some eighteen months later, however, the South sought estimates from "Col. Clay" on 8- and 9-inch, wrought-iron rifles. The correspondence is sketchy, but does explain that he ". . . forges his guns hollow and screws in the breech pieces and his work is very thorough. . . ." The letters stop before revealing whether any weapons were ordered at Clay's price of £400 for the 8-inch and £500 for the 9—the former to weigh 95 cwt. (10,640 pounds) and the latter between 7 and 8 tons.

The Armstrong was the brainchild of Baron William George Armstrong (1810-1900) who produced his first rifle in 1855. Successful trials with his weapons led to their adoption by the British government and establishment of the Elswick Ordnance Company in 1859. Although Armstrong supervised manufacture of his weapons, he had no financial connection with the enterprise until, after re-armament of the services, the government withdrew from the firm in 1862 and it was amalgamated with other Armstrong interests into the Sir W. G. Armstrong Co.[3] The government's connection with the company explains why no Armstrongs were available during the early part of the Civil War, yet became easily obtainable after 1862.

The Armstrong initially was a wrought-iron weapon built-up of tubes made from spiral coils. All parts except breech piece and trunnion rings were formed from bars welded into a single length of roughly 120 feet with a 5-inch thickness at top tapering to 3 at the bottom. The bar, narrow side down, was coiled in tight spirals around a mandrel, then upset and the joints welded with pressure and heat. The ends were recessed about an inch on a lathe so that one fitted into another. Two thus joined were drawn together by a heavy bolt run through them, the nut tightened by the power of ten men swinging on a 12-foot wrench, and a welding heat applied in the furnace. After the bolt was removed, the tube was machined and a larger hoop shrunk on after heating. This in turn was machined and larger tubes added in similar fashion until the piece attained requisite size for that caliber rifle.

Toward the end of 1864, Armstrong began making the main tube of steel, but continued to use bands of wrought iron formed around a mandrel.[4] Two systems of rifling were used, "compression" and "shunt." The former (Fig. VIII-1) consisted of a large number (seventy-six in the 110-pounder) of small, shallow grooves which gave an overall sawtooth appearance. This form was used with breechloaders and took a projectile covered with a thin coating of lead which was squeezed into the grooves as the shell

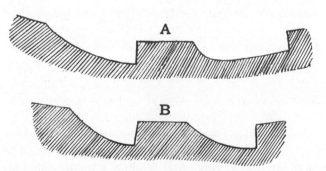

FIGURE: VIII-1 IDENTIFICATION: Armstrong Compression Rifling. REMARKS: A — 6-Pounder (2.5-Inch) Breechloader. Rifling — 32 x 32. B — 12-Pounder (3-Inch) Breechloader. Rifling — 38 x 38. SOURCE: Holley.

progressed through the bore. The system was discarded early in 1863 after breech-loading proved a failure in Armstrong's heavy guns forcing return to muzzle-loading for new designs and conversion of existing 70- and 110-pounders to this form. Conversion was accomplished by replacing the breech mechanism with a solid block and re-rifling the bore in the shunt system which was considerably more ingenious than the compression method. Shunt rifling involved a small number of grooves—3 to 10—and use of a projectile with a similar number of rows of projections which at first were zinc strips and later brass studs.

Figures VIII-2 and -3 illustrate the projectile entering the bore and emerging. The grooves at the muzzle were cut deeply on one side and shallow on

the other and continued in this form for several inches into the bore (the distance varied with caliber, being 8 inches, for instance, in the 110-pounder). Here the high side began to taper gradually deeper until both were the same depth. This point also varied with caliber, but was 14 inches in the case of the 110-pounder, or a total of 22 from the muzzle face. In loading, the studs fitted easily into the deep grooves and the direction of rotation, forced by the rifling, kept them hugging the deep side.

However, well down in the bore, past the end of the taper, the studs struck a curve, or switch, which "shunted" them to the opposite side, which here, of course, was of equal depth. This placed the studs against the correct side of the rifling when, upon starting out, the direction of rotation was reversed. Held against the side of the rifling, the projectile slid along the bottom of the tube until the taper was struck. This gradually lifted it as the studs drove onto the shallow side and by the time the round emerged, it was tightly nipped by all studs equally and lined up for a perfect release. Figure VIII-4 shows shunt rifling of an 8-inch Armstrong at West Point.

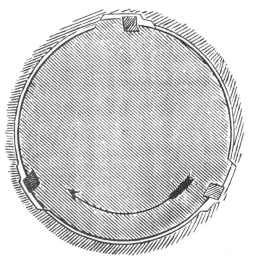

FIGURE: VIII-2 IDENTIFICATION: Armstrong Shunt Rifling. REMARKS: Projectile entering bore during loading. Note studs in deep groove. SOURCE: Holley.

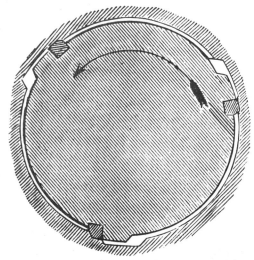

FIGURE: VIII-3 IDENTIFICATION: Armstrong Shunt Rifling. REMARKS: Projectile emerging from bore during firing. Note studs in shallow grooves. SOURCE: Holley.

FIGURE: VIII-4 LOCATION: West Point, N.Y. IDENTIFICATION: Armstrong Shunt Rifling. REMARKS: Muzzle face of 150-Pounder (8-Inch) Armstrong with 6 x 6 shunt rifling. See Fig. VIII-9.

139

Armstrongs were made in a variety of calibers ranging from 6-pounder to 600 and although the latter—as well as many other calibers—were not sent to this country, it is difficult to pinpoint those that were. Consequently, the table of weapons in the appendices includes a reasonably full listing of Armstrong calibers many of which doubtless saw service only with the British and were not brought to America.

Figure VIII-5 shows top and side elevations of an early Armstrong breech-loading 12-pounder and Figure VIII-6 a muzzle-loader of similar caliber. The latter rifle is displayed at West Point where records state it was made by Sir W. G. Armstrong Co. in 1864. Bore is 3 inches and weight 1,009 pounds, about 13 over the 996 "standard" for this model. Figure VIII-7 is a 20-pounder breechloader on field carriage with its limber. This type was adopted into the British service in 1859 as a 25-pounder with a bore diameter of 3.75 inches. Experiment, however, led to reduction in the weight of the projectile to 21 pounds and the piece was redesignated a 20-pounder.

The reverse occurred in the case of the 100-pounder which was found capable of handling a 110-pound projectile and so designated. The first of these 110-pounders (7-inch) weighed 8,400 pounds and although one hundred were built, they were not accepted into service. Later rifles of this caliber were strengthened and the weight increased to 9,184 pounds (Fig. VIII-8). This was the standard service model although a few weighing 9,632 pounds were constructed. Both types, after breech-loading was found unsuccessful, were converted to muzzle-loaders and re-rifled on the shunt system. Since these were British service types, it is doubtful if any were exported.

Perhaps the most interesting of Armstrong's weapons in this country is the 150-pounder (Fig. VIII-9) in the West Point collection. This magnificent specimen on its original carriage was one of the major weapons in Fort Fisher. It fell into federal hands by right of capture at the reduction of that fortification 15 January 1865. The piece is an excellent example of Armstrong's built-up construction of heavy weapons and the six-wheel carriage and side compressor is a type seacoast carriage seldom seen in this country. Bore diameter measures 8 inches between lands, instead of the 8.5 which Holley[5] records for this caliber. It is rifled with 6 grooves in the shunt system. Weight marked on the right trunnion is 15,737 pounds in contrast to the "standard" 14,896. Length overall is 131 inches compared to the 129.75 listed for this type weapon by Holley.[6] The piece is marked on the left trunnion: "Sir W. G. Armstrong Co., No. 1207, 1864" and on the right, along with the weight, "150-Pdr."

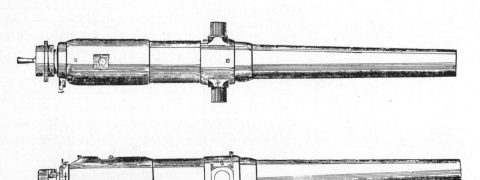

FIGURE: VIII-5 IDENTIFICATION: Armstrong, Field, 3-Inch, B.L.R., Iron. BORE: Diameter — 3. Rifling — 38 x 38, compression. Length — 73.5. LENGTH O/A: 83. SOURCE: Holley. COMMON NAME: 12-Pounder Armstrong B.L.R. Or, 3-Inch Armstrong B.L.R.

FIGURE: VIII-6 LOCATION: West Point, N.Y. IDENTIFICATION: Armstrong, Field, 3-Inch, Rifle, Iron. BORE: Diameter — 3. Rifling — 3 x 3, shunt. Length — 67.5. LENGTH O/A: 76. TRUNNIONS: Diameter — 3.5. Length — 3.5. REMARKS: Marks obscured by paint. Military Academy records state piece was made by W.G. Armstrong & Co., England, in 1864. COMMON NAME: 12-Pounder Armstrong. Or, 3-Inch Armstrong.

FIGURE: VIII-7 IDENTIFICATION: Armstrong, Field, 3.75-Inch, B.L.R., Iron. BORE: Diameter — 3.75. Rifling 44 x 44, compression. Length — 93. LENGTH O/A: 96. REMARKS: Redesignated from 25-Pounder when weight of projectile reduced. SOURCE: Holley. COMMON NAME: 20-Pounder Armstrong B.L.R. Or, 3.75-Inch Armstrong B.L.R.

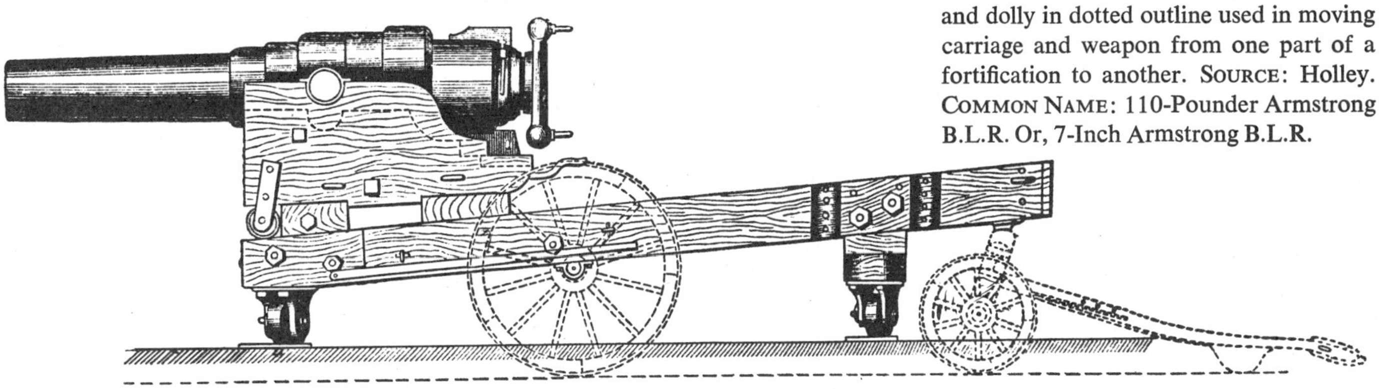

FIGURE: VIII-8 IDENTIFICATION: Armstrong, Seacoast and Navy, 7-Inch, B.L.R., Iron. BORE: Diameter — 7. Rifling — 76 x 76, compression. Length — 99.5. LENGTH O/A: 120. REMARKS: Wheels and dolly in dotted outline used in moving carriage and weapon from one part of a fortification to another. SOURCE: Holley. COMMON NAME: 110-Pounder Armstrong B.L.R. Or, 7-Inch Armstrong B.L.R.

FIGURE: VIII-9 LOCATION: West Point, N.Y. IDENTIFICATON: Armstrong, Seacoast and Navy, 8-Inch, Rifle, Iron. BORE: Diameter — 8. Rifling — 6 x 6, shunt. Length — 96v. LENGTH O/A: 131. TRUNNIONS: Diameter — 8. Length — 6.25. MARKINGS: Left Trunnion — Sir. W.G. Armstrong & Co., No. 1207, 1864. Right Trunnion — Weight 15737 Lbs., 150-Pdr., Prep. 809 Lbs. REMARKS: British barbette carriage. Note six traverse wheels and side compressors. COMMON NAME: 150-Pounder Armstrong. Or, 8-Inch Armstrong.

In addition to the previously mentioned Huse letter regarding drawings from which the South might manufacture Armstrongs, the Official Records have at least two other references to this possibility. A Southern hearing regarding the fall of New Orleans brought forth the comment:[7] "We learned that Mr. John Clarke (sic) had taken a contract from the Government for making the Armstrong guns and was about to erect buildings, furnaces and hammer for that purpose. . . ." John Clark, presumably the same man, made a few brass weapons for the Confederacy, but capture of the city would have ended any attempt to manufacture the Armstrong.

A later attempt is mentioned in a letter[8] to U.S. Navy Secretary Gideon Welles dated 18 December 1864 describing Confederate activity in the Norfolk area: "There are three Englishmen now in the [navy] yard who have been imported to manufacture Armstrong guns. They have got the furnaces up and are putting up a heavy trip hammer and I think they will be ready to commence work by the 1st of January. . . . Although I do not wish or intend to dictate to the Government, I think that this yard ought to be taken as soon as possible before they get to manufacturing those Armstrong guns. . . ."

Since the letter was written only a few months before Appomattox, the shaky condition of the Confederacy makes fabrication of a new weapon doubtful despite the January target date. However, the possibility remains that one or more "Confederate Armstrongs" were made and may some day be recognized as such.

Armstrongs are exceedingly rare in America today and the next English rifle, the Whitworth, is only a little more prevalent. Sir Joseph Whitworth (baronet) was born near Manchester in 1803 and became an engineer working with various machinists until 1833 when he formed a tool-making business near his home and became a leader in this field. Because of his reputation, the government in 1854 asked him to design machines for making rifled muskets. Finding no guides to follow, Whitworth began experiments which resulted in a form of rifling which instead of grooves utilized a polygon shape with gently rounded edges and similarly shaped projectiles that permitted them to ride on wide bearing surfaces.

This same form of hexagonal rifling (Fig. VIII-10 and 11) was used in Whitworth's cannon that, competing against the Armstrong during trials of 1864-65, gave results which Sir Joseph and others felt were superior although his rifles were not adopted by the government. They were, however, available to both North and South throughout the war and while the few imported by the Union saw little use, the Confederates were quite fond of them.

The weapon was made of steel, carefully annealed to increase its ability to withstand pressure. Instead of shrinking on bands, Sir Joseph tapered the barrel very slightly and forced the band on cold by hydrostatic pressure using great care and accuracy. Threads were cut in ends of the bands and they were screwed together instead of being welded as in the Armstrong. For larger guns, a harder steel was used for bands over the breech than was used for the tubes. The principle of initial tension was not used at first, but was applied to later weapons. Both breech and muzzle-loaders were made. Whitworth's first successful rifles were breechloaders, but the method proved a failure for larger calibers and later fell into disuse even for field pieces.

Whitworth, like most inventors, made weapons in various calibers. Those mentioned in texts of the period are listed in the appendix with such statistics as are available. Bore diameters of Whitworths are often confusing since the hexagonal shape makes measurement difficult. Those selected are the distance between flats in conformity with today's practice of measuring diameter between lands. However, the reader will find Civil War era texts often refer to slightly different caliber for these same weapons. Thus we find the 12-pounder mentioned as 3-inch, the 70 as 5.5, and the 120 as 7-inch. These are

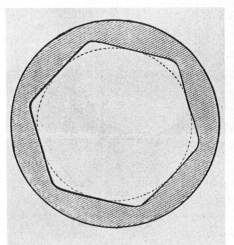

FIGURE: VIII-10 IDENTIFICATION: Whitworth Rifling SOURCE: Holley.

FIGURE: VIII-11 IDENTIFICATION: Whitworth Rifling. REMARKS: Muzzle face of 5-Inch at West Point (Figs. VIII-17 and 18) illustrates typical hexagonal appearance of all Whitworth calibers. Bore diameter should be measured across flats (the lands) not angles.

FIGURE: VIII-12 IDENTIFICATION: Whitworth, Field, 2.75-Inch B.L.R., Steel. REMARKS: 1865 photograph of 12-Pounder Whitworth mounted on field carriage which is stamped "Richmond Arsenal, 1864." Note elevating screw linked to piece and carriage and folding trail handspike which apparently pivoted to lie flat on the stock when not in use.

merely the distance between angles rather than flats. In addition, some texts, including the Official Records on occasion, refer to the 70-pounder as an 80, obviously to conform with the weight of the projectile. Now and then the 120 will be termed a 130, presumably for the same reason. Future references here, except in direct quotation, will adhere to the terminology of the table for the sake of uniformity.

Several types of Whitworths were used in this country, but the main calibers seem to have been the 12-pounder (2.75-inch), both breech and muzzle-loading, and the 70-pounder (5-inch). Most were purchased by the South, but one of the first batteries to arrive in America went North. This was a six-piece battery of 2.75-inch breechloaders complete with carriages, ammunition, and machinery for making more projectiles. It was donated to the United States in 1861 by a group of American citizens residing abroad. A letter[9] from the government dated 17 June 1861, acknowledged the gift and stated: ". . . that the government will take good care to place the battery in the hands of those who know how to make it serve the patriotic purposes of the donors. . . ."

Future events, however, failed to bear out the promise for after being dragged through the Peninsular Campaign, the weapons wound up in the de-fenses of Washington where they were fired only for practice. They were excellent rifles, but the North had many excellent weapons and an odd battery needlessly complicated administrative and supply problems.

Charles Knap, testifying[10] before the Senate Committee in 1864, probably put it as well as anyone when he said of the Whitworth: "As a toy it is the most wonderful gun in the world, but it is not fit for actual service for it requires . . . very delicate manipulation and common soldiers in action are not very delicate fellows in handling their projectiles and those guns would be very apt to jam . . . It is a perfect thing to show the state of the art, but for actual service, in my opinion, it is not worth carrying into the field. . . ."

The piece, as Knap said, was a "wonderful gun." In tests in England a 12-pounder delivered 2,600-yard ranges with 5° elevation, 4,500 with 10°, 7,000 with 20°, and an unprecedented 10,000 with 35°. One of these weapons captured from the Confederacy is shown in Figure VIII-12. The stock of the American-made carriage is stamped "Richmond Arsenal, 1864."

However, a far more interesting Whitworth (Fig. VIII-13) is owned by the Washington Navy Yard and was photographed in 1964 while on loan to Fort Fisher. The piece, which is missing its breechblock, is on its original carriage resting on a post-war, ornamental cast iron stand in lieu of wheels. The 12-pounder was captured near Fort Fisher 23 August 1863, thereby removing a thorn which had been pricking federal blockaders with considerable regularity. The piece had been salvaged from the blockade runner *Modern Greece*, which ran ashore near the fort in June, 1862, and had become part of a two-gun "Flying Battery" used to protect other runners.

Whenever one of these shallow-draft steamers neared the coast and was fired on by a federal warship, she made for shore, then turned toward Wilmington and ran for the harbor entrance while hugging the beach as closely as possible. Here the "Flying Battery" went into action. A fast team dragged the guns down the long strip of beach, stopping to unlimber and toss a few rounds at pursuing Yankees whenever the chance offered. The Whitworth far outranged anything the Union vessels could bring to bear with any accuracy and although the rifle's projectile was small, it carried a sting that discouraged close acquaintance. More than once the battery went into position behind sand dunes and for days at a time protected salvage of unlucky runners that piled ashore either by accident or design when pursuers were close.

The high regard in which the gun was held was emphasized by General W.H.C. Whiting, commander of Southern forces around Wilmington[11] in a plea for replacement after it was lost: "The efforts of the enemy to stop our steamers are increasing. . . . I have met with a serious and heavy loss in that Whitworth, a gun that . . . has saved dozens of vessels and millions of money to the Confederate States. . . ."

Similarly, a Northern report[12] on the Whitworth's activities: "There is . . . a light battery of Whitworth guns [sic] . . . [that] is shifted from point to point as its services are required. Our blockading squadron has been a good deal annoyed by it . . . . Blockade runners . . . when chased . . . invariably make for shoal water and, if likely to be captured, increase their head of steam, beach the vessel and allow the engines to work until she is driven so high on the beach it is almost a work of impossibility to drag her off. On these occasions, as soon as the report of our guns are heard . . . the light batteries [sic] of Whitworth guns [sic] are brought down and used. . . ."

The "Flying Battery's" luck played out in August, 1863.[13] A runner, the *Hebe*, had gone ashore 18 August, while hotly pursued by the *U.S.S. Niphon,* a 153-foot screw steamer mounting a 20-pounder Parrott, four 32-pounders of 42 cwt. and two 12-pounder rifles. The *Hebe* had loaded in England during May with coats, blankets, shoes, and other goods desperately needed by the Confederacy during the winter months. She was trying to get into Wilmington, but when headed off, drove ashore about 9 miles from Fort Fisher rather than return to sea where she no doubt would have run out of coal before reaching a safe port.

Despite heavy seas and gale winds, the *Niphon* followed her in and when the *Hebe's* men abandoned, sent a prize crew aboard the beached ship. While they gathered combustibles to burn her if necessary, a second boat arrived with a line from the *Niphon*. Their small craft swamped, however, and they waded ashore not far from the *Hebe*. With their boat damaged, they attempted to launch one of the *Hebe's* abandoned on the beach by the fleeing blockade runners, but before they could get away, three cavalrymen arrived and the unarmed seamen were taken prisoner.

Reinforcements now began arriving for both sides. Another vessel, the 181-foot *Shokokon,* a double-ended side-wheeler mounting a pair of 30-pounder Parrotts and four 24-pounders, joined the *Niphon* and more cavalry and the "Flying Battery" showed up on the beach. The Southern cavalry opened small-arms fire on the *Hebe* and the battery lobbed shells at the warships, apparently with little result. Return fire from the vessels was equally wild due to the heavy seas which made accurate shooting impossible.

The position of the men aboard the *Hebe* be-

FIGURE: VIII-13 IDENTIFICATION: Whitworth, Field, 2.75-Inch, B.L.R., Steel. BORE: Diameter — 2.75. Rifling — 6 x 6. Length — 105. LENGTH O/A (excludes missing breechblock): 105. TRUNNIONS: Diameter — 3.7. Length — 3.75. MARKINGS: Left Trunnion — Whitworth Ordnance Co., Manchester, No. 46, Patent 1861. Right Trunnion — Whitworth Ordnance Co., Manchester, No. 46, Patent 1861. REMARKS: Weapon is part of the Washington Navy Yard collection and was on loan to Fort Fisher, N.C., when photographed. Original iron carriage mounted on ornamental iron stand in lieu of wheels. COMMON NAME: 12-Pounder Whitworth B.L.R. Or, 2.75-Inch Whitworth B.L.R.

came more precarious as the minutes passed, so they set fire to the ship and warped their boat alongside the vessel to leave. But during the process the seas slammed the craft against the *Hebe* and stove her, so the crew scrambled back aboard, doused the fires and signaled for help. That brought boats from both blockaders, but none were able to come alongside and one swamped in the attempt, the crew either drowning or being taken captive on shore. Four men managed to make it from the *Hebe* to the boats, but the rest were poor swimmers and stayed aboard.

Finally, all hope of rescue abandoned, the boats returned to their vessels. The *Shokokon* fired a shot across the *Hebe's* bow to warn the men to abandon her and surrender. Then, as they struggled ashore from the bow, both blockaders opened a heavy fire on the beached vessel. Twice the *Hebe* was set afire and each time the seas extinguished the flame. At last a shell exploded near her stack, her decks blazed up and continued to burn as the blockaders hauled off shore leaving fifteen men dead or captured and three boats.

This ended the first round, a victory for the Confederates due more to the sea than their efforts. The battery had cut up the *Niphon's* rigging a bit, but was otherwise ineffective. Federal fire seems to have done nothing except set the *Hebe* on fire and it took about three hours intensive shelling to do that.

During the next few days, the Confederates began salvaging water-soaked goods from the stranded runner, the working party protected by the "Flying Battery" dug in back of the dunes. The federals watched from a distance and on the morning of the 23rd the warships returned—and this time they meant business.

First came the *Niphon* and the *James Adger,* a 215-foot side-wheeler with a 9-inch Dahlgren, six 32-pounders of 42 cwt. and a 20-pounder. They were to make soundings and cut off escape down the beach of any Confederates as well as enfilade their position. Next came two other gunboats, the *Western World* with four 32s and a 30-pounder Parrott, and the *Stockton,* armament not listed, but probably comparable. Finally, the frigate *Minnesota* lumbered into position. This 3,300-ton screw steamer mounted an 8-inch and four 6.4-inch Parrotts, one 11- and thirty-eight 9-inch Dahlgrens, and four 12-pounder howitzers. Her armament, discounting the *Stockton,* brought a total of sixty-eight guns against the two on the beach—and this time no sea was running.

The Confederates threw a few rounds at the *Adger*—hitting her three times—and cut two planks on the *Minnesota*. But when the frigate's broadside rippled from bow to stern, the Southerners abandoned their guns and pulled out. Apparently there wasn't time to spike them, but the gunners did take the breechblock of the Whitworth making the piece useless except as a trophy. What happened to the block is still a mystery, but probably it was tossed into the marsh and disappeared under the mud. The vessels then turned their power against the *Hebe,* destroying her beyond hope of salvage, and sent boats ashore for the guns.

Pierce Crosby, fleet captain aboard the *Minnesota,* listed the materiel captured:[14]

"One Whitworth rifled gun, 3-inch caliber [sic], extreme length 8′ 10″, length of bore 8′ 4″ and marked 'Whitworth Ordnance Co., No. 46, Patent 1861, Manchester' [markings which may still be seen on the weapon], one field carriage for same marked No. 220, 1 caisson for same, 1 limber for the same, 3 ammunition boxes for the same, 24 shot for the same, 8 shell, 3 sights, 35 charges for the Whitworth gun, 1 extractor for the same. One rifled 4-inch caliber, extreme length 6′ 11″, length of bore, 5′ 5″, marked 'Fawcett, Preston & Co., Liverpool, 1862', one field carriage for the same, 1 sight for same, 18 shell for same. . . ."

Northern reports, particularly Crosby's coldly statistical statement, make the Confederate version[15] of the affair seem overly dramatic to say the least:

"Yesterday," Gen Whiting informed Richmond, "the enemy took a fancy to destroy what remained of the wreck of the *Hebe* . . . from which a company of the garrison at Fort Fisher were engaged in saving property. The steam frigate *Minnesota* and five [sic] other gunboats approached the beach and, under a terrific fire, attempted to land, but were gallantly repulsed by Capt. [Daniel] Munn with a Whitworth and two [sic] small rifle guns of short range. The site was about 9 miles from Fort Fisher on a narrow and low beach between the sounds and the ocean and completely under the fire of the enormous batteries of the enemy. A portion of the squadron, steaming farther up the beach, effected a landing some 2 miles off in largely superior force, and came down upon Captain Munn still gallantly fighting his little guns against the *Minnesota,* they being moved by hand and having fired his last round, the Whitworth [sic] disabled, 1 gunner killed, lieutenant and four men wounded, Captain Munn with his small party was compelled to fall back under a heavy enfilade fire toward Fort Fisher with the loss of his guns. . . ."

Although Northern accounts are more plausible in many particulars of the engagement, Whiting's casualty figures are probably more accurate than the

FIGURE: VIII-14 LOCATION: Petersburg, Va. IDENTIFICATION: (Front) — Whitworth, Field, 2.75-Inch, B.L.R., Steel. BORE: Diameter — 2.75. Rifling — 6 x 6. Length — 104. LENGTH O/A: 108. TRUNNIONS: Diameter — 3.75. Length — 3.5. REMARKS: Note breech differs from Figs. VIII-12 and 13. COMMON NAME: 12-Pounder Whitworth B.L.R. Or, 2.75-Inch Whitworth, B.L.R.
IDENTIFICATION: (Second from front) — Whitworth, Field, 2.75-Inch, Rifle, Steel. BORE: Diameter — 2.75. Rifling — 6 x 6. LENGTH O/A: 86. TRUNNIONS: Diameter — 3.75. Length — 3.5. MARKINGS: Left Trunnion — The Manchester Ordnance and Rifle Co., No. 202, 1864, cwt.-9, qrs.-1. COMMON NAME: 12-Pounder Whitworth. Or, 2.75-Inch Whitworth.

FIGURE: VIII-15 LOCATION: Washington Navy Yard, D.C. IDENTIFICATION: Whitworth, Field, 2.75-Inch, Rifle, Steel. BORE: Diameter — 2.75. Rifling — 6 x 6. LENGTH O/A: 85. TRUNNIONS: Diameter — 3.75. Length — 3.5. REMARKS: Breech is bronze. COMMON NAME: 12-Pounder Whitworth. Or, 2.75-Inch Whitworth.

eight Confederate dead reported by U.S. Major General John G. Foster who also erroneously called the second rifle captured—which will be discussed later in this chapter—an Armstrong.

In addition to the Washington Navy Yard Whitworth, excellent specimens of the breechloader will be found at Gettysburg, which has two mounted on reproduction American field carriages, and Petersburg, which displays a breechloader and a muzzle-loader together (Fig. VIII-14) Note slightly different form of reinforce on the breechloader compared to the Washington piece. Measurements are about the same.

Fort Sill also has a muzzle-loader and there is one at Washington Navy Yard (Fig. VIII-15). The latter piece measures 85 inches overall, about an inch shorter than the Petersburg and Fort Sill weapons. Markings, if any, on the Washington Whitworth are concealed by paint. However, both trunnions of the Fort Sill rifle are marked in a circle around the outer edge of the face: "Manchester Ordnance & Rifle Co." Inside the circle is "Cwt. 9, Qts. 1, Whitworth Pa-

tent, No. 200, 1864." Based on this, the weight is 1,090 pounds. All have the typical Whitworth hexagonal bore of 2.75 inches.

Two 70-pounder Whitworths, part of a four-gun shipment for the Confederacy, wound up being used against the former owners in 1863, but not very successfully. The guns were captured aboard a blockade runner and two were set ashore on Morris Island during July in battery with a pair of 8-inch Parrotts. The "Naval Battery" as it was called (Fig. VIII-16) was manned entirely by sailors, but was under operational control of the Army.

The Whitworths, although an expensive gun for the day—70-pounders cost the South £700 each—failed to stand hard usage. Reporting on them, Brigadier General John W. Turner, General Gillmore's chief of artillery on Morris Island, remarked:[16]

"These guns opened fire with shell, but it was found necessary to abandon their use entirely in consequence of their repeated and constant premature explosions, which greatly endangered our troops in the advance trenches and of the probable injury it would do the guns. Solid shot was then used exclusively.

"There appeared to be much difficulty experienced at times in loading these guns by the projectile wedging when part way down. It could then be rammed home only by heavy blows of a handspike or by attaching a powerful purchase . . . [a practice the Naval Battery commander, F. A. Parker, reported[17] cost the lives of four men by premature explosion of the charge].

"They were very unsatisfactory in point of accuracy, shooting very wild, seldom hitting Fort Sumter at a distance of 3,980 yards. In comparison with the 8-inch Parrotts in the same battery, they fell far short in accuracy and subsequently one of them became disabled by the gun apparently sliding through the reinforce to the rear. A displacement of nearly an inch took place closing the vent completely. The other, being considered unsafe after this, further use of it was discontinued. . . ."

A plate from Gillmore's book on operations against Charleston (Fig. VIII-17) explains the disabling of this rifle which the general terms an 80-pounder, but gives the correct caliber, 5-inch.

Today the piece is at West Point. Its breech (Fig. VIII-18) is slightly different, and at 134 inches the overall length is two more than the 70-pounder (Fig. VIII-19), one of a pair at the Washington Navy Yard. Both Washington pieces measure 132 inches and only marking visible is "Whitworth" stamped across the reinforce at the breech. Lettering on the base of the breech apparently was engraved by

146

FIGURE: VIII-16 IDENTIFICATION: Whitworth, Seacoast & Navy, 5-Inch, Rifle, Steel. REMARKS: Pair of captured 5-Inch Whitworths used in the Federal "Naval Battery" on Morris Island to bombard Fort Sumter in 1863. See Figs. VIII-17 and 18.

the Navy after the war. Records at the yard state the weapons were made in 1862 and with two others were captured aboard the "Anglo-Confederate Pirate and Blockade Runner *Princess Royal.*"

Whether the West Point and Washington guns were originally together is a possibility, but thus far not proved. Breech differences would normally indicate separate models and shipments and probably this was the case. However, it is an interesting conjecture that the guns may once have been together in the hold of the *Princess Royal,* an iron screw steamer which was beached 29 January 1863 on what is today known as the Isle of Palms, directly across the harbor entrance from Morris Island where the Naval Battery Whitworths were employed.

Other Whitworth calibers also seem to have been used in small numbers. Alexander mentioned a 6-pounder (2.15-inch), a 3-pounder (1.5-inch) is noted occasionally, and the Official Records[18] place two 32-pounders aboard the Confederate cruiser *Shenandoah.* Available records list the 32-pounders as having a 4.14-inch bore. However, the author believes this is a diameter across angles and the correct caliber should be approximately 3.6-inch. In addition, the Confederates either had or were expecting a 120-pounder (6.4-inch) for shells to fit this caliber (see Chapter XIII) have been salvaged from the wreck of a blockade runner off Fort Fisher. No records of the rifle have been found,

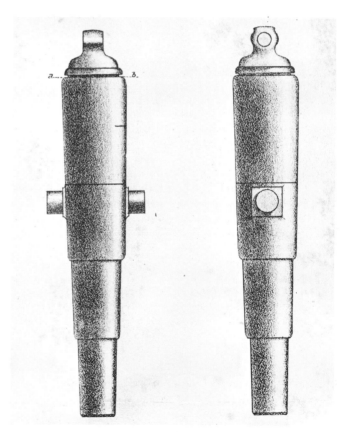

FIGURE: VIII-17 IDENTIFICATION: Whitworth, Seacoast & Navy, 5-Inch, Rifle, Steel. REMARKS: 5-Inch Whitworth of U.S. "Naval Battery" on Morris Island, S.C., disabled at 111th round by inner cylinder slipping rearward through outer jacket forming separation at "a — b" and closing vent. SOURCE: Gillmore.

FIGURE: VIII-18 LOCATION: West Point, N.Y. IDENTIFICATION: Whitworth, Seacoast & Navy, 5-Inch, Rifle, Steel. BORE: Diameter — 5. Rifling — 6 x 6. Length — 114v. LENGTH O/A: 134. TRUNNIONS: Diameter — 8.25. Length — 6.5. REMARKS: Naval Battery weapon (Figs. VIII-16 and 17) disabled by inner cylinder slipping to rear through reinforce. Note gap between sight bracket and tube. COMMON NAME: 70-Pounder Whitworth. Or, 80-Pounder Whitworth (erroneous). Or, 5-Inch Whitworth (preferred).

FIGURE: VIII-19 LOCATION: Washington Navy Yard, D.C. IDENTIFICATION: Whitworth, Seacoast & Navy, 5-Inch, Rifle, Steel. BORE: Diameter — 5. Rifling — 6 x 6. Length — 111v. LENGTH O/A: 132. TRUNNIONS: Diameter — 8. Length — 6.5. REMARKS: Marks obscured by paint. Navy Yard records state piece was made by Whitworth Ordnance Co., Manchester, England, Patent 1862. Captured aboard blockade runner *Princess Royal.* COMMON NAMES 70-Pounder Whitworth. Or, 80-Pounder Whitworth (erroneous). Or, 5-Inch Whitworth (Preferred).

but perhaps future diving operations will uncover the weapon in the same vessel. If so, it will be interesting to see which of two 6.4-inch Whitworth models[19] was exported. One, manufactured by the Royal Gun Factory at Woolwich, was built on the Armstrong principle of affixing bands by heat and shrinkage. This was the heavier type, weighing 16,660 pounds. The other, built by Whitworth's firm, with the bands forced on by hydrostatic pressure, weighed 13,440

pounds. Both were rifled on the Whitworth principle.

April 12, 1861, found shot and shell weighing up to 130 pounds raining down on Fort Sumter from Confederate guns ringing the island bastion. But the piece that worried Major Robert Anderson's beleaguered garrison was a single little gun on Morris Island—a 12-pounder Blakely rifle which sent its projectiles across 1,250 yards of water with unprecedented accuracy to slam into the gorge wall. Lasting damage was slight, but officers and men kept a wary ear cocked to the sound of the rifle's shot boring into the bricks. It was the sound of the future, and Anderson and his men knew it.

The rifle was one of the few guns mentioned specifically in official reports and takes up several paragraphs of the "Engineering Journal" of the engagement.[20] This report lists penetration of the 12-pounder bolt as 11 inches, but one struck the stone cheek of an embrasure chipping it and sending fragments into the casemate, painfully, although not seriously, wounding a sergeant and three men. The spent projectile tumbled in with the fragments and there is a good chance the Blakely round illustrated in Chapter XIII and now at the Military Academy, is the same one. The rifle fired only eleven shot and nineteen shells during the fight due to limited ammunition[21] and since this is reported to be one of the shot, donated to the Academy by a member of Anderson's command,[22] there is a good chance it is the same round—it certainly would have been handy to pick up. If the same, it is interesting to note that the shot probably tumbled or at least yawed in flight since the base, not the point, was crushed by the impact.

Although rifled cannon had been fired in the United States before, the 12-pounder was the first rifled piece used in this country in combat. South Carolina Governor F. W. Pickens in a letter[23] to Secretary of War L. P. Walker mentioned arrival of ". . . a fine rifled cannon from Liverpool of the latest maker—Blakely gun—an improvement upon Armstrong, of steel rolls or coils with an elevation of seven and one half degrees to a mile. It throws a shell or twelve-pound shot with the accuracy of a dueling pistol and with only one and a half pounds of powder. Such, they write me, is this gun, and I hope to have it in position by tonight." The letter is dated 9 April 1861.

Two days after the capture of Sumter, General Beauregard wrote[24] Walker: "We have a remarkable rifled cannon, 12-pdr., superior to any other here. Others ought to be ordered." The piece was a gift to the people of South Carolina from Charles K. Prioleau of Frazer & Co. in London and is said to have borne a plaque inscribed:[25] "Presented to the State of South Carolina by a citizen resident abroad in commemoration of the 20th December, 1860"—the day the state seceded from the Union.

Holly, probably a bit more accurately than Governor Pickens, describes the piece:[26] "The following are particulars of the first gun sent by Capt. Blakely to the Confederates, obtained from a drawing dated May 15, 1860. The gun, made by Fawcett, Preston & Co., was of cast iron reinforced by a solid wrought-iron hoop made thin at the edges." Holley also reported the rifle fired more than 3,000 rounds during its career and listed statistics as follows:

Total length of gun	84 inches
Length of bore	75.5 "
Diameter of bore	3.5 "
Diameter of cast iron under hoop	9.1 "
Maximum diameter of hoop	12.1 "
Length of hoop	22.2 "
Diameter of muzzle	6.0 "

The only drawing which we know definitely to be this piece (Fig. VIII-20) was published in *Harper's Weekly* 18 May 1861. However, another sketch from the publication four years later (Fig. VIII-21) may well show the same piece. Accompanying text:[27] explains that General Sherman's army in its swing through the South had moved into South Carolina and advanced elements had crossed Lynch's Creek: ". . . as the rebels fled across the river, Maj. Gen. [Joseph A.] Mower sent after them a few shells from a Blakely gun which he had captured and which had been presented to the state of South Carolina by citizens residing abroad." Although it is entirely possible more than one Blakely was presented to the state, tubes in both drawings appear similar and use of almost the exact wording of the first Blakely plaque in describing the piece fired by General Mower would indicate the rifles were the same, although carriages, of course, are different.

Despite the stir created by the piece initially, the first Blakely apparently was forgotten when rifles became more common and no mention of it has been found in the Official Records after the opening engagement. Whether it survived the war is problematical, but it may some day turn up resting in a town park or lying in the corner of a museum storage room. Fortunately, it should be easy to recognize from the dimensions and either the plaque on the breech, if still present, or the holes by which it was attached.

FIGURE: VIII-20 IDENTIFICATION: Blakely, Field, 3.5-Inch, Rifle (Type 1), Iron. BORE: Diameter — 3.5. Length — 75.5. LENGTH O/A: 84. REMARKS: First rifled cannon fired in combat in the United States. Sketch of piece on Morris Island, S.C., from where it bombarded Fort Sumter in 1861. SOURCE: *Harper's Weekly,* 18 May, 1861. COMMON NAME: 12-Pounder Blakely, Type 1. Or, 3.5-Inch Blakely, Type 1.

FIGURE: VIII-21 IDENTIFICATION: Blakely, Field, 3.5-Inch, Rifle (Type 1), Iron, (Tentative). REMARKS: Federal troops firing captured Blakely across the Pee Dee River during invasion of South Carolina in 1865. Piece, now mounted on field carriage, is believed to be the same as in Fig. VIII-20. SOURCE: *Harper's Weekly,* 1 April 1865.

Although this was the first Blakely fired in America, it was far from the last and a fortunately high survival rate has left a fair number of these weapons scattered North and South. The inventor, former Royal Artillery Captain Alexander Theophilis Blakely, was recognized in England as a pioneer in the banding of cannon. However, the captain had bad luck in getting his guns accepted, or even tested, by a government partial to Armstrongs. Consequently, he sold a great many to other nations—particularly Russia and the Confederacy—testifying before the Ordnance Select Committee in 1863 that more than four-hundred had gone to foreigners, half made of steel and the others of cast iron strengthened with steel.[28] These were the preferred materials for Blakelys, especially larger calibers, although he apparently used wrought iron occasionally in early models as evidenced by the previously described 12-pounder.[29]

Unlike Armstrong and Whitworth, Blakely, at least in the beginning, had no foundry and his designs were produced by various firms including Fawcett, Preston & Co., Low Moor Iron Co., George Forrester & Co., and, later, Blakely Ordnance Co. of London in which he presumably had an interest.

Inconsistency of material and manufacturer are but two of many problems encountered in any attempt to identify Blakely rifles, particularly the field guns where few factors remain constant. He apparently engaged in continuous experiment in an effort to improve his weapons and no doubt dumped previous models on such eager foreigners as the Confederates. This may account for the wide variety of shapes, sizes, and apparent model changes found today. Some are stamped with both manufacturer's name and the words "Blakely's Patent" making identification certain. Others are probably Blakelys, but carry only a manufacturer's label, and at least one is marked "Blakely's Patent," but may not be his design.

Consequently, in an effort to bring some order out of the confusion and to establish a system of reference, known, or even possible Blakely field calibers are divided into categories and listed according to type. First is the 12-pounder which fired against Fort Sumter and which is too well documented as a Blakely to deny. This piece, although it may no longer exist, for the sake of convenience will be identified as Type 1. Next are three varieties, each stamped in clear lettering with a manufacturer's name and Blakely's—evidence which establishes their identity beyond reasonable doubt.

One of these (Fig. VIII-22) is the most common form of small Blakely. West Point has one, and there are a number in national and state parks including Shiloh and Chickamauga-Chattanooga. The illustrated piece is at Fort Pemberton near Greenwood, Mississippi. Bore is 3.6 inches rifled with 7 straight—type lands and grooves, although other

models have a hook—slant rifling similar to, but with a more rounded "hook" than that of the Brooke which probably was adapted from it. Overall length is 58 inches and the piece is marked on the tube between the trunnions and breech: "Blakely's Patent No. 34, Fawcett, Preston & Co., Liverpool, Makers, 1861." All of this model have approximately the same measurements and are similarly marked with exception of the number which changes, of course, and is sometimes stamped on the trunnions. This variety is already known as Type 2.[30]

Type 3 (Fig. VIII-23) is an extremely rare weapon, this being the only one thus far discovered. Located at the Military Academy, it measures 60.5 inches overall and has a bore diameter of 3.5 rifled

FIGURE: VIII-22 LOCATION: Greenwood, Miss. IDENTIFICATION: Blakely, Field, 3.6-Inch, Rifle (Type 2), Iron. BORE: Diameter — 3.6. Rifling 7 x 7, straight. Length — 49. LENGTH O/A: 58. TRUNNIONS: Diameter — 3.62. Length — 2.75. MARKINGS: Tube, rear of trunnions — Blakely's Patent No. 34, Fawcett Preston & Co., Liverpool, Makers, 1861. COMMON NAME: 12-Pounder Blakely, Type 2. Or, 3.6-Inch Blakely, Type 2.

FIGURE: VIII-23 LOCATION: West Point, N.Y. IDENTIFICATION: Blakely, Field, 3.5-Inch, Rifle (Type 3), Iron. BORE: Diameter — 3.5. Rifling — 6 x 6, hook-slant. Length — 55. LENGTH O/A: 60.5 TRUNNIONS: Diameter — 3.5. Length — 2.62. MARKINGS: Left Trunnion — Forrester & Co., Liverpool, 1862. Right Trunnion — Blakely Patent. COMMON NAME: 12-Pounder Blakely, Type 3. Or, 3.5-Inch Blakely, Type 3.

with 6 lands and grooves. The piece is marked on the left trunnion: "Forrester & Co., Liverpool, 1862" and on the right, "Blakely Patent."

The Beaufort, South Carolina Museum boasts the only specimens of Type 4 the author has discovered. There are two of the rifles, both identical in form and exhibiting the same rounded breech without cascabel of Type 3. But instead of banding, the entire breech area is cast in bulbous shape which pinches flat for the trunnion band, then changes to a straight taper to the muzzle. Trunnions and band of the illustrated piece (Fig. VIII-24) are bronze. The companion weapon has an iron band of similar size and shape. Its trunnions originally were smaller than the other—about 3.1-inch—but have been sleeved to roughly 3.6 by what appear to be sections of iron pipe. This method of increasing trunnion diameter to fit standard carriages also has been noted in a Type 2 Blakely at Chickamauga-Chattanooga National Military Park. The weapons have a 3.6-inch bore diameter with 6 lands and grooves and are excellent examples of one, though by no means only, form of Blakely's hook-slant rifling. Figure VIII-25 shows his "hook" is sharply rounded leading to a gently curved "shank" which continues to a section which bends only in conformity with the bore. Contrast this with the similar rifling of the Blakely 9-inch and the simplified hook-slant of the Brooke and other Confederate weapons in which the "hook" is almost a right angle leading to a slant which curves with the bore. (See Figs. VII-1 and 2.) Overall length of the Beaufort Blakelys is 66.5 inches. The illustrated weapon is marked on the tube in rear of the trunnion band: "Blakely's Patent, No. 50, Fawcett, Preston & Co., Liverpool, Makers, 1862." The other is similarly marked except for the number which is 48.

FIGURE: VIII-25 IDENTIFICATION: Blakely Rifling. REMARKS: Muzzle face of Beaufort weapon (Fig. VIII-24) illustrates typical hook-slant Blakely rifling.

FIGURE: VIII-26 LOCATION: Shiloh, Tenn. IDENTIFICATION: Blakely, Field, 3.6-Inch, Rifle (Type 5), Iron. BORE: Diameter — 3.6. Rifling — 7 x 7, straight. Length — 49. LENGTH O/A: 58. TRUNNIONS: Diameter — 3.62. Length — 2.75. REMARKS: Similar to Type 2 with exception of band forward of trunnions (See text). COMMON NAME: 12-Pounder Blakely, Type 5. Or, 3.6-Inch Blakely, Type 5.

FIGURE: VIII-24 LOCATION: Beaufort, S.C. IDENTIFICATION: Blakely, Field, 3.6-Inch, Rifle (Type 4), Iron. BORE: Diameter — 3.6. Rifling — 6 x 6, hook-slant. Length — 60. LENGTH O/A: 66.5. TRUNNIONS: Diameter — 3.6. Length — 3. MARKINGS: Tube, rear of trunnions — Blakely's Patent No. 50, Fawcett-Preston & Co., Liverpool, Makers, 1862. REMARKS: Trunnions and Trunnion Band are bronze. Similar weapon nearby has iron Trunnions and Trunnion Band. COMMON NAME: 12-Pounder Blakely, Type 4. Or, 3.6-Inch Blakely, Type 4.

Type 5 (Fig. VIII-26) apparently lacks the definite marking of previous forms and identification is more tenuous. However, with exception of the extra band in front of the trunnions, the piece seems as accurate a copy of Type 2 as Civil War fabrication permits and on this basis is placed in the category of a "very probable" Blakely. The purpose of the front band is a mystery, but it probably added either strength or weight to the piece. Normally, banding accomplished the former, but here location argues against this since there is little strain in front of the trunnions and the piece seems to have adequate metal at this point. Moreover, if banded to correct a design

151

FIGURE: VIII-27 LOCATION: Rivers Bridge State Park, S.C. IDENTIFICATION: Blakely, Field, 3.6-Inch, Rifle (Type 2), Iron. BORE: Diameter — 3.6. Rifling — 7 x 7, straight. Length — 49. LENGTH O/A: 54.5. TRUNNIONS: Diameter — 3.62. Length — 2.75. MARKINGS: Left Trunnion — 31. Right Trunnion — 31. Tube, rear of trunnions — Blakely's Patent, Fawcett-Preston & Co., Liverpool, Makers, 1861. REMARKS: Note missing cascabel (See text). COMMON NAME: 12-Pounder Blakely, Type 2. Or, 3.6-Inch Blakely, Type 2.

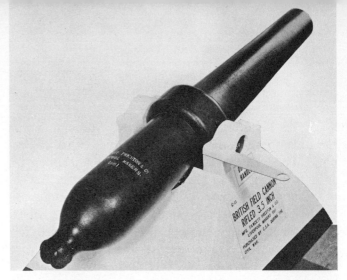

FIGURE: VIII-28 LOCATION: John M. Browning Memorial Museum, Rock Island Arsenal, Illinois. IDENTIFICATION: Blakely, Field 3.5-Inch, Rifle (Type 6), Iron. BORE: Diameter — 3.5. Rifling — 7 x 7, straight. Length — 58. LENGTH O/A: 67.25. TRUNNIONS: Diameter — 3.25. Length — 3. MARKINGS: Left Trunnion — 69. Right Trunnion — 69. Tube — Fawcett-Preston & Co., Leverpool, Makers, 1861. COMMON NAME: 12-Pounder Blakely, Type 6. Or, 3.5-Inch Blakely, Type 6.

weakness, we could expect to find other Type 2s modified to conform and even, perhaps, mention of weapon failure in reports. This is not the case. Only two of these rifles, both at Shiloh, have thus far come to light and no statement has been found of Type 2 Blakely tube weakness. Even General Alexander, in his previously quoted remarks, fails to mention any failures. But he does offer a possible clue to the band in the words: "The only advantage . . . for this gun is its lightness, but this was found to involve the very serious evil that no field carriage could be made to withstand its recoil. . . ."

The Type 2 Blakely weighed roughly 700 pounds and it is obvious that addition of a light band would add little to the total. But even a small addition—or subtraction—would change the balance. Speculative it is, but the author believes that the "kick" of the Blakely may have been due to improper preponderance and the Confederates not only knew it, but tried to correct it, possibly experimentally, by addition of a small weight forward of the trunnions. This theory is somewhat substantiated[31] by the type of iron in the band which apparently is wrought, not cast, a material Blakely seldom used, but one quite often utilized by the Confederates.

A Type 2 (Fig. VIII-27) at Rivers Bridge State Park in South Carolina may also strengthen the change-in-balance theory. It is modified in different fashion, but one which would have also changed the preponderance. The cascabel has been removed and saw marks testify that it was done deliberately and carefully. Certainly it was not removed in any attempt at destruction, for use of the piece is little, if any, impaired and less effort applied to a trunnion would have accomplished far more. Removal of the appendage to increase elevation would have been of little help in this case since the bottom of the breech would hit the carriage stock before the cascabel.

Consequently, the author feels that here again—in this case a field expedient—was an attempt to reduce the "kick" of the Blakely and preserve its carriage.

The next two models differ from previous types and the only connection appears to be the same manufacturer, Fawcett, Preston & Co. No records have been found attributing cannon design to this firm, and since we know that Blakely utilized its services for fabricating his rifles, the weapons bearing the firm name can be listed as "probable" Blakelys.

First in this category is Type 6. There are at least two of these weapons, one at Chickamauga-Chattanooga National Park and the other (Fig. VIII-28) in the John M. Browning Memorial Museum at Rock Island Arsenal, Illinois. The weapons appear to be identical and have the same measurements and markings. Bore diameter is 3.5 inches rifled with 7 lands and grooves, and overall length 67.25 inches. Tubes of both are marked "Fawcett, Preston & Co., Liverpool, Makers, 1861." Trunnions of the Rock Island piece are each marked with the number "69." No trunnion marks were found on the National Park weapon.

Type 7 (Fig. VIII-29) has entirely different appearance and measurements, but the tube is marked "Fawcett, Preston & Co., Liverpool, 1862." In this case, the muzzle face bears the number 921, presumably the weight, and the right trunnion "136," the gun number. This is the companion piece to the Whitworth captured in the 23 August 1863 attack on Confederates salvaging the *Hebe* near Fort Fisher

FIGURE: VIII-29 LOCATION: Washington Navy Yard, D.C. IDENTIFICATION: Blakely, Field*, 4-Inch, Rifle (Type 7), Iron. BORE: Diameter — 4. Rifling 6 x 6, hook-slant. Length — 65v. LENGTH O/A: 83. TRUNNIONS: Diameter — 4. Length — 3.5. MARKINGS: Muzzle Face — 921. Right Trunnion — 136. Tube — Fawcett-Preston & Co., Liverpool, 1862. REMARKS: *Weapon was captured near Fort Fisher, N.C., while employed in a field capacity. However, in view of the caliber, siege and garrison may be a more appropriate category. Piece at rear is a 2.9-Inch Confederate Navy Parrott (Fig. VI-30). COMMON NAME: 18-Pounder Blakely, Type 7. Or, 4-Inch Blakely, Type 7.

and erroneously termed an Armstrong in General Foster's report of the affair.[32]

Captain Pierce Crosby's previously quoted description still holds: ". . . 4-inch caliber, extreme length 6'11" (83 inches), length of bore 5'5" (65 inches). . . ." The bore is rifled with 6 lands and grooves in typical Blakely hook-slant fashion. The piece is now at the Washington Navy Yard and is stamped: "Captured by Adm. Lee near Ft. Fisher, N.C. 23 Aug. 1863." Based on bore diameter, it would be about an 18-pounder and perhaps should be catalogued as a siege piece. However, in view of its known employment in field service with the Whitworth, it is listed here with the slightly smaller weapons.

Although Types 8, 9, and 10 may be Blakelys, attribution to the captain is dubious and until further evidence is acquired, they should be rated no higher than "possible."

Type 8 (Fig. VIII-30) is on display at Shiloh where there are three of this model. Bore diameter is 3.4 rifled with 10 lands and grooves and overall length 73.5 inches. None of the pieces is marked and although in the past they have been attributed to Blakely, there is a good chance they may be experimental U.S. models.

Type 9 (Fig. VIII-31) is a Charleston rifle and the only one of its kind thus far discovered. Rust has corroded the bore making accurate measurement difficult and the apparent 3.75-inch diameter probably was closer to 3.5 originally. Bore length is 63.5 inches and length overall, 75. The piece is rifled with

8 lands and grooves which appear octagonal, but likely were hook-slant, seemingly more of the Brooke type than Blakely's.

On the other hand, the reinforcing band is stamped "Blakely's Patent" which would seem proof of identification. But the lettering is extremely crude and differs in form and size from that found on other marked types. This crude appearance extends to the entire piece which, even discounting the ravages of rust, lacks the finished, symmetrical lines of the other weapons. Moreover, the design seems to fly in the

FIGURE: VIII-30 LOCATION: Shiloh, Tenn. IDENTIFICATION: Blakely*, Field, 3.4-Inch, Rifle (Type 8), Iron. BORE: Diameter — 3.4. Rifling 10 x 10. Length — 66.5v. LENGTH O/A: 73.5. TRUNNIONS: Diameter — 3.75. REMARKS: *Blakely designation is entirely tentative. Piece may be an experimental U.S. model. COMMON NAME: 12-Pounder Blakely, Type 8. Or. 3.4-Inch Blakely, Type 8.

FIGURE: VIII-31 LOCATION: Charleston, S.C. IDENTIFICATION: Blakely*, Field, 3.5-Inch, Rifle (Type 9), Iron. BORE: Diameter — 3.5. Rifling — 8 x 8, hook-slant. Length — 64.5v. LENGTH O/A: 75. TRUNNIONS: Diameter — 4.5. Length — 3. MARKINGS: Tube — Blakely's Patent. REMARKS: *Despite name stamped on tube, identification as a Blakely is dubious (See text). Bore diameter of 3.5 is conjectural since due to rust and scaling bore measures about 3.75. COMMON NAME: 12-Pounder Blakely, Type 9. Or, 3.5-Inch Blakely, Type 9.

face of traditional theories for rifled weapons of the day which generally demanded strength over the seat of the charge either by banding or extra thickness of tube. Not so this piece. The vent and bottom of the bore are behind the reinforce and circumference of the tube at the vent is 2.5 inches less than immediately in front of the band.

It could, of course, be some sort of experimental Blakely, but design and crudeness argue more for a very early Confederate-made piece, possibly cast in South Carolina before local mechanics learned more advanced principles of rifled artillery. The "Blakely's Patent" may mean exactly what it says and be a trademark of one of the captain's weapons. On the other hand, it could have been stamped by a Confederate founder as acknowledgment of partial imitation, or be nothing more than instructions for artillerymen to use Blakely ammunition.

Wartime history of the piece is not known. It appeared in Charleston about the turn of the century aboard a raft on which it had been ferried across the harbor from the vicinity of Morris Island. The Negro fishermen who brought it were vague as to specific location, but indicated it had been found in one of the tidal creeks which traverse the marsh back of the island. It was sold to a scrap metal firm and planted muzzle down at the entrance as an advertisement. Years passed. The company moved. Offices were built on the site and the street widened. Yet the cannon remained—now dangerously near the curb where it took a far heavier toll of automobile fenders than it probably ever did of the enemy. During the

Civil War Centennial, it was hauled out of the ground, scraped, and mounted in its present location at the Municipal Yacht Basin.

Type 10, with two identical specimens at the Washington Navy Yard (Fig. VIII-32), has only a tenuous hold on the Blakely title. The weapons are heavily painted which precludes thorough scraping. However, both test strongly magnetic and hence presumably are iron. Statistics are the same with bore diameter 2.9 inches rifled with 6 lands and grooves. Length overall, 36.5 inches, compares favorably with 37.21 of the 12-pounder Mountain Howitzer (Chapter II) and trunnions are exactly the same diameter, 2.7, and at 2.5 are only a quarter inch longer. Thus the rifles were ideally suited for the standard mountain howitzer carriage and may have been designed as companions to the smoothbore only to be later supplanted by the Confederate 2.25-inch Mountain Rifle described in Chapter IX.

Absence, or concealment, of marks leaves only superficial means by which the pieces may be classified. Measurements place them in no established category, but the rifling is Blakely's form with a pronounced "hook" and the trunnion band and general shape is similar to Type 6.

Based on this admittedly sketchy evidence, the weapons are classified as "possible" Blakelys despite a rumor at the yard that the cannon were cast locally as ornaments. This theory is unacceptable to the author without supporting data since it seems highly unlikely that the Navy Yard would go to the trouble of rifling two ornaments—especially in a highly complicated, foreign manner. Even the possibility that they were cast locally to test Blakely's form of rifling seems improbable because of the small size. Similarly, the supposition that they may have been scale models is not tenable at this time due to absence of an original piece for copying. Finally, with all the genuine weapons available at the yard, fabrication of ornaments seems a waste of time and effort and the author feels they are more likely small Blakely rifles captured from the Confederates.

The captain's larger rifles, although varied in appearance and covering a wide range of caliber, are a bit easier to identify than field guns since most are plainly marked. However, not all calibers came to this country, so those mentioned in the following pages are either available today or can be documented as having been ordered or used during the war. The list is believed to be complete, but future research may reveal weapons that should be added.

Most heavy Blakelys, like the field guns, were purchased by the Confederacy, but apparently he

FIGURE: VIII-32 LOCATION: Washington Navy Yard, D.C. IDENTIFICATION: Blakely*, Mountain, 2.9-Inch, Rifle (Type 10), Iron. BORE: Diameter — 2.9. Rifling — 6 x 6, hook-slant. Length — 26.5. LENGTH O/A: 36.5. TRUNNIONS: Diameter — 2.7. Length — 2.5. REMARKS: *Blakely identification tentative (See text). COMMON NAME: 10-Pounder Blakely, Type 10. Or, 2.9-Inch Blakely, Type 10.

made eight 9-inch and four 11-inch rifles for the State of Massachusetts.[33] The 9-inch fired a 248-pound bolt with a charge of 30 pounds and the 11-inch burned 37.25 pounds with a 375-pound projectile. In tests, the latter, loaded with 52.5 pounds of powder, drove a 525-pound shot through 45 feet of earth.

Smallest Blakely in the siege and seacoast category seems to have been a 4-inch. Several were listed in the 1864 defenses of South Carolina, Georgia, and Florida and at least one of these pieces is also called an 18-pounder Blakely siege gun.[34] Bore diameter is the same as the previously mentioned Type 7, but since data and description of the siege 4-inch is lacking, there is insufficient evidence to transfer Type 7 to the siege category—especially since the only known specimen was being used in a field capacity when captured.

The slightly larger 4.5-inch (Fig. VIII-33) we know was used as a garrison weapon in Fort Pulaski which had a pair of the rifles. They were part of a shipment of four that arrived at Savannah in November 1861, aboard the steamer *Fingal* which, converted to the ironclad *Atlanta*, gained a niche in history through her battle with the *Weehawken*.

After the *Fingal's* cargo was distributed, the two Blakelys remained at Pulaski only to be picked up by U.S. forces at the capture of that fort the following April. Sent north, they were deposited at West Point and returned to Pulaski in the 1930s. Both rifles have 7 lands and grooves and are 96 inches overall. Tube markings, with exception of the number, are identical. The illustrated piece is stamped: "Blakely's Patent, No. 43, Fawcett, Preston & Co., Liverpool, Makers, 1861."

FIGURE: VIII-34 LOCATION: Washington Navy Yard, D.C. IDENTIFICATION: Blakely, Seacoast and Navy, 7-Inch, Rifle, Iron and Steel. BORE: Diameter — 7. Rifling — 9 x 9, Straight. Length — 96.25v. LENGTH O/A: 119.5. TRUNNIONS: Diameter — 7.5. Length — 6. MARKINGS: Left Trunnion — 80. Right Trunnion — J.D.B. Tube — Blakely's Patent No. 37, Fawcett-Preston & Co., Liverpool, Makers, 1861. COMMON NAME: 120-Pounder Blakely. Or, 7-Inch Blakely.

Although no 6.4-inch Blakely 100-pounder has been found, we know that at least one was used, for this was the pivot rifle aboard the *Alabama* which slammed a shell into the rudderpost of the *Kearsarge*. Dimensions of the *Alabama* weapon are not available, but Holley[35] lists a 100-pounder, 6.4-inch Blakely as having 8 lands and grooves, a bore length of 96 inches and weight of 8,000 pounds.

Figure VIII-34 is a 7-inch, 120-pounder at the Washington Navy Yard. The piece is 119.5 inches overall and rifled with 9 lands and grooves. Breech markings are "Blakely Pat. No. 37, Fawcett, Preston & Co., Liverpool, 1861." Navy Yard records state it was captured aboard the "Anglo-Confederate Pirate Ship *Florida*."

A slightly larger weapon, 7.5 inch[36] bore, became known to Confederate defenders of Vicksburg as the "Widow Blakely," reportedly because it was the sole specimen of the captain's art in the city defenses. Mounted overlooking the river, one of its own shells exploded in the tube during the 22 May 1863 action against Union gunboats. The blast took off a section of the muzzle, but since the remainder of the piece was undamaged, the ragged ends were trimmed even and the rifle used as a mortar during the rest of the siege. After the fall of Vicksburg, the "Widow" was hauled off to West Point where it was displayed mistakenly identified as "Whistling Dick," another "name" rifle discussed in Chapter I. Its true nature was recognized a few years ago, and the piece returned to Mississippi after an absence of ninety-six years. It has been mounted by the Park Service about a mile south of its position during the siege.

The "Widow" (Fig. VIII-35) is rifled with 12 lands and grooves in typical Blakely hook-slant fashion and has an overall length of 100 inches. It is marked on the left trunnion "Low Moor," a firm which made weapons for Blakely, and, for some undetermined reason, twice with the date, "1861."

FIGURE: VIII-33 LOCATION: Fort Pulaski, Ga. IDENTIFICATION: Blakely, Siege & Garrison or Navy, 4.5-Inch, Rifle, Iron and Steel. BORE: Diameter — 4.5. Rifling — 7 x 7, hook-slant. Length — 76.5v. LENGTH O/A: 96. TRUNNIONS: Diameter — 4.62. Length — 4.25. MARKINGS: Tube — Blakely's Patent No. 43, Fawcett-Preston & Co., Liverpool, Makers, 1861. COMMON NAME: 4.5-Inch Blakely.

FIGURE: VIII-35 LOCATION: Vicksburg, Miss. IDENTIFICATION: Blakely*, Seacoast and Navy, 7.5-Inch, Rifle, Iron. BORE: Diameter — 7.5. Rifling — 12 x 12, hook-slant. LENGTH O/A: 100 (muzzle has been cut back). TRUNNIONS: Diameter — 7.25. Length — 6. MARKINGS: Left Trunnion — Low Moor, 1861, 1861. Tube — Blakely's Patent, 1861. REMARKS: *Piece appears to be reworked British 42-Pounder (6.97-Inch) of 67 cwt. (See text). COMMON NAME: the "Widow Blakely." Or, 7.5-Inch Blakely. Or, British 42-Pounder (6.97-Inch) of 67 cwt. Banded and Rifled to 7.5-Inch.

FIGURE: VIII-36 LOCATION: Washington Navy Yard, D.C. IDENTIFICATION: Blakely*, Seacoast and Navy, 7.25-Inch, Rifle, Iron. BORE: Diameter — 7.25. Rifling — 12 x 12, hook-slant. Length — 104.6v. LENGTH O/A: 124. TRUNNIONS: Diameter — 7.25. Length — 6. MARKINGS: Left Trunnion — Low Moor. Tube — Blakely's Patent, 1861. REMARKS: *Piece appears to be reworked British 42-Pounder (6.97-Inch) of 67 cwt. (See text). COMMON NAME: 150-Pounder Blakely. Or, 7.25-Inch Blakely. Or, British 42-Pounder (6.97-Inch) of 67 cwt. Banded and Rifled to 7.25-Inch.

FIGURE: VIII-37 LOCATION: Washington Navy Yard, D.C. IDENTIFICATION: Blakely*, Seacoast and Navy, 6.3-Inch, Rifle, Iron. BORE: Diameter — 6.3. Rifling — 8 x 8, hook-slant. Length — 73v. LENGTH O/A: 88.5. TRUNNIONS: Diameter — 5.75. Length — 5.5. MARKINGS: Left Trunnion — Low Moor, 1856 (probable date, see text). REMARKS: *Piece appears to be reworked British 32-Pounder (6.3-Inch) of 32 cwt. (See text). COMMON NAME: 100-Pounder Blakely. Or, 6.3-Inch Blakely. Or, British 32-Pounder (6.3-Inch) of 32 cwt., Rifled.

FIGURE: VIII-38 LOCATION: West Point, N.Y. IDENTIFICATION: Blakely, Seacoast and Navy, 8-Inch, Rifle, Iron. BORE: Diameter — 8. Rifling — 3 x 3, hook-slant. Length — 119v. LENGTH O/A: 136. TRUNNIONS: Diameter — 8.5. Length — 6.5. MARKINGS: Left Trunnion — Low Moor, 1862. Cascabel —A crown and P.1158. REMARKS: Piece at left is the "Window Blakely" before transfer to Vicksburg, Miss. (Fig. VIII-35). COMMON NAME: 200-Pounder Blakely. Or, 8-Inch Blakely.

The tube is stamped "Blakely's Patent, 1861." It no doubt originally resembled the Washington Navy Yard Blakely (Fig. VIII-36) acquired after it was abandoned by the Confederates at Shipping Point on the Potomac River in 1862[37]. The bore is blocked, but diameter appears to be 7.25 inches rifled in similar fashion to the "Widow." It measures 124 inches overall and is marked on the tube "Blakely's Patent, 1861," and on the left trunnion, Low Moor

Difference in length indicates the "Widow" lost about 2 feet of tube.

Although both pieces are clearly marked with Blakely's name, they differ considerably in appearance from most of this inventor's large calibers and seem more an adaptation than a new model. Consequently, it is the author's belief they were originally standard British service smoothbores, or new pieces cast in the service pattern, then rifled, banded, and stamped with his brand.

Compare the Washington Navy Yard 6.3-inch (Fig. VIII-37) also rifled on Blakely's plan, but with 8 lands and grooves. Rout off the base ring, top of the sight bracket and lock piece, sweat on a band and, barring size and missing muzzle on the "Widow," they could be triplets. No weights have been found, but based on measurements, the smaller conforms to the British 32-pounder (6.3-inch) of 32 cwt., and the others to the 42-pounder (6.97-inch) smoothbore of 67 cwt. British texts[38] state the 32 was bored-up to this caliber from 24-pounder (5.75-inch) of 33 cwt., which would account for the small diameter trunnions (5.75-inch) that in a gun of this weight would normally be expected to conform in size to bore diameter. Moreover, the left trunnion, through heavy layers of paint, appears to have the date 1866 which obviously is in error and could well be 1856 which would conform nicely to the time of change in the 24-pounders.

Assuming the weapons are simply reworked service smoothbores, it is the author's belief they should be termed British 32-pounder (6.3-inch) of 32 cwt., rifled, and British 42-pounder (6.97-inch) of 67 cwt., banded and rifled to 7.25-inch (7.5-inch in the case of the "Widow"), and have no more right to the Blakely designation than the rifled American smoothbores to the name James. However, since "Widow Blakely" is a far more romantic designation than "British 42-pounder (6.97-inch) of 67 cwt., banded and rifled to 7.5-inch" and the chances of change after a hundred years are slight, the weapons will be listed in the Blakely column for the romanticist with a footnote to what the author believes is their proper description for those who are sticklers for technical accuracy.

Figure VIII-38 pictures the "Widow" during its stay at the Military Academy. The large piece in front of it is a 200-pounder Blakely, still in the West Point collection. It has an 8-inch bore rifled with 3 lands and grooves and measures 136 overall. The left trunnion is marked "Low Moor, 1862." The right, which may have held reference to Blakely, is missing. The cascabel is marked with a crown and "P-1158." The weapon was captured 23 August 1864 at Fort Morgan which is listed in the Official Records[39] as having two 8-inch Blakelys in its defenses. Another photograph (Fig. VIII-39) shows the breech with scar left by the missing trunnion.

Confederates at Wilmington, North Carolina, about the middle of August, 1863, cheered the steamer *Gibraltar* as she slipped into port after eluding federal blockaders off the bar. By this stage of the war, arrival of any blockade runner was cause for rejoicing and the *Gibraltar* was doubly welcomed since her cargo included two huge cannon, so long they had to be ferried across the ocean standing vertical, muzzles protruding from the hatches to give the vessel the appearance of a three-stacker with only one streaming smoke. The guns were 12.75-inch[40] Blakelys, products of George Forrester & Co., Vauxhall Foundry, Liverpool. Tubes (Fig. VIII-40) were cast iron with a bronze air chamber at the breech. Reinforcing also was cast iron with exception of a steel band over the powder chamber. They were 194 inches long, had a maximum diameter of 51

FIGURE: VIII-39 LOCATION: West Point, N.Y. IDENTIFICATION: Blakely, Seacoast and Navy, 8-Inch, Rifle, Iron. REMARKS: Breech of weapon in Fig. VIII-38. At right is 4.2-inch Confederate Parrott.

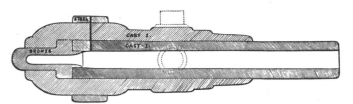

FIGURE: VIII-40 IDENTIFICATION: Blakely, Seacoast, 12.75-Inch, Rifle, Iron, Steel and Bronze. BORE: Diameter — 12.75. Rifling — 4 x 4, hook-slant. Length — 184. LENGTH O/A: 194. REMARKS: Made by Forrester & Co., Vauxhall Foundry, Liverpool. SOURCE: Holley. COMMON NAME: 650-Pounder Blakely. Or, 600-Pounder Blakely. Or, 700-Pounder Blakely. Or, 900-Pounder Blakely. Or, 13-Inch Blakely. Or, 12.75-Inch Blakely (preferred).

inches, and weighed a bit more than 27 tons each, or 60,480 pounds based on the long ton.

The Blakelys were the largest rifles in the Confederacy and their arrival drew an immediate bid from General Beauregard who bombarded Richmond with telegrams soliciting them for Charleston where their obvious power would protect the inner harbor against federal ironclads tempted to run past the forts guarding the entrance.

Despite half-hearted attempts to keep the guns at Wilmington, they were dispatched to Charleston where the first was unloaded 29 August and promptly damaged through sheer negligence. Records are vague, but apparently in a hurried effort to get the piece operational, it was tested before the manufacturer's instructions were received. The officer in charge cut down a powder bag and loaded the 6.4-inch diameter air chamber with powder which, since the bronze walls were only 3 inches thick, gave way under pressure of the blast. The damaged chamber eventually was repaired by Charleston mechanics and the piece returned to service, but the accident placed

Beauregard in an embarrassing position with Richmond and later mention of the Blakelys was restricted to essentials. The general did, however, report successful firing of the second rifle 2 October. With charges varying from 30 to 55 pounds and 2 degrees elevation, it lofted 470-pound shells up to a mile and a quarter. The cartridges, this time, were placed correctly in front of the air chamber.

Civil War artist Conrad Wise Chapman painted one of the Blakelys mounted in Charleston's White Point Gardens, better known today as "The Battery." The finished canvas hangs today in the Valentine Museum at Richmond, but since the rifle is only a small object in a corner, Chapman's preliminary sketch (Fig. VIII-41) has been substituted. It seems a faithful rendition of the tube, as illustrated by Holley, although a bit of artistic license may have been taken with the carriage.

The rifles were never fired against the enemy and spent the war as expensive (they cost about £10,000 each) ornaments.[41] Despite initial enthusiasm and the reportedly successful test of 2 October, the Blakelys failed to meet expectations and Johnson[42] called them ". . . of very little account because of the inferiority of their projectiles. These failed generally to take the grooves and would tumble like nail kegs without ever attaining their proper range. . . ."

At the evacuation of Charleston 18 February 1865, both guns were loaded with excessive charges and blown. The view of "The Battery" piece that met Federal troops entering the city is shown in Figure VIII-42. The massive breech, 51 inches in diameter, was carted to the repossessed U.S. Arsenal where it appears in the background of a photograph of ammunition in Chapter XIII. The breech and part of the tube are now at West Point. Figures VIII-43 and 44 are front and rear views which clearly show the bronze air chamber in the breech and the type rifling (4 grooves) in the section of tube beside it. Figure VIII-45 is a sketch of one of the grooves.

Another part of the Blakely is still in Charleston, but not on view to the public. The huge piece of cast iron, which must weigh about two tons, is in the attic of a three-story residence, blown there by the force of the blast a hundred or more yards down the street. Rather than risk the weight on the stairs, beams beneath it were shored to stand the strain and the iron relic of a century ago has remained where it landed, mute tribute to the power of black powder. Figure VIII-46, an 1865 view of Charleston's East Battery, shows the Blakely carriage in foreground and the residence (arrow) which houses the section of iron.

FIGURE: VIII-41 IDENTIFICATION: Blakely, Seacoast, 12.75-Inch, Rifle, Iron, Steel and Bronze. REMARKS: Preliminary sketch by Civil War artist Conrad Wise Chapman of 12.75-Inch Blakely mounted at Charleston, S.C. The finished painting, of which this is but a very small section, hangs today at the Valentine Museum, Richmond, Va. Drawing is dated 29 Oct. 1863.

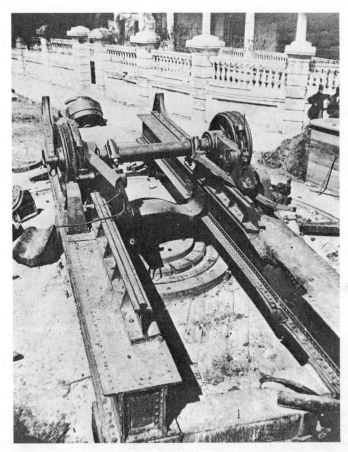

FIGURE: VIII-42 IDENTIFICATION: Blakely, Seacoast, 12.75-Inch, Rifle, Iron, Steel and Bronze. REMARKS: Remains of carriage and weapon destroyed at evacuation of Charleston 18 Feb. 1865. Note breech (now at West Point) in background.

158

FIGURE: VIII-43 LOCATION: West Point, N.Y. IDENTIFICATION: Blakely, Seacoast, 12.75-Inch, Rifle, Iron, Steel and Bronze. REMARKS: Breech and section of tube of weapon deliberately blown at Charleston 18 Feb. 1865. Breech is 51 inches in diameter. Bronze air chamber (center of breech) is 12.75 exterior and 6.4 interior diameter. Tube (left) is rifled 4 x 4, hook-slant. See rear view, Fig. VIII-44.

FIGURE: VIII-44 LOCATION: West Point, N.Y. IDENTIFICATION: Blakely, Seacoast, 12.75-Inch, Rifle, Iron, Steel and Bronze. REMARKS: Rear view of breech and tube. See Fig. VIII-43.

FIGURE: VIII-45 IDENTIFICATION: Rifling of 12.75-Inch Blakely. SOURCE: Holley.

FIGURE: VIII-46 LOCATION: Charleston, S.C. IDENTIFICATION: Blakely, Seacoast, 12.75-Inch, Rifle, Iron, Steel and Bronze. REMARKS: Section of rifle remains in residence (arrow) where it landed 18 Feb. 1865 when weapon was blown to prevent capture. Portion of carriage in foreground.

NOTES

1. E. P. Alexander, "Confederate Artillery Service," *Southern Historical Society Papers*, Vol. XI, 1883, p. 108.
2. *Official Records*, Series IV, Vol. 1, letter 21 May 1861, pp. 343–346.
3. *Encyclopaedia Britannica*, 1946.
4. *Official Navy Records*, Series II, Vol. 2, pp. 774–775.
5. Alexander L. Holley, *A Treatise on Ordnance and Armor*, 1865, p. 15.
6. *Ibid.*
7. *Official Records*, Series I, Vol. 6, p. 627.
8. *Official Navy Records*, Series I, Vol. 6, pp. 482–483.
9. *Official Records*, Series III, Vol. 1, pp. 274–275.
10. Reports of committees of the U.S. Senate, 2nd session, 38th Congress, "Heavy Ordnance," p. 89.
11. *Official Records*, Series I, Vol. 29, Part 2, pp. 670–671.
12. *Ibid.*, Vol. 33, pp. 425–426.
13. *Official Navy Records*, Series I, Vol. 9, pp. 165–172.
14. *Ibid.*, p. 171.
15. *Official Records*, Series I, Vol. 29, Part 2, pp. 670–671.
16. *Ibid.*, Vol. 28, Part 1, p. 223.
17. *Official Navy Records*, Series I, Vol. 14, pp. 471–472.
18. *Ibid.*, Series II, Vol. 1, *C.S.S. Shenandoah*, p. 267.
19. Holley, *op. cit.*, pp. 28–29, 34, Table VIII.
20. *Official Records*, Series I, Vol. 1, pp. 21–24.
21. *The Charleston Mercury*, 2 May 1861, p. 1.
22. Capt. Truman Seymour. West Point Museum officials believe there was once a letter from Seymour attesting the validity of the shot, but that it disappeared some years ago.
23. *Official Records*, Series I, Vol. 1, pp. 292–293.
24. *Ibid.*, p. 316.
25. Samuel Wylie Crawford, *The Genesis of The Civil War, The Story of Sumter, 1860–61*, 1887, p. 397. *The Charleston Mercury*, 29 April 1861, p. 2.
26. Holley, *op. cit.*, pp. 38, 47, 50.
27. *Harper's Weekly, a Journal of Civilization*, 1 April 1865. Gen. Mower was commander, 1st Division, XVII Corps.
28. Holley, *op. cit.*, p. 36.
29. *Ibid.*, paragraph 57: "No wrought iron is used . . . on account of its liability to become permanently stretched. . . ." However, paragraph 72 mentions Blakely's first gun as having wrought iron bands, his second a wrought iron tube, and paragraph 73 describes the wrought iron band of the first rifle sent to the Confederates.
30. It received the name from Mr. Jac Weller of Princeton, N. J.
31. For the determination of the type of iron in the band, the author is indebted to Mr. Edwin H. Olmstead of Mount Holly Springs, Pa., who has made an extensive examination of the Shiloh weapons and states that band and tube are definitely of different materials and the former is probably wrought iron.
32. *Official Records*, Series I, Vol. 29, Part 1, pp. 77–78.
33. Holley, *op. cit.*, p. 42.
34. *Official Records*, Series I, Vol. 35, Part 2, pp. 415, 464–465.
35. Holley, *op. cit.*, Table X.
36. Although the author's measurements confirm 7.5, Vicksburg's plaque lists the bore as 7.44, and perhaps is more accurate. Holley, op. cit., in a sketch of what appears to be an identical, undamaged piece, records, 7.5, yet the same weapon, to be discussed shortly, today measures 7.25. Consequently, rust and time have made exact measurement difficult if not impossible and the reader is free to take his choice.
37. Holley, *op. cit.*, p. 39, illustrates this Shipping Point piece and states bore diameter is 7.5 inches.
38. Sir Howard Douglas, *A Treatise on Naval Gunnery*, 1860, p. 605, Table XXIV. George Will and J. C. Dalton, *The Artillerists Handbook of Reference*, 1879, Appendix IV, table of smoothbore ordnance.
39. *Official Records*, Series I, Vol. 39, Part 2, p. 786.
40. The Blakelys were also called 13-inch as a matter of convenience and 900-, 700-, and 600-pounders. However, since the solid shot delivered for their use at Charleston weighed 650 pounds, this designation has been arbitrarily assigned although 12.75-inch is a more accurate identification.
41. Josiah Gorgas, "Contributions to The History of The Confederate Ordnance Department," *Southern Historical Society Papers*, Vol. XII, 1884, p. 94.
42. John Johnson, *The Defense of Charleston Harbor, 1863–65*, 1890, p. 71.

Chapter 9

Cannon Miscellaneous

PREVIOUS CHAPTERS HAVE DEALT PRIMARILY with rifles and smoothbores which, through multiplicity of caliber and number might be considered weapons systems rather than single models. This chapter is devoted to miscellaneous pieces that fail to meet the requirements of a system although several were fine weapons which gave efficient service throughout the war and perhaps deserve more extensive treatment than is possible here. Others have a much lighter hold on distinction and many were out-and-out failures.

Most important both in number and general achievement was the U.S. 3-inch, wrought iron field rifle M-1861 known and admired on both sides of the line as the "Ordnance Rifle" or "Ordnance Gun." The piece also had two other names which through the years have added confusion to its origin and development. These are "Griffen Gun" and "Rodman Rifle," and while there is considerable justification for the first, there seems little or none for the second.

John Griffen,[1] a native of Mamaroneck, New York, was an ingenious young man with considerable experience in Pennsylvania iron foundries when in 1854 he turned his talents to invention of a wrought iron field gun. He developed a process[2] whereby strips of wrought iron about ¾-inch thick and 4½

wide were wrapped by lathe around an iron core. Five layers were laid on in alternate spirals until the tube, with a thin covering of iron staves on the outside, was built to requisite thickness. The core was removed and an iron plug driven into the breech to close it and form the cascabel. The metal was then brought to a welding heat and upset 2 inches in a press. Finally, it was rolled out from 4.5 to 7 feet, trunnions were welded on, the bore reamed out, and the chase reduced to proper size by turning in a lathe.

Griffen's first piece,[3] a 3.67-inch smoothbore which resembled the M-1841, bronze 6-pounder, was tested successfully in 1855 by the founder, Phoenix Iron Co. of Phoenixville, Pennsylvania, and a year later passed Army proving with flying colors, not bursting until filled with 7 pounds of powder and thirteen balls. However, Army orders failed to materialize and attempts to market improved models abroad met with little more success. Griffen was now superintendent of the firm—a post he held until his death in 1884—but he had to wait until the outbreak of war before government contracts were received by the company which he had put into the gun-making business.

161

An early wartime Griffen smoothbore (Fig. IX-1) is displayed at the Gettysburg Wax Museum. The piece—marked "Phoenix, 1861" with the weight "1030" on the left trunnion and "Patented Dec. 25, 1855" on the righ'.—has a 3.67-inch bore 63.25 inches long and is 72.25 overall. Superficially, this wrought iron smoothbore resembles the Ordnance Rifle, but lacks the clean lines of the 3-inch which seems to have originated with a letter dated 22 June 1861 from Secretary of War Simon Cameron to the Ordnance Department:[4] "The Colonel of Ordnance will take measures to procure 300 wrought iron field pieces, 6-pounder caliber, from Phoenix Iron Company . . . a portion (two thirds) of these guns to be rifled. . . ."

Three days later Lieutenant Colonel J. W. Ripley replied:[5]

"In compliance with your instructions . . . I shall order from the Phoenix Iron Company 300 iron field pieces—200 rifled, 100 smoothbore. Before giving the order it will be necessary to furnish the company with a drawing to work by. That drawing is now in preparation by the Ordnance Board. Permit me to suggest and recommend that all these guns be rifled. This is essential to uniformity of ammunition and will secure efficiency for all the guns instead of only two-thirds of them. The bore cannot exceed 3.35 inches without making the projectile . . . too heavy for convenient transportation in the field. This bore will give such projectiles about 10 pounds weight. I propose to fix the price at $250 per gun, which will be about 25 cents per pound of wrought iron, as I estimate the finished gun's weight to be not more than 1,000 pounds, under this weight rather than above. . . ."

The correspondence has been quoted at some length, since it explains certain factors relating to development of the rifle.

Since Griffen's original models were smoothbores and Ripley's letter clearly states the Ordnance Board was drafting a design for submission to the founder, it seems evident that Griffen's connection with the Ordnance Rifle was the process of construction—the form was a product of the Ordnance Bureau and hence the name.

Rodman's connection, if any, is decidedly tenuous. His method of interior cooling used in manufacture of certain columbiads, obviously didn't apply here since the Ordnance Rifle was wrought, not cast, iron. He could, of course, have designed it for the Ordnance Bureau, but contemporary records fail to bear out this supposition and the only link of the inventor with the gun found thus far is Benton's:[6] "The form of this piece . . . is the same in its general character as all the guns of the Rodman pattern. . . ."

FIGURE: IX-1 LOCATION: Wax Museum, Gettysburg, Pa. IDENTIFICATION: Griffen, Field, 3.67-Inch, Model 1855, Wrought Iron. BORE: Diameter — 3.67. Smoothbore. Length — 62.75v. LENGTH O/A: 72.25. TRUNNIONS: Diameter — 3.67. Length — 2.75. MARKINGS: Left Trunnion — Phoenix, 1861, 1030 lbs. Right Trunnion — Patented Dec. 25, 1855. Breech — 13. COMMON NAME: 6-Pounder Griffen. Or, 3.67-Inch Griffen.

FIGURE: IX-2 LOCATION: West Point, N.Y. IDENTIFICATION: Rifle, Field, 3-Inch, Model 1861, Wrought Iron. BORE: Diameter — 3. Rifling — 7 x 7, straight. Length — 65. LENGTH O/A: 73.3. TRUNNIONS: Diameter — 3.67. Length — 2.8. MARKINGS: Muzzle Face — T.T.S.L., No. 100, P.I. & Co., 1861, 815 lbs. REMARKS: Left piece of Capt. Samuel S. Elder's Battery B, 1st U.S. Artillery. It is said to have fired the last artillery round prior to Gen. Lee's surrender at Appomattox 9 April 1865. COMMON NAME: Ordnance Rifle (preferred). Or, Ordnance Gun. Or, Griffen Gun. Or, Rodman Rifle (erroneous).

A possible explanation may lie in the remark of Colonel R. O. Tyler, siege train commander during the Peninsular Campaign, quoted by Abbot:[7] "Upon June 20, I was ordered to bring up a battery of five 4½ inch Rodmans. . . ." This piece, the 4.5-inch siege rifle, resembled the 3-inch Ordnance Rifle closely in appearance and was often called an Ordnance Rifle. It was, however, cast iron, not wrought, and thus was erroneously supposed by a number of artillery and ordnance men to have been fabricated by Rodman's method. Consequently, since both calibers were outwardly similar, it is possible that attribution to Rodman occurred through a combination of confusion and error.

Despite confusion of name, the 3-inch Ordnance Rifle gave excellent service and won praise both

North and South. Confederate artillerymen were particularly fond of these weapons which Alexander describes[8] as: "The beautiful United States Three-Inch Ordnance Rifles. . ." and of which Colonel William Allan, chief of ordnance, 2nd Corps, ANV, remarked:[9] "We especially valued the 3-inch rifles which became the favorite field pieces. . . ."

Federal tributes were more restrained, but Brigadier General George D. Ramsay, chief of ordnance, said of them:[10] "The experience of wrought iron field guns is most favorable to their endurance and efficiency. They cost less then steel and stand all the charge we want to impose on them. . . ."

The Ordnance Rifle (Fig. IX-2) is in the West Point collection and is reported to have fired the last artillery round before Lee's surrender.[11] It was the left piece of Captain Samuel S. Elder's Battery B., 1st U.S. Artillery at Appomattox Court House 9 April 1865. Marks show the piece was No. 100 made at the Phoenix Iron Co. in 1861 and was inspected by T.T.S. Laidly. It weighs 815 pounds, 5 lighter than standard.

After the original 300 guns, all of which were rifled, Phoenix turned out about 1,100 more,[12] a total production which has left a high number of these weapons scattered throughout the Eastern seaboard, particularly in the National Parks. Not all have been examined, but those that have conform very closely to specifications of the standard 3-inch listed as Model 1861 in the Ordnance Manual[13] and recorded in the appendix. Typical rifling (Fig. IX-3) consists of lands .5-inch wide and grooves .84 wide. The illustrated piece, No. 265, was made by Phoenix Iron Co. in 1862, was inspected by Laidly, and weighs 816 pounds. It is displayed at the Beaufort, South Carolina, Museum.

Toward the end of the war, Hotchkiss and Schenkl projectiles were mainly used with Ordnance Rifles although various others could be fired including the Dyer with which a test piece elevated 10° gave 2,788 yards range and at 20°, 3,972 yards. The charge in both cases was a single pound with a 9-pound shell.[14]

Following the war, an attempt was made to retain use of the Ordnance Rifles through conversion to breechloaders and beefing up the weight of the projectile.[15] The bore of a number of rifles was reamed to 3.2-inch and a steel breechblock installed, but the attempt seems to have met with little favor despite enthusiastic reports by ordnance boards through 1881.

The Ordnance Rifle (Fig. IX-4) in the Petersburg collection is one of these conversions. The bore measures 3.2 inches and the length overall 68.75 inches, roughly 4.5-inches shorter than standard due to removal of the cascabel. Muzzle markings are difficult to read, but appear to be JGB, 1866, 945, PI & Co., 816 lbs. The right trunnion is stamped "Patented Dec. 9, 1862, Phoenix Iron Co." On the tube is "U.S."

FIGURE: IX-3 LOCATION: Beaufort, S.C. IDENTIFICATION: Rifle, Field, 3-Inch, Model 1861, Wrought Iron. REMARKS: Muzzle face of typical Ordnance Rifle.

FIGURE: IX-4 LOCATION: Petersburg, Va. IDENTIFICATION: Rifle, Field, 3-Inch, Model 1861, Wrought Iron. Converted to 3.2-Inch B.L.R. BORE: Diameter — 3.2. Rifling — 7 x 7, straight. Length — 68.75. LENGTH O/A (excludes missing breechblock): 68.75. TRUNNIONS: Diameter — 3.67. Length 2.8. MARKINGS: Muzzle Face — J.G.B., 1866, 945, P.I. & Co., 816 lbs. Right Trunnion — Patented Dec. 9, 1862, Phoenix Iron Co. COMMON NAME: 3.2-Inch B.L.R.

FIGURE: IX-5 LOCATION: Chattanooga-Chickamauga National Park. IDENTIFICATION: Singer-Nimick, Field, 3-Inch, Rifle, Cast Steel. BORE: Diameter — 3. Rifling — 7 x 7, straight. Length — 63. LENGTH O/A: 73. TRUNNIONS: Diameter — 3.67. Length — 2.8. MARKINGS: Muzzle Face — No. 1, J.S., 834 lbs. Left Trunnion — Singer-Nimick & Co., Pittsburg, Cast Steel, 1862. Right Trunnion — Singer-Nimick & Co., Pittsburg, Cast Steel, 1862. COMMON NAME: 3-Inch Singer-Nimick Rifle.

FIGURE: IX-6 LOCATION: Petersburg, Va. IDENTIFICATION: Rifle, Field, 3-Inch, Model 1863, Iron. BORE: Diameter — 3. Rifling — 7 x 7, straight. LENGTH O/A: 71.5. TRUNNIONS: Diameter — 3.5. Length — 3. MARKINGS: Tube — U.S. REMARKS: Trunnions paint covered, but park records list markings as H.N.H. & Co., No. 1, 1863. COMMON NAME: 3-Inch Rifle Model 1863. Or, 3-Inch Henry N. Hooper Rifle.

Chickamauga-Chattanooga National Military Park has a pair of 3-inch rifles (Fig. IX-5) which may be the only survivors of a reported half dozen made of cast steel on the Ordnance Rifle pattern. The pieces resemble the wrought iron version closely, with 3-inch bores rifled with 7 lands and grooves and overall lengths 73 inches, less than half an inch short. However, the bores are only 63 inches long compared to a standard 65. Left and right trunnion faces are marked "Singer-Nimick & Co., Pittsburg, Cast Steel, 1862." Muzzle faces are stamped with the weights, 834 pounds, initials of the inspector, John Symington, and piece numbers, 1 and 5.

In view of the bore length discrepancy, difference in metal and hence manufacturing method, purists may object to these weapons being called "Ordnance Rifles." However, since they were made in the same pattern, seemingly with intent at duplication in a different material, it is the author's belief they have as much right to this colloquial identification as the wrought-iron 3-inch provided a qualifying term such as "Singer-Nimick" or "cast steel" is also used.

A 3-inch at Petersburg (Fig. IX-6) at first glance appears to be an Ordnance Rifle, but on closer examination registers numerous differences. The piece has similar rifling, 7 lands and grooves, but overall length, 71.5 is almost two inches short. General appearance is slightly different, particularly the breech which is more hemispherical than in the Phoenix Company rifles. Paint obscures identifying information, but Petersburg records list trunnion marks as "HNH [Henry N. Hooper] & Co., No. 1, 1863." The tube is stamped "U.S." Whether this should be classed as a Hooper Company attempt to manufacture a standard Ordnance Rifle or simply a similar appearing experimental weapon is a question that must await availability of additional records.

Jumping from the field to siege, a weapon that is generally considered a companion to the 3-inch Ordnance Rifle and often bears a similar name is the 4.5-inch Siege Rifle M-1861. This piece, as previously mentioned, was almost identical in form to the 3-inch, but was made of cast iron cooled from the exterior since the bore was too small for practical use of Rodman's process.[16]

The rifle met mixed reaction. Its endurance was distrusted by many artillerymen since the trial gun burst after only eight hundred rounds and the piece, as issued, was not bouched, a neglect which resulted in rapid erosion around the vent.[17] On the other hand, bouching was relatively easy and with this deficiency corrected, the weapons seem to have rendered excellent service for Abbot says of them:[18] "The two siege batteries of 4.5 ordnance guns which accompanied the Army of the Potomac in all its movements from Fredericksburg until the final crossing of the Rapidan were of great use from their superior range and accuracy, in silencing troublesome field batteries and in other field service and could be moved with the reserve artillery without impeding the march of the army. . . ."

The mobility of these weapons was extolled by Captain F. A. Pratt, commander Battery M, 1st Connecticut Artillery, who, in recalling that his unit kept pace with others in the Army of the Potomac over difficult terrain, wrote:[19] "I consider it in every way practical to take batteries of this kind with a moving army and from observation believe they are more readily moved than the 20-pounder Parrott batteries whose weight is thrown on the rear axle. It always . . . excited surprise and comment . . . that guns apparently so cumbrous could be so readily and rapidly moved. . . ." Three 1st Connecticut rifles (Fig. IX-7) overlooked Fredericksburg during the war. Although in position, the pieces were ready for traveling with implements loaded and trails of the siege carriages hooked to limbers.

The 4.5 in firing position (Fig. IX-8) at Ft. Allen Park, Portland, Maine, is one of a pair made at Fort Pitt Foundry in 1866. They were inspected by Clifton Comly and are Nos. 108 and 110, weighing 3,557 and 3,615 respectively. With 10° elevation, the 4.5 delivered a range of 3,265 yards using 3.25 pounds of powder and a 25.5-pound Dyer shell,[20] although 30-pound Hotchkiss or Schenkl projectiles were more likely used in the field.

A former Canadian, working for the United States during the war, invented several pieces of light ordnance which, although apparently excellent weapons, do not seem to have been particularly popular. Norman Wiard (1826-1896)[21] was born in Ontario where at an early age he became foreman of a foundry and began experiments with ordnance. During the Civil War he served as Superintendent of Ordnance Stores, a post which offered considerable opportunity for his inventive proclivities and incidentally brought him into consultation regarding weapons development with both the President and Secretary of War Stanton.

Writing in 1863,[22] Wiard described his weapons as being made of semi-steel (a low-carbon cast iron in which scrap steel replaces part of the pig iron of the charge) in two calibers—6-pounder rifle of 2.6-inch bore and a 12-pounder, 4.62-inch smooth-

FIGURE: IX-7 IDENTIFICATION: Rifle, Siege & Garrison, 4.5-Inch, Model 1861, Iron. REMARKS: Three rifles of a Connecticut battery on hills overlooking Fredericksburg in February, 1863. Although in position, the pieces are limbered and in traveling order.

FIGURE: IX-8 LOCATION: Portland, Me. IDENTIFICATION: Rifle, Siege & Garrison, 4.5-Inch, Model 1861, Iron. BORE: Diameter — 4.5. Rifling — 9 x 9, straight. Length — 120. LENGTH O/A: 133. TRUNNIONS: Diameter — 5.3. Length — 4. MARKINGS: Muzzle Face — No. 110, 3557, C.C., Ft. Pitt, Pa., 1866. COMMON NAME: 4.5-Inch Siege Rifle (preferred). Or, 4.5-Inch Ordnance Rifle. Or, 4.5-Inch Rodman Rifle (erroneous).

FIGURE: IX-9 LOCATION: Shiloh, Tenn. IDENTIFICATION: Wiard, Field, 3.6-Inch, Rifle, Semi-Steel. BORE: Diameter — 3.6. Rifling — 8 x 8. Length — 57.5v. LENGTH O/A: 63.5. TRUNNIONS: Diameter — 4.62. Length — 3.5. COMMON NAME: 12-Pounder Wiard. Or, 3.6-Inch Wiard.

bore howitzer. The latter, he wrote, replaced ". . . my original 12-pounder rifle, thus requiring but one size of carriage for my 12-pounder smoothbore [howitzer] and my 6-pounder rifle field gun. . . ."

One of his 12-pounder rifles (Fig. IX-9) at Shiloh has a bore of 3.6 inches rifled with 8 (another at the same park has 12) lands and grooves. Length overall is 63.5 inches. Marks, if any, are obscured by paint. The 6-pounder and the howitzer each weighed 725 pounds, according to Wiard, although a 6-pounder at Petersburg is marked 837. He said the rifle with a single ounce of powder at 35° could lob a projectile 800 yards, with two ounces, 1,200, and with 12, more than 4 miles.

Surviving Wiards do not conform in all respects to the illustration accompanying the inventor's article. His diagram of the 2.6-inch rifle and the smoothbore howitzer (Fig. IX-10) shows that while general design is similar, both had cascabels, appendages which are lacking in Wiards known today even though rifles have been found dating before and after the article.

Wiard rifles of either caliber are far from common and the smoothbore is extremely rare. An excellent specimen of the 6-pounder rifle is in the Petersburg collection (Fig. IX-11). The piece has a standard 2.6-inch bore rifled with 8 lands and grooves and is 53 inches overall. The right trunnion is marked "N.W., N.Y.C., O.F." Other marks, if any, are concealed by paint, but identical pieces at West

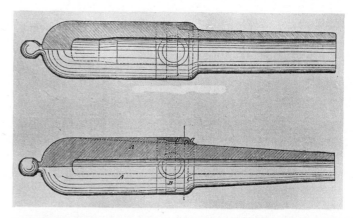

FIGURE: IX-10 IDENTIFICATION: (Top) Wiard, Field, 4.62-Inch (Smoothbore), Howitzer, Semi-Steel. COMMON NAME: 12-Pounder Wiard Howitzer. Or, 4.62-Inch Wiard Howitzer. IDENTIFICATION: (Bottom) Wiard, Field, 2.6-Inch, Rifle, Semi-Steel. REMARKS: Main tube designated A. B, C, and D are reinforces. COMMON NAME: 6-Pounder Wiard. Or, 2.6-Inch Wiard. SOURCE: Wiard's System of Artillery.

FIGURE: IX-11 LOCATION: Petersburg, Va. IDENTIFICATION: Wiard, Field, 2.6-Inch, Rifle, Semi-Steel. BORE: Diameter — 2.6. Rifling — 8 x 8. Length — 46.8. LENGTH O/A: 53. TRUNNIONS: Diameter — 3.67. Length — 3. MARKINGS: Right Trunnion — N.W., N.Y.C., O.F. COMMON NAME: 6-Pounder Wiard. Or, 2.6-Inch Wiard.

FIGURE: IX-12 IDENTIFICATION: Wiard, Field, 2.6-Inch, Rifle, Semi-Steel. REMARKS: Note Wiard, Field, Carriages. Vertical rounds are Wiard canister, horizontal is Hotchkiss shot.

Point and Shiloh bear the same marks on the right trunnions as well as 1862 and 1864, respectively, on the left. However, this form of marking does not hold true in all cases, for a 6-pounder in private hands has been thoroughly examined and has no marks at all.[23]

A Civil War photograph (Fig. IX-12) shows two of these rifles on Wiard's specially designed field carriage which had high, wide-spread cheeks which permitted much greater elevations than standard carriages. Various features of this ingenious carriage are illustrated in a diagram (Fig. IX-13) from Wiard's article. The cheeks, although resting on top of the axle, were connected by "U" bolts beneath it for additional strength. This not only allowed greater elevation, but one carriage could be shoved under another to conserve space during ship and rail transportation. The cheeks were strapped with an iron band which could be tightened to counteract wood shrinkage. Implements were carried above the axle instead of below as in conventional carriages and were thus less vulnerable to being ripped off by stumps.

Instead of the customary trail plate, which dug into the ground during recoil forming a hole that hindered subsequent aiming, Wiard made his trail plate almost flat. This had a tendency to slide rather than dig, and to insure that it slid straight, he affixed a narrow, metal keel which cut a shallow groove and prevented the trail from slewing to the side.

Wiard also devised an ingenious brake for his carriage. The conventional way to slow descent on steep hills was to stop the carriage and chain one or both wheels to prevent rotation. This method took time to affix the chains and was hard on iron tires since prolonged sliding wore one spot. Wiard overcame this difficulty with a metal shoe linked to the stock by chain. While the carriage continued to roll, the shoe was dropped into the road where the carefully measured chain stopped it exactly under a wheel. The wheel then rode on top of the shoe without rotating. At the bottom of the hill, the brake was released by tripping a special link in the chain; this added enough length for the wheel to roll off the shoe which bounced along behind and could be drawn back aboard the carriage and, without stopping, be reset for later use.

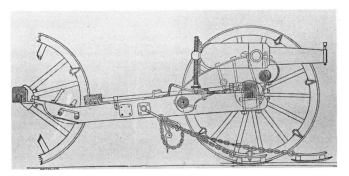

FIGURE: IX-13 IDENTIFICATION: Wiard's Field Artillery Carriage. REMARKS: Note brake (bottom of wheel) shown in on and off positions. SOURCE: *Wiard's System of Artillery.*

Wheels of Wiard carriages (Fig. IX-14) also were unusual. They were made with a number of bolts and wedges which could be adjusted to overcome wood shrinkage, a subject of annoyance in conventional wheels. This feature also made repair quick and easy by replacement of damaged parts. In fact it was Wiard's boast—backed up by demonstration—that using only a wrench "I can singly repair the wheels of artillery carriages constructed according to my invention, faster than a man with an axe can destroy them. . . ."

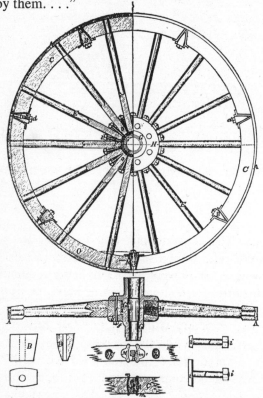

FIGURE: IX-14 IDENTIFICATION: Wheel for Wiard's Field Artillery Carriage. REMARKS: A—Tire; B—Wedges; C—Felloes; D—Tire Bolts, d. Tire Bolt Nuts; E—Spokes; F—Bolts, f. Nuts; G—Part of hub bearing on axle; H—Ring; I—Bolt at hub, i. Nut; J—Hub Wedges; M—Malleable iron castings, m. Flanges. SOURCE: *Wiard's System of Artillery.*

Wiard also developed a boat howitzer, the product of a specialized need. In October, 1861, Major General Ambrose E. Burnside received permission to organize a division-size strike force equipped with shallow-draft steamers to facilitate landings from which quick raids inland could be made to disrupt communications.[24] This "Burnside Expedition," which sailed in January for operations in the coastal areas of North Carolina, included newly organized Marine Artillery units outfitted by the Superintendent of Ordnance Stores[25] with ". . . 12 steel, 12-pounder, rifled boat howitzers . . . of my fabrication, each with a sliding and field carriage, implements and ammunition. . . ." Both carriages were standard types used with the Dahlgren boat howitzers. However, Wiard designed a limber—a double-shafted rig (Fig. IX-15) drawn by two horses in tandem—to be used with the field carriage to give the pieces extended maneuverability on land.[26]

The limber carried three ammunition boxes, each holding a dozen rounds for the rifle or nine for the 12-pounder, smoothbore boat howitzer. It also held a spare articles box, mess chest, and a box for the men's pea jackets. A water breaker was slung beneath and a drag rope, lashed around the boxes, could be used in various emergencies, even slinging the tube beneath the limber to save it if the carriage should be disabled.

One of Wiard's rifled boat howitzers in the Washington Navy Yard collection (Fig. IX-16) has a 3.4-inch bore rifled with 12 lands and grooves. Length overall is 64.5 inches. It presumably has a loop buried in the concrete. Marks, other than an anchor on the tube, are obscured, but Navy Yard records state the piece to be a U.S. rifled, 12-pounder Wiard, dated 1861, with a weight of 785 pounds, two heavier than the "standard" recorded by the inventor in his article. A duplicate weapon at the yard is

FIGURE: IX-15 IDENTIFICATION: Field Carriage for Dahlgren Boat Howitzer with Wiard Limber. REMARKS: Crew marched beside the piece carrying the implements. SOURCE: Wiard, *Marine Artillery.*

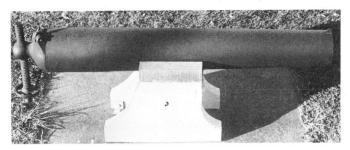

FIGURE: IX-16 LOCATION: Washington Navy Yard, D.C. IDENTIFICATION: Wiard, Boat Howitzer, 3.4-Inch, Rifle, Semi-Steel. BORE: Diameter — 3.4. Rifling — 12 x 12. LENGTH O/A: 64. MARKINGS: Tube — Anchor. REMARKS: Loop concealed by mounting. COMMON NAME: 12-Pounder Wiard Rifled Boat Howitzer. Or, 3.4-Inch Wiard Rifled Boat Howitzer.

FIGURE: IX-17 LOCATION: Charleston, S.C. IDENTIFICATION: Boat Howitzer, 3.5-Inch, Rifle, Confederate (Tentative), Iron. BORE: Diameter — 3.5. Rifling — 12 x 12. Length — 54.5 LENGTH O/A: 64: REMARKS: Piece is unmarked, but presumed to be Confederate. COMMON NAME: 12-Pounder Rifled Confederate Boat Howitzer. Or, 3.5-Inch Rifled Confederate Boat Howitzer.

marked with identical data on the tube, including the 785-pound weight.

The iron boat howitzer (Fig. IX-17) owned by the Charleston (S.C.) Rifle Club is said to have been found many years ago hidden, presumably by retreating Confederates, on a tiny, uninhabited island in the nearby Ashley River. The bore is 3.5 inches, rifled with 12 lands and grooves. Length overall is 64 inches, less than an inch shorter than the Wiard. No markings have been found and the author is inclined to believe this is a Confederate-made piece. The field carriage originally was complete, but the wheels were removed to discourage youngsters from pushing the piece around the club grounds to the detriment of the shrubbery.

The next weapons—Ames and James—have little in common but a rhythmical sound and a hundred years of confusion. A few hours in text or park trying to untangle the maze of Ameses and Jameses is guaranteed to ruffle the most even-tempered ordnance buff and bewildered hobbyists will find scant consolation in knowing that the puzzle also plagued Civil War officers—right up to the highest ranks. The problem is more a matter of semantics than ordnance and stems from too casual weapons identification considering the number of persons and firms involved. Specifically, there were three men, a company, and two foundries named Ames and a single representative of the James clan. The weapons are properly two—one of each name—but many smoothbores rifled during the early stages of the war were called "James Rifles" and every now and then the Ames name is improperly attached to cannon which happened to be cast by that firm.

Best known of the lot was Charles Tillinghast James who was born in West Greenwich, Rhode Island in 1804 or 1805, depending on which biography you read.[27] He received little formal schooling, but seems to have been a man of tremendous energy. Starting as a carpenter, James taught himself mechanics and worked to the top in the textile industry. He became an exponent of utilizing steam engines to operate cotton factories and acquired a reputation for reviving dying mills.

Long interested in politics, James began to take active part after 1848. He became a major general of militia, and in 1851 was elected to the United States Senate, a post he held until 1857. However, during this period, his financial position deteriorated. He refused to offer for re-election, retired from politics, and devoted his talents to perfecting several inventions including the James projectile for rifled cannon which is illustrated in Chapter XIII. In addition, the general developed a 14-pounder rifle which, to the author's way of thinking, is the only true "James Rifle." Existing smoothbores, as described in Chapter I, rifled to use the general's projectiles were called "James Rifles" or "James Guns," but the term is misleading and the simple "Rifled 6 (or other) pounder" is more accurate and leaves the name "James" free for description of the 14-pounder.

The weapon, normally bronze although a few were made of steel, is found in most of the field-gun parks and two excellent specimens (Fig. IX-18) grace the entrance to the science building at Louisiana State University at Baton Rouge. Bores measure 3.8 inches rifled with 10 lands and grooves (an occasional piece will be found with 7), and length

FIGURE: IX-18 LOCATION: Baton Rouge, La. IDENTIFICATION: James, Field, 3.8-Inch, Rifle, Bronze. BORE: Diameter — 3.8. Rifling — 10 x 10, straight. Length — 64. LENGTH O/A: 73. TRUNNIONS: Diameter — 3.67. Length — 2.75. MARKINGS: Muzzle Face — G.T.B. Left Trunnion — 1861. Right Trunnion — Ames Co., Founders, Chicopee, Mass. REMARKS: A few made of steel. COMMON NAME: 14-Pounder James. Or, 3.8-Inch James.

overall is 73 inches. Both are marked on the right trunnion "Ames Co., Founders, Chicopee, Mass.," on the left "1861," and on the muzzle face, "GTB."

Accompanying historical plaques[28] state they fired at Fort Sumter and were presented to the University after the war by General W.T. Sherman. The latter part of the statement is doubtful, and the former certainly is not borne out by fact. The pieces obviously did not fire on Fort Sumter, since the previously discussed Blakely (Chapter VIII) was the only rifle on hand at the initial bombardment and the 14-pounder was far too light for demolition work during 1863.

All James rifles thus far checked have been dated 1861-62 and probably none were made after the latter date since by then the general's projectiles had fallen into disfavor and he was dead, the victim of one of his own shells. Wounded when a shell exploded 16 October 1862 while he was experimenting with it at Sag Harbor, New York, he died the following day.

Although the 14-pounder appears to be the only gun actually invented by the general, many Civil War officers referred to the rifled smoothbores as "James" guns, terminology which often led to considerable confusion as evidenced by correspondence between Major General George B. McClellan and Secretary of War E. M. Stanton 22 June 1862.[29] McClellan started the exchange in a message timed 4:30 A.M.: "I am informed General James now has completed two batteries of bronze, rifled guns and one battery of steel rifled guns, all of 3.80 caliber. These guns have been tried by others in whom I have confidence and I should be glad to have you order them for this army as early as practicable. . . ."

Stanton replied at 4:30 P.M.: "James is not known as a manufacturer of guns and it is not known

that he makes any pretension of having invented one. Ames, of Chicopee, manufactures guns, and is the manufacturer of James' projectile, about the merits of which there are conflicting reports and the purchase of which you declined to recommend last spring. . . ."

McClellan answered this at 7:25 P.M. with: ". . . the guns referred to are rifled cannon which General Charles T. James claims to have invented as perfectly adapted to his patented projectile. They are manufactured by Ames of Chicopee, Mass. A member of my staff, who is a good artillery officer, experimented with these guns and James' patent projectiles in December last and pronounced them the best he had seen. . . ."

Thus far McClellan seems to know exactly whereof he speaks for the "3.80 caliber" is unquestionably the 14-pounder and not the 3.67-inch rifled to handle 12-pound James projectiles. However, with the next sentence, he falls into the James' conversion trap: "They are highly recommended by other officers and are said to have been the most efficient of all those used in the siege of Fort Pulaski. . . ." As far as can be determined, no 14-pounders were used in this engagement and the "James" gun were simply rifled 6-, 24-, 32-, and 42-pounders.

Other Civil War officers also confused the 14-pounder with older weapons rifled to fire James ammunition and even a first-class ordnance officer like Benton, in testimony before the Senate Committee on Heavy Ordnance[30] denied existence of a distinct James gun. However, the 3.8 caliber described by McClellan is clearly the 14-pounder and since there is no reason to doubt the general's veracity, the author is convinced the piece was indeed designed by General James and produced by the Ames Co.

Although few if any James rifles were produced after 1862, what appears to be a James 6-pounder smoothbore made in 1864 is mounted at Fort McHenry (Fig. IX-19). With exception of caliber, the piece is a copy of the 14-pounder rifle. It is clearly dated 1864 and although battered, a trunnion face has sufficient lettering to establish that Ames was the founder. Stamped on the breech is "State of Conn." and "W.A.B."—William A. Buckingham, Civil War governor whose initials have been found on conventional James rifles.

Why Connecticut would order one, possibly several, small-caliber smoothbores at this stage of the war is difficult to imagine. The piece might have been the last of an order for 14-pounders and, being filled months after the rifle had fallen from favor, was bored as a 6-pounder in an attempt to salvage

FIGURE: IX-19 LOCATION: Fort McHenry, Md. IDENTIFICATION: James, Field, 3.67-Inch, Bronze. BORE: Diameter — 3.67. Smoothbore. Length — 64. LENGTH O/A: 73. TRUNNIONS: Diameter — 3.67. Length — 2.75. MARKINGS: Left Trunnion — 1864. Right Trunnion — Ames Co., Founders, Chicopee, Mass. Tube at Breech — W.A.B. (Governor William A. Buckingham) State of Conn. COMMON NAME: 6-Pounder James. Or, 3.67-Inch James.

something from a bad bargain. It could have been a bonafide 1864 order with the James form considered an improvement over the M-1841 6-pounder design. Perhaps Ames had a few unbored castings left from the days of James popularity and Connecticut snapped them up as 6-pounders at a reduced price. Such possibilities seem endless and the piece remains a fascinating mystery until future research uncovers records of the transaction.

Since Ames manufactured the 14-pounders and also converted many of the old smoothbores to use James ammunition, it seems logical to take up this firm next—and the brothers who owned it. Nathan Peabody Ames (1803-1847) and James Tyler Ames (1810-1883) were born at Chelmsford, Massachusetts, and in 1829 began making swords for the government. Nathan apparently was head of the firm which shortly after opening moved to Chicopee (Springfield) and was incorporated in 1834 as the Ames Manufacturing Co. In 1836 a foundry was added for casting bronze cannon, church bells, and, later, statues. The ordnance-making part of the business seems to have prospered for in 1840 we find Nathan visiting Europe to inspect various armories and by 1844 the firm was turning out machines for the British to be used in the manufacture of muskets. At Nathan's death in April, 1847, his younger brother took over the business and piloted it until retirement in 1874. For this reason, varying initials are found on Ames-made weapons at different periods.

Those made before the older brother's death are stamped "N.P. Ames, Founder, Springfield, Mass." After 1847 they are marked "Ames Co., Founders, Chicopee, Mass.," "Ames Mfg. Co., Chicopee, Mass.," or "A.M.Co."

Insofar as known, all products of the firm were brass with exception of the previously mentioned steel 14-pounders. However, there is also an iron Ames gun, the product of Horatio Ames whose address is variously given as Salisbury and Falls Village, Connecticut. Since the two are quite near, it is probable that the foundry was at Falls Village and his residence at Salisbury.[31] Ames, apparently no relation to the Massachusetts brothers, developed several wrought iron rifles. In 1862 he delivered the first of five 50-pounders ordered by the Navy. The piece (Fig. IX-20) which resembled the Dahlgren iron rifles, had a bore of 5.1 inches and weighed 5,500 pounds. Test firing continued until the rifle had survived 1,630 rounds of 37-pound shot fired with charges of 3.5 pounds. A second gun was bored to 80-pounder, 6-inch bore, and fired 438 times with 5-pound charges and 67-pound shot. The remaining three weapons plus another were then accepted by the Navy and the order terminated due to the excessive cost.

The following year Ames received an order from President Lincoln for fifteen 100-pounder rifles with the tacit understanding that he would make the largest guns possible with his existing works. Consequently, a 7-inch rifle, which Ames called a 125-pounder (Fig. IX-21) was delivered in September, 1864, and tested at Bridgeport, Connecticut. It was fired seven-hundred times with charges ranging from 13 to 30 pounds and Hotchkiss shot and shell varying from 104 to 127 pounds. The ammunition gave considerable trouble, stripping its packing under high charges, and proper instruments for checking the range didn't arrive until late in the tests. However, random shots gave the following results: Charge, 25 pounds, shot 108 pounds, elevation 30°—8,700

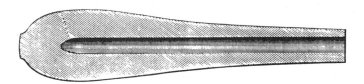

FIGURE: IX-20 IDENTIFICATION: Ames, Navy, 5.1-Inch, Rifle, Wrought Iron. BORE: Diameter — 5.1. Length — 92 (estimated). LENGTH O/A: 106.5 (estimated). SOURCE: Holley. COMMON NAME: 50-Pounder Ames Rifle. Or, 5.1-Inch Ames Rifle.

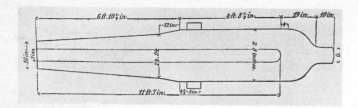

FIGURE: IX-21 IDENTIFICATION: Ames, Seacoast, 7-Inch, Rifle, Wrought Iron. BORE: Diameter — 7 (later bored to 8). Length — 139. LENGTH O/A: 168.13. TRUNNIONS: Diameter — 8. Length — 4.5. SOURCE: U.S. Senate Committee Reports, 38th Congress. COMMON NAME: 125-Pounder Ames. Or, 7-Inch Ames. Or, (after reboring) 8-Inch Ames.

yards, charge, 30, shot, 125, elevation 30°—8,960; charge 25, shell 106, elevation 34° 30'—9,230 yards.

Concluding the tests, the board reported:[32] Ames wrought iron guns possess to a degree never before equaled by any cannon of equal weight offered to our service the essential qualities of great lateral and longitudinal strength and great powers of endurance under heavy charges. . . . They are not liable to burst explosively and without warning even when fired under very high charges. . . . They are well adapted to the wants of the service generally, but especially whenever long ranges and high velocities are required. . . ." The board also recommended that the 7-inch pieces be reamed up to 8.

This was high praise indeed from normally conservative Army officers, but their faith was not fulfilled. The test piece, when bored to 8 inches, burst on the twenty-fourth round and subsequent firing of the other guns proved what cast iron advocates had been saying for some time—that wrought iron was an excellent material, but the art of working iron had not reached a state where perfect welds could be made with sufficient regularity. One wrought iron piece might stand ten thousand rounds and the next not go ten. This, and the price—almost ten times that of cast iron weapons of equal caliber—discouraged further purchases of the Ames guns. The pieces were made by welding a number of rings one after another to a solid breech. Each ring was made by wrapping a bar of wrought iron around a mandrel and welding the ends, then boring a hole in the center into which was fitted a similarly made, smaller circle.[33]

Massachusetts could boast a number of ordnance manufacturers and inventors during the 19th century and one of the more interesting was Daniel Treadwell (1791-1872).[34] A native of Ipswich, he

turned his inventive genius to many fields and during the 1820s developed a power printing press which was used extensively in larger towns along the Atlantic seaboard, first for books and later newspapers. He also devised a method of spinning hemp and his machine for a time produced most of the Navy's cordage.

In 1840, Treadwell filed a caveat in the U.S. Patent Office describing a method of constructing cannon by building up a series of wrought iron rings welded together and reinforced by bands.[35] He spent some three years setting up furnaces and in 1843

FIGURE: IX-22 LOCATION: Washington Navy Yard, D.C. IDENTIFICATION: Treadwell, Seacoast or Navy, 6.4-Inch, Wrought Iron. BORE: Diameter — 6.4. Smoothbore. LENGTH O/A: 84.5. TRUNNIONS: Diameter — 4.75. Length — 4.25. MARKINGS: Tube — Daniel Treadwell. COMMON NAME: 32-Pounder Treadwell. Or, 6.4-Inch Treadwell.

FIGURE: IX-23 LOCATION: West Point, N.Y. IDENTIFICATION: Rifle, Field, 3-Inch, Experimental, German Silver. BORE: Diameter — 3. Rifling — 7 x 7, straight. Length — 64. LENGTH O/A: 73.5. TRUNNIONS: Diameter — 4.2. Length — 3.2. MARKINGS: Muzzle Face — No. 2, H.N.H. & Co., 1864, 1372. COMMON NAME: Rifled Napoleon (erroneous) Or, Experimental 3-Inch Rifle.

completed about half a dozen 6-pounder field guns for the Army and a year later finished four light 32-pounders for the Navy. Despite successful tests, however, he failed to seriously interest the government in adopting his weapons, probably due to a necessarily high price. This disappointment, coupled with the later conviction, culminating in an unsuccessful suit in 1863, that Parrott had appropriated his idea, so preyed upon his mind that he lost interest in his earlier activities and spent the last ten years of his life in virtual retirement.[36]

Two of Treadwell's four 32-pounders are in the Washington Navy Yard collection (Fig. IX-22). The pieces are identical and although apparently neither saw service during the war, deserve careful preservation as historic relics as well as interesting specimens of experimental ordnance.

Another Massachusetts weapon—manufactured by Henry N. Hooper of Boston—is the experimental 3-inch rifle (Fig. IX-23) in the West Point collection. The piece, as mentioned in Chapter I, is sometimes called a "Rifled Napoleon," but has little in common with this traditional smoothbore 12-pounder other than similarity of appearance to the so-called "Southern" model. The bore is rifled with 7 lands and grooves and the 73.5-inch weapon, said to be made of German silver, weighs 1,372 pounds. It is No. 2 of a very limited quantity turned out by the Hooper firm in 1864.

A Washington Navy Yard weapon (Fig. IX-24) is identified by records there as a 30-pounder Sawyer. The piece has a bore diameter of roughly 4.62 inches rifled with 6 lands and grooves and measures 78.5 inches overall. It was made by Cyrus Alger & Co. of Boston in 1856, according to trunnion marks, and was captured by the Confederates aboard the tug *Fanny*.

This craft, an iron-hulled propeller, was picked up[37] by Southern vessels 1 October 1861 while trying to take provisions to a detachment of troops at Chickamicomico, near Loggerhead Inlet, North Carolina. She fired nine shots, then was run ashore and surrendered after her crew panicked. Most records simply mention her "two guns," but a federal report[38]

FIGURE: IX-24 LOCATION: Washington Navy Yard, D.C. IDENTIFICATION: Sawyer, Siege & Garrison or Navy, 4.62-Inch, Rifle, Iron. BORE: Diameter — 4.62. Rifling — 6 x 6, straight. Length — 61.5v. LENGTH O/A: 78.5 TRUNNIONS: Diameter — 5.5. Length — 4. MARKINGS: Muzzle Face — 1. Left Trunnion — 1856. Right Trunnion — C.A. & Co. COMMON NAME: 30-Pounder Sawyer. Or, 4.62-Inch Sawyer (preferred).

states: "She had the best armament of all tugs, one being a Sawyer's rifle gun. . . ." and a Confederate tabulation of ordnance stores[39] a few days after the capture lists: "One 32-pdr. rifled cannon . . . and one 8-pdr. rifled cannon. . ." Either could have been a Sawyer, but presumably the former was the piece in the Navy Yard today.

References to the Sawyer are few and misleading. Abbot[40] mentions the siege train in the Richmond campaign having an experimental 24-pounder (5.862-inch) and a 6-pounder (3.67-inch) rifled on the Sawyer plan. The 24 burst at the tenth round, he recalls, and the smaller caliber was seldom used and emplaced only to repel assaults. In this case, although speaking of rifles, Abbot refers to equivalent smoothbore caliber. Rifled projectile weight varied considerably, but a 3.67-inch probably would go 18 to 20 pounds and a 5.862 in the neighborhood of 45. This explains the apparent bore diameter and weight discrepancy in the "30-pounder Sawyer" and the 6- and 24-pounders.

Abbot furnished no statistics on the siege train rifles, but a 24-pounder Sawyer tested at Fort Monroe in 1859 had the following dimensions and weights:[41] bore diameter, 5.862-inch rifled with 6 lands and grooves, the latter .25-inch deep; length of bore 110 inches and weight of the piece, 8,822 pounds. At 13°30' with 5.5 pounds of powder, it fired the inventor's 45-pound projectiles an average 4,359 yards. Note bore diameter was .042 larger than the standard 5.82-inch 24-pounder.

Brigadier General J. W. Phelps at Ship Island, Mississippi, had a much higher opinion of the Sawyer than Abbot for he wrote to Washington 29 January 1862:[42] "The 9-inch shellgun on Navy carriage is being put up to the number of ten, but I am in hopes that Sawyer's rifled 24-pounder and 8 and 10-inch columbiads will be sent to replace them. I would take this occasion to state, as my opinion, that if the 42-pounder were bored for Sawyer's 24-pounder, it would be the best heavy ordnance that we have either for land or sea service. . . ."

Writing in December, 1861, General B. F. Butler told Major General George B. McClellan:[43] "I have also nearly ready eight heavy rifled 5 and 6 inch guns of the Sawyer pattern. . . ." Speaking in round numbers, these may well have been the 4.62, such as in Washington Navy Yard, and the 5.862-inch, or "24-pounder."

The projectile for the Sawyer had six flanges which mated with grooves of the bore. The gun, despite early enthusiasm, wasn't particularly successful and was phased out of service as rapidly as

FIGURE: IX-25 IDENTIFICATION: Cochran Breechloader. RE-MARKS: 1861 view of weapon being tested at the Naval Practice Battery, Washington Navy Yard. SOURCE: *Leslie's Illustrated Newspaper* 21 Sept. 1861.

possible. The inventor was Sylvanus Sawyer (1822-1895) of Templeton, Massachusetts.

Another unsuccessful weapon, the Cochran Breechloader, is largely a mystery. The invention of J. Webster Cochran, who published a pamphlet about it in 1860,[44] the piece seems to have utilized a breechblock which, to judge from a contemporary sketch (Fig. IX-25), was pierced by a screw which turned into the breech.

One biographer[45] states that Cochran, who was born at Enfield, New Hampshire in 1814, by the time he was twenty had invented ". . . a revolving breechloading, rifled cannon in which the cylinder was automatically rotated by a cocking of the hammer, the same principle that afterward secured the success of the revolving pistol. . . ." This, of course, is an earlier model than the illustrated piece and one which, based on the description, seems impractical if not downright dangerous for heavy ordnance of the day. It does, however, establish that Cochran was working with rifled, breech-loading ordnance as early as 1834. He lived in France from 1835 until 1847 when he returned home and engaged in the manufacture of firearms and projectiles as well as perfecting various other inventions.

The following thirteen cannon—Attick, Atwater, Bishop, Bomford, Butler, Dimick, Dyer, Ericsson, Lyman-Haskell, Read, Schenkl, Stockton, and Woodruff—saw limited or no service, but since their names are sprinkled through texts of the period, to skip them would be remiss.

Attick's rifle (Fig. IX-26) was more an alteration than a separate weapon since the piece consisted of a standard 42-pounder, rifled and reinforced with a composition band forced on by hydrostatic pressure. The composition was a trade secret, but is believed to have been a form of bronze. The gun, mounted aboard the Stevens Battery, was tried with 14- and 16-pound charges and 100-pound James projectiles. It burst after a short period of service.

Holley mentions an 80-pounder (5.85-inch) Atwater, rifled with 12 lands and grooves, being tested at the Washington Navy Yard. Chief feature of the piece was the method of rifling (Fig. IX-27). Atwater believed pressure of the column of air in front of the projectile in the bore was greater than the gas behind it. In accord with this theory, he increased windage by cutting away alternate lands for 12 calibers (roughly 70 inches) from the bottom of the 144-inch bore. The piece was cast iron, 21 inches thick at the breech where it was double-banded with 6- by 2-inch wrought iron rings. The first band had six rings and the second five, all shrunk on with heat. The rifle weighed 11,625 pounds.

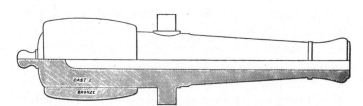

FIGURE: IX-26 IDENTIFICATION: Attick, Seacoast, 7-Inch, Rifle, Iron and Bronze. BORE: Diameter — 7. Length — 110. LENGTH O/A: 129. TRUNNIONS: Diameter — 7. Length — 6.5. REMARKS: Standard 42-Pounder, Model 1841, rifled and banded with composition reinforce which was a trade secret, but basically bronze. SOURCE: Holley. COMMON NAME: 100-Pounder Attick Rifle. Or, 7-Inch Attick Rifle.

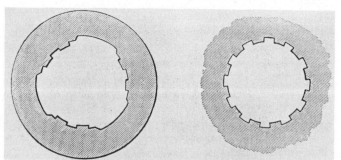

FIGURE: IX-27 IDENTIFICATION: Atwater Rifling. REMARKS: Approximately half the bore was rifled 12 x 12, straight (right). Certain lands of the remainder were removed to insure windage and, theoretically, reduce pressure from the column of air in front of the projectile. Although texts state alternate lands were cut away, the illustration shows a somewhat different form. SOURCE: Holley.

Apparently Mr. Atwater's theory was not successful for it receives only casual mention in contemporary texts. However, at least one other piece was rifled in this fashion for one of the three Navy 15-inchers, mentioned in Chapter V, which were cast at Pittsburg with 12-inch bores and rifled, was grooved according to Atwater's method.[46]

The 12-pounder Bishop Breechloader (Fig. IX-28) was patented in 1856 by G. W. Bishop. The cast iron smoothbore, now at West Point, was found at Fort Richmond in New York Harbor where it apparently had lain unmounted since the early part of the Civil War. The bore is 4.62 inches, length to end of breech 52 inches and to end of breechblock hinge, 59.5 inches. The block, apparently conical, is missing.

Colonel George Bomford, inventor of the columbiad (q.v.) also designed a 12-inch smoothbore which was made at the South Boston Foundry of Cyrus Alger in 1846.[47] This cast iron Bomford gun had a total length of 134 inches and a bore length of 116.2. Weight was 25,510 pounds and maximum range 5,800 yards with 28 pounds of powder and a 181-pound shell. In 1862 the piece (Fig. IX-29) was reinforced with a band of 1-inch wide wrought iron rings 4 inches thick, giving it a maximum diameter of 46 inches. It was never introduced into service.

About 1845, Bomford devised a plan for testing pressure at various points within the bore.[48] He drilled ten small holes through the tube at intervals of approximately a caliber and dropped a steel ball into each. When the piece was fired, the velocity with which each ball was projected could be determined and from this pressures deduced for the various points. The piece in Figure IX-30 is listed in West Point records as a 3-inch Bomford breechloader used in the experiments. The cascabel and block, which screwed into the breech, are missing. Length to the breech opening is 64 inches.

References to the Butler gun are few and not entirely clear. Statistical data[49] on the 1,000-ton sailing ship *Morning Light,* which was captured by the Confederates off Sabine Pass, Texas, 21 January 1863, and burned two days later to prevent recapture, lists her armament as eight 32-pounders of 57 cwt. and "1 rifled Butler gun."

This terminology, which is echoed by a Confederate report[50] of the capture, would indicate the inventor's name was Butler. However, a correspondent's story of the action for a Houston newspaper states:[51] "I forgot to mention she [the *Morning Light*] had on board a very pretty little breechloading gun presented by the Beast [Maj. Gen.

FIGURE: IX-28 LOCATION: West Point, N.Y. IDENTIFICATION: Bishop, Field, 4.62-Inch, Breechloader, Iron. BORE: Diameter — 4.62. Smoothbore. Length — 52. LENGTH O/A: 59.5 (to end of breechblock hinge). TRUNNIONS: Diameter — 5. Length — 4. REMARKS: Patented in 1856. COMMON NAME: 12-Pounder Bishop Breechloader. Or, 4.62-Inch Bishop Breechloader.

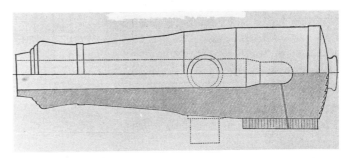

FIGURE: IX-29 IDENTIFICATION: Bomford, Seacoast, 12-Inch, Model 1846, Banded, Iron. BORE: Diameter — 12. Smoothbore. Length — 116.2. LENGTH O/A: 134. TRUNNIONS: Diameter — 12. Length — 10 (estimated). REMARKS: Split cascable with ratchet-type elevation. Drawing was made after original piece was banded with wrought-iron reinforce in 1862. SOURCE: Holley. COMMON NAME: 12-Inch Bomford.

FIGURE: IX-30 LOCATION: West Point, N.Y. IDENTIFICATION: Bomford, Experimental, 3-Inch, Breechloader, Iron. BORE: Diameter — 3. Smoothbore. Length — 64. LENGTH O/A: 64 (excludes threaded cascabel which served as breechblock). TRUNNIONS: Diameter — 3.67. Length — 2.5. REMARKS: Used in experiments to determine bore pressure. COMMON NAME: 3-Inch Bomford Breechloader.

Benjamin F. Butler]. . . . However, were the hyena in the same fix with his munificent present, he would be in very bad plight for while in the act of firing it a [Confederate] shell . . . exploded which resulted in the gunner losing part of his hand and carrying away a portion of the breech and spoiling the gun considerably. . . ."

The presentation theory may have been correct or the dream of a vindictive Southern newspaperman. Partial substantiation, however, is found in the 1925 Bannerman catalogue[52] which advertised a 34-inch, iron Civil War muzzle-loader with a 2-inch bore roughly resembling the Cadet 6-pounder of Chapter I. The weapon was marked in large letters on the breech: "Gen. Butler, 1861." Price, including a gunner's outfit, was $38. Whether the little muzzle-loader was presented by the general or named for him and its connection, if any, with the *Morning Light* breechloader, is strictly conjectural and positive identification must await supporting evidence.

The Army in 1859 tested at Fort Monroe a 6.4-inch rifle invented by Horace E. Dimick.[53] It had 6 lands and grooves, bore length 101 inches and weight 9,300 pounds. With a 6-pound charge, the piece fired a 51-pound projectile of Dimick's design.

Tested at the same time were two rifles built on the plan of Alexander B. Dyer (1815-1874), later major general and chief of ordnance 1864-74. A 2.9-inch Dyer, which had 8 lands and grooves, bore length 44.5 inches and weight 250 pounds, gave 3,270 yards average range with a 1-pound charge, elevation 13°30' and a 9-pound projectile. His 3.67-inch had 16 lands and grooves, a bore length of 57.5 and weighed 880 pounds. It fired a 14-pound projectile using a 1.25-pound charge, but no range was recorded.

John Ericsson (1803-1889), who designed and built the *Monitor* in 1861, turned his talents two years later to construction of wrought iron, smoothbore ordnance for the ironclads *Puritan* and *Dictator*. As one biographer put it:[54] "In 1863 he designed and built for acceptance by the government a thirteen-inch wrought iron gun. The design was a distinct advance on the practice of the day, but it placed demands on the makers of forgings which they were unable to successfully meet and in test the gun developed some slight cracks. This failure led to a controversy between Ericsson and the Naval Bureau of Ordnance which prevented further consideration of his design. . . ."

Captain Fox amplified this a bit in testimony before the Senate committee 21 January 1865:[55] "Capt. Ericsson made us a gun and although it has not burst, it is opening so as to render its use dangerous. . . ."

The Ericsson[56] consisted of a wrought iron tube reinforced with a series of rings ⅜-inch wide and 9¼ thick, cut from boiler plate and forced on by hydrostatic pressure. The reinforce began at a flange at the end of the breech and extended for 8 feet down the tube where a large nut tightened around the chase forced the rings together and back against the flange. Total length was 152 inches, maximum diameter 42, and weight, 47,000 pounds.

The odd-looking "accelerating gun" (Fig. IX-31) was patented by Azel S. Lyman of New York 3 February 1857.[57] Although a smoothbore, the piece seems to have fired an elongated solid projectile shown in the bore (b). This was loaded through the breech, after the threaded cap (a) was removed, and backed by a small charge of powder. Similar caps were removed and the twin tubes (d) loaded with larger charges. An air-tight material was placed over the muzzle (f) and the air of the bore exhausted through an opening (e) to eliminate pressure from in front of the projectile. At ignition through the vent (c), the projectile started down the bore and was accelerated by explosion of the additional charges in the two tubes. A 2.9-inch rifle constructed on Lyman's plan was later partially tested, but condemned by the government as too dangerous.

Four rifles tested at Fort Monroe in 1859[58] are listed as the design of "Dr. Reed." This appears to be Dr. John Brahan Read (1816-1899), Tuscaloosa, Alabama physician and inventor of the celebrated Read projectile (q.v.)—which also is often misspelled "Reed".[59] The smallest was a 3.69-inch with 3 lands and grooves, bore length 103.4 and weight 1,200. It burned a 1.5-pound charge to fire a 12-pound projectile. Two had almost the same bore diameter and identical 7 land and groove rifling

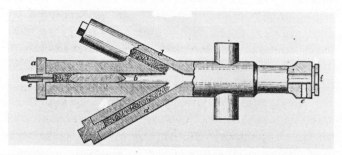

FIGURE: **IX-31** IDENTIFICATION: Lyman, Experimental, Accelerating, Iron. REMARKS: Drawing from patent 3 Feb. 1857. Bore diameter not specified. Smoothbore. a. Threaded breech cap; b. Bore; c. Vent; d. Acceleration tubes; e. Air exhaust port; f. Airtight diaphram. SOURCE: Holley.

which varied in depth from .03 to .08 inch and sounds suspiciously like the hook-slant form later adopted by the Confederacy and generally termed "Brooke." Bore of one, designated a siege piece, was 4.854 inches in diameter and 109 long. It weighed 5,000 pounds and burned a 3-pound charge to loft a 22-pound projectile. The field model had a 4.636-inch bore 74 inches long. Weight was 1,900 pounds, charge 2 and projectile weight 15. The final model tested by the doctor, who worked for the Confederacy during the war, was a 6.425-inch with 3 lands and grooves, bore length 110 inches and weight 8,500. With 6 pounds of powder, elevation 11°30′, it fired a 50-pound projectile an average 3,655 yards.

Commander William A. Parker, skipper of the *U.S.S. Cambridge,* reported 12 November 1861:[60] ". . . while bombarding an encampment of Rebel soldiers near the town of Urbana, the Schenkle [sic] rifled gun was split for the distance of 10 inches from the muzzle. The caliber of the gun is 4 9/16 (4.56) inches, weight of projectile 19 pounds. The crack is so slight that the gun can still be used on an emergency. I am unable to account for the cause of this fracture. . . ."

No other statistical data has been found on this weapon which no doubt was designed by J. P. Schenkl, inventor of a form of projectile (Chapter XIII) used throughout the war by federal forces. The inventor's name is spelled in contemporary records both with and without a final "e." The spelling and initials used here were copied from the bronze fuse of a Schenkl shell in possession of the author.

During the 1840s, U.S. Navy Commodore Robert Field Stockton (1795-1866) supervised construction of three 12-inch, wrought iron smoothbores which became known as Stockton Guns.[61] The first, called the "Oregon," was made in England and after considerable testing with charges of 20 and 30 pounds and 216-pound balls, cracked through the reinforce, but was banded and fired again, apparently without injury. It was then set aside and in 1864 was reported still at the Philadelphia Navy Yard.[62]

After qualified success of the "Oregon," a second gun was forged, this time at the United States firm of Ward and Co. This was the celebrated "Peacemaker" which narrowly missed killing President John Tyler in 1844 when it exploded while being fired aboard the *U.S.S. Princeton* during an excursion on the Potomac River.[63]

Destruction of the Peacemaker brought a return to England for fabrication of the third Stockton gun (Fig. IX-32). Almost an exact copy of the others, it was made at the Mersey Iron Works in 1845.[64]

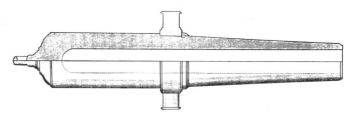

FIGURE: IX-32 IDENTIFICATION: Stockton, Navy, 12-Inch, Wrought Iron. BORE: Diameter — 12. Smoothbore. Length — 144. LENGTH O/A: 169. TRUNNIONS: Diameter — 8.5 (estimated). Length — 8 (estimated). REMARKS: Made at Mersey Iron Works, England, in 1845. One of three Stockton guns (See text). SOURCE: Holley. COMMON NAME: "The Mersey Gun." Or, 12-Inch Stockton.

Total length was 169 inches, bore length 144 inches, diameter over the chamber 28 inches, and weight 16,700 pounds. It was never mounted for service since investigation of the Peacemaker explosion convinced the government that existing industry was incapable of producing a safe wrought iron cannon of large caliber and that their use should be abandoned. Before being laid to rest, however, the third piece was fired successfully—with 45 pounds of powder and a 224-pound shot.

The Woodruff was a steel 2-pounder which weighed 140 pounds. Sole reference to its use found thus far is in Brown's book on Grierson's Raid.[65]

The Confederates, although far more limited in resources than the North, managed to produce a fair share of miscellaneous weapons of which the most prevalent today is a bronze, 3-inch rifle, easily identified by a pronounced base ring and straight, sharply tapered tube. An excellent collection of these weapons is displayed at Petersburg. All were made by Quinby & Robinson of Memphis, Tennessee (Fig. IX-33) or A.B. Rand Brothers of Vicksburg, Mississippi (Fig. IX-34), although fabrication of the 3-inch may not have been restricted to these two firms.

Products of both are basically similar, but exhibit certain noticeable differences probably due more to lack of exact patterns and standards than a deliberate model change. Weapons from the Vicksburg shop have a slightly narrower base ring than the Quinby and Robinson guns and are rifled with 6 lands and grooves of the "Brooke" fashion. Markings are on the right trunnion and on the illustrated piece are: "A.B. Rand Bros., V. Burg, Miss., 1862, No. 3." The other is marked on the left trunnion: "1862" and on the right: "Quinby & Robinson, Memphis, Tenn." It is rifled with 12 lands and grooves of the straight type.

FIGURE: IX-33 LOCATION: Petersburg, Va. IDENTIFICA-TION: Rifle, Field, 3-Inch, Confederate, Bronze. BORE: Di-ameter — 3. Rifling — 12 x 12, straight. LENGTH O/A: 65.5. TRUNNIONS: Diameter — 3.67. Length — 3.25. MARKINGS: Left Trunnion — 1862. Right Trunnion — Quinby & Robin-son, Memphis, Tenn. COMMON NAME: 3-Inch Quinby & Rob-inson. Or, 3-Inch Confederate Rifle.

FIGURE: IX-34 LOCATION: Petersburg, Va. IDENTIFICA-TION: Rifle, Field, 3-Inch, Confederate, Bronze. BORE: Di-ameter — 3. Rifling — 6 x 6, hook-slant. LENGTH O/A: 63. TRUNNIONS: Diameter — 3.67. Length — 2.75. MARKINGS: Right Trunnion — A.B. Rand Bros., V. Burg., Miss., 1862, No. 3. REMARKS: Muzzle has been cut back 2.5 inches. Standard overall length is 65.5. COMMON NAME: 3-Inch Rand. Or, 3-Inch Confederate Rifle.

In general, rifles of both foundries are 65.5 inches long. The illustrated Rand, however, is an exception. Measurements show 2.5 inches have been turned off the muzzle, possibly to eliminate an imper-fection in casting, making the length 63 inches. In other respects, the piece seems to be a duplicate of companion Rands. Trunnion diameters of all are 3.62 inches, but those of the Rands are a bit shorter—2.75 inches compared to 3.25.

The South also manufactured bronze rifles in the U.S. 6-pounder M-1841 pattern as mentioned in Chapter I. A Fort Monroe 3-inch (Fig. IX-35) was cast at Tredegar in 1861 and rifled with 12 lands and grooves. Leeds and Co. of New Orleans turned out the 3.3-inch rifle in Figure IX-36. There are three of this caliber at West Point, all rifled with 7 lands and grooves and cast in 1861-62.

A cast iron 3-inch rifle, Model 1861, was listed in the 1863 Confederate Ordnance Manual[66] as in service, but not considered permanently adopted. Su-perficially the piece (Fig. IX-37) resembled the U.S. Ordnance Rifle, but lacked the wrought iron weap-on's streamlined appearance. Length was 72 inches and weight 967 pounds.

Figure IX-38 shows a Petersburg National Mili-tary Park 3-inch 71.5 inches long rifled with 12 lands and grooves in contrast to 5 for the Model 1861. Paint covers marks, but Park records list the piece at an even 1,000 pounds. Muzzle swell and noticeable

breech reinforce give the rifle a distinctive, if not particularly uniform, appearance.

Also boasting a muzzle swell, but trimmer shape, was the 4.62-inch siege rifle, Model 1862 (Fig. IX-39). This piece, listed in the 1863 manual,[67] had 7 lands and grooves, overall length 118 inches and weight 4,362 pounds. A heavier Confederate 4.62 was discussed in Chapter VII on the Brooke.

By 1862, the South had developed a light mountain rifle which presumably was made in limited quantities and is one of the rarest of Confederate ordnance items today. Despite extensive travel and

FIGURE: IX-35 LOCATION: Fort Monroe, Va. IDENTIFI-CATION: Rifle, Field, 3-Inch, Confederate, Bronze. BORE: Di-ameter — 3. Rifling — 12 x 12, straight. Length — 57.5. LENGTH O/A: 65.5. TRUNNIONS: Diameter — 3.67. Length — 2.8. MARKINGS: Muzzle Face — 1169. Left Trunnion — 1861. Right Trunnion — J.R.A. & Co., T.F. REMARKS: Cast in pattern of 6-Pounder, Model 1841. COMMON NAME: 3-Inch Confederate Rifle.

FIGURE: IX-36 LOCATION: West Point, N.Y. IDENTIFICATION: Rifle, Field, 3.3-Inch, Confederate, Bronze. BORE: Diameter — 3.3 Rifling — 7 x 7, Straight. Length — 56.5v. LENGTH O/A: 65.5. TRUNNIONS: Diameter — 3.67. Length — 2.8. MARKINGS: Left Trunnion — 1861. Right Trunnion — Leeds & Co., New Orleans, La. COMMON NAME: 3.3-Inch Leeds Rifle. Or, 3.3-Inch Confederate Rifle.

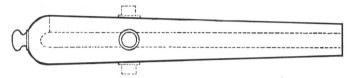

FIGURE: IX-37 IDENTIFICATION: Rifle, Field, 3-Inch, Model 1861, Confederate, Iron. BORE: Diameter — 3. Rifling — 5 x 5, straight. Length — 62.5. LENGTH O/A: 72. TRUNNIONS: Diameter — 3.67. Length — 2.75. REMARKS: Listed as in service, but not considered permanently adopted. SOURCE: *Ordnance Manual* (Confederate) 1863. COMMON NAME: 3-Inch Confederate Rifle.

FIGURE: IX-38 LOCATION: Petersburg, Va. IDENTIFICATION: Rifle, Field, 3-Inch, Confederate, Iron. BORE: Diameter — 3. Rifling 12 x 12, straight. Length — 62.5. LENGTH O/A: 71.5. TRUNNIONS: Diameter — 3.67. Length — 2.75. COMMON NAME: 3-Inch Confederate Rifle.

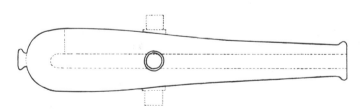

FIGURE: IX-39 IDENTIFICATION: Rifle, Siege & Garrison, 4.62-Inch, Model 1862, Confederate, Iron. BORE: Diameter — 4.62. Rifling — 7 x 7, straight. Length — 106. LENGTH O/A: 118. TRUNNIONS: Diameter — 5.82. Length — 5. SOURCE: *Ordnance Manual* (Confederate) 1863. COMMON NAME: 4.62-Inch Confederate Siege Rifle.

correspondence, the author has been unable to locate a drawing, photograph, or existing piece. However, its statistics are recorded in the 1863 manual,[68] and

identification should be easy and positive if one of the weapons is discovered. The mountain rifle was bronze with 2.25-inch bore 40 inches long. Length overall was 44 inches and weight 200 pounds. This was the piece referred to in Chapter VIII which may have taken the place of the little 2.9-inch weapon at Washington Navy Yard listed as a Type 10 Blakely.

Another very rare Confederate item is the 14-pounder Cameron rifle (Fig. IX-40) at the United Daughters of the Confederacy Museum in Charleston. Bore diameter is 3.56 rifled with 6 lands about 1.25-inch wide and grooves .63 inch. Length overall is 83.5 inches. No founder's marks have been found, but the trunnion band is stamped: "To The State of South Carolina From Plowden C.J. Weston." He was lieutenant governor in 1863, but the donation was made after the war.

Newspaper stories through the years have built a history for the piece based more on imagination than documentation. However, two contemporary articles,[69] which quote eyewitnesses, seem credible and establish that a rifled cannon was under construction in May and June 1861 at Cameron's shop in Charleston. Particulars of fabrication are more accurately reported in excerpts from a letter in museum files written in 1906 by Maurice Quinlivan, one of the men who built the piece.

"It gives me great pleasure to state to the best of my knowledge and belief the circumstances attending the manufacture of the rifled cannon now at the Confederate Museum, Charleston, S.C. The gun was made at the machine shops of Cameron, Taylor and Johnson, Charleston, S.C.

FIGURE: IX-40 LOCATION: Charleston, S.C. IDENTIFICATION: Cameron, Field, 3.56-Inch, Rifle, Wrought Iron. BORE: Diameter — 3.56. Rifling — 6 x 6, straight. Length — 71. LENGTH O/A: 83.5. TRUNNIONS: Diameter — 3.1. Length — 2.9. REMARKS: No apparent foundry marks (see text). Original carriage. COMMON NAME: 14-Pounder Cameron. Or, 3.56-Inch Cameron.

Mr. Archibald Cameron superintended the construction, my brother, Michael Quinlivan, had charge of the forging of the same and I assisted him. My brother is now lying so ill that he could not give the information desired.[70]

"I know that the iron used was a tough, wrought iron formerly used as tires on the wheels of locomotives of the South Carolina Railroad which locomotives were in 1861 in the scrap heap in the yard of that railroad. I believe my brother told me that the tires were from the wheels of one of the earliest locomotives used on that railroad, the first long railroad built in the world. . . ."

Wartime service of the piece is largely conjectural, but the gun is reported to have been used along the coast near Georgetown, South Carolina, against Union gunboats and later taken to Columbia where it eventually was picked up by Sherman's men only to be repurchased after the war by the Cameron firm in a sale of government property.

There is a rumor that Sherman's men found the piece too tough to destroy, but damaged the muzzle in the attempt. Repairs, so the story goes, required that the tube be cut back a foot—but why, since the war was about over, and by whom is left unanswered. Furthermore, if the federals had really wanted to destroy the piece, Yankee ingenuity and sledges would have found a way, and certainly not by pounding on the muzzle.[71]

If the tube was ever longer than at present—a supposition which is extremely doubtful—it probably was cut back by the Confederates in an attempt to improve handling and firing characteristics. However, based on the present very light preponderance, an extra foot of muzzle weighing 50 pounds or so would have necessitated props under the chase or straps at the breech to maintain elevation—obviously absurd conditions which the Cameron firm was far too experienced to perpetrate.

Although newspaper articles and correspondence refer to a single Cameron, there is evidence that the firm may have made more than one. According to the Official Records,[72] Beauregard at Charleston 14 July 1863 ordered Brigadier General H. W. Mercer at Savannah, Georgia: "Send also [to Charleston] two Cammeron [sic] rifled 14-pounder guns, sent from here for siege train. . . ." The piece is mounted on an original Confederate field carriage which, considering years of braving the elements outside the museum, is in surprisingly good condition and may be almost as rare a specimen as the tube.

Cannon in most town parks seldom get a second glance, even from tourists, but City Hall at Athens, Georgia, has a strange looking 4-pounder (Figs. IX-41 and 42) that attracts more than normal attention.

FIGURE: IX-41 LOCATION: Athens, Ga. IDENTIFICATION: Gilleland, Experimental, 3.13-Inch, Double-Barrel, Iron. BORE: (Both barrels) Diameter — 3.13. Smoothbore. Length — 46.5. LENGTH O/A: 56.5. TRUNNIONS: Diameter — 4.2. Length — 3. REMARKS: Designed to fire shot from each barrel linked with chain. Unsuccessful. COMMON NAME: 4-Pounder Gilleland. Or, Double-Barreled 4-Pounder. Or, 3.13-Inch Gilleland.

FIGURE: IX-42 LOCATION: Athens, Ga. IDENTIFICATION: Gilleland, Experimental, 3.13-Inch, Double-Barrel, Iron. REMARKS: Distance across both barrels is 12.75 inches. See Fig. IX-41 for statistics.

The experimental piece is a double-barrel smoothbore which probably should be called a "Gilleland Gun" in honor of its inventor, John Gilleland, a private in the "Mitchell Thunderbolts," an elite home-guard outfit of business and professional men barred from active service by age or disability.

Cast at a local foundry, it was designed to fire two balls linked together by chain which, theoretically, would whir through the air like a giant scythe mowing down lines of enemy troops.[73]

Taken to a field outside town for testing, the piece was loaded with a ball in each barrel, the chain dangling from the twin muzzles. But Gilleland had neglected one vital factor—there was no way to insure simultaneous ignition of both charges. One barrel fired an instant before the other. The chain parted and each ball with a few links attached, went its separate and erratic way, more danger to friend than foe.

That ended both the test and the gun's wartime career. It was returned to town where its only service until mounted at City Hall was occasional celebration of political victories where simultaneity in firing blank charges made little difference to cheering throngs.

Diameter of both bores is 3.13 and length 46.5 inches. Length overall is 56.5 and horizontally across the muzzle 12.75. The homemade carriage is simple and sturdy.

Columbus, Ga., boasts a Confederate-made, 2.75-inch breech-loading rifle (Fig. IX-43) with straight type lands and grooves too rusted for accurate count. The piece, 61.25 overall excluding the breechblock link, has a chamber 4.87 inches wide and 5.87 long. An accompanying plaque states the weapon was bored from the wheel shaft of a river steamer in 1863 at the Columbus Iron Works Co. which during the war became the Confederate Naval Iron Works.

A fascinating little cannon that, based on the number reportedly made, should have survived the war, but thus far has escaped discovery, was the Hughes Breechloader. Principal reference is an article in the *Confederate Veteran*[74] which states it was the invention of D.W. Hughes, a native of Ohio who entered the Confederate Gun Works at Memphis, Tenn., in 1861.

Some 50 Hughes guns, apparently smoothbores, were made in Memphis during 1862–63 and put to use at various points, including a battery ordered for General M. Jeff Thompson which was used in the vicinity of New Madrid, Missouri. Statistics given in the article are somewhat nebulous—bore 1.5 to 2 inches, length 34-inch average and weight about 80 pounds. Some were made of bronze, others from old railway car axles which probably would have been wrought iron. Mounted on a light carriage, the piece was maneuvered entirely by manpower and in tests at Memphis projected a lead ball approximately 3 miles.

Adaptation of the revolver principle to cannon intrigued inventors on both sides during the war, but they met with little better success than Cochran's previously mentioned "revolving, breech-loading rifled cannon." A Southern attempt (Fig. IX-44) is said to have been designed by Henry Clay Pate, Petersburg, Virginia, lawyer. A pair were cast by one of the city's foundries, Tappey & Lumsden, but explosion of one during tests

in May, 1861, proved the weapon too dangerous for use and the other, set aside for duration of the war, today graces the lawn of Petersburg's Centre Hill Mansion Museum. It is a 4-pounder (3.13-inch), five-shot smoothbore with an overall length, including lock-up crank, of 70 inches. Bore length, exclusive of cylinder, is 48 inches. The lock-up crank forced the 13.5 in. long cylinder (which was loaded from the front) against the barrel to minimize escape of gas during discharge. Overall construction appears light, if not flimsy, in a weapon expected to stand the stresses of rapid fire in field use.

The piece goes by a variety of names including "Revolving Cannon," "Tappey & Lumsden" and "Pate, Tappey & Lumsden." Although Pate's claim as designer is somewhat tenuous, the author prefers "3.13-Inch Pate, Tappey & Lumsden Revolving Cannon" as being more descriptive.

If historians some day discover hints that the Confederates in 1865 had under development a secret weapon to retrieve their waning fortunes, West Point has a piece which is a possible choice for the honor. This bizarre weapon, in the foreground of the line of cannon in Figure V-26, is 71.5 inches long. General appearance is novel, but the bore is even stranger—it's a rectangle, 6.5 by 1.5 inches. West Point records call it an "improvised cannon" captured by Union

FIGURE: IX-43 LOCATION: Columbus, Ga. IDENTIFICATION: Confederate, Field, 2.75-Inch, B.L.R., Iron (probably Wrought). BORE: Diameter — 2.75. Rifling — Straight-type lands and grooves too rusted to count. Length — 55.38 excluding 5.87-inch chamber. LENGTH O/A: 61.25 (excluding breechblock link). TRUNNIONS: Diameter — 3. REMARKS: Cannon was doubtless first breechloader made by the Naval Iron Works, but not first of the war. COMMON NAME: Confederate 2.75-Inch B.L.R.

troops at Richmond during the course of manufacture. The cast iron freak with wrought iron bands may be nothing more exciting that a test vehicle for powder or metal. But if romanticists ever start looking for a Confederate secret weapon, this Richmond enigma should be an odds-on favorite.

Two Southern weapons—Anderson and Ripley—are mentioned in Civil War texts, but probably existed more in imagination than reality. Sole reference to the Anderson seems to be a shell found by Abbot's men at Richmond. In his drawings of Confederate ammunition[75] he lists this projectile as "Copper ratchet sabot. One sample found at Naval Laboratory marked 'Anderson Rifle 7″ ' . . ."

Since ratchet sabot ammunition was used in Brooke rifles which were made by Anderson's Tredegar Foundry, and since there appears to be no other record of an Anderson 7-inch rifle, chances are it was simply another term for the Brooke.

Similarly, only one reference has been found to the Ripley. This is a letter from Lorin Blodgett, secretary of the Philadelphia Board of Trade, to Gideon Welles, quoting a Mr. F.T. Sharratt who had left Charleston, South Carolina, 29 November 1861 and arrived at Philadelphia 3 December.[76] According to Blodgett, Sharratt said: "General [Ambrosio José] Gonzales has [in] a new 4-gun battery near Beaufort [S.C.] a new style of gun, VIII-inch howitzers, 5 feet, invented by General [Roswell S.] Ripley, which now lie partly masked, back of Beaufort. They were sent secretly and it is supposed that our troops are not aware of their existence. . . ." Since the Ripleys do not appear in ordnance inventories and are not mentioned during the later years of war by the normally verbose Southerners, chances are this invention was pure rumor, perhaps circulated deliberately for benefit of such line-crossing travelers as Mr. Sharratt.

If this supposition is correct, the battery, which was "partly masked" may have been intended for discovery and consisted of nothing more lethal than carefully aimed logs—better known as "Quaker Guns" (Fig. IX-45). Such "ordnance" was used by both sides and is defined by Webster's Dictionary as: "A dummy piece of artillery, usually of wood — so called because the sect of Friends, or Quakers, hold to the doctrine of nonresistance." The illustrated "piece" was emplaced by the Confederates at Centerville, Virginia.

A form of naval ordnance, long obsolete by 1861 and not in production, was mounted ashore as secondary defense by Confederates in a number of

FIGURE: IX-44 LOCATION: Centre Hill Mansion Museum, Petersburg, Va. IDENTIFICATION: Pate, Tappey & Lumsden, Field, 3.13-Inch, Iron. BORE: Diameter — 3.13. Smoothbore. Length— 48 (excluding cylinder). LENGTH O/A: 70. TRUNNIONS: Enclosed, diameter not available, but very small for a piece of this size. REMARKS: Paint conceals marks, if any. Cylinder holds five rounds. COMMON NAME: Revolving Cannon. Or, Tappey & Lumsden. Or, Pate, Tappey & Lumsden. Or, 3.13-Inch Pate, Tappey & Lumsden Revolving Cannon (preferred).

instances and occasionally even by the North. Known as a "Carronade," the piece is unusual and for this reason is worth more discussion than its slight importance to the war effort of either side would warrant. Invented in England in 1774 by General Robert Melville (1723-1809), the first one—an 8-inch (68-pounder) weighing 3,500 pounds—was cast at a foundry in Carron, Scotland, in 1779. This was the forerunner of a relatively short, light weapon designed for shipboard use to project a large, heavy ball with minimum velocity on the theory this would cause maximum splintering of wooden hulls. For this reason, early models were called "Smashers," a term that stuck as an alternate although the weapons were commonly known as "Carronades" for the original foundry despite their later manufacture by other nations.

General Melville recognized the suitability of the piece for shells, but the British Navy seems to have subordinated this on the premise that since England ruled the seas, the status quo was in her favor and it was desirable to suppress major weapons improvement which, if adopted, would spur enemies to follow suit, possibly to the detriment of British naval supremacy. This, however, was forlorn hope and by the turn of the century, shells had been added to carronade lockers of all major navies although solid shot seems to have remained the basic projectile.

Carronades became so popular that during the War of 1812, they formèd the major armament of many American and British ships to the neglect of traditional long guns. This situation was fine if two carronade-armed vessels met. They could slug it out at close quarters on relatively equal terms. But when a carronade vessel met one armed with a preponderance of long guns, it was often a different story. The smart skipper put distance to advantage, staying just out of range of the carronades, and cut his adversary to pieces with impunity. Despite this occasional humiliating—and fatal—occurrence, carronades retained a disputed popularity and in our Navy remained aboard ships until 1845 when the entire system of armament was reorganized and the weapons set ashore to gather rust until the Civil War.

Documented use of carronades by the Union is rare, but federal defenses at Jacksonville and Palatka, Florida, listed three such weapons—a 32- and two 42-pounders—as late as March, 1864[77]. On the other hand, the South often put these weapons to work, generally for flank defense of fortifications. Shell, grape, and, doubtless, canister were used. Traditional solid shot probably saw little, if any, service in this role. Although during the heyday of the carronade they were made in relatively small calibers for light vessels and a few even had trunnions instead of the usual loop, all references found thus far show carronades used during the Civil War were 42- or 32-pounders.

One of the former (Fig. V-19) at West Point measures 71.5 inches overall. The bore is flared to 7.9 at the muzzle face from an interior diameter of 7 inches. It is marked on the breech "No. 98," on the reinforce "42-1822," and on the cascabel "I.C. & Co., B.F., Va." Records state the piece was captured at Fort Walker on Hilton Head Island, South Carolina, after that sand work had been battered into submission by Admiral Samuel F. DuPont's fleet 7 November 1861. This is substantiated by Major Francis D. Lee of South Carolina Engineers, who built Fort Walker defenses. He reported[78] two 42-pounder carronades arrived a short time before the bombardment, but without carriages. Consequently, they were ". . . simply buried in the sand to such depth and with such directions as to enable us to have at least one fire in the event of an attempt to storm the work. . . ."

A number of reproduction 32-pounders are aboard the U.S.S. Constitution, moored today at the Naval Shipyard, Boston, Massachusetts. They are representative of the original armament and were made according to government blueprints from which measurements in Appendix C were taken. Bore diameter of these weapons is 6.4 inches, flared to 7 at the muzzle face. Length overall is 65 inches. They have trunnions although others of the period used a loop.

Actual combat use of carronades during the Civil War was probably slight, but a 42-pounder in Battery Wagner battered federal sappers digging their way through the sands of Morris Island. C.E. Chickchester wrote 16 August 1863:[79] "I would also suggest the 42-pounder carronade, now used for flank defense, be removed to the extreme right face of this work where it can be advantageously used to the front upon the enemy's working parties with shell and grape. . . ." The piece was moved and the report of 24 August from Battery Wagner stated:[80] "Fire was also opened from the 42-pdr. carronade on salient and was kept up 'til morning, when the embrasure was closed to mask the gun from the enemy. . . "

English rifles were the best foreign weapons used by the Confederates. However, cannon were also purchased from other countries in Europe, particularly Austria which supplied a number of field pieces, many of which are still around today.

General Gorgas, writing in the Ordnance Bureau Field Manual of 1862, stated:[81] ". . . twenty-

FIGURE: IX-45 IDENTIFICATION: "Quaker Gun" REMARKS: Log shaped to resemble cannon. Both sides used these dummy or "Quaker Guns" to deceive the enemy.

seven [his figures total 24] bronze field pieces have been introduced into the C.S. service from Austria. Seven are 24-pounder howitzers cast in Vienna in 1857-59 of caliber 5.87 instead of 5.82. The remaining 17 are 6-pounders cast in Vienna in 1826 and 1859 of caliber 3.74 instead of 3.67. By having the balls enclosed in canvas, the ordinary ammunition issued for the approximate calibers in C.S. service may be used with these guns and howitzers. . . ."

A 24-pounder howitzer (Fig. IX-46) at Gettysburg has a bore of 5.87 and is 59.5 inches long. Markings on the base ring are: "No. 15, 632 lbs., Wien, 1858." A companion piece, No. 35, weighs 665 pounds and was made in 1859.

Fort Sill, Petersburg, Fort Monroe, and probably other museums and parks have specimens of the Austrian 6-pounder gun which is easily recognized by its handles and pronounced muzzle swell. The illustrated piece (Fig. IX-47) in the Washington Navy Yard collection measures 62 inches overall and

is marked on the tube: "7c [centner of 110.23 pounds] 6f [pfund of 1.23 pounds] B. N:815, Z, S.A." and on the base ring: "Bronn Major In Wien 1843." Most of these 6-pounders are smoothbore, but the illustrated piece is rifled with 6 lands and grooves. Bore length is 53 inches and the diameter 3.74.

Although Gorgas listed the dates of the 6-pounders as "1826 and 1859," in view of the 1843 Washington specimen and an 1832 date on one at Fort Sill, it is probable he meant "between" rather than specifically these dates.

Weapons of Continental countries other than Austria seem to have seen little use in America. Miller's Photographic History[82] mentions a few bronze French 12-pounders used by the South and here and there a Spanish piece, captured in the Mexican War, probably saw a bit of service. Two such weapons (Fig. IX-48) are at the Washington Navy Yard. These bronze, 12-pounder smoothbores

FIGURE: IX-46 LOCATION: Gettysburg, Pa. IDENTIFICATION: Austrian, Howitzer, Field, 5.87-Inch, Bronze. BORE: Diameter — 5.87. Smoothbore. Length — 50.5 LENGTH O/A: 59.5. TRUNNIONS: Diameter — 3.67. Length — 3.25. MARKINGS: Base Ring — No. 15, 632 lbs., Wien, 1858. Breech — 7H 6B S. COMMON NAME: Austrian 24-Pounder Howitzer. Or, Austrian 5.87-Inch Howitzer.

FIGURE: IX-47 LOCATION: Washington Navy Yard, D.C. IDENTIFICATION: Austrian, Field, 3.74-Inch, Rifle, Bronze. BORE: Diameter — 3.74. Rifling — 6 x 6, straight. Length — 53. LENGTH O/A: 62. TRUNNIONS: Diameter — 3.5. Length — 3.25. MARKINGS: Base Ring — Bronn Major In Wien, 1843. Breech — 7C 6F B, N:815, Z, S, A, REMARKS: Also found as smoothbore. COMMON NAME: Austrian 3.74-Inch Rifle.

FIGURE: IX-48 LOCATION: Washington Navy Yard, D.C. IDENTIFICATION: Spanish, Field, 12-Pounder, Bronze. BORE: Diameter — 4.75. Smoothbore. Length — 76.5. LENGTH O/A: 88.5. TRUNNIONS: Diameter — 4.6. Length — 4.6. MARKINGS: Base Ring — Barcelona, 1 de Mayo de 1767. Tube, chase — El Toro. Tube, breech — Crest of Charles III. REMARKS: Identical piece at rear bears the name "El Tosigo" (poison). Both apparently were captured during the Mexican War and used by the Confederates at Norfolk. COMMON NAME: Spanish 12-Pounder.

apparently had been captured during the Mexican War, acquired by the Confederates, probably in the Norfolk area, then lost to federal forces in the reoccupation of the Norfolk Navy Yard in May, 1862. Measurements of both are approximately the same— bore length 76.5 inches, diameter 4.75 inches, and length overall, 88.5 inches. Tubes at the breech are ornately engraved with the crest of Charles III of Spain and marks on the base ring state they were made at Barcelona in 1767. The chase of the piece in foreground is inscribed "El Toro" (The Bull) and the other "El Tosigo" (Poison).

Both North and South used a variety of machine guns such as the Gatling, Billinghurst-Requa, Union Repeating, and Parmenter and Bromwell on the federal side, and Williams Breechloader and the English-made Vandenburg Volley Gun by the Confederates. All are fascinating weapons and although generally employed by artillerymen in Civil War days, they are more properly infantry armament and outside the province of this book.

There has been little attempt to counterfeit cannon for financial gain, but it has been done on occasion, particularly by the Park Service, in an honest effort to recreate specific types of ordnance that for one reason or another are no longer available. This is particularly true of pre-Civil War varieties such as the 6-inch smoothbore (Fig. IX-49) which is an obvious fake and so listed. The "weapon" is now mounted at Fort Pulaski and was obtained from the Yorktown area. Apparently a number of this type were made, for others are mounted at Newport, Rhode Island and Orono, Maine. Simi-

larly Chalmette National Park at New Orleans has several pieces—one of which is shown in Chapter X —all clearly marked as reproductions.

Occasionally, however, a fake does wind up masquerading as an authentic piece. Such is the cannon in Figure IX-50. When photographed in 1964, it was at Chancellorsville and appeared to be a Northern-made Napoleon. The bore measured a standard 4.62 inches, smooth—for 4 or 5 inches. Then it narrowed abruptly to 3.67 inches and was rifled with

FIGURE: IX-49 Location: Fort Pulaski, Ga. Identification: Fake 6-Inch Smoothbore. Remarks: Mounted on reproduction casemate carriage.

FIGURE: IX-50 Location: Chancellorsville, Va. Identification: Fake Napoleon. Remarks: Standard 6-Pounder, Model 1841, Rifled, altered to resemble a Napoleon by routing off chase and breech molding and enlarging bore to 4.62-inch for five or six inches near muzzle.

15 lands and grooves. The puzzle was compounded by the length, which was short for a Napoleon, and the breech which was too flat and narrow.

Solution to the problem is due to Dr. Hazlett whose knowledge of ordnance, clever reasoning, and painstaking research of Parks Service records revealed that such weapons are altered 6-pounders. The change was made some years ago when it was found a number of Napoleons were needed to complete a section of the reconstructed lines at Gettysburg. Napoleons in this quantity were not available, but 6-pounders were. So the 6s, both smooth and rifled, were sent to the lathes. The bores were routed to 12-pounder caliber for a few inches in depth and the astragal and fillets of the chase and base rings were turned off. Now the pieces passed all but close muster as Napoleons.

In fairness to the Park Service, no deception was intended. Anyone asking would have been told the "Napoleons" were altered 6-pounders. But years passed. Personnel familiar with the change were transferred. The pieces were rolled in from the field for routine painting and maintenance and sent back to other locations—even different parks. Now they are probably fairly well scattered and ordnance enthusiasts may run into these fakes, probably unmarked, at any time and should recognize them for what they are.

NOTES

1. H. Paul Jeffers, "Mr. Griffen's Gun," *Civil War Times Illustrated,* Vol. III, No. 7, November 1961, p. 9.
2. Alexander L. Holley, *A Treatise on Ordnance and Armor,* 1865, pp. 363–365.
3. Jeffers, *loc. cit.,* pp. 9–10.
4. *Official Records,* Series III, Vol. 1, pp. 289–290.
5. *Ibid.,* pp. 295–296.
6. J. G. Benton, *A Course of Instruction in Ordnance and Gunnery Composed and Compiled for Cadets of The United States Military Academy,* 1875, p. 181.
7. Henry L. Abbot, "Siege Artillery in The Campaigns Against Richmond With Notes on The 15-Inch Gun," *Professional Papers No. 14, Corps of Engineers,* 1867, p. 139.
8. E. P. Alexander, "Confederate Artillery Service," *Southern Historical Society Papers,* Vol. XI, 1883, p. 107.
9. William Allan, "Reminiscences of Field Ordnance Service With The Army of Northern Virginia 1863–65," *Southern Historical Society Papers,* Vol. XIV, 1886, p. 137.
10. *Official Records,* Series III, Vol. 4, p. 469.
11. West Point records. Also, *Official Records,* Series I, Vol. 46, Part 1, p. 1225.
12. Jeffers, *loc. cit.,* p. 10.
13. *Ordnance Manual for The Use of Officers of The United States Army,* 1861, pp. 17–18.
14. Benton, 1875, *op. cit.,* p. 525.
15. William E. Birkhimer, *Historical Sketch of The Organization, Administration, Materiel and Tactics of The Artillery, United States Army,* 1884, pp. 274–footnote, 294–295.
16. Benton, 1875, *op. cit.,* p. 184. Reports of committees of the U.S. Senate, 2nd session, 38th Congress, "Heavy

Ordnance," p. 90, testimony of Charles Knap, proprietor Fort Pitt Foundry, 4 February 1864. When asked how small a gun he was manufacturing on the Rodman principle, Knap replied: "We are not manufacturing less than 8-inch caliber on this principle. It might be valuable for the 6-inch (sic) gun, or what is known as the 32-pdr. . . ."

17. Abott, *op. cit.*, p. 86; *Official Records*, Series I, Vol. 1, p. 983.
18. Abott, *op. cit.*, p. 124.
19. *Ibid.*, p. 154.
20. Benton, 1875, *op. cit.*, p. 525.
21. *Encyclopedia Americana.*
22. Norman Wiard, "Wiard's System of Field Artillery," *War Pamphlets*, pp. 3–38.
23. The piece is owned by Dr. Robert H. MacLeod of Morris Plains, N. J.
24. *Battles and Leaders of The Civil War*, Vol. 1, pp. 660–670.
25. Norman Wiard, "Marine Artillery . . . Invented and Adapted by Norman Wiard," *War Pamphlets*, Introduction, p. 17.
26. *Ibid.*, pp. 26–27, 28–30.
27. *Appleton's Cyclopaedia of American Biography*, 1895.
28. The author is indebted to Lt. Col. Arthur V. Crego of The Louisiana State University for a majority of information on the weapons. Col. Crego dug out available records in the Baton Rouge area and found they fail to link the cannon with either Fort Sumter or Gen. Sherman. He attributes the basis of the plaques largely to legend.
29. *Official Records*, Series I, Vol. 2, Part 3, pp. 240–242.
30. Reports of committees of the U.S. Senate, *op. cit.*, p. 71.
31. *Ibid.*, pp. 130–135, 146–149.
32. *Ibid.*, pp. 4–5.
33. *Ibid.*
34. *Appleton's Cyclopaedia*, op. cit.
35. Daniel Treadwell, "On The Construction of Hooped Cannon, Being a Sequel to a Memoir On The Practicability of Constructing Cannon of Great Caliber," *Memoirs of The American Academy of Arts and Sciences*, 1864, p. 6.
36. *Dictionary of American Biography*, 1928.
37. *Official Navy Records*, Series I, Vol. 6, pp. 275–276. Also, Vol. 1, p. 252.
38. *Ibid.*, Vol. 6, p. 280.
39. *Ibid.*, p. 738.
40. Abbot, *op. cit.*, p. 85.
41. Joseph Roberts, *Hand-Book of Artillery for The Service of The United States Army and Militia*, 1861, pp. 172–173.
42. *Official Records*, Series I, Vol. 6, p. 679.
43. *Ibid.*, Vol. 53, pp. 506–509.
44. J. Webster Cochran, *Improvements in Ordnance, Firearms and Projectiles*, 1860.
45. *Appleton's Cyclopaedia*, op. cit.
46. Reports of committees of the U.S. Senate, *op. cit.*, p. 24, 87.
47. Holley, *op. cit.*, p. 78.
48. J. G. Benton, *A Course of Instruction in Ordnance and Gunnery Composed and Compiled for Cadets of The United States Military Academy*, 1861, pp. 143–144.
49. *Official Navy Records*, Series II, Vol. 1, pp. 151, 260.
50. *Ibid.*, Series I, Vol. 19, p. 566.
51. *Ibid.*, pp. 570–572.
52. Francis Bannerman & Sons, *60th Anniversary Catalogue*, 1925, p. 147.
53. Roberts, *loc. cit.*, pp. 172–173.
54. *Dictionary of American Biography*, 1928.
55. Reports of committees of the U.S. Senate, *op. cit.*, p. 168, testimony of Capt. G. V. Fox, assistant secretary of the Navy, 21 January 1865.
56. Holley, *op. cit.*, pp. 88–89.
57. *Ibid.*, p. 885.
58. Roberts, *loc. cit.*, pp. 172–173.
59. *Alabama Genealogical Register*, Vol. III, No. 4, December 1961, p. 181. Also, *Official Records*, Series I, Vol. 28, Part 2, pp. 277–278, letter signed by John B. Read and indorsements by Capt. Francis D. Lee.
60. *Official Records*, Series I, Vol. 6, pp. 424–425.
61. *Appleton's Cyclopaedia*, op. cit.
62. Holley, *op. cit.*, p. 87.
63. *Ibid.*, p. 357.
64. *Ibid.*, p. 86.
65. D. Alexander Brown, *Grierson's Raid*, 1962, pp. 6, 56, 87.
66. *Ordnance Manual for The Use of Officers of The Confederate States Army*, 1863, pp 9–13.
67. *Ibid.*
68. *Ibid.*
69. *The Charleston Mercury*, 18 May and 17 June 1861.
70. Michael died six weeks later. His obituary in *The Charleston News and Courier* 20 January 1907, p. 3, states that to his skill ". . . was entrusted the forging of the first wrought iron rifled cannon used in the South. . . . The rifled cannon is now in possession of the Charleston Chapter, United Daughters of The Confederacy. . . ."
71. Another version is that failure to break the trunnions led to jamming trunnions, broken from another piece, down the bore necessitating cutting the tube to remove the obstruction. This is doubtful on several counts including: a broken trunnion would hardly be in proper condition for blocking a bore, and very few weapons had trunnions of suitable diameter (see tables in appendix). Since the muzzle face is too smooth and accurate for a hacksaw job, any removal of metal must have been done in a lathe and any obstruction could be drilled out far easier than setting up the piece for turning. Shells or shot jammed down the bore and wedged would be far more traditional —and effective.
72. *Official Records*, Series I, Vol. 28, Part 2, p. 199.
73. Historical marker erected by the Georgia Historical Commission.
74. *The Confederate Veteran*, Vol. XVI, 1908, p. 44; *Official Records*, Series I, Vol. 52, p. 600.
75. Abbot, *op. cit.*, Plate IV, Fig. 20.
76. *Official Navy Records*, Series I, Vol. 12, p. 380.
77. *Official Records*, Series I, Vol. 35, Part 2, p. 25.
78. *Ibid.*, Vol. 6, pp. 18–20.
79. *Ibid.*, Vol. 28, Part 1, p. 516.
80. *Ibid.*, p. 444.
81. *Field Manual, Confederate States of America, Ordnance Bureau, Richmond, Va.*, 1 July 1862, p. 21.
82. *Photographic History of The Civil War*, Vol. 5, p. 156.

Chapter 10

Carriages

CANNON CARRIAGES, WHETHER WOOD OR METAL, Army or Navy, serve two vital functions—they hold the piece for firing and dissipate the shock of recoil. In addition, and incidentally, certain types provide a convenient method of transportation.

Historically, carriage development afloat remained fairly static until about mid-nineteenth century, the 4-truck broadside carriage changing little in almost three-hundred years.[1] Ashore, however, war or threat of war brought about major innovations in field carriages beginning about the middle of the 18th century. This was particularly true in England and France where improvement in the military arts was vital to national survival.

The British seem to have made the first move and developed a series of carriages based on the "bracket" trail system, described by John Muller in his 1757 *Treatise on Artillery*. The French countered in 1765 with the "flask" system developed by General Jean Baptiste Gribeauval (1715-1789).[2] It is not the intention here to go into the merits of the two systems, suffice it that both were major improvements over the haphazard arrangement that existed previously and neither remained static for long, but was altered and improved as new knowledge was gained.

Both systems, first the British and then the French, gradually gave way to the "stock" or "block" trail system which was refined into the field carriage of the 1860s. Initial steps in development of this type were taken by Sir William Congreve[3] as early as 1776 and by 1794 its main features had become part of British artillery materiel. It was adopted and improved by the French in 1827.[4]

Benton[5] traces the ancestry of the American carriage to Gribeauval. However, Birkhimer,[6] who seems to have gone somewhat deeper into history, states that the English bracket system was the forerunner. This system was used during the Revolution since it was the one with which Americans were familiar and, Birkhimer says, "So far as is known, Professor Muller's work on gunnery was the only textbook for artillery construction extant in this country prior to 1797. . . ." Tubes and other materiel were imported from France, he says, but no carriages[7].

By 1800, copies of a French treatise on the materiel portion of the Gribeauval system had been translated and a few such carriages made. Others were acquired in New Orleans in 1803 after the Louisiana Purchase.[8] However, it was not until 18 April 1809 that the government actually ordered

189

FIGURE: X-1 LOCATION: Chalmette New Orleans, La. IDEN-TIFICATION: Carriage, Field, 6-Pounder, Old English, Wood. REMARKS: Reproduction carriage and tube.

FIGURE: X-2 LOCATION: Chalmette, New Orleans, La. IDENTIFICATION: Carriage, Field, Gribeauval, Wood. REMARKS: Reproduction carriage which seems to be a combination of 4- and 8-pounder models. Authentic French 6-pounder tube.

construction of Gribeauval carriages and this form was introduced into service.[9]

During the War of 1812, the British used stock trail carriages which were infinitely superior to both the bracket and flask systems. American contact with British artillery seems to have been too slight for this to have been impressed upon most officers, although one, Colonel Decius Wadsworth, commissary general and then chief of ordnance 1812-21, tried in 1817 to introduce a carriage based on the new English system.[10] His carriage, however, was turned down by an ordnance board in favor of the Gribeauval which, to all nations but the British, had the reputation of being the ultimate for field artillery. This was in 1818 and when the colonel retired in 1821, the Gribeauval system reigned supreme until 1829, although two years earlier even the French had been forced to admit the superiority of the British stock trail and had adopted it with modifications and improvements. Complete drawings and tables of construction were obtained from the French by a young American lieutenant, Daniel Tyler, and by July, 1830, preliminary work had started in the United States toward construction of field carriages based upon these drawings.[11]

The transition was not abrupt, however, and Gribeauval carriages remained in the system until the Ordnance Board of 1835 resolved:[12] "That the system of carriages for field artillery, recently adopted after much trial and minute investigation by the government of France, is the best hitherto devised for

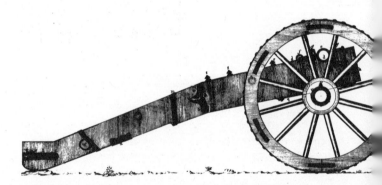

FIGURE: X-3 IDENTIFICATION: Carriage, Field, 6-Pounder, Old English, Wood. SOURCE: Muller, 1757.

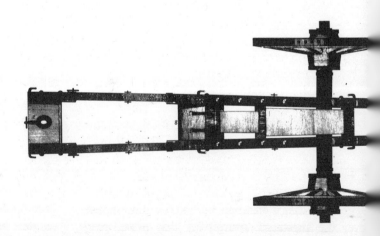

FIGURE: X-4 IDENTIFICATION: Carriage, Field, 6-Pounder, Old English, Wood. SOURCE: Muller, 1757.

the service of the United States and that it ought to be received with no further alterations than may be found necessary for the adoption of the respective carriages to our guns and roads." The board adjourned after recommending use of the same system in field trains, and the report was approved 8 July 1836,[13] thereby setting a specific date for the official adoption of stock trail carriages which, with minor alterations, carried the cannon of the Civil War.

Specimens of bracket trail (Fig. X-1) and flask (Fig. X-2) are exhibited at Chalmette in New Orleans. Both are reproduction carriages, but conform closely to illustrations in contemporary texts. The English resembles Muller's 6-pounder carriage (Figs. X-3 and 4). The Gribeauval seems to be a combination of 4- and 8-pounder mounts. An 8 (Figs X-5 and 6) was taken from an 1809 work by Louis de Tousard, former inspector of artillery. A number of Tousard's plates—confirming continued use of the carriage—are reprinted in a 1820 volume for U.S. service[14] and an 1834 abstract[15] for South Carolina militia. Sketches of a 4-pounder (Figs. X-7 and 8) from the 1834 work show the carriage ready for action and with limber and ammunition chest.

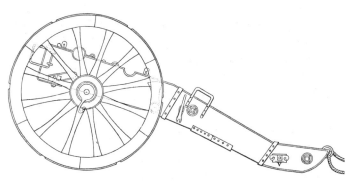

FIGURE: X-5 IDENTIFICATION: Carriage, Field, 8-Pounder, Gribeauval, Wood. SOURCE: Tousard.

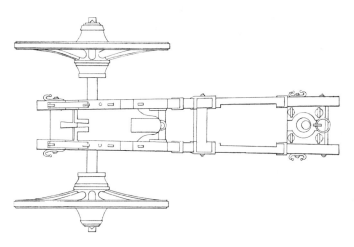

FIGURE: X-6 IDENTIFICATION: Carriage, Field, 8-Pounder, Gribeauval, Wood. SOURCE: Tousard.

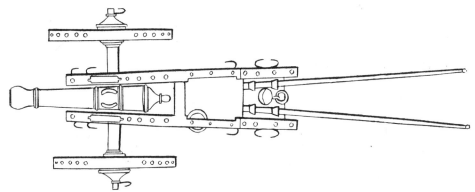

FIGURE: X-7 IDENTIFICATION: Carriage, Field, 4-Pounder, Gribeauval, Wood. SOURCE: Wilson.

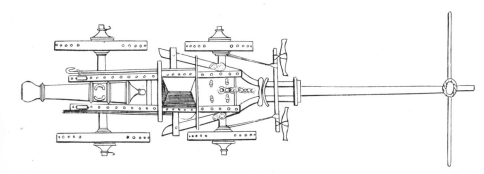

FIGURE: X-8 IDENTIFICATION: Carriage, Field, 4-Pounder, Gribeauval, Wood. SOURCE: Wilson. REMARKS: Carriage limbered. Note ammunition chest with sloping cover resting rear of the breech.

191

Reproductions of Civil War field carriages have been shown so often in previous chapters that another would be needless repetition. Instead, the following diagrams will illustrate the transition from 1841 to 1861. Figure X-9 of a 6-pounder carriage was taken from the Ordnance Manual of 1841; Figure X-10 of 6- and, similar but larger, 12-pounder mounts from Mordecai's *Artillery for the Land Service of the United States,* 1849, and Figure X-11 of a 6-pounder carriage from the 1861 Ordnance Manual. Although dimensions were altered a bit during the twenty-year period, comparison of the illustration will show little change in appearance by the time of the Civil War.

In 1841 there were three carriages,[16] almost identical to look at, but differing slightly in dimen-

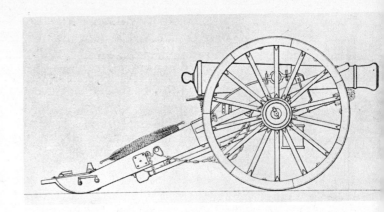

FIGURE: X-9 IDENTIFICATION: Carriage, Field, 6-Pounder, ca. 1841, Wood. SOURCE: *Ordnance Manual,* 1841.

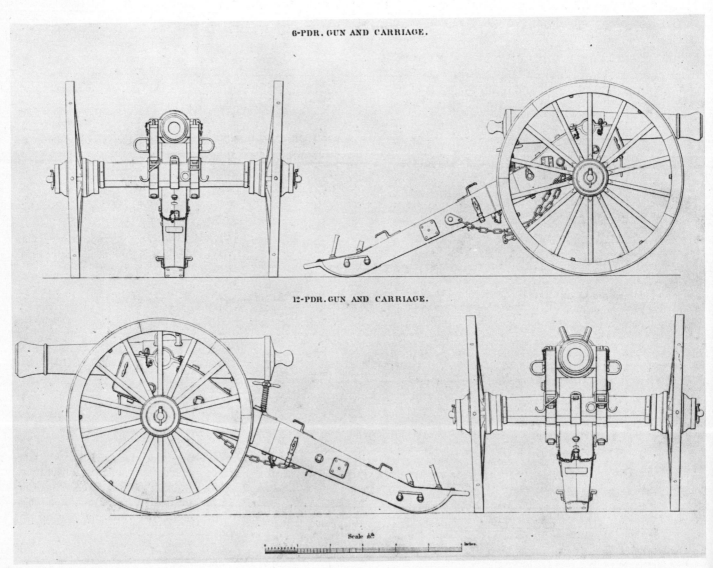

6-PDR. GUN AND CARRIAGE.

12-PDR. GUN AND CARRIAGE.

Scale

FIGURE: X-10 IDENTIFICATION: (top) Carriage, Field, 6-Pounder, ca. 1849, Wood. (bottom) Carriage, Field, 12-Pounder, ca.-1849, Wood. SOURCE: Mordecai.

sion, for use with the following pieces: one for the 6-pounder gun or 12-pounder howitzer; another for the 24-pounder howitzer; and a third for the 12-pounder gun, model 1841. The 32-pounder howitzer, introduced in 1844, was mounted on the 12-pounder gun carriage. Adoption of the 12-pounder, Model 1857 (Napoleon), however, was a greater problem. The 24-pounder howitzer carriage was modified to accommodate the new weapon by altering the length of the cheeks and making a slight change in location of the elevating screw.[17]

Consequently, at the start of the conflict, there were, technically, four field carriages, all generally the same, but differing very slightly in size to accommodate different weight weapons.[18] Detailed specifications are of interest only to someone attempting to reproduce one of these carriages and in this case, the 1861 Ordnance Manual will be found an excellent reference with a complete listing of wood and metal parts as well as dimensions. However, since certain weights and measurements will be desired by students of tactics, an abbreviated list giving the most important dimensions of field and other carriages will be found in the Appendices. Wiard's carriage, since it was part of his field artillery "system" and used with his

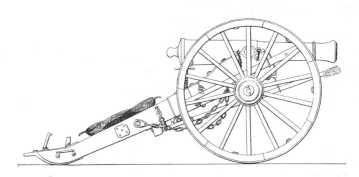

FIGURE: X-11 IDENTIFICATION: Carriage, Field, 6-Pounder, ca. 1861, Wood. SOURCE: *Ordnance Manual*, 1861. REMARKS: Type field carriage used throughout the Civil War.

weapons alone, was discussed in the previous chapter.

All field carriages used the same limber,[19] a two-wheel vehicle with a single chest over the axle and a pintle at the rear over which the lunette, an iron ring at the end of the carriage trail, could be dropped and locked. This converted the two-wheel gun carriage into a four-wheel vehicle with single point connection which permitted an extremely short turning radius. The field carriage, limbered (Fig. X-12), was drawn by six horses[20] hitched in pairs, although casualties no doubt occasionally reduced

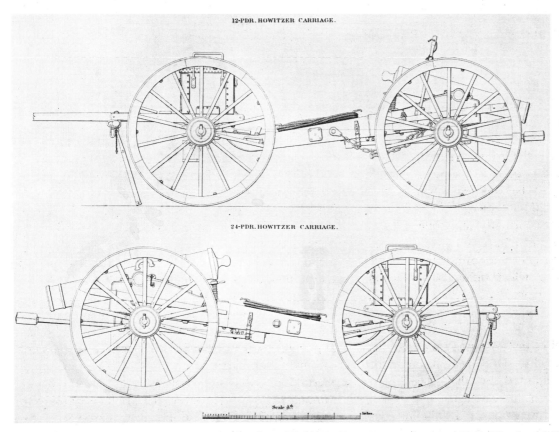

FIGURE: X-12 IDENTIFICATION: (Top) Carriage, Field, 12-Pounder Howitzer, ca. 1849, Wood, with Limber attached. (Bottom) Carriage, Field, 24-Pounder Howitzer, ca. 1849, Wood, with Limber attached. SOURCE: Mordecai. REMARKS: Virtually the same limber was used during the Civil War.

FIGURE: X-13 IDENTIFICATION: 3-Inch Ordnance Rifle on Field Carriage, Limbered, en route to Cedar Mountain, Va., 9 Aug. 1862, halts in stream to cool hoofs of the horses. REMARKS: Note 4-horse team instead of customary 6.

teams, particularly in the Confederacy, to four. Such a team, this one Federal, cools its hooves (Fig. X-13) in a brook near Cedar Mountain, Virginia, 9 August 1862. The weapon is a 3-inch Ordnance Rifle.

Artillery horses and harness is a subject in itself and detailed discussion is beyond the scope of this book. However, since without horses field and siege artillery would have been virtually immobile, typical artillery harness is shown in Figure X-14. It was used with both field and siege carriages, although standard wagon harness of the day, which differed a bit, could be used with the latter. Horses, as previously stated, were linked in pairs termed "lead,' "swing,' and "wheel." Each left or "near" horse was ridden by a driver and its companion or "off" horse carried the man's belongings in a valise. Draft was through the "trace." The pole, supported by the wheel pair, served only for guidance of the carriage.

A horse traveled 400 yards at a walk in four and a half minutes, at a trot in two minutes and at a gallop in one—a matter which had to be calculated against loading time when defending a position

against charging cavalry. An artillery horse weighed an average 1,000 pounds and in ranks occupied a front of 40 inches and a 10-foot depth. He could carry a soldier and equipment (225 pounds) 25 miles in an 8-hour day. A pack horse could carry 250 to 300 pounds 20 miles a day and a draft animal could haul 1,600 pounds, carriage included, 23 miles in the same period. This, however, was predicated on good roads. Artillery horses, expected to maneuver across country, were restricted, if possible, to 700 pounds each, carriage included[21].

Information on Southern field carriages is sketchy, but insofar as materials availability permitted, they probably followed the U.S. models in appearance and dimension—especially since specifications for all carriages in the Confederate Ordnance Manual of 1863 are copied directly from the U.S. Manual of 1861. However, the South apparently did experiment with a new howitzer carriage, for an article in the 1898 *Southern Historical Society Papers*[22] mentions fabrication of a joint, or as it would be called today, "split" trail model to permit use of

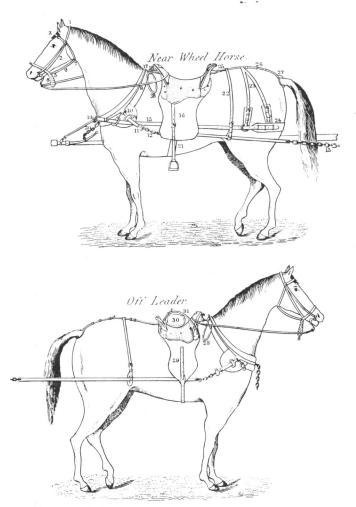

Near Wheel Horse.

Off Leader.

FIGURE: **X-14** IDENTIFICATION: Typical Artillery Harness.
SOURCE: *Instruction for Field Artillery.*
REMARKS:

	Halter	Bridle
1.	Crown Piece	Crown Piece
2.	Cheek Strap	Cheek Strap
3.	Brow Band	Brow Band
4.	Nose Band	Throat Lash
5.	Chin Strap	Bit (Curb).
6.	Throat Strap	Reins
7.	Throat Lash	
8.	Hitching Strap	

9. Collar and Hames with joint loops for Trace Tugs.
10. Trace Tugs with Safe.
11. Trace Hook.
12. Trace.
13. Trace Chain.
14. Safe.
15. Breast Strap.
16. Saddle.
17. Hame Strap.
18. Collar Strap.
19. Sliding Loop.
20. Chain and Toggle.
21. Girth.
22. Loin Strap.
23. Hip Strap.
24. Breech Strap.
25. Back Strap, of Crupper.
26. The Body, of Crupper.
27. The Dock, of Crupper.
28. Trussing Strap.
29. Valise Saddle.
30. Valise.
31. Valise Strap.

howitzers as mortars in high-angle fire. Lack of other references to this carriage would indicate that it probably met with little success and few were made.

In addition to the weapons, each of which carried a basic ammunition supply in the chest on its limber, batteries had certain support vehicles—caissons, a battery wagon, and a forge. The caisson was used to haul extra ammunition and generally one was attached to each piece of light artillery and two to the heavy, although wise battery commanders probably "liberated" an additional caisson or two to insure adequate ammunition as well as spare horses to provide against casualties.

Theoretically, the light battery of 1861 had four 6-pounder guns and two 12-pounder howitzers, six caissons, a battery wagon, and a forge, total fourteen. With six horses per carriage and one-twelfth spares, it had ninety-one draft animals and carried 1,112 rounds of assorted shot, shell, spherical case, and canister. The heavy battery had four 12-pounders, two 24-pounder howitzers, twelve caissons, a battery wagon, and forge, total twenty. Horses, including one-twelfth spares, totaled one hundred and thirty, and ammunition, 1,218 rounds. Two 32-pounder howitzers with four caissons carried 210 rounds.[23]

The caisson (Fig. X-15), a surprisingly efficient ammunition carrier which could follow the guns any-

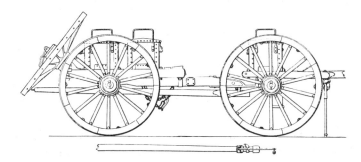

FIGURE: **X-15** IDENTIFICATION: Caisson. SOURCE. *Ordnance Manual.* 1861. REMARKS: Vehicle consisted of a Body, holding two ammunition chests, and a standard Field Limber with a single chest. A spare wheel was attached to the Body and a spare pole slung beneath.

FIGURE: X-16 LOCATION: Manassas, Va. IDENTIFICATION: Caisson. REMARKS: Reproduction.

where, was composed of a body, containing two ammunition chests, and a standard field limber. It carried a spare wheel at the rear, an extra pole slung beneath, and in emergencies its limber could be detached in a matter of seconds and substituted for the disabled limber of a gun thus saving a valuable weapon at the loss of a relatively inexpensive cart. An excellent reproduction (Fig. X-16) is exhibited at Manassas.

Ammunition chests on the body and limber were of standard size and, consequently, the number of rounds carried[24] varied inversely to increase in caliber (Fig. X-17). Packed properly, a chest for the 6-pounder gun carried twenty-five shot, twenty spherical case, and five canister, all with cartridges attached or "fixed," two spare cartridges, seventy-five friction primers, 2 yards of slow match and two portfires, a total of fifty rounds weighing 376.52 pounds. This gave the piece 200 rounds in the four boxes of gun limber, caisson body, and caisson limber. The 12-pounder gun, Model 1841, had twenty shot, eight case, four canister, all fixed, total thirty-two rounds which, with requisite primers, spare cartidges, etc., weighed 499.83 pounds. The Model 1857 carried twelve shot, fixed, twelve case, four shells, and four canister, separate loading, total thirty-two rounds, weight 484.11 pounds.

The 12-pounder howitzer had fifteen shells, twenty case, and four canister, all fixed, total thirty-nine rounds, weight 479.6 pounds. The 24-pounder howitzer box carried twelve shells, eight case strapped with sabot, and three canister, total twenty-three rounds, weight 564.69 pounds. The 32-pounder howitzer had eight shells, six case, strapped, and one

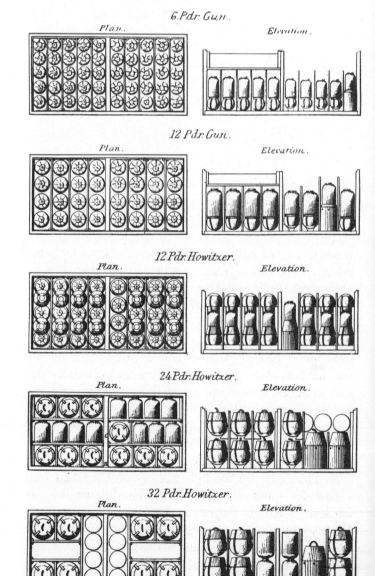

FIGURE: X-17 IDENTIFICATION: Ammunition Chests. SOURCE: *Instruction for Field Artillery.*

FIGURE: X-18 IDENTIFICATION: Battery Wagon. SOURCE: *Instruction for Field Artillery.*
REMARKS:

1. Lunette
2. Stock
3. Guard Plate
4. Lock Chain
5. Lock Chain Bridle
6. Lock Chain Hook
7. Studs (Iron)
8. Side Rails
9. Upper Rails
10. Hinges
11. Cover Boards
12. Cover Strap and Turnbuckles
13. Bottom Rails
14. Bows (Iron)
15. Hasp.
16. Forage Rack Chains
17. Sides of Forage Rack
18. Bars of Forage Rack
19. Side Boards
20. Side Stays

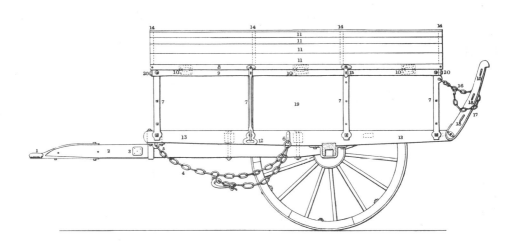

FIGURE: X-19 IDENTIFICATION: Traveling Forge. SOURCE: *Instruction for Field Artillery.* REMARKS:

1. Roof of Bellows House
2. Studs
3. Girders to Support Bellows
4. Bellows
5. Ribs of Bellows
6. Side Rail
7. Windpipe
8. Air Back
9. Back of Fire Place
10. Fire Place
11. Stock
12. Stock Stirrups
13. Coal Box
14. Handles
15. Turnbuckle and Hasp
16. Bellows Hook
17. Fulcrum and Support for Bellows Pole
18. Vice
19. Prop

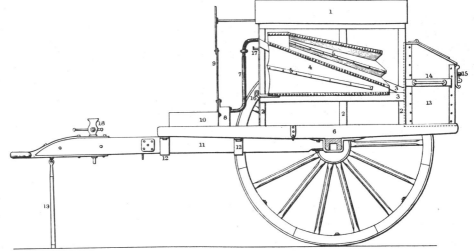

canister, total fifteen rounds, weight 492.33 pounds. These were textbook breakdowns at the start of the war and probably were altered as combat conditions and ammunition availability dictated.

The battery wagon (Fig. X-18) was a traveling warehouse of supplies necessary to keep wood, cloth, and leather items of the battery in operation. In limber and wagon body it carried more than one hundred twenty-five different items ranging from axes, saws, planes, and gauges of the carpenter's trade to saddler's stores of needles, shears, thimbles, awls, and beeswax—all in the limber chest—and oil, paint, felling axes, sponge and rammer heads, spikes for spiking cannon, spokes for wheels, halters, harness leather, spades, an elevating screw, tarpaulins, scythes for gathering forage, and a grindstone, all in the wagon body. Excluding 20 pounds of nails and a hundred needles, the number of individual articles totaled almost five hundred. A forage rack, protruding from the rear of the wagon, could carry a surprising amount of fodder if properly pressed and lashed.

The forge (Fig. X-19) held about seventy-five different items[25] ranging from 280 horseshoes and miscellaneous bolts, washers, nails, and assorted iron

197

FIGURE: X-20 IDENTIFICATION: Traveling Forge. REMARKS: Forge is limbered, but anvil has been removed. Background is camp of 5th New York Volunteers between Yorktown and Richmond in the spring of 1862.

bars, to an excellent inventory of smith's tools. Most were carried in the limber chest (not shown) which was identical in size and appearance to the standard ammunition chest. The remainder, except vise and anvil, went into a storage compartment of the body beneath the bellows known as the "iron room." The bellows fed air through pipes to the air box in the rear of the fireplace where the anvil, which was taken off for use, traveled. The vise was attached to the shaft and the box in rear carried coal. A Civil War photograph (Fig. X-20) shows a battery forge with anvil removed and ready for business during McClellan's march from Yorktown toward Richmond in May, 1862.

Mountain artillery batteries were far more Spartan than their field associates, yet adequately equipped for their job. The main criterion was the ability to be broken down into suitable loads for pack animals, generally horses during the Civil War. Thus the 12-pounder mountain howitzer shown on reproduction carriage in Chapter II, when mounted on an authentic carriage (Fig. X-21) could be packed on two animals with a third for ammunition and traverse territory too rough for vehicles, or, with twin shafts attached to the trail, be drawn by a single horse over favorable ground.

The mountain howitzer carriage, like the field, changed a bit in dimension between 1841 and 1861, although appearance remained about the same. Major differences, other than size, between field and mountain carriages, were that the cheeks of the latter were formed of a single piece by hollowing out the head of the stock, and the axle-tree was made of wood since it was not expected to take hard usage under draft.[26] The tube (220 pounds) and shafts (30 pounds) were packed on one horse, the carriage and implements (287 pounds) on another, and ammunition in two chests on a third. Two chests, carrying carriage-maker's tools for repairs, formed the load for a horse as did a portable forge, anvil, and smith's tools, packed in similar fashion. The same harness and saddle, weighing 47 pounds, were used for all.[27]

Each ammunition chest contained one shell, six spherical case, and one canister, all fixed, a total of eight rounds which, with a dozen friction primers, 18 inches of slow match, and a single portfire, weighed 97.82 pounds and, including chest, 112 pounds. Thus an ammunition horse packed sixteen rounds weighing 224 pounds plus harness and saddle.[28]

Ordnance tables[29] allowed the battery six howitzers, seven carriages, thirty-six ammunition chests (forty-eight rounds per piece), two chests of forge and smith's tools, two of carriage-maker's tools, thirty-three pack saddle and harness, and thirty-three horses or mules.

The mountain howitzer was found to be an excellent weapon for operations on the Western plains against Indians. However, the pack capability of the carriage was unnecessary and its unsuitability to steady draft a liability. Consequently, the carriage was altered a bit during the 1850s to give it larger wheels, wider track, an iron axle, and a limber which carried two mountain-type ammunition chests (see Appendix). This prairie carriage, as it was called, had a single pole and was drawn by two horses abreast.[30]

The caisson—known as the prairie ammunition cart—was a two-wheel vehicle with double shafts drawn by a single horse although hooks on the shafts permitted harnessing of another in tandem for rough going. It carried four chests of ammunition and one for implements. This gave the piece, between limber and cart, forty-eight rounds.

Siege and garrison carriages followed the field through the stages of bracket trail to Gribeauval and final order for conversion to stock trail 8 July 1836.[31] Like the field, they changed a bit in dimension, but little in appearance, between 1841 and 1861.

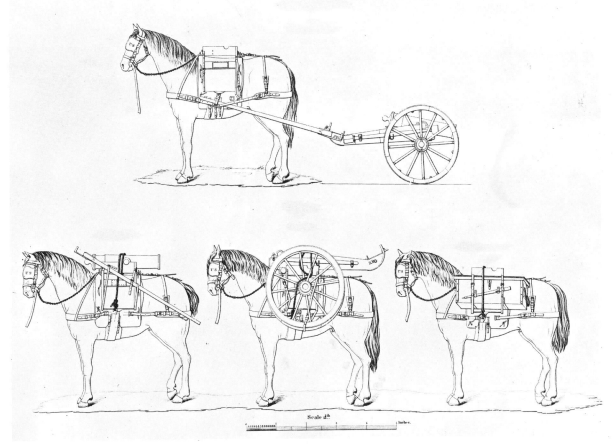

FIGURE: X-21 IDENTIFICATION: Carriage, Mountain Howitzer, 12-Pounder, Wood. SOURCE: Mordecai. REMARKS: (Top) Limbered for Draft. (Bottom) Packs. Tube and shafts (left); Carriage (center), and Ammunition Chests (right).

FIGURE: X-22 IDENTIFICATION: Carriage, Siege and Garrison, Wood. REMARKS: 8-Inch Siege Howitzers, Model 1861, mounted on Siege carriages in unidentified battery during the Civil War.

There were three separate carriages,[32] similar except for size—one for the 12-pounder siege gun, one for the 18-pounder, and one for either the 24-pounder gun or 8-inch siege howitzer. In the latter case a quoin had to be used for elevation since the 8-inch was too short to reach the screw. A Civil War photograph (Fig. X-22) shows two Model 1861 howitzers on siege carriages in an unidentified battery, probably in the Washington defense.

With the advent of rifles during the war, the 18-pounder carriage was adapted to the 30-pounder Parrott and the 12-pounder to the 4.5-inch siege rifle[33] which is illustrated mounted on this carriage in traveling position in Chapter IX. Authentic siege carriages today are rare and reproductions are not too prevalent. One of the latter supporting a cut-off 32-pounder at Vicksburg was illustrated in Chapter I along with diagrams of the 18- and 24-pounder siege carriages. An excellent contemporary photograph (Fig. X-23) shows two 4.2-inch Parrotts on siege carriages in Battery Putnam, Morris Island, about 1864.

Since the siege carriage was not expected to maneuver with troops, it differed in certain respects from the field model. It was larger and heavier, factors of little consequence for it could be brought into combat with relative leisure. There were no hooks for implements since these were carried separately in a wagon and the heavy trail attached to the limber in a manner intended to help counterbalance the weight of the pole on the horses. This eliminated the metal lunette, a prominent feature of the field model.

Noticeable features are the so-called traveling trunnions and the bolster. It was found that when limbered, the position of the trunnion bed threw too much weight of the heavy piece on the rear wheels. To correct this, the bolts at the rear ends of the cheeks were enlarged to form an additional trunnion bed and the piece was shifted to these when limbered, the breech resting in a groove formed in a block of wood known as the bolster (Fig. X-24). The operation necessitated removal of the elevating screw which was reversed in its nut and permitted to hang beneath the carriage. A leather strap kept the handle from unwinding and dropping off. The same limber was used for all three carriages and the mortar wagon,[34] and was distinctive in that it had no chest since immediate supply of ammunition was unnecessary. Instead, projectiles, strapped with sabot, but with the charges separate, were normally hauled by wagon.[35]

FIGURE: X-23 IDENTIFICATION: Carriage, Siege & Garrison, Wood. REMARKS: 4.2-Inch Parrotts on Siege Carriages in Battery Putnam, Morris Island, S.C., about 1864.

FIGURE: X-24 IDENTIFICATION: Carriage, Siege & Garrison, Wood. SOURCE: Mordecai. REMARKS: 24-Pounder, Model 1839, in traveling position.

Transportation of the 24-pounder gun took ten horses and five drivers, and the 12-, 18-, 8-inch, and mortar wagon, eight horses and four drivers. The battery wagon and forge were the field type and each required six horses and three drivers.[36]

The mortar wagon, a sturdy, flat-bed vehicle (Figs. X-25 and 26) was designed for hauling siege mortars, spare guns, or large shot and shell. It consisted of the standard siege limber, a body equipped with removable stakes along the side to secure the load and a windlass, or winch, at rear to assist in loading heavy objects by dragging them up the stock.[37]

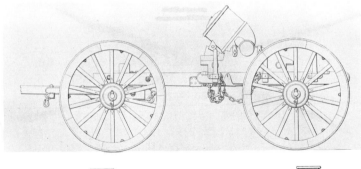

FIGURE: X-25 IDENTIFICATION: Mortar Wagon. SOURCE: Mordecai. REMARKS: 10-Inch Siege Mortar, Model 1841, with its bed loaded on Mortar Wagon.

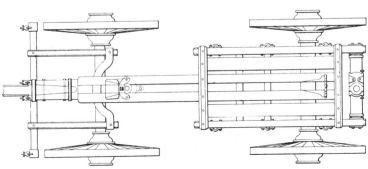

FIGURE: X-26 IDENTIFICATION: Mortar Wagon. SOURCE: Instruction for Heavy Artillery. REMARKS: Note winch at rear. In loading, limber was detached, stock lowered to ground and mortar on its bed was winched up the stock to body of the wagon.

FIGURE: X-27 IDENTIFICATION: 8-Inch Siege Mortar, Model 1841 and Bed. SOURCE: *Instruction for Heavy Artillery.* RE-MARKS:

1. Cheeks
2. Maneuvering Bolts
3. Middle Transom
4. Front Transom
5. Cap Squares
6. Cap Square Straps
7. Bolster
8. Quoin
9. Sleeper
10. Deck Planks
11. Eye Bolts

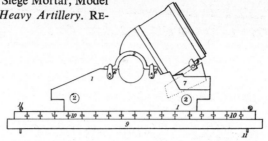 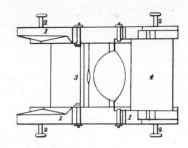

Mortars, both siege and seacoast, were mounted on carriages known as "beds" and during the Civil War were mainly of two types—1841 and 1861, the former of cast iron and the latter of wrought. The 1841 siege models (Fig. X-27) fitted the 8- and 10-inch calibers as well as the stone mortar which was suppressed by 1861.[38] Except for dimensions, all were alike and consisted of two cheeks and two connecting transoms, all cast in a single piece. A wood bolster, grooved to fit the elevating quoin, was bolted to the front transom. Maneuvering bolts at the ends of the cheeks were made of wrought iron and placed in the mold before the carriage was poured. Cap squares held the trunnions in place, but were needed only when the piece was fired at very low angles of elevation.[39] The West Point stone mortar (Chapter III) bed differs a bit in profile and may have been a slightly earlier version or a founder's adaptation of the standard mount.

The 1841 seacoast model was similar except that the cheeks turned up in front to receive the front transom through which worked an elevating screw. Although cheeks were cast iron, the transoms were wood, mortised and tenoned to the cheeks and secured by bolts, one of which was left long. This bolt and the projecting ends of the cheeks were used for maneuvering.[40] Two of these beds are pictured in Chapter III with 10-inch seacoast Model 1841-44 mortars at the Crows Nest near Dutch Gap. Several illustrations of the 1861 seacoast bed are also shown in the same chapter mounting 13-inch mortars.

The 1861 siege variety was similar, but lacked the front steps (Fig. X-28). This is an 8-inch siege mortar in Fort C.F. Smith, part of the Washington defenses. A similar mount at the Mariner's Museum, Newport News, Virginia, is illustrated in Chapter III.

All these mortars were, of course, United States models. The Confederacy acquired many of the 1841 type, both siege and seacoast, at the start of the war and probably a few of the 1861 siege variety were picked up later through capture. It is exceedingly doubtful if any new seacoast models were obtained.

However, the Confederates no doubt used older types such as that in the Chapter III drawing of a Morris Island battery of 10-inch, Model 1819 seacoast mortars. The wheels used for training were not on eccentrics and presumably the axles were subject to terrific strain when the piece fired. In addition, to judge by the apparent 8-inch siege mortar in the Chapter III picture of captured materiel at Richmond, the Southerners fabricated a few beds. This one seems to have been made of wood, a material frowned upon for heavy mortar beds because of its elasticity, but one which was readily available in the iron-starved South. The pattern is similar to the 1841 U.S. model with, perhaps, changes suggested by the wooden Coehorn bed. The quoin is intended to be used from the side, a natural, safe arrangement preferable to that of the U.S. model which was designed for front use of the quoin although in practice it was generally inserted obliquely.[41] The little Coehorn also was listed in the siege category and an excellent specimen of a reproduction bed is illustrated in Chapter III. Handles were placed on either side and it was normally carried by four men.[42]

Seacoast carriages were of three general types—barbette, casemate, and flank casemate—based on the designated portion of the fortification they were intended to defend. They also were divided into wood or iron models and barbette carriages were further classified as front or center pintle. In addition, like field and siege carriages, although general appearance remained the same within each category, dimensions differed minor amounts to accommodate various caliber weapons.

All, regardless of material or type, consisted of two parts, a top section which carried the weapon, known as the "gun carriage" or "top carriage" (hereafter to be designated by the latter term to differentiate it from the entire carriage) and a bottom frame called the "chassis." Each had specific functions and if these are understood in principle, operation of all these carriages will be easier to visualize. The chassis determined direction of the piece. The top carriage permitted elevation. Together they absorbed recoil. A brief study of the various illustrations will explain more adequately than words the method of pivoting the chassis from front or center to give direction. Elevation is equally evident whether performed by quoin, screw, ratchet, or a combination of these.

Methods of controlling recoil are a bit more difficult. In all cases the shock of discharge was dissipated by sliding friction. When the piece fired, the entire top carriage slid back along the chassis and by the time it struck stops or "counterhurters" at the rear, most of the momentum was gone. This was fine

insofar as recoil went—the "kick" of the piece could push the top carriage with considerable facility. But shoving it back to the front of the chassis, or "in battery," for each succeeding shot would have exhausted the crew after a few rounds. To overcome this difficulty, the top carriage could have been equipped with wheels or rollers. But these, although excellent for getting the piece into battery, obviously would eliminate the initial requirement—sliding friction to take up recoil. Consequently, early carriages involved a compromise—part rolling, part sliding friction—which like most compromises was workable, but far from perfect.

Then a far better method was developed. The wheels or rollers were mounted on "eccentrics," an arrangement which permitted the top carriage to roll into battery then be dropped onto the chassis for firing. This was often accomplished by using a heavy axle with the spindles for the wheels being affixed

FIGURE: X-28 IDENTIFICATION: 8-Inch Siege Mortar, Model 1861, on Bed. REMARKS: Fort C.F. Smith, Washington defenses, about 1864. Note mortar platform. Men are serving a 12-Pounder Bronze Field Howitzer. Siege carriages at far rear.

203

near the rim of the ends instead of the center as would normally be the case. Thus, when the axle was rotated with lever or wrench, the spindles and attached wheels were lowered or raised. There were also other methods, but whether simple or complex, an eccentric of some sort was the secret of most seacoast carriage operation.

Historically, until about 1840 most seacoast weapons were mounted on 4-truck carriages similar to the Navy broadside model, but with larger, iron wheels replacing the wood trucks. This form remained relatively unchanged until 1819 when cast iron was adopted for carriage frames in the interests of economy and longer life. The metal held sway during the 20s and 30s although during the latter part of its tenure, military authorities became increasingly aware that enemy shot would shatter such carriages with deadly effect on the gun crews.[43]

This led the Ordnance Board of 1838 of its final report, January, 1839, to advocate a return to wood, a material which reigned supreme until wrought iron was formally suggested to the 1856 Ordnance Board and adopted in 1859 for seacoast carriages.[44] An exact date for introduction of the two-part—chassis and top carriage—form is not available. Birkhimer states such carriages in wood, front pintle (presumably barbette) models were "in vogue" after 1800 although he gives no hint regarding their appearance.

The type which was introduced in the 1830s, and with certain alterations was still in use at the outbreak of war, came to America in the same fashion as field and siege models—from France via plans and specifications acquired in 1829. Initial use of these "French" barbette carriages is established by a letter dated 27 September 1872 from Major Alfred Mordecai:[45]

"My actual service in the Ordnance Department began on the 1st of January, 1833, when I joined Captain [John] Symington at Washington Arsenal . . . [who] was just finishing the first of the barbette carriages which were . . . copied from the French system. . . . The first of these barbette carriages was sent in the winter or spring of 1833 for the armament of Fort Moultrie on account of the political disturbances in South Carolina. I can have, therefore, no hesitation in saying that the first full knowledge of the French system which we copied in field, siege and barbette carriages, was derived from the complete drawings and tables of construction which were furnished by Lieutenant [Daniel] Tyler to the Ordnance Office."

The history of these carriages is carried a bit further by a confidential engineer report on Fort Moultrie armament dated 22 January 1835:[46]

"The sum of the lengths of the three sea fronts is about 500 feet. Twenty-four guns can be mounted on these fronts if the new French seacoast barbett [sic] carriage is used, or a still greater number if the old truck carriage is employed. The use of the truck carriage, however, would require an embrasure or a platform so elevated as greatly to expose the men and would, of course, not be resorted to unless in case of urgent necessity. Eight guns are at present mounted on the French carriages, the platforms of which are in perfect order. . . . It is understood that there are 8 more carriages of the new pattern in store at Fort Moultrie. . . ."

Basic components of these carriages were wood. However, to judge from a recommendation in the Ordnance Board report of 1839 that cast iron no longer be used for transoms of casemate and barbette carriages, it may be inferred that transoms of the type sent to Fort Moultrie were made of cast iron until introduction in 1839 of the wood, front pintle, barbette carriage (Fig. X-29) which, with a few changes, remained standard for twenty years.

Nevertheless, minor improvements did continue during this period and by the end of the decade, the carriage had reached the form (Fig. X-30) of an 1849 drawing. This version differed from the earlier model primarily in slight dimension changes and such visible additions as a tongue prop and chassis rail plates. It received even fewer alterations during the succeeding years and was still defending the nation's fortifications at the outbreak of war. A contemporary photograph in Chapter I shows 32-pounders at Fort Totten mounted on this carriage. The mount in the drawing also supports a 32-pounder, but others of this type, identical except for dimension, were used with 12-, 18-, 24-, and 42-pounder guns. The 8-inch seacoast howitzer utilized the 32-pounder carriage without alterations and only slight modification of width was necessary to adapt the 42-pounder gun carriage to the 10-inch howitzer.

In the permanent installation of the drawing, a pintle—an iron pin with key or nut at top—anchored the front of the chassis to a stone block, often protected from wear on top by an iron circular or square "pintle plate." This permitted the rear of the carriage to swing in a 180° arc on traverse wheels that ran on an iron track also set on stone.

In temporary fortifications, the pintle plate was bolted to a wooden bolster, instead of a stone block, attached to a wood cross picketed firmly to the ground. The iron traverse circle, or track, was spiked to planks pinned to sleepers and connected with the cross. This form was relatively light and planks probably were replaced by heavy timbers in the semi-

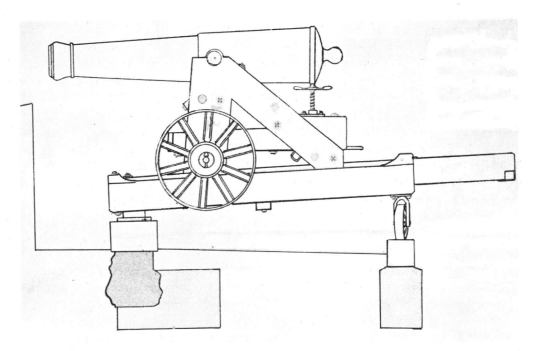

FIGURE: X-29 IDENTIFICA-
TION: Carriage, Seacoast, Front
Pintle, Barbette, Model 1839,
Wood. SOURCE: *Ordnance
Manual,* 1841.

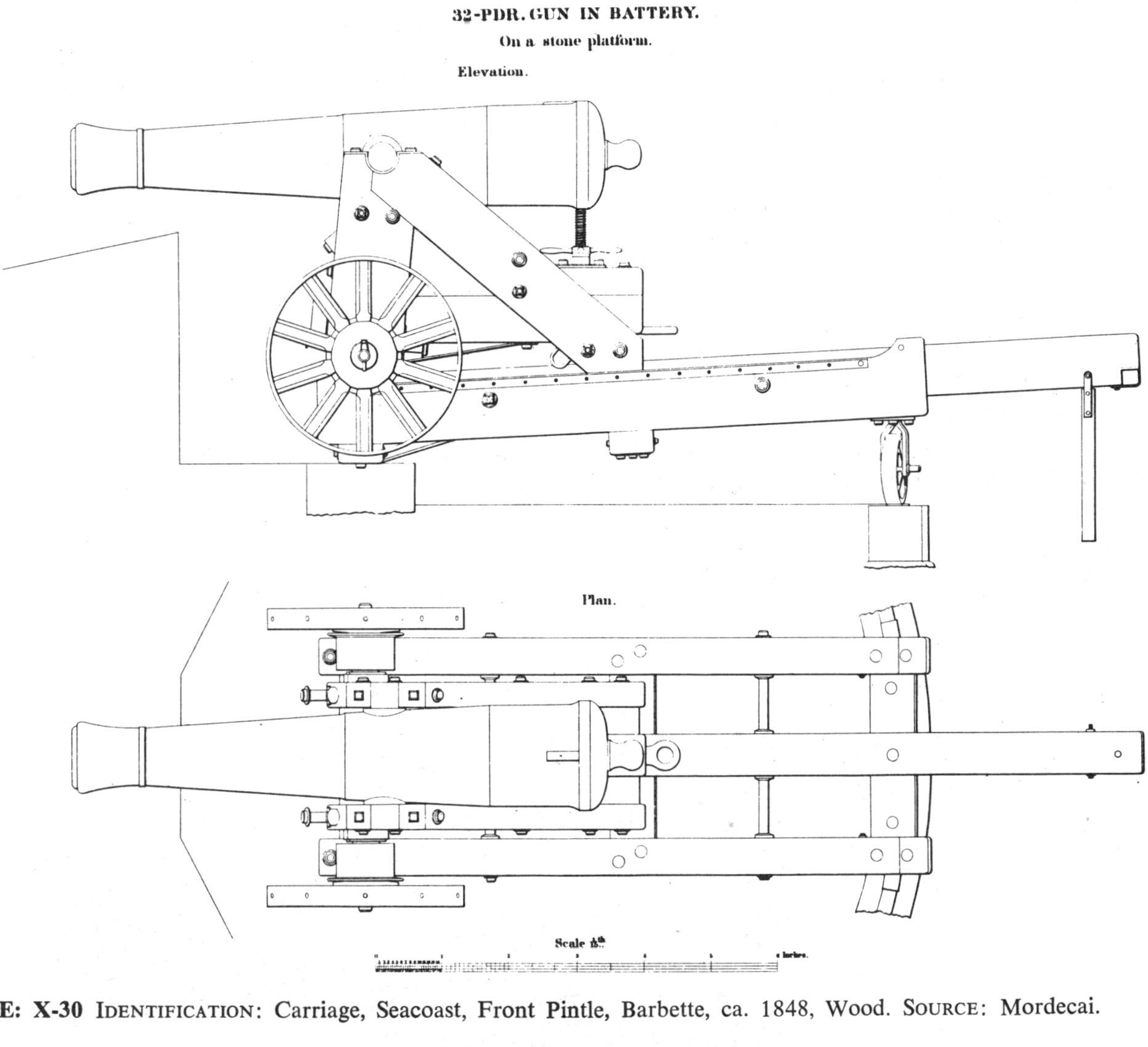

32-PDR. GUN IN BATTERY.

On a stone platform.

Elevation.

Plan.

Scale ⅟₁₂

FIGURE: X-30 IDENTIFICATION: Carriage, Seacoast, Front Pintle, Barbette, ca. 1848, Wood. SOURCE: Mordecai.

permanent Confederate sand batteries. The pintle plate and track, however, were definitely used and specimens have been found by the author buried in the remains of such batteries in the Charleston area.

The chassis of this carriage was formed of two side rails connected at front, center, and rear by transoms and held together by bolts. They were protected on the outer edges by iron "rail plates" and had curved "hurters" and "counterhurters" front and rear. In the center was a long wood "tongue" supported by a "prop" to sustain the heavy weight of the top carriage and weapon at the end of recoil. Cheeks of the top carriage were formed of two "uprights" and two diagonal "braces" connected by axle tie and transoms, all mortised, tenoned, and bolted together. Most prominent features are the two large wooden wheels. These, as illustrated in the overhead view of the drawing, were connected on the inside to smaller wheels, known as "top carriage rollers," made of iron with flanges on the outer rims to hold the top carriage straight on the rails.

Unlike later carriages, these wheels and rollers were not on eccentrics. Here was the compromise between rolling and sliding friction. The rollers remained in constant contact with the rails and at all times supported a share of the top carriage weight. Remaining weight, at rear, rested on the tongue and provided the required sliding friction. The piece was moved into, and when necessary out of, battery by men heaving on 5½-foot handspikes. These were inserted between the spokes of the top carriage wheels and using the spokes for leverage, the top carriage moved jerkily to and fro. It was hot work and gun crews no doubt were enthusiastic over the newer models equipped with eccentrics. Top carriage wheels were shod with iron and occasionally used for transporting the weapon from one part of a fort to another. Details of this maneuver will be explained in the following chapter.

Successor to this carriage was the wrought iron, front pintle, barbette carriage authorized in 1859 and listed in the Ordnance Manual of 1861 in three models which differed only in dimension—one for the 10-inch columbiad, one for the 8-inch columbiad and 42-pounder gun, and one for the 32- and 24-pounder guns. Later they were modified to fit Parrott rifles as in Figure X-31 which shows these carriages mounting six 100-pounder Parrotts in Battery No. 1 which opened 1 May 1862 during the siege of Yorktown. Elevation in this case was by quoin. Projectiles, lower left, are Parrott bolts. This temporary battery also illustrates in dim outline the previously discussed circular iron pintle plate and iron traverse circle.

The top carriage consisted of two triangular pieces of boiler plate strengthened by ribs bolted to the inner sides and connected by transoms. Flanges inside the cheeks held the top carriage on the chassis. The rails were two "I-beams" connected by transoms. The top carriage truck wheels were on an eccentric axle, activated by the "truck handspike" shown attached to the chassis rail directly below the top carriage. A concerted heave on two of these, fitted over the truck spindles on either side of the top carriage, brought the wheels into play. This still left the rear of the top carriage on the rail to be dragged along with standard maneuvering handspikes worked in holes in the trucks. Later operation of this carriage was improved by addition of a form of eccentric known as the roller handspike. This, as the name implies, had a small roller a few inches from the end. By shoving the tips of two handspikes under the projecting metal shoes of the top carriage, the rear could be lifted and the entire unit rolled into or out of battery on trucks and roller handspikes.

Advanced versions of this carriage are shown in Chapter IV mounting two 10-inch Rodman columbiads at West Point and in Chapter V holding the 11-inch *Keokuk* Dahlgren at Charleston. The *Keokuk* carriage and the one at rear in the West Point picture have been improved mainly in the chas-

FIGURE: X-31 IDENTIFICATION: Carriage, Seacoast, Front Pintle, Barbette, Model 1859, Wrought Iron. REMARKS: U.S. Battery No. 1 at Yorktown consisting of one 8-Inch and five 6.4-Inch Parrotts. Opened fire 1 May 1862.

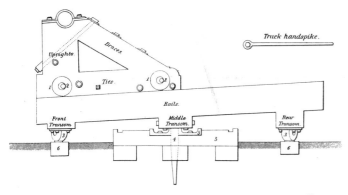

FIGURE: X-32 IDENTIFICATION: Carriage, Seacoast, Center Pintle, Barbette, ca. 1850, Wood. SOURCE: *Instruction for Heavy Artillery*. REMARKS: 8-Inch Columbiad Carriage.

1. Truck Wheels
2. Eccentric Axles
3. Traverse Wheels
4. Pintle
5. Pintle Plate and Bed
6. Traverse Circle

sis—eccentric wheels have been added in front to assist in traversing the piece. In addition, steps have been added in the West Point version. The carriage in foreground at the Military Academy is equipped with a winch to haul the top carriage out of battery and four trucks which would permit it to roll into battery of its own accord. Lack of time prevented close examination of this carriage during the author's only visit to West Point. However, to judge from the photograph, the rear trucks are on eccentrics and the front so placed that they automatically touch the rails when those at rear are engaged.

Primary disadvantages of the front pintle barbette carriage were limited traverse—180° maximum —and lack of support under the center of the chassis when heavy columbiads were fired at high elevation. The center pintle corrected both these deficiencies. It permitted 360° traverse and the strongest support was directly under the point of greatest strain.

No date of introduction has been found for the wood, center pintle, barbette carriage (Figs. X-32 and 33) designed for 8-and 10-inch columbiads. It was omitted from Mordecai's drawings of U.S. ordnance in 1849, yet was ordered supplanted by a wrought iron model in 1859 on the basis of recommendations three years earlier. Since Mordecai places the 1844 8-inch columbiad on a casemate carriage and gives no mount for the 10 which is, however, listed in the section on tubes, chances are this carriage was under development and, to judge from the numbers in coastal fortifications by the beginning of the war, probably went into production in the late 40s or early 50s. Installation of these carriages at Fort Moultrie, for instance, was budgeted in 1855 for completion prior to June, 1856.[47]

At any rate, the carriage gave excellent service and was used extensively by the South for such weapons as the banded 10-inch "Confederate Rodman" and Model 1858 columbiad illustrated in Chapter IV and the 10-inch (Fig. X-34) in Battery Semmes overlooking the James River.

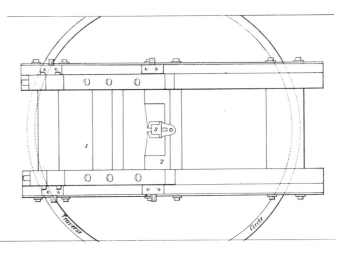

FIGURE: X-33 IDENTIFICATION: Carriage, Seacoast, Center Pintle, Barbette, ca. 1850, Wood. SOURCE: *Instruction for Heavy Artillery*. REMARKS: 8-Inch Columbiad Carriage.
1. Front Transom
2. Rear Transom
3. Elevating apparatus.

FIGURE: X-34 IDENTIFICATION: Carriage, Seacoast, Center Pintle, Barbette, Confederate, Wood. REMARKS: 10-Inch "Confederate Rodman" in Battery Semmes on the James River. Top Carriage Wheels have been removed to disable the piece in this ca.1865 photograph.

FIGURE: X-35 IDENTIFICATION: Carriage, Seacoast, Center Pintle, Barbette, ca. 1850, Wood. REMARKS: May, 1861 photograph of 10-inch, Model 1844 columbiads on Fort Sumter.

A rare 1861 photograph (Fig. X-35) shows South Carolinians and center pintle, barbette carriages at Fort Sumter shortly after Major Anderson's surrender. A 10-inch columbiad mounted on a similar carriage was wrecked through carelessness of Private John Carmody, a wild Irishman in Anderson's command who, against orders, and with more enthusiasm than sense, climbed to the terreplein during the bombardment and touched off the piece toward Morris Island. Damage from the shot seems to have been negligible, but in his haste Carmody forgot to throw the eccentrics out of gear. The top carriage slammed back against the counterhurters and left the chassis to crash in splinters, and, incidentally, demonstrate a major danger of all carriages equipped with eccentrics.

Top carriage and chassis construction, as indicated in the diagram, were generally similar to the front pintle model. The tongue was omitted and the transoms of the top carriage extended below the tops of the rails to hold alignment. The entire tops of the rails were shod with iron rail plates and hurters and counterhurters were stronger, although apparently insufficient alone to stop the recoil. Four iron traverse wheels ran on the circular track. Foundation construction could be stone or wood with an iron pintle plate required for both types.

The wrought iron, center pintle, barbette carriage of 1859 was designed for 8- and 10-inch columbiads, but was later adapted for 6.4-, 8- and 10-inch Parrotts. A beautiful specimen (Fig. X-36) mounting a 6.4-inch Parrott in the Washington defenses shows the same top carriage was used for iron front and center pintle models and the chassis was similar with obvious difference of pintle placement. Traverse wheels of the front pintle model were 18 inches in diameter, those of the center pintle 14.6 in rear and 11.63 in front. The approximate 3-inch difference provided part of the necessary forward inclination of the rails which was the same 5.23 inches in one-hundred for all wrought iron carriages. The remaining portion of the slant came from different length "traverse wheel forks." The photograph illustrates a screw method of elevating the Parrott. The chassis has movable counterhurters which could be clamped at any point along the rails to limit recoil.

Development of the 15-inch Rodman necessitated a still stronger carriage and resulted in a new wrought iron, center pintle, barbette model. The top carriage was equipped with two or four trucks on eccentrics and the chassis was made heavier to carry the tremendous weight of the tube. Figure X-37 shows a 15-inch on a two-truck top carriage in the Civil War defenses of Alexandria, Virginia, and Figure X-38 a four-truck (rear missing) model currently displayed in Fort McHenry, Baltimore, Maryland.

A front pintle model was also used with the 15-inch for platforms to fit this type have been found in permanent fortifications. Based on the platforms, this carriage had wheels on eccentrics at the pintle, rear traverse wheels some 15.75 feet from the pintle and an additional set of wheels about 7.5 feet from the pintle to take the strain off the middle of the chassis. The top carriage may have had two or four trucks on eccentrics, more likely the latter.

While barbette guns were mounted atop the

FIGURE: X-36 IDENTIFICATION: Carriage, Seacoast, Center Pintle, Barbette, Model 1859, Wrought Iron. REMARKS: Fort Stevens, Washington defenses. 6.4-Inch Parrott. Note elevating screw.

FIGURE: X-37 IDENTIFICATION: Carriage, Seacoast, Center Pintle, Barbette, ca.1861, Wrought Iron. REMARKS: 15-Inch Rodman in Battery Rogers near Alexandria, Va.

FIGURE: X-38 LOCATION: Fort McHenry, Md. IDENTIFICATION: Carriage, Seacoast, Center Pintle, Barbette, ca. 1861, Wrought Iron. Top Carriage — Length 106.5. Width, excluding eccentrics, 57. Chassis — Length 240. Width 61. REMARKS: 15-Inch Rodman. Note this is a 4-truck top carriage in contrast to two on the carriage in Fig. X-37.

terreplein firing over the parapet, exposed to shot and shell, casemate weapons were buried below in the fortification shooting through narrow slits where blinding powder smoke soon made aiming difficult and breathing little better. Casemate carriages were generally lower than the upper deck models necessitating a different top carriage, and the size of the embrasures limited both traverse and elevation to the point where the center pintle arrangement was unnecessary and the front pintle insufficient. Consequently, the chassis of these mounts had traverse wheels front and rear and an iron "tongue" anchored by a pintle in the center of the embrasure. This extended the pivot to a point directly under the muzzle of the piece thereby insuring all possible traverse under extremely limited conditions.

Initially, these carriages, like the early barbette models, compromised between rolling and sliding friction as in Figure X-39, an illustration from the 1841 Ordnance Manual showing the mount for a 32-pounder gun. The same carriage, with minor changes in dimension, was also used for 24- and 42-pounders.[48] Although the top carriage was equipped with four trucks, an ingenious arrangement of slanted chassis rails permitted the weight to rest on all only when the piece was in battery (see drawing). The forward truck wheels at all times remained on the outer rails which were capped with iron rail plates and sloped upward to the rear parallel to the long, wooden tongue. The rear trucks, while the weapon was in battery, rested on the inner rails which were horizontal. When the piece started back in recoil, the rear of the top carriage, held level by the horizontal line followed by the rear trucks, soon struck the

rising slant of the wood tongue. This lifted the rear trucks off the rails and sliding friction took over to reduce recoil. Handspikes worked in holes bored in the treads of the front wheels levered the piece back into battery where in the last few inches the rear trucks again touched the rails and lifted the rear of the top carriage.

The reason for having the top carriage rest on wheels when in battery was twofold: it placed the top carriage in the same relative plane of elevation for each shot and, by making movement easy, ensured the front trucks of rolling against the hurters thus placing the muzzle fully into the embrasure. The difference in slant of the rails is clearly visible in the casemate carriage mounting the fake gun in Fort Pulaski (Chapter IX). This is a reproduction of a later model which has a more sophisticated top carriage, but utilizes approximately the same chassis.

This new model, which the reproduction copies, probably was developed during the middle to latter part of the 1840s, although no exact date is available. It is, however, the casemate carriage illustrated (Fig. X-40) in Mordecai's book of 1849 which, allowing a few months for publication, would indicate a top limit of 1848. This carriage, like its predecessor, was used with minor dimension changes for 24-, 32-, and 42-pounder guns as well as the 8-inch columbiad shown in the diagram.

Scarcely detectable changes were made in the chassis, but the top carriage, in addition to the obvious "squaring" of the cheek ends, had three important alterations: an eccentric roller was installed, the rear trucks removed, and the rear transom notched over the wood tongue to serve as a guide. This seems

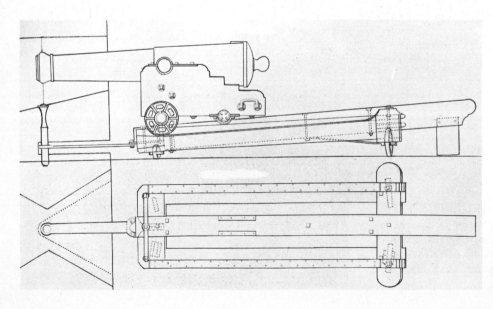

FIGURE: X-39 IDENTIFICATION: Carriage, Seacoast, Casemate, Model 1839, Wood. SOURCE: *Ordnance Manual* 1841. REMARKS: Mounting 32-Pounder Gun, Model 1841.

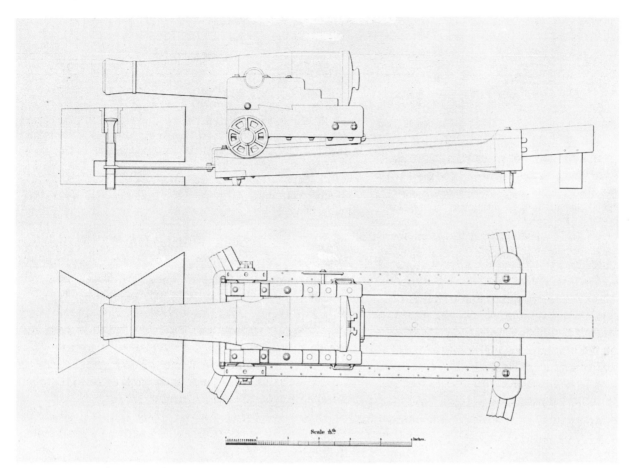

Scale ¹⁄₁₂ᵗʰ

Inches.

FIGURE: **X-40** IDENTIFICATION: Carriage, Seacoast, Casemate, ca. 1848, Wood, SOURCE: Mordecai. REMARKS: Mounting 8-Inch Columbiad, Model 1844.

to have been an excellent carriage and, although technically superseded by an iron model in April, 1859, mounted the guns with which Major Anderson's small garrison defended Fort Sumter two years later.

The 1859 wrought iron, casement carriage which replaced the wood variety was built in two models that differed only in dimension—one for the 8-inch columbiad and 42-pounder gun, and a scaled-down version for 24- and 32-pounders. Chassis construction was generally similar to iron barbette types, but with substitution of the casemate principle of front and rear traverse wheels and embrasure pintle holding the tongue. The top carriage also copied the barbette form, but was somewhat smaller. Operation was the same with trucks working on eccentrics and roller handspikes being adopted later to facilitate movement.

Like barbette carriages, the casemate variety was adapted to handle the Parrotts and eleven of the small model, mounting 6.4-inch rifles, are displayed today at Fort Sumter (Fig. X-41) where, as explained in Chapter VI, they were installed shortly after the war.

FIGURE: **X-41** LOCATION: Fort Sumter, S.C. IDENTIFICATION: Carriage, Seacoast, Casemate, Model 1859, Wrought Iron. REMARKS: Mounting 6.4-Inch Parrott.

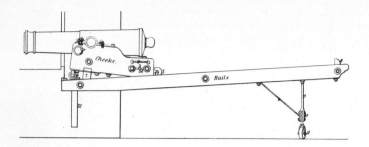

FIGURE: **X-42** IDENTIFICATION: Carriage, Seacoast, Flank Casemate, ca. 1844, Wood. SOURCE: *Instruction for Heavy Artillery.* REMARKS: 24-Pounder, Siege & Garrison Howitzer, Model 1844. 1. Maneuvering Ring. 2. Trail Handles. 3. Trail Roller. 4. Eccentrics. 5. Rollers. 6. Elevating Screw Handle. 7. Front Transom (Iron). 8. Counterhurters. 9. Prop and Brace. 10. Fork. 11. Traverse Wheel. 12. Pintle.

Final standard mount in the seacoast category is the flank casemate carriage (Figs. X-42 and 43) designed for the 24-pounder siege and garrison howitzer and intended to protect the moat or ditch of a fortification against infantry assault.

An excellent reproduction (Fig. X-44) mounting a bronze, 12-pounder field howitzer in lieu of the iron 24, guards the moat of Fort Pulaski. This model pivoted in the sole of the embrasure on a pintle directly under the front of the chassis which consisted of two rails hooked together by bolts and transoms and separated by a narrow groove. The top carriage had brass rollers in front and a trail roller on eccentrics at rear. The latter was made with flanges in the center that fitted into the groove between the chassis rails and held the rear of the top carriage in line. The front was positioned by a tenon on the bottom of the iron front transom which ran in the groove.

The front rollers were not on eccentrics, but unlike trucks of previously described early model wood carriages, they bore on the rails only at specific times. The top carriage front transom, a few inches behind the rollers, extended a carefully determined distance below the cheeks. This was so calculated that when the eccentrics of the trail roller were engaged, elevation of the rear was sufficient to lift the transom and place the front rollers on the rails for easy movement of the piece by hand. Disengagement of the eccentrics dropped the front transom back to the rails thereby lifting the rollers and permitting sliding friction to reduce recoil. Elevation was set by a screw apparatus and since the piece and top carriage were relatively light, a single handspike, consisting of a handle with two branches, worked the eccentrics.

A wrought iron, flank casemate carriage was listed in the 1861 Ordnance Manual to replace the

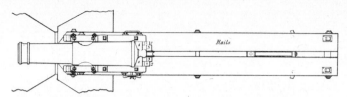

FIGURE: **X-43** IDENTIFICATION: Carriage, Seacoast, Flank Casemate, ca. 1844, Wood. SOURCE: *Instruction for Heavy Artillery.* REMARKS: Overhead view of carriage in Fig. X-42. 24-Pounder, Siege & Garrison Howitzer, Model 1844. 1. Elevating Screw Handle. 2. Eccentrics. 3. Trail Roller. 4. Rear Transom (Iron).

wood model,[49] but development had not progressed sufficiently by publication date for inclusion of drawings or specifications. In view of its relatively insignificant role, the new carriage probably was shelved for the duration of the war. The manual does note, however, that the pivot was being moved forward some two feet for improved traverse. This necessitated alterations to embrasures and the use of an iron tongue with new carriages or wood models adapted for the changed opening.

Before leaving Army carriages, two innovations developed by federal forces bombarding Fort Sumter, 1863-65, are worthy of mention. The first was a built-up platform (Fig. X-45) to permit extreme range with 4.2-inch Parrotts mounted on standard siege carriages. Although the practice of digging in the trails of such carriages for increased range had long been known, this arrangement allowed far greater elevations and at the same time provided a platform for the trail plate to slide on thus limiting strain on the stock.

The second device (Fig. X-46) might be called a field expedient for the standard barbette carriage

FIGURE: **X-44** LOCATION: Fort Pulaski, Ga. IDENTIFICATION: Carriage, Seacoast, Flank Casemate, ca. 1844, Wood. REMARKS: Reproduction carriage mounting 12-Pounder Field Howitzer, Model 1841.

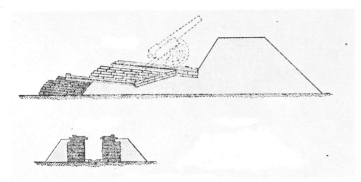

FIGURE: X-45 IDENTIFICATION: Platform, Siege, Improvised, Wood. SOURCE: *Official Records,* Vol. 28. REMARKS: Cross section and front view of platform improvised for 30-Pounder (4.2-Inch) Parrotts on Black Island firing against Fort Sumter during the Siege of Charleston.

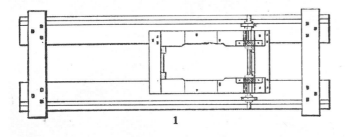

1

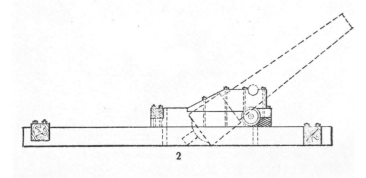

2

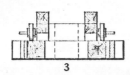

3

FIGURE: X-46 IDENTIFICATION: Carriage, Seacoast, Barbette, Field Expedient, Wood. SOURCE: *Official Records,* Vol. 28. REMARKS: Improvised carriage for 6.4-Inch Parrott utilized at Black Island, S.C., for firing on Fort Sumter 1863–65. 1. General Plan. 2. Side Elevation. 3. End View.

which was in short supply. The drawing is self-explanatory and this simple carriage,[50] which utilized two trucks on eccentrics, seems to have been quite efficient in a static position where extended firing at a stationary target such as Fort Sumter required a minimum of traverse. All wood parts were hewn from long-leaf pine in which the area abounded. Ironwork was founded by portable forges and at shops of the supply base on Hilton Head Island a few miles down the coast.

Navy carriages during the Civil War were of three basic types: broadside, pivot, and monitor. Broadside mounts operated from the sides of ships, generally through ports, and although there had been numerous experimental types prior to the war, three models may be considered standard: the 4-truck, Marsilly, and an iron carriage for the 8-inch Dahlgren of 6,500 pounds.

Best known was the 4-truck carriage. This veteran had served navies of the world for three centuries and although obsolescent was by no means obsolete, carrying many of the nation's shipboard cannon at the beginning of the conflict. One of these venerable carriages (Fig. X-47) mounting a 42-pounder was among several salvaged from the *U.S.S. Cairo* and now displayed at Vicksburg. Diagrams explaining the various parts (Figs. X-48 and 49) were taken from an 1864 text on naval ordnance.

The ancient 4-truck had numerous faults, but since correction of one emphasized another or eliminated one of its good points, the carriage spanned the years with little change simply because no one could produce a better. Furthermore, the following advantages, although few in number, were vital factors and far outweighed the defects:

FIGURE: X-47 LOCATION: Vicksburg, Miss. IDENTIFICATION: Carriage, Navy, 4-Truck, Wood. LENGTH O/A: 73.25. HEIGHT: (excludes cap squares) 28.13. REMARKS: 42-Pounder Gun, Model 1841, and original carriage salvaged from *U.S.S. Cairo.* Gun is marked on muzzle face — No. 20, B.H.; left trunnion — 1856; right trunnion — K & W, F.P.F.; tube — U.S.,; base ring — 8,397.

FIGURE: X-48 IDENTIFICATION: Carriage, Navy, 4-Truck, Wood. SOURCE: Brandt. REMARKS: Nomenclature side and overhead (Fig. X-49) views:

WOOD PARTS
- A. Brackets
  - a. Jog
  - b. Trunnion Holes
  - c. Steps
  - d. Quarter Rounds
  - e. Arch
- B. Transom
- C. Breast Piece
- D. Front and Rear Axle Trees
  - f. Body (square)
  - g. Arms
- E. Front and Rear Trucks
- F. Dumb Trucks
- G. Bed and Stool
- H. Quoin

METAL PARTS
1. Two Cap Squares
2. Four Cap Square Bolts and two Keys
3. Two Bracket Bolts
4. Two Rear Axle Tree Bolts
5. Two Side Tackle Eye Bolts
6. One Train-Tackle Eye Bolt
7. One Transporting Eye Bolt
8. Two Breast Bolts
9. Two Hinges of Breast Pieces
10. Two Transom Bolts (Upper and Lower)
11. Two Breeching Side-Shackles and Pins
12. Bed Bolt
13. Four Axle Tree Bands (Fig. X-49)
14. Chafing Plates of Steps and Brackets
15. Four Linch Pins and Washers (Not Shown)
16. Quoin Plate and Stop (Not Shown)
17. Ratchet for Quoin Stop (Not Shown)
18. Four Training Loops
19. Breeching Thimble (cast iron)
20. Side-Shackle Bolts for Breechings
21. Shackle Pin, Plates and Keys
22. Two Axle Stays

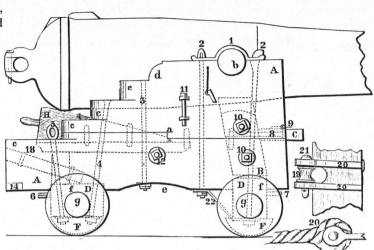

FIGURE: X-49 IDENTIFICATION: Carriage, Navy, 4-Truck, Wood. SOURCE: Brandt. REMARKS: See Fig. X-48 for nomenclature.

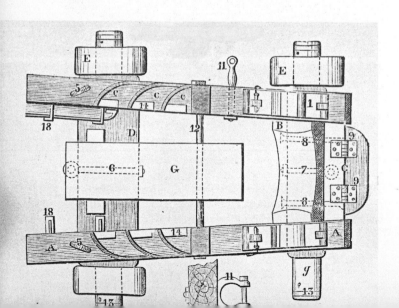

1. Strength. The carriage was extremely rugged and could take not only the beating of heavy seas, but glancing blows of enemy shot. A direct hit, of course, would disable it, but even in this case there was little danger to adjacent crews from flying pieces except in a few experimental models made of cast iron. Wrought iron was also tried at a late date, but was generally more favored for the similar garrison model than at sea.

2. Simplicity. This becomes more apparent with careful study of the diagrams. The carriage was easily manufactured, yet ingenious in design. Every part had its function and during the centuries all but essentials had been whittled away.

3. Stability. Wide axles and low silhouette made these carriages exceedingly difficult to overturn in a seaway despite their heavy burden.

4. Transportability. Transfer of pieces from one part of the ship to another was feasible with this carriage, an advantage of some moment under combat conditions. This also insured return of the piece to action if a breeching gave way since it could be pushed back to the port for reeving a new tackle.

Objectionable features were at least ten:

1. Wood decayed, particularly in tropical climes and iron was not entirely satisfactory as a substitute.

2. Recoil was very hard on breechings, necessitating constant examination and replacement.

3. Truck friction made it difficult to run inboard for loading, but if this were eased, it would increase strain on the breeching.

4. In a seaway, the carriage generally worked out of the center of the port and under much heel was only brought back with considerable difficulty.

5. Training was slow and unsteady through a limited sweep since the trucks had to be skidded sideways on the deck.

6. The piece could not be fired instantly when the aim came on target since warning had to be given the crew to get clear of recoil.

7. When the vessel was heeling, crews could not take in slack of lee gun training tackle fast enough during recoil to hold the piece out of battery for reloading. This cost effort and delay to haul it back inboard.

8. Management of side tackles of weather guns was difficult under heel in a seaway.

9. When trained either fore or aft, the strain on the breeching and bolts was unequal.

10. If under heel a lee gun ran out violently, it was apt to open seams when it struck the waterway, start the shot from its seat—which could cause explosion—and cause other damage to carriage or ship.

Operation of the carriage was simple yet ingenious. Take the breast plate, for instance. This was merely a hinged piece of wood at the front of the carriage, yet was vital to both security and traverse. Raised and the carriage run forward, it permitted the trucks to rest squarely on the waterway while the ends of the brackets were snugged against the spirketing—heavy timbers which ran from the waterway to the bottom of the port. Lashed in this position by the training tackle, the carriage was immobilized and strain evenly distributed, an important consideration in heavy seas.

On the other hand, it was a matter of seconds to cast off the lashings and drop the breast plate. In this position, its curved portion held the trucks well back from the waterway permitting the piece to be trained laterally, an obvious impossibility with the plate up and carriage run fully forward.

Recoil was controlled primarily by the elasticity of heavy breeching rope rove through the carriage shackles and cascabel of the weapon and secured to the side of the vessel. However, the trucks also played a part in checking recoil. These solid wheels in later years were made of lignum vitae, an especially heavy, tough wood, but difficult to obtain in large diameters. For this reason, trucks were uniformly 15 inches with proportionately large axles to increase friction and make the carriage difficult to roll. They also slid on the deck for an instant in recoil before starting to turn.

Elevation generally was maintained by a quoin with an iron projection at the bottom which hooked into a ratchet on the bed below to prevent its being kicked out by the shock of discharge. However, an elevating screw was sometimes used instead.

Gunports were normally 3 feet high and 3½ feet wide, the opening starting 20 to 24 inches from the deck. Carriages were designed to place the center of the trunnions in a horizontal plane one-half caliber below the center of the port, which provided 11° elevation and 7° depression compared to the plane of the deck. This was considered desirable, for although ships seldom heeled more than 4° or 5°, even a 7° list would insure weather guns being able to fire level with the horizon and lee weapons with 4° elevation.

The advent of heavy Dahlgrens brought about adoption of the Marsilly, or Navy 2-truck, carriage for broadside weapons. A development of the French, it became the specified mount for 9-inch Dahlgrens in broadside and gradually replaced the 4-truck carriage for other heavy cannon. Major differences, as illustrated in the diagrams (Figs. X-50

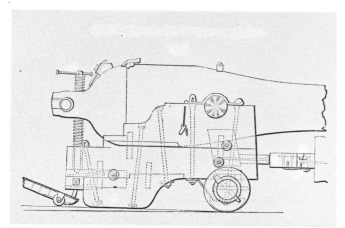

FIGURE: X-50 IDENTIFICATION: Carriage, Navy, Marsilly, Wood. SOURCE: Brandt. REMARKS: Mounting 9-Inch Dahlgren. Note Roller Handspike at rear. Also see Fig. X-51, overhead view. Often called Navy 2-Truck Carriage.

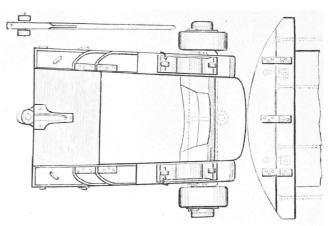

FIGURE: X-51 IDENTIFICATION: Carriage, Navy, Marsilly, Wood. SOURCE: Brandt. REMARKS: Overhead view of carriage in Fig. X-50. Note accompanying Roller Handspike.

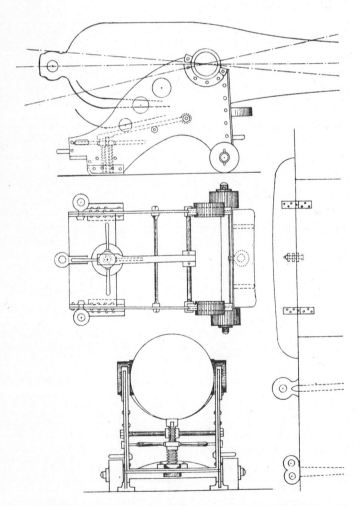

FIGURE: X-53 IDENTIFICATION: Carriage, Navy, for 32-Pounder of 4,500 Pounds, 8-Inch of 6,500 Pounds and 9-Inch, Wrought Iron. SOURCE: *Ordnance Instructions for the U.S. Navy,* 1866. REMARKS: Side, overhead and rear views.

and 51) are obvious. The rear trucks were removed and the brackets extended to the deck to serve as slides. A roller handspike under the rear moved the carriage into battery or to other ports. The breast plate was stationary, but a hinged sweep piece attached to the side of the ship performed the same function. Elevation was by screw through the cascabel instead of quoin.

One of the main objections to adoption of the Marsilly carriage was the fear that it would be deficient in transportability. However, tests[51] showed a 9,000-pound, 9-inch Dahlgren could be fired, sponged, loaded, run to a port on the opposite side of the vessel, and fired again in 1 minute, 45 seconds. The roller handspike was used under the rear and the piece shoved along like a wheelbarrow. It also was found that with this carriage heavy Dahlgrens could be worked with ease in a seaway. Although seldom used on land, 9-inch Dahlgrens on these carriages (Fig. X-52) were emplaced opposite Yorktown in 1862.

The iron carriage (Fig. X-53) for Dahlgren's 32-pounder of 4,500 pounds, 8-inch of 6,500 and 9-inch obviously was adapted from the Marsilly mount. Front trucks and sliding friction from the brackets in rear, use of roller handspikes, and breast plate with hinged sweep piece were all similar. Screw elevation was retained, but differed in operation. Major difference between the two carriages was material. The Marsilly was made of wood and the new carriage of wrought iron. An excellent example of the iron mount (Fig. X-54) carries a 9-inch Dahlgren at

FIGURE: **X-54** LOCATION: American-Swedish Historical Museum, Philadelphia, Pa. IDENTIFICATION: Carriage, Navy, for 32-Pounder of 4,500 Pounds, 8-Inch of 6,500 Pounds, and 9-Inch, Wrought Iron. MARKINGS: Carriage — No. 218, 1336 lbs., 20-In. 9-Inch Dahlgren: Left trunnion — P., T.A.H. Right trunnion — IX-In., 1863. Breech — C.A., & Co., No. 481, 9240 lbs. REMARKS: Note elevation method differs from diagram, Fig. X-53.

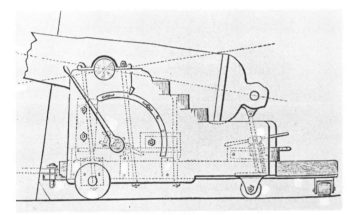

FIGURE: **X-55** IDENTIFICATION: Carriage, Navy, Van Brunt, Wood. SOURCE: Simpson. REMARKS: Experimental broadside carriage.

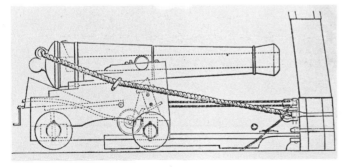

FIGURE: **X-56** IDENTIFICATION: Carriage, Navy, Ward's Novelty Carriage, Wood. SOURCE: Simpson. REMARKS: Experimental carriage developed by Cmdr. James H. Ward, USN.

Philadelphia, Pa. It utilizes conventional cascabel screw elevation in lieu of the more elaborate arrangement of the diagram, but whether this was standard procedure is not known.

Before leaving broadside carriages, two experimental mounts that probably saw little use except in literature of the period, should be mentioned. These were the Van Brunt and the Ward, both developed by United States Navy officers in an effort to overcome the deficiencies of the 4-truck carriage.

Captain Gershom J. Van Brunt's mount (Fig. X-55) was in some respects a radical departure. It was a friction model with top carriage and chassis, or slide, as it was called in the Navy.[52] The four trucks were used to run the piece into battery and move it about the deck. Prior to firing, the matching levers were hove down which operated an eccentric axle against the top of the slide and clamps beneath to control recoil. In addition, it had an automatic compression feature. If crewmen forgot to throw the levers, the start of recoil tripped a spring and catch apparatus which turned the eccentric axle to the compression position. The slide was attached to the side of the vessel by a pintle and ran on rear rollers for traverse.

Commander James H. Ward's "Novelty Carriage" (Figs. X-56 and I-38) utilized a 4-truck mount as the top carriage modified by addition of a fore and aft piece to ride on the slide and a fixed roller handspike immediately beneath the trunnions. In this carriage, the four trucks remained off the deck except when it was necessary to move the piece from one port to another. Recoil was controlled by sliding friction and the piece moved into battery with the aid of the fixed roller. An especially made roller handspike, slipped under the rear of the slide, facilitated traverse.[53]

Broadside carriages were fine so long as sailing ships with long, unencumbered sides were standard in the world's navies. But introduction of steam brought about a change in both armament and tactics. Early steam warships were primarily sidewheelers with much of their interior occupied by engine and coal bunkers which forced a sharp reduction in the number of men and guns. Moreover, the huge wheels took up valuable rail space amidships and were highly vulnerable to shot and shell. Consequently, instead of moving in to slug it out at close quarters with relatively light guns as in sailing days, the steamers kept a respectful distance from the enemy. This led to installation of a few large caliber, heavy weapons near bow and stern with wide traverse, pivot carriages to handle them.

FIGURE: X-57 IDENTIFICATION: Carriage, Navy, Pivot, Wood. REMARKS: Gun crew practicing in 1864 with 9-Inch Dahlgren mounted on pivot carriage aboard the *U.S.S. Mendota*, 205-foot schooner-rigged, sidewheel steamer.

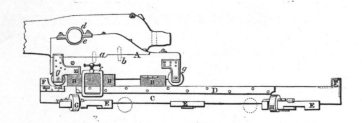

FIGURE: X-58 IDENTIFICATION: Carriage, Navy, Pivot, Wood. SOURCE: Brandt. REMARKS:

CARRIAGE
A. Brackets
B. Transoms
a. Jog
b. Dowels
d. Cap Squares
e. Trunnion Plates
f. Compressor, with Screw and Lever
g. Rollers and Journal Plates

SLIDE
C. Rails
D. Compressor battens
E. Transoms
F. Hurters
G. Shifting Trucks
H. Training Trucks

FIGURE: X-59 IDENTIFICATION: Carriage, Navy, Pivot, Wood. SOURCE: *Ordnance Instructions for the U.S. Navy, 1866*. REMARKS: X. Battens and Slats; Y. Preventer Breechings; Z. Upper Pivot Plate; 1. Middle Roller Plate; 2. Eyes for Tackles; 3. Hurter Straps; 4. Rail Plates.

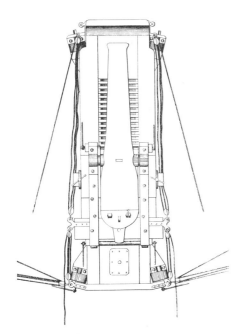

FIGURE: X-60 IDENTIFICATION: Carriage, Navy, Pivot, Wood. SOURCE: *Ordnance Instructions for U.S. Navy, 1866.* REMARKS: 11-Inch Dahlgren loaded and ready to be run out to leeward.

FIGURE: X-61 IDENTIFICATION: Carriage, Navy, Pivot, Wood, modified to Center Pintle, Barbette. REMARKS: Double-Banded Brooke Rifle of undetermined caliber in Battery Dantzler overlooking James River in 1864.

Some years later, when the screw replaced paddles, emphasis shifted again. Now machinery and screw were below the waterline and with open decks once again, broadside guns returned as main batteries and pivot weapons were relegated to a secondary, although still important role. Favorite arms for pivot mounts were 6.4- and 8-inch Parrotts or 11-inch Dahlgrens. The lighter, 9-inch Dahlgren also was used in pivot, however, as aboard the *U.S.S. Mendota* (Fig. X-57), a wood sidewheel steamer of 974 tons carrying a battery of two 6.4-inch Parrotts, four 9-inch Dahlgrens, two 20-pounder Dahlgren rifles, and two 24-pounder Dahlgrens.

Termed a friction carriage, the pivot mount (Figs. X-58 and 59) consisted of a top carriage and slide with additional check on recoil provided by compressors. Major parts of both top carriage and slide were wood, the former composed of brackets held together by front and rear transoms which bore

on the rails of the slide. The compressors were affixed to the top carriage front transom and to battens attached to the slide rails.

Top carriage and slide rollers were all on eccentrics. Those of the top carriage permitted friction to check recoil, while the latter let the slide lie flat on the deck for solid support when firing. Pivoting was by means of stout bolts through the transoms that dropped into sockets set in the deck. An 11-inch on pivot carriage run in for loading (Fig. X-60) shows compressors, training tackle, and handspikes attached to eccentrics of top carriage

An interesting Confederate adaptation of a pivot carriage to barbette use ashore (Fig. X-61) mounted a Brooke in Battery Dantzler, part of the heavy weapons complex guarding James River approaches to Richmond. Top carriage brackets differ a bit from the U.S. model, but transoms and rollers seem identical. The slide has been shortened and equipped for

219

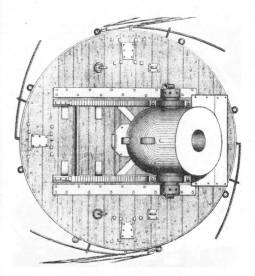

FIGURE: X-63 IDENTIFICATION: Mortar Circle, Navy, Wood. SOURCE: *Ordnance Instructions for the U.S. Navy,* 1866. REMARKS: Circle or platform on eccentrics for mounting 13-Inch Mortar, Model 1861, and its bed aboard ship. Note four Circle Eccentic Bars for activating eccentric rollers during traverse.

FIGURE: X-62 IDENTIFICATION: Carriage, Navy, Pivot, Wood, modified to Center Pintle, Barbette. REMARKS: Double-Banded Brooke Rifle of undetermined caliber in Confederate battery near Richmond, 1864.

center pintle. The compressor, left of carriage, was assisted in controlling recoil by the breeching rope which originally went through the hole in the cascabel to shackle to the right side of the slide.

Another Brooke, on a similar carriage (Fig. X-62), was sighted on the Dutch Gap area of the James River. Close examination reveals minor differences between the two, particularly in the shape of the top carriage brackets and slide transoms and in platform construction.

Monitor turrets normally were armed with a 15-inch Dahlgren and either one of the admiral's 11-inchers or an 8-inch Parrott. Carriages for all were similar except for dimension and consisted of a top carriage and slide as in the hypothetical monitor turret armed with two different type 15-inch Dahlgrens illustrated in Chapter V.

Because of limited space within the turret, mechanical aids were used to considerable extent including a crank to work the trucks when moving the piece in or out of battery and a handwheel to set

or release the compressor. Overhead traveling bars carried shellwhips to assist in loading the heavy projectiles. Slide rails were set flat on deck. Rollers were not needed since traverse was accomplished by revolving the turret. The port admitted 8° elevation.

Mortar schooners mounting the 13-inch, M1861 seacoast mortar for heavy bombardment were equipped with a circular platform (Fig. X-63) set on eccentric rollers engaged by four levers for traverse or disengaged to let the platform rest on solid support during firing. A side view of the platform in Chapter III shows a square port for one of the removable levers. In addition to the main ship carriages, the Navy also used boat and field carriages for the Dahlgren boat howitzers, discussed in Chapter V, and a light deck carriage for the admiral's 20-pounder rifle and probably other light weapons. This friction carriage (see 20-pounder rifle in Chapter V) seems to have been adapted from the boat model. It consisted of a wood top carriage and slide and utilized two compressors in tandem.

NOTES

1. Edward Simpson, *A Treatise on Ordnance and Naval Gunnery,* 1862, p. 126.
2. J. G. Benton, *A Course of Instruction in Ordnance and Gunnery Composed and Compiled for Cadets of The United States Military Academy,* 1861, p. 106.
3. Sir William Congreve, lieutenant general, commandant of the Royal Artillery, comptroller of the Royal Laboratory at Woolwich and superintendent of military machines during the late 18th and early 19th centuries. His eldest son, Sir William Congreve (1772–1828) was the inventor of the Congreve Rocket (Chapter XIV).
4. William E. Birkhimer, *Historical Sketch of The Organization, Administration, Materiel and Tactics of The Artillery, United States Army,* 1884, pp. 237–238.
5. Benton, 1861, *op. cit.,* pp. 103–108.
6. Birkhimer, *op. cit.,* pp. 225–226.
7. *Ibid.,* p. 224.
8. *Ibid.,* pp. 229, 231.
9. *Ibid.,* p. 231.
10. *Ibid.,* pp. 232–237.
11. *Ibid.,* p. 239.
12. *Ibid.,* p. 248.
13. *Ibid.,* p. 248.
14. H. Lallemand, *A Treatise on Artillery,* Vol. 1, 1820.
15. John L. Wilson, *Abstract of a System of Exercise and Instruction of Field Artillery and The Exercise of Heavy Artillery in Battery . . . for Use of South Carolina Militia,* 1834.
16. *Ordnance Manual for The Use of Officers of The United States Army,* 1841, p. 34.
17. *Ordnance Manual for The Use of Officers of The United States Army,* 1861, p. 74 footnote.
18. *Ibid.,* p. 44.
19. *Ibid.,* p. 45.
20. *Ibid.,* p. 362.
21. *Ibid.,* p. 455.
22. William LeRoy Broun (sic), "The Red Artillery, Confederate Ordnance During The War," *Southern Historical Society Papers,* Vol. XXVI, 1898, p. 372.
23. *Ordnance Manual,* 1861, *op. cit.,* p. 362.
24. *Ibid.,* pp. 335–336.
25. *Ibid.,* pp. 340–341; Benton, 1861, *op. cit.,* p. 227.
26. Benton, 1861, *op. cit.,* p. 229.
27. Alfred Mordecai, *Artillery for The United States Land Service,* 1849.
28. *Ordnance Manual,* 1861, *op. cit.,* pp. 75, 336.
29. *Ibid.,* p. 363.
30. Benton, 1861, *op. cit.,* p. 230.
31. Birkhimer, *op. cit.,* pp. 248, 253.
32. *Ordnance Manual,* 1861, *op. cit.,* pp. 59–62.
33. J. G. Benton, *A Course of Instruction in Ordnance and Gunnery Composed and Compiled for Cadets of The United States Military Academy,* 1875, p. 239.
34. *Ordnance Manual,* 1861, *op. cit.,* p. 61; Benton, 1861, *op. cit.,* p. 231.
35. *Ordnance Manual,* 1861, *op. cit.,* p. 365.
36. John Gibbon, *The Artillerist's Manual, Compiled From Various Sources and Adapted to The Service of The United States,* 1860, p. 194; *Ordnance Manual,* 1861, *op. cit.,* p. 364.
37. Gibbon, *op. cit.,* pp. 196–197.
38. Birkhimer, *op. cit.,* p. 286.
39. Gibbon, *op. cit.,* p. 197.
40. *Ibid.,* pp. 217–218.
41. *Ibid.,* p. 197.
42. *Ibid.,* p. 198.
43. Birkhimer, *op. cit.,* pp. 254–255.
44. *Ibid.,* pp. 254–255.
45. *Ibid.,* p. 240.
46. National Park Service records, Fort Sumter National Monument, Headquarters, Fort Moultrie, Charleston, S. C.
47. *Ibid.* Engineer reports on Fort Moultrie.
48. *Ordance Manual,* 1841. *op. cit.,* pp. 54–55 list both cypress and cast iron top carriage for this model.
49. *Ordnance Manual,* 1861, *op. cit.,* pp. 62, 66.
50. Q. A. Gillmore, *Engineer and Artillery Operations Against The Defenses of Charleston Harbor, 1863,* 1865, p. 288.
51. *Edward Simpson, A Treatise on Ordnance and Naval Gunnery,* 1862, p. 130.
52. *Ibid.,* p. 139.
53. *Ibid.,* p. 128.

Chapter 11

The Art of the Artilleryman

ANCIENT ARTILLERY IS SUCH A VAST and varied field that exhaustive discussion of all minor facets would prove more boring than beneficial. Yet a general knowledge of these topics is essential for a thorough understanding of the subject. How, for instance, were cannon loaded and fired: mounted on carriages, aimed, manufactured, or spiked? These and many other nagging questions have little to do with identification, but plague and discourage the beginner and occasionally even the expert.

This chapter, then, is designed to catch up such loose ends, the miscellanies of the artilleryman's art. Basically, it encompasses such diverse topics as implements for handling and firing weapons, manufacture, markings, gunpowder, and fortification. It will not answer every question and is no more intended to cover each subject in its entirety than to train modern readers as Civil War cannoneers. If it adds to the reader's general knowledge and understanding of ancient artillery, it will have served its purpose. And if a few questions are answered in the process, so much the better.

Other than location of rest rooms, one of the most persistent questions asked of park personnel is, "How does it shoot?" The answer is of considerable magnitude, embracing loading, aiming, firing, and the various implements to accomplish these functions.

The process of loading a muzzle-loader, whether Army or Navy, involved three basic steps: cleaning bore and vent, insertion of propellant and projectile, and attachment of an igniter. They differed a bit depending on service and type weapon and were somewhat more complicated in practice than in the telling, but each of the three had to be accomplished before firing.

Constant drill of gun crews insured that no step would be overlooked in the confusion of combat. Each operation, often each motion, was performed in specified manner and prescribed order. Detailed instructions covering several pages were provided for each type weapon including service of a 32-pounder mounted on a wood, front pintle, barbette carriage for which a condensed version follows:

The gun crew, four cannoneers and a gunner, fell in at rear of the piece and at the command "Take Implements" ran to their posts which were numbered—odd customarily serving on the right of the piece, even and gunner on the left.

Mounting the tongue, the gunner took off the vent cover (Fig XI-1)—which he handed to No. 2 to be placed against the parapet—and put on the gunner's pouch, a leather container which normally hung from the cascabel, but during firing was worn around the waist. It held various implements for aiming and firing including a buckskin finger stall with a pad of hair that the gunner pulled over his second finger, left hand, like a glove for protection while closing the vent during sponging. Often the thumb was used instead in which case the little glove was called a thumb stall (Fig. XI-1).

The gunner now elevated or depressed the piece to convenient position for loading and with the gunner's level (Fig. XI-2), a metal device with a spirit level, determined the high point of the base ring and marked it with chalk for use in aiming with breech sight or tangent scale. Permanent marks on the base ring of heavy weapons fired from level platforms and improved sighting equipment often rendered this duty unnecessary.

The cannoneers picked up handspikes, embarred through the spokes of the top carriage wheels, and at the gunner's command "Heave," moved the piece until the face of the muzzle was about a yard in the rear of the parapet where the gunner commanded "Halt." They unbarred, chocked the rollers, and resumed their posts. (See Fig. XI-7 for casemate clock.)

At the command "Load," No. 2 removed the tampion (also spelled tompion), which closed the bore against weather or entry of foreign materials, and placed it near the vent cover to remain until completion of firing.

No. 1 picked up the sponge (Fig. XI-3). This implement consisted of a sponge-head of elm or poplar about 1 inch less than the bore in diameter

FIGURE: XI-1 IDENTIFICATION: Miscellaneous Implements. SOURCE: Mordecai.

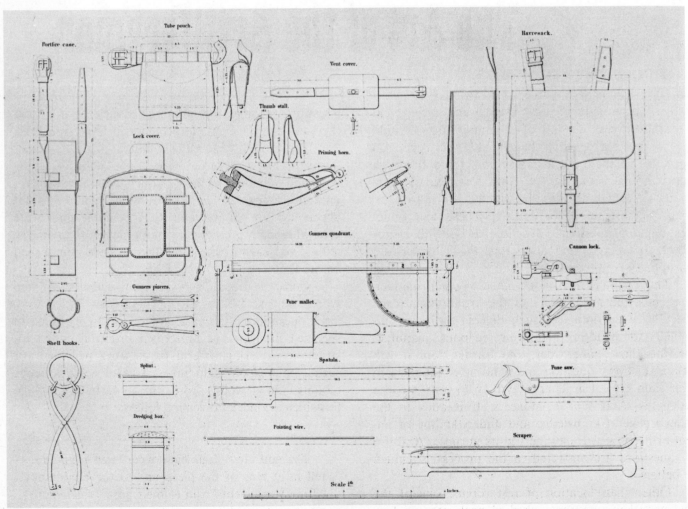

and, for seacoast weapons, 8 inches long. It was covered with wool and mortised to receive the tenon of an ash stave, 125.33 inches long for the 32-pounder.

Nos. 1 and 2 together drove the sponge to the bottom of the bore, turned it three times clockwise and three times counterclockwise, then withdrew it. During sponging, the gunner stopped the vent with his finger protected by the stall. This prevented air from whistling out and perhaps carrying smoldering material with it that would remain and prematurely ignite the cartridge. Whether or not to stop the vent was the subject of considerable debate and instructions for service of different weapons may vary on this point. The argument also extended to wet or dry sponges. The former did a better job of extinguishing smoldering cartridge bag embers, but formed a

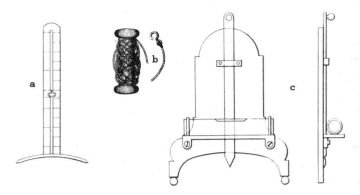

FIGURE: XI-2 IDENTIFICATION: Miscellaneous Firing Implements. SOURCE: Instruction for Heavy Artillery, 1861. REMARKS: a. Breech Sight. b. Lanyard and handle. c. Gunner's Level.

FIGURE: XI-3 IDENTIFICATION: Rammers, Sponge Heads and Staves. SOURCE: Mordecai.

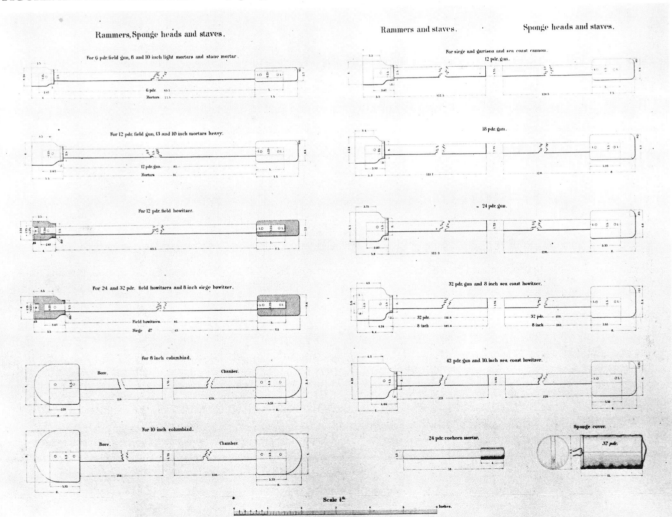

paste of charred matter which was difficult to remove.

During sponging, No. 4 picked up the pass box (Fig. XI-4) and went a few paces to the rear for a cartridge. The box was a 7 × 14-inch white pine container with a hinged top secured by hook and staple. It had a handle on one end and was used for conveying the cartridge to the gun from the budge barrel (Fig. XI-4), a strongly-made oak barrel hooped with copper bands. The top was formed of leather tacked around the rim and closed at the center by a drawstring to permit quick access, yet secure closure against rain or sparks. It held a quantity of cartridges as an intermediate point between gun and magazine.

Putting down the pass box, No. 4 opened it and handed the cartridge to No. 2 who inserted it into the bore while No. 1 exchanged sponge for rammer with No. 3.

The rammer head (Fig. XI-3) was made of hard wood, generally elm or beech, and for a 32-pounder was 6.4 inches long and 5.6 inches in diameter tapering sharply to 3 at the end where it was mortised to receive the tenon of a 125.86-inch stave. Rammer heads used with shell were generally recessed slightly to protect the fuse. Light weapons often had sponge and rammer at opposite ends of the same stave (Fig. XI-3).

Working together, Nos. 1 and 2 shoved the cartridge to the bottom of the bore, then withdrawing the stave a full arm's length, rammed with a single stroke and removed the rammer.

By this time No. 4 had obtained a ball and handed it to No. 2 who introduced it into the bore while No. 1 held the rammer ready for use in the same manner as was done with the cartridge. If a wad, often made of hay in the Army or junk in the Navy, was used, it was inserted after the ball to hold it secure against the charge. A ring, or grommet, of the same materials sometimes per-

FIGURE: XI-4 IDENTIFICATION: Miscellaneous Implements. SOURCE: Mordecai.

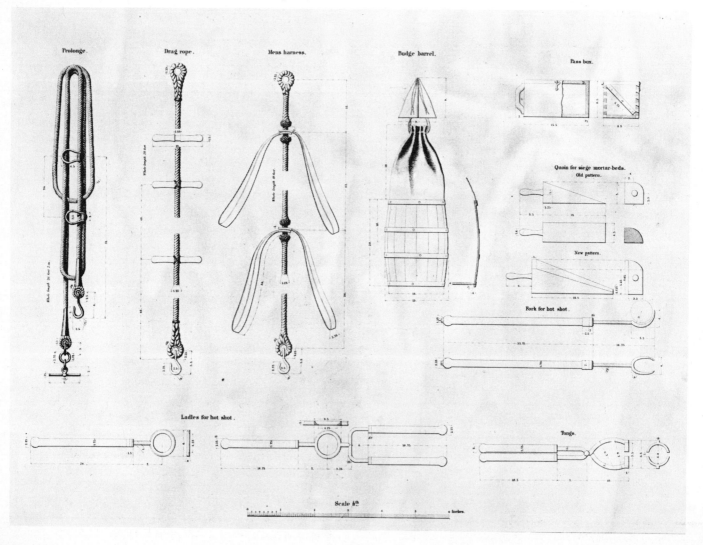

226

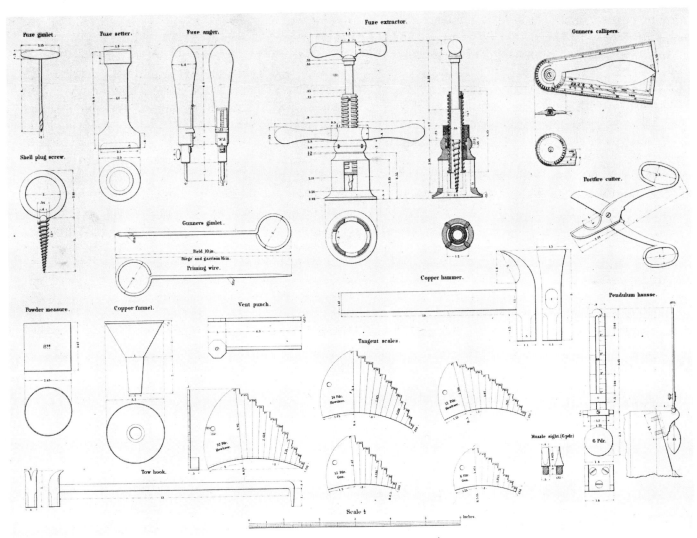

FIGURE: XI-5 IDENTIFICATION: Miscellaneous Implements. SOURCE: Mordecai.

formed this function. Shells, strapped to a wood block recessed at one end to fit the round projectile and known as a sabot, were always loaded with fuse outward. They were not rammed, but shoved gently home.

The gunner now inserted a priming wire (Fig. XI-5) into the vent and pricked through the wool, occasionally flannel, cartridge bag into the powder. This wire implement had a slightly smaller diameter than the vent. One end was sharpened to a point, the other bent into ring form for easy handling.

Leaving the priming wire temporarily in the vent, the gunner adjusted the sight for proper distance. Nos. 1 and 2 unchocked the rollers, with Nos. 3 and 4 embarred handspikes, and at the gunner's command, ran the piece into battery. Other forms of carriage at this point, of course, involved throwing the eccentrics out of gear and dropping the top carriage onto the chassis rails.

With the piece in battery, cannoneers resumed their posts. No. 3 put down his handspike and removed a friction tube and lanyard (Fig. XI-2) from the tube pouch (Fig. XI-1) which, like the pouch worn by the gunner, he had strapped on at the beginning of action. Passing the hook at one end of the lanyard through the eye of the friction tube, he waited while Nos. 1 and 4 embarred under the traverse wheels or fork bolts.

The gunner removed the priming wire and directed Nos. 1 and 4 in traversing the piece commanding "Left" or "Right" and at the same time tapping on the right side of the breech for No. 1 to move the chassis left, or left side for No. 4 to move it right. Aided by breech (Fig. XI-2) or other sighting apparatus, the gunner gave the piece proper elevation correcting direction as necessary to stay on target, then announced "Ready" at which Nos. 1 and 4 unbarred and resumed their posts.

Removing the sighting device, the gunner received the friction tube from No. 3, inserted it in the vent, and stepped off the tongue to windward to observe effect of the shot.

No. 3 uncoiled and stretched taut the lanyard while Nos. 1 and 2 picked up the roller chocks.

At the command "Fire"—generally prefaced by the number of the piece—i.e., "Number One, Fire"—No. 3 gave the lanyard a quick, steady pull. Immediately after discharge, Nos. 1 and 2 chocked the rollers and all resumed their posts. No. 3 recoiled the lanyard in the form of a St. Andrew's Cross around the handle and stowed it in the tube pouch.

During action, a trained gun crew performed its duties smoothly, with little lost motion, to the following commands of the gunner: "From Battery—Load—In Battery—Point—Ready—Fire," the sequence con-

tinuing until "Cease Firing" was ordered by the officer in overall charge.

Rate of fire depended largely on the type of weapon and carriage. Field guns could be discharged, with careful aim, twice a minute and, when pressed, a good crew firing canister could double that rate. Siege cannon generally fired twelve rounds an hour—which allowed sufficient time for the tube to cool between shots—but were capable of twenty when necessary. No rate has been found for a 32-pounder on seacoast mount, but a trained crew could load and fire the 15-inch Rodman in 1 minute 10 seconds of which the majority was spent in traverse and elevation.

In addition to the implements with which each piece was equipped, there were others used in common by two or more weapons. A single gunner's level, previously described, and two vent punches, for instance, customarily sufficed for up to six pieces.

FIGURE: XI-6 IDENTIFICATION: Ladles and Worms. SOURCE: Mordecai.

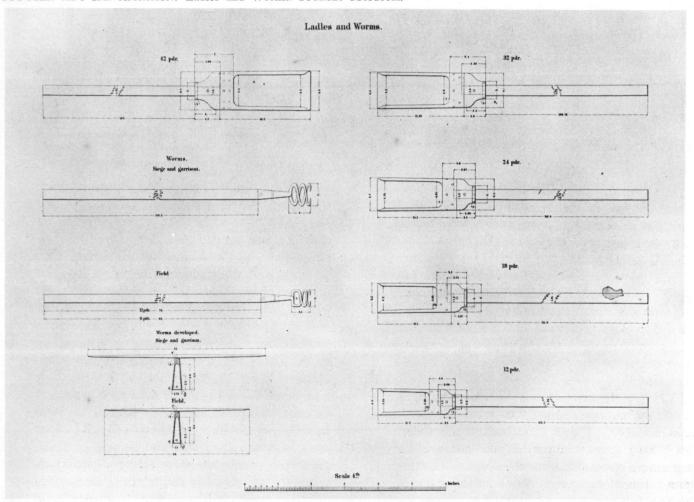

The vent punch (Fig. XI-5) was the same diameter as the priming wire, but had one end flat for insertion in the vent and the other brazed to an octagonal iron head with a hole in it for insertion of a nail to aid in withdrawal. It was used to drive an obstruction through the vent into the tube from which it could be removed. The gunner's gimlet (Fig. XI-5) and gunner's pincers (Fig. XI-1) also were used by several weapons. The first, a wire with screw-type end, was used to bore out broken priming wires or similar obstructions. The second was made of iron with steel jaws for removing obstructions which extended outside the vent. One arm was tipped with a claw for drawing nails or spikes.

A single worm and one ladle also served up to six pieces. The worm (Fig. XI-6), an iron implement shaped like a double corkscrew, was attached to the end of a stave and used to withdraw unfired cartridges, rags, or other debris from inside the bore. The ladle (Fig. XI-6) was made of sheet brass tacked to a wood head mortised for a stave. It had the general form of a kitchen flour scoop and served prior to invention of cartridge bags for conveyance of the loose powder charge to the bottom of the bore. In later years, however, the device removed projectiles when a piece had to be unloaded without firing. The thin, metal ladle could be shoved under the ball and both withdrawn from the tube. Other type ladles (Fig. XI-4), consisting of an iron ring and one or three handles, were used to carry hot shot and will be discussed in the following chapter.

Mortar and howitzer batteries were also equipped with a scraper (Fig. XI-1), used to remove the residue of powder from the bore. It consisted of an iron handle with a spade-shaped steel scraper at one end and a spoon of the same material at the other for collecting and removing the scrapings.

Aiming Civil War cannon, or "pointing" as it was commonly called, involved both deflection and elevation. The first was relatively simple and depended on the gunner's eye-sighting between front and rear sights as in a modern rifle. This brought scathing criticism from Abbot[1] who found it highly inconsistent to provide an infantry sniper's rifle, expected to shoot 500 or 600 yards, with fine telescopic sights, yet furnish a Parrott, firing 3,000 or 4,000 yards, with sights ". . . far coarser than those of any old smoothbore musket. . . ."

The forward sight was generally placed on the muzzle as in the 6-pounder (Fig. XI-5). However, many Navy broadside weapons, that smashed muzzle sights on the ports, and certain heavy Army pieces with little or no muzzle swell, which involved a large angle between rear sight and muzzle, affixed the blade to a bracket cast on the tube approximately between the trunnions. This boss was termed a reinforce sight piece by the Army and reinforce sight mass by the Navy, usually abbreviated in both cases to sight piece or sight mass. Many weapons, large and small, also utilized side sights, affixing the blade on the rimbase above a trunnion, whence the name rimbase, or trunnion, sights.

Elevation was far more complicated than deflection and there were several implements to obtain it. One of the oldest was by gunner's quadrant (Fig. XI-1), a 22.3-inch wood arm with a quarter circle of 6-inch radius at one end. The outer edge of the circle was graduated in degrees and was crossed by a plumb line attached to the center. The arm was laid against the muzzle face, the quarter circle extending back over the tube. A plumb bob stretched the line across the degree scale and by elevating or depressing the tube, it could be made to read the desired elevation. A brass model with a 22-inch arm and a 6-inch quadrant was equipped with a spirit level in the middle and a vernier instead of the plumb line. Before the war started, the quadrant had gone out of style except for use with mortars and long pieces when fired at exceptionally high elevations.

Other methods of elevation were by tangent scale (Fig. XI-5), breech sight, or pendulum hausse. The first was made of sheet brass with a flange along the base cut to fit the curve of the base ring. The top was cut in a series of steps, each representing a carefully calculated range. Each step had a notch in the center for convenience of sighting and the gunner elevated the piece until his line of sight between the notch in a particular step and the front sight came on target. It was not particularly accurate and was discarded in favor of either of the following methods:

The breech sight (Fig. XI-2) resembled the leaf sight on a modern rifle and consisted of an upright sheet of brass supported on a foot cut to fit the base ring. The upper part had a slit in the center and a scale at one side. A slide moved up and down and could be tightened by a screw at any point on the scale. The slide had a small hole in the center through which the gunner lined up the front sight and target. When the breech sight was used, it was imperative for accurate aim that it be centered exactly on the high point of the breech either permanently notched in the base ring—accurate only if the trunnions were level—or marked with chalk after being established by the gunner's level.

A more sophisticated sight, particularly for field pieces, was the pendulum hausse (Fig. XI-5) adopted from the Russians. The main objection to the breech sight was the necessity for finding the high point of the base ring, which took valuable time in pieces of maneuver. The pendulum hausse solved this problem. Basically, it was nothing more than a breech sight suspended to permit front and rear as well as lateral movement. This was accomplished by replacing the foot beneath the brass sight column with a bulb filled with lead and attaching it at a single point to a horizontal pin. This permitted the column to swing left or right. The pin extended on each side of the column and the ends were turned into tiny journals. In use, the journals fitted a bracket bolted to the rear of the breech and permitted the column to swing back and forth in line with the axis of the bore. Consequently, with the column able to swing in four directions, the bulb centered it exactly vertical regardless of whether the trunnions were level and allowed sighting without distortion. The pendulum hausse could be used with a rimbase front sight by changing the position of the breech bracket.

Each of these sighting devices was removed prior to firing and each, with exception of the gunner's quadrant, was made to fit a particular caliber weapon.

Cannon equipped with handles, such as the heavy 12-pounder gun, the early Napoleons, or the 24-pounder field howitzer, could be fired by graduating the rear of the handles in degrees and holding a string across the required points while elevating the piece.[2] It obviously was an inaccurate method and probably used only in emergency.

The Navy often utilized a special trunnion sight for high elevations, particularly with its pivot guns. This consisted of a wood sighting bar with a spirit level and a graduated metal semicircle at the center. The device was affixed by thumbscrew to the center of a trunnion face and when the cipher in the semicircle was aligned with a mark stamped in the metal of the trunnion, and the bubble was centered, the piece was level. Elevation was set by loosening the thumbscrew, turning the semicircle to align the required degree with the trunnion mark, then elevating or depressing the piece until the bubble was again centered. The gunner lined up sights on the sighting bar with the target for deflection.

Artillery could also be fired at night, but not with daytime accuracy.[3] Where area targets, such as a city or fort, were available harassing fire at night was not only feasible, but highly effective for its nuisance value albeit physical destruction was generally light compared to better aimed bombardment during the day. The previously discussed "Swamp

Angel," for instance, was fired during darkness against Charleston and bombardment of Fort Sumter continued around the clock during certain periods of 1863-64 to discourage Confederate work crews from repairing at night damage caused by more accurate daytime fire. There are other instances of night firing when similar effect was desired and considered worth the expenditure of ammunition.

Visual pointing was difficult if not impossible at night, so pieces to be fired after dark were laid during the day. The correct deflection was retained during firing by chocking traverse wheels of seacoast weapons, or by nailing strips of wood on the platforms near the wheels of siege carriages to serve as guides. The strips were placed an inch or two away from the wheels and a stick of proper width laid between during adjustment, then removed before firing to prevent the shock of recoil from ripping away the guide strips.

Elevation could be set by marking the elevation wheel or cutting a stick the exact distance between the breech and a convenient spot beneath it on the stock. Deflection for night firing of mortars was set in similar fashion by nailing guides on the platform for the bed. Proper elevation was retained by marking the quoin or nailing a cleat on the bolster.

Sighting mortars[4] in the daytime was a bit more difficult than with longer weapons since the pieces generally were in deep defilade where the gunner was unable to sight over the tube and see the target. Consequently, one method of determining deflection was to drive a stake into the crest of the epaulement just above the piece and another a few feet farther forward and in line with the target. A string tied to the forward stake was carried rearward across the center of the first and affixed to a third driven behind the piece. The string now established a line of sight to the target and by using a plumb line, the mortar could be moved until the line of its bore exactly coincided with the string, or target line. Elevation was set by gunner's quadrant as previously explained.

Firing devices, or igniters, evolved during the years into the friction primer, the main type used on land during the Civil War, and the quill percussion primer, generally used afloat. The evolution, however, was a long, slow process that began in early cannon with loose powder poured into the vent and ignited probably by a glowing coal.

An early improvement was slow match, made of 6-inch diameter twisted cotton or treated hemp rope which burned at the rate of 4 or 5 inches an hour. It was attached to the end of a wooden stick, or linstock (Fig. XI-7), tipped at one end with an iron point for

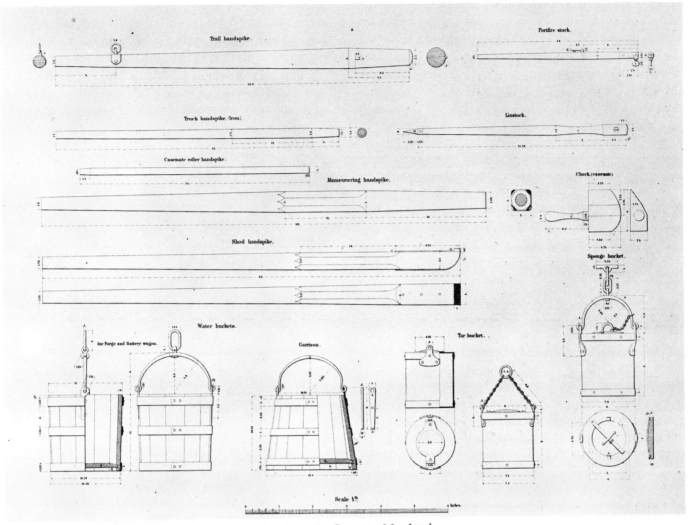

FIGURE: **XI-7** IDENTIFICATION: Miscellaneous Implements. SOURCE: Mordecai.

holding it between rounds in either a match tub or the ground. The vent was still filled with loose powder and a short train was laid along the top of the barrel to prevent the blast from the vent affecting the match.

Slow match was replaced by portfire, a flammable composition driven into a paper case ½ inch in diameter and 22 inches long. It burned with an intense flame that could not be extinguished by water and necessitated cutting it off with portfire cutters (Fig. XI-5) below the burning section when firing ended. Slow match was used in many cases to light the portfire which could be held in a portfire stock (Fig. XI-7).

A major step forward came with introduction of the quill priming tube (Fig. XI-8) which did away with the necessity for priming with powder from a flask or priming horn (Fig. XI-1). The tube was made from the quill of a large feather by splitting the wider end into seven, or other odd number, parts bent

FIGURE: **XI-8** IDENTIFICATION: Quill Priming Tube. SOURCE: Gibbon.

231

outward and formed into a small cup by interweaving fine woolen yarn in basket fashion. Tube and cup were then packed with a powder composition moistened into a paste with camphorated alcohol or spirits of wine. A thin wire was inserted longitudinally through the entire quill which, upon being withdrawn after the composition dried, left a hole that ensured almost simultaneous ignition throughout the tube. A strand of quick match was pasted with powder composition across the top and the whole capped with a paper cover over the cup and twisted tight beneath.

The tube was inserted into the vent and ignited by the hammer of a lock striking an explosive wafer laid on top of the cup just prior to firing. However, this method proved unsatisfactory since more often than not the wafer was blown away by wind or a blast from adjacent guns and the hammer struck only the cup, smashing but failing to ignite it. As a result, the Navy tried forming the wafer into a cap which fitted over the nipple cast on the hammer. This worked so well initially that the quill was found to be superfluous, the flame from the cap alone, since it was channeled directly into the vent, being sufficient to fire the charge.

In later years increased caliber lengthened the vent to the point where flame from the cap often failed to reach the charge and the Navy was forced back to the quill. Both elements were now combined by placing the explosive wafer within the cup and instead of laboriously weaving a basket of wool yarn, a paper disk was pasted under the quill prongs. The Navy also replaced the composition with grained powder which seemed more resistant to moisture.

In addition to the quill, the Army used a similar shaped tube of brass. It was punched from a small disk into cup shape, drawn through dies until the proper diameter was attained, then loaded and used in approximately the same fashion as the quill.

Locks used in firing both metal and quill tubes also went through considerable evolution. Even prior to the tube, flint locks similar to those used with smallarms were adapted to firing cannon primed with loose powder. However, introduction of the tube brought the lock into its own. Basically, a lock was nothing more than a mechanism designed to ignite the charge by the blow of a piece of metal known as the hammer. Accomplishing this was relatively simple through springs or pull of a lanyard. But removing the head of the hammer from the vent before the blast destroyed the lock springs or slammed the hammer back against the tube was a difficult problem.

Various methods were tried in Europe and America including devices for covering the hammer

with a protective layer of leather, to take the shock of rebound, or kicking it to the side as the cap was struck, but none was particularly successful. Best for our service seems to have been the product of E. Hidden who invented a lock in the early '40s which was used extensively by both Army and Navy and was based on removing the hammer laterally. This was a complicated device, however, and Hidden later patented a simple yet effective model that became standard in the Navy during the war. It removed the hammer from the vent by drawing it rearward through continued pressure on the lanyard. A further improvement cast lock lugs directly on the breech of many weapons, such as the Dahlgrens, to which the hammer from the Hidden Lock attached directly and functioned in the normal manner. Figure XI-9 illustrates several Navy locks and Figure XI-1 an Army cannon lock which utilized the Hidden principle.

Although the Navy would have preferred to give up the quill and lock in favor of the Army ignition method, the problem of safety prevented it. The quill was almost entirely destroyed during firing and any pieces remaining were harmless. Not so the metal tube

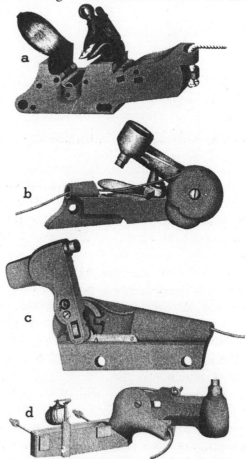

FIGURE: XI-9 IDENTIFICATION: Locks, Navy. SOURCE: Simpson. REMARKS: a. Navy Flint Lock; b. Hidden's Navy Rebounding Lock; c. Hidden's Navy Lock of 1840; d. Hidden's Navy Lock in use during the Civil War.

or Army friction primer. These were made of brass, and bits of metal flying through the air in the close confines of shipboard created a hazard to gun crews, particularly since sailors habitually went barefoot during action. The danger extended to the Army's casemate weapons where quill tubes and locks often were used.

However, most Army cannon, North and South, were fired by friction primer (Fig. XI-10), an ingenious device which was simple and quick to use, yet extremely effective. It consisted of two small brass tubes, a serrated wire, friction composition, and musket powder. Starting with a sheet of thin brass, disks a little smaller than a dime were punched out, then formed into the shape of a cup which was forced through a series of dies until it was a tube .19 inch in diameter, closed at one end. Cutters trimmed it to 1¾ inch, measured from the closed end near which a .15-inch hole was drilled, and at the same time opposite it, a .06-inch hole. The short part of the tube, which had been cut off, was now forced through two more dies and reduced sufficiently to fit the larger hole drilled in the long tube where it was soldered securely. A wood plug was inserted in the long tube while the short one was filled with a paste of friction composition hollowed with a conical drift before being permitted to harden.

A piece of wire, flattened on one end and serrated, was pushed partly through the small tube and out the .06-inch hole in the large tube directly behind it leaving the serrated portion surrounded by friction composition, but not imbedded in it. The small tube was now pinched closed at the open end and the short piece of serrated wire sticking out was crimped over to hold the serrations motionless. The other end of the wire was twisted into a loop to receive the hook of the lanyard and the head of the small tube was dipped into shellac mixed with lamp black and dried. The long tube, after removal of the wood plug, was filled with musket powder, the bottom sealed with shoemaker's wax and both ends touched with varnish. After thorough drying, the wire loop was bent parallel to the long tube for convenience in handling and the primers packed, ten bundles of ten each to a tin box.

In use, the wire was bent upward, hooked to the lanyard and the long tube inserted into the vent. A steady, quick pull on the lanyard dragged the serrated wire across the friction composition igniting it and setting off the musket powder which flashed down the tube and vent to the charge. It was a convenient and generally sure method of ignition, and had the added advantage of giving little flash to betray the piece

during night firing. Unused and fired primers are shown in Fig. XI-11.

It was a sad day when artillerymen lost their guns, but one that occurred so often the Ordnance Manual[5] was constrained to prescribe various methods of rendering weapons useless to the enemy—and, conversely, putting captured ordnance into service. There were numerous ways to disable a piece and that selected depended on such factors as time available and chances of recapture. Quickest and easiest was spiking the vent. Done properly, this required a jagged, hardened steel spike with a soft point which was driven into the vent flush with the top of the tube, then the soft point clinched in the bore below by hitting it with the rammer. However, if such spikes, carried in the battery wagon, had been mislaid, one or more heavy nails with the heads cut off would serve as a substitute. If recapture was considered imminent, a spring spike with a shoulder might be used. It could be removed, but only with considerable difficulty.

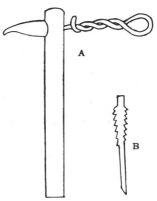

FIGURE: XI-10 IDENTIFICATION: Friction Primer. SOURCE: Simpson. REMARKS: A. Complete primer, also called Friction Tube. B. Serrated wire (enlarged).

FIGURE: XI-11 IDENTIFICATION: Friction Primers. REMARKS: Left pair loaded, one cleaned the other encrusted from years of being buried in gun position. Two at right have been fired.

Spiked vents could be cleared in one of several ways. If the spike was not clinched and the bore open, a one-third charge packed with junk wads could be set off by laying a board down the bore with a groove on the underside for a length of quick match. This generally blew out the spike. If not, it might be drilled out of an iron piece or a new vent bored. If a weapon was bronze, sulphuric acid pored around the spike often loosened it enough to be blown out by a charge. If that failed, the vent piece could be unscrewed and cleared or a new one inserted.

Spiked cannon could be fired although the process was somewhat tedious. The bore was loaded in the customary way and a strand of quick match laid along the bottom from the muzzle to the charge. Then, as the Ordnance Manual instructs: "Apply the fire to the quick match, and get out of the way." If sufficient lengths of quick match were not available, a small piece could be inserted in the cartridge and another at the muzzle. A few handfuls of powder tossed down the bore would carry the flame between them. The quick match in the cartridge could even be omitted if three or four holes were punched in the bag before loading.

Spiking, although traditional and ordinarily used, was not a particularly successful method of disabling a piece and only delayed a capable enemy for a short time. Colonel William Allan, chief of ordnance, 2nd Corps, Army of Northern Virginia, for instance, recalled after the war[6] that twenty spiked pieces captured at Winchester in 1863 were all back in action within a day, under command of their new owners.

A more efficient way, generally coupled with spiking, was to ram a projectile down the bore then block it with iron wedges driven home with the rammer. Wood wedges were not satisfactory since they could be burned out, but removing iron was a much tougher job. It could be done, however, by removing the vent piece and driving a narrow wedge behind the shot to start it forward. Then it could be eased back and the wedges removed with a hook. Sometimes, if the vent were open or vent piece removed, powder could be introduced and the shot fired out. As a last resort, a hole could be drilled in the breech, the shot driven out and the hole plugged with a screw. Removal was further complicated if the bore was filled with projectiles such as the rifled 24-pounder mentioned in Chapter I.

If time permitted and it was obvious the piece would not be recaptured, destruction was the only certain method of denying it to an enemy. This could be accomplished in a number of ways. Firing at high elevation with an overload of charge and projectiles or with the bore filled with sand would generally burst a cast iron piece, or two pieces could be fired muzzle to muzzle, or one fired against the chase of the other. Breaking off one or both trunnions was a traditional method although, as mentioned in a previous chapter, a breeching with trunnions could be made for such cannon.

Bronze weapons were seriously damaged by causing shells to burst in the bore or firing broken shot with heavy charges. Building a fire under the chase and striking it with a sledge also disabled bronze pieces.

If recapture after a long delay was a possibility, the tubes could be spiked or blocked, but left undamaged, and the carriages destroyed. Major Anderson resorted to this method when he moved to Fort Sumter in December, 1860. Behind him he left the armament of Fort Moultrie spiked, and the barbette carriages in flames. However, since fire failed to destroy the ironwork and timber was plentiful, the South Carolinians had the pieces in action again before the first shot on Sumter four months later.

Another method is shown in the photograph of the banded 10-inch, Model 1844 columbiad at Fort Johnson (Chapter IV). A section of top carriage brace has been neatly sliced out with an axe, leaving the piece mounted, but incapable of standing the strain of firing.

Heavy weapons, siege and seacoast, were generally fired from platforms to give a stable, level foundation for the carriage. Platforms in permanent seacoast fortifications were often made of beautifully fitted granite blocks on top of which iron traverse circle and pintle plate were bolted. Temporary platforms were made of wood. Both forms are illustrated in Chapter X.

Siege platforms, including those for mortars, could be made of planks sized exactly to Ordnance Manual tables, carefully doweled together and designed to accompany the weapons. However, in country as heavily wooded as that along the east coast, it is probable that in many cases platforms were fabricated on the spot from local materials. This was particularly true in the Richmond and Charleston campaigns. Speaking of the former, Abbot said:[7] "The siege gun platforms issued by the Ordnance Department are designed for breaching batteries where the direction of the gun is but slightly changed. For batteries of position, they are entirely too small. We made very little use of them, preferring to improvise larger platforms of lumber obtained from neighboring buildings." At Charleston, federal forces made platforms of local pine lumber,[8] including the most famous platform of all—that for the "Swamp Angel," described in the chapter on Parrott rifles.

Although firing was the artilleryman's main duty, he also had the more prosaic job of putting his guns in position to shoot. Mounting a light mountain howitzer on its carriage was merely a matter of lifting it with the aid of handspikes. Even field pieces could be manhandled by placing a handspike under the cascabel and shoving another well into the muzzle. But mounting siege and seacoast weapons was a different matter, although it could be accomplished with surprising ease by an experienced crew using simple equipment.

The main implement for handling field weapons —and also needed with heavier pieces—was the handspike. This versatile item of artillery equipment came in several shapes and sizes for special work, but basically all were poles of hickory or oak or bars of iron.[9]

Field weapons used the trail handspike (Fig. XI-7) which was 52.5 inches long tapering from 1.5 inches at the top to 3 near the center then down to 2.2 at the lower end. Weight was 7.25 pounds.

The shod handspike (Fig. XI-7) had an iron shoe at the lower end and was used with mortars. It was 62 inches long and tapered from 1.75 inches at top to 2.5 at the bottom. Weight, 12 pounds.

Mountain howitzers used a 45.58-inch handspike tapered from 1.65 inches at either end to 2 in the middle where there were two small holes through which a 15-inch loop of rope was attached for use in placing the piece on the pack saddle. It weighed 5 pounds.

Maneuvering handspikes for siege and seacoast use (Fig. XI-7) were octagonal in the middle and square near the lower end which was beveled at the tip to facilitate sliding it under objects. Generally it was 66 inches long ranging from 1.8 to 3 inches in diameter and weighing 8.25 pounds. However, a 7-foot model weighing 12 pounds was also used with seacoast weapons.

The gin handspike (Fig. XI-18) was round on the large end to fit into the socket of the gin windlass. It was 66 inches long and varied from 1.6 to 3.25 inches in diameter. Weight was 11.25 pounds.

Handspikes for iron carriages and wooden casemate carriages were made of iron and technically known as bars. Maneuvering types for all iron carriages were 58.5 inches long, varied from 1 to 1.25 inches in diameter, and weighed 30.75 pounds. Elevating bars were 53 inches long, 1 to 1.5 inches in diameter, and weighed 19 pounds.

Truck handspikes, or bars, (Fig. XI-7) for wood casemate carriages were 42 inches long, 1.1 to 1.4 inches in diameter, and weighed 18.5 pounds. The roller model was 34 inches long, varied from .85 to 1 inch in diameter, and weighed 7 pounds. Eccentric handspikes, or bars, had a rounded piece at one end containing a hexagonal opening which fitted over the head of the eccentric axle after the fashion of a wrench. Such an implement is held by one of the men at right in Figure XI-18.

Equipment for mounting and moving heavy weapons—so-called "mechanical maneuvers"—was relatively simple consisting mainly of blocks, jacks, gins, and sling carts.

Blocks, termed rollers if rounded, were made of wood in numerous sizes ranging from 1 to 4 feet long and up to 8 inches in diameter. Shapes were equally varied including, in cross section, squares, oblongs, circles, triangles, wedges, and combinations such as an oblong with a rounded side. Figure XI-12 shows a random selection and Figure XI-13 the use of blocks to raise a siege gun sufficiently for mounting. Other uses depended primarily on need and ingenuity.

Since blocks as well as other apparatus often required a means of lifting one end of a piece, a jack of some sort was a necessity. Four types are mentioned in the Ordnance Manual, based on the simple screw, lever, geared screw, and hydraulics.

The screw jack was merely a tubular cast iron stand with a nut on top through which a screw worked. Handles turned the nut to raise or lower the screw. It was 19 inches tall, weighed 25 pounds, and was used primarily by field batteries, especially to lift carriage wheels for greasing.

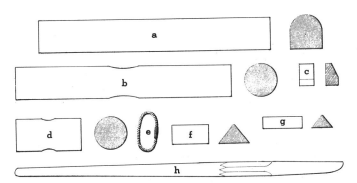

FIGURE: XI-12 IDENTIFICATION: Miscellaneous Rollers. SOURCE: *Instruction for Heavy Artillery*, 1861. REMARKS: a. Half Roller, 46 x 6 inches. b. Long Roller, 42 x 6 inches. c. Gun Chock, 3.6 x 2.75 inches. d. Short Roller, 12 x 7 inches. e. Trunnion Loop, 18 inches circumference. f. Wheel Chock, 7 x 6 x 3 inches. g. Roller Chock, 7 x 3 x 2 inches. h. Maneuvering Handspike, 66 inches (for mechanical maneuvers, 72 inches).

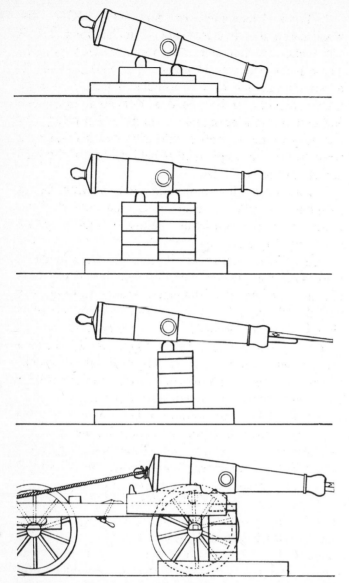

FIGURE: XI-13 IDENTIFICATION: Use of Blocks to Mount a Gun on its Carriage. SOURCE: *Instruction for Heavy Artillery,* 1861.

The lever jack (Fig. XI-14) consisted of a stand, which formed an adjustable fulcrum, and a 15-foot, 5.5-inch diameter wood lever weighing 150 pounds. The 2-foot high stand, which weighed 100 pounds, was composed of a bed and two uprights, held rigidly a few inches apart by a transom and bolt. An iron fulcrum pin was inserted through any of eight pairs of holes drilled at different levels in the uprights. Two brass plates, screwed to the bottom of the lever, were notched to fit over the fulcrum pin. This prevented slipping and provided a way of changing the amount of leverage by using different notches.

A versatile device for seacoast use was the lifting jack (Fig. XI-14). The screw of this iron jack was geared to a crank and when placed under an object, lifted in the same fashion as the simple screw. How-

ever, a foot, attached at the bottom of the screw through a slot in the stand, could lift objects having little floor clearance. The jack, with handle and bed, was 20 inches long, 12 inches wide, and 29.2 inches high. It weighed 160 pounds.

The hydraulic jack was an improvement over the lifting jack and could be used in similar fashion. It was patented and procured ready-made, generally in 10-ton capacity size which had a height of 25.5 inches, lift 10 inches, largest diameter 9 inches, length of foot 4 inches, and length of lever 26.5 inches. Total weight, including lever, was 117.25 pounds.

Gins were little more than tripods with a rope and pulley system for lifting weights. There were three types, field and siege, garrison, and casemate, differing mainly in dimension. All were composed of two spruce legs, held together in an inverted "V" by bolts and braces and with a windlass between, a third leg of the same material, termed a "pry pole," and an array of nuts, bolts, pulleys, and other iron and brass parts.

Legs of the field and siege gin (Fig. XI-15) were 15-feet long, 6.5 inches wide, and 5.5 inches thick. The pry pole was similar in length, but 5.5 inches in both width and thickness. The windlass, 68 inches long, had a 9-inch barrel.

The garrison gin (Fig. XI-16) had legs and pry pole 22 feet long tapering from 6.5 inches at the top to 9 near the windlass which was 104 inches long with an 11-inch barrel.

Since it was designed to operate beneath a ceiling, the casemate gin (Fig. XI-17) had legs only 15 feet long, but in other respects was generally similar to the garrison model. Both differed visibly from the field and siege gin in having cleats attached to the pry pole, eleven for the garrison and six for the casemate. Ninety feet of 4-inch rope was used with the field and siege gin and 120 feet of 5-inch with the others.

Figure XI-18 shows victorious federal troops using a garrison gin to dismount a "Confederate Rodman" The process was roughly the same regardless of the type gin employed. A heavy rope sling was looped around the cascabel and a maneuvering handspike shoved well into the muzzle. The gin fall was attached to the sling, the windlass manned, and the piece raised out of the trunnion holes. At this stage, field and siege carriages could be hauled away and the tube lowered to the ground.

Barbette and casemate carriages presented a different problem. After the piece cleared the trunnion holes, the carriage was traversed as far as possible to the side on which both legs were located.

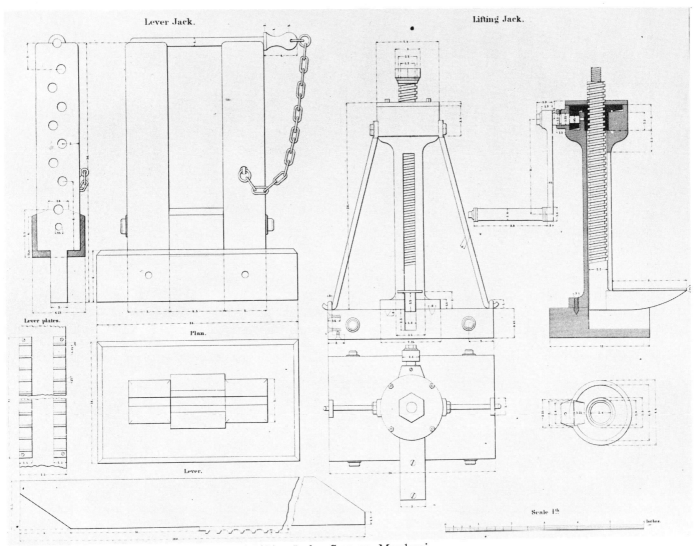

FIGURE: **XI-14** IDENTIFICATION: Lever and Lifting Jacks. SOURCE: Mordecai.

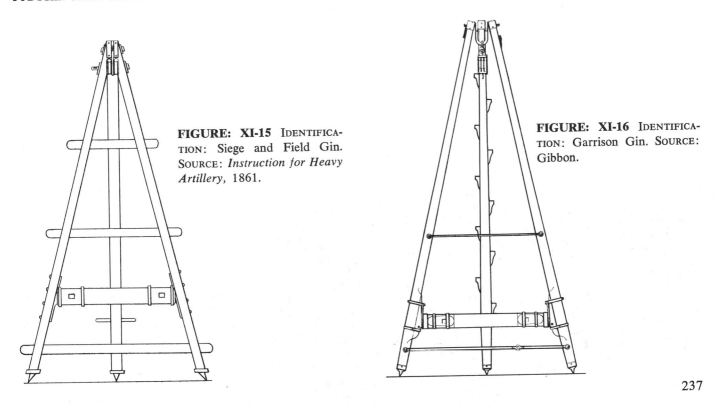

FIGURE: **XI-15** IDENTIFICATION: Siege and Field Gin. SOURCE: *Instruction for Heavy Artillery,* 1861.

FIGURE: **XI-16** IDENTIFICATION: Garrison Gin. SOURCE: Gibbon.

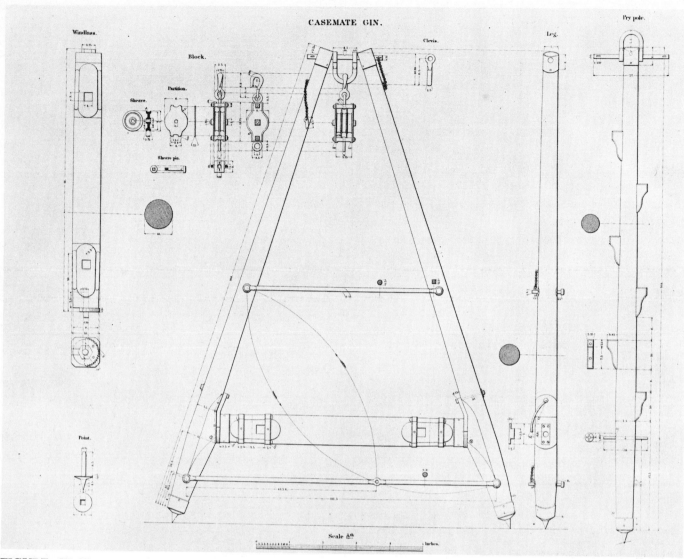

FIGURE: **XI-17** IDENTIFICATION: Casemate Gin. SOURCE: Mordecai.

FIGURE: **XI-18** IDENTIFICATION: Garrison Gin. REMARKS: Confederate Columbiad being removed from carriage at Fort McAlister after capture by Sherman's forces December, 1864.

This removed it from directly beneath the weapon which now could be lowered to blocks or a casemate truck for removal. Placing the piece on its carriage required a reverse of the process.

Mounting a 15-inch Rodman, because of its weight, presented a special problem. Using blocks and heavy timbers for skids, the tube first had to be rolled onto the chassis which had the top carriage removed. Now with garrison gins front and rear as well as lifting jacks, muzzle and breech were alternately raised and shored up with block scaffolding. When the proper height was reached, the iron top carriage was simply assembled beneath the trunnions and the piece lowered into position. Dismounting necessitated a reverse of the procedure.

The ease with which iron carriages were put together recommended a simplified version of this method for mounting smaller weapons, particularly in casemates. The piece was simply raised on block scaffolds with the lifting jack and both chassis and top carriage built beneath it.

Weapons mounted on the wood, front pintle, barbette carriage could be moved short distances using the top carriage wheels, shod with iron tires, and a standard field limber with the ammunition chest removed. The maneuver (Fig. XI-19) involved removing the prop, taking off the traverse wheels, and lowering the end of the chassis. Then the limber could be backed up, planks installed parallel to the chassis rails, the pole raised to engage limber pintle and top carriage lunette, and the piece rolled away on the wheels of limber and top carriage. A reverse of the procedure installed the top carriage on another chassis. The maneuver made a relatively quick replacement of a disabled gun possible and enabled a fortification commander to move weapons from one front to another as the military situation warranted.

However, movement of heavy weapons in most cases required that the piece be dismounted and transported in one of several vehicles. Mortars and longer weapons, that were not too heavy, could be carried in the mortar wagon. Abbot, for instance, preferred this method for carrying such weapons as the 6.4-inch Parrott after disabling a number of the type vehicle traditionally assigned this role—the sling cart.

Figure XI-20 shows a diagram of a sling cart and Figure XI-21, one in Fort Johnson at Charleston shortly after the war. This 2,500-pound vehicle had two 8-foot diameter wheels and a long pole. It was backed over the piece to be slung, the breech in direction of the pole. A prolonge—an 18-foot length of 3.5-inch rope (Fig. XI-4)—was attached to the end of the pole which was raised until vertical. The movement pivoted the axle lowering two hooks at rear about 8 inches and to which a chain looped around the trunnions was hooked.

Hauling on the prolonge brought the pole level and at the same time, like a huge lever with axles as a fulcrum, lifted the piece a few inches. If necessary to raise it higher, the weapon was blocked at this point and the process repeated to gain a few more inches. In either case, the piece was now approximately balanced and the cascabel could be lashed in position to hold the tube level. A standard siege limber[10] was connected to the pole for transportation by horses. However, since the sling cart limbered was roughly 35 feet long, it was difficult to handle on narrow, twisting roads and, as Abbot discovered, subject to having the pole broken.

An even larger, 4-wheel sling cart (Fig. XI-22), was built by the Confederates specifically to move the two 12-inch smoothbores under construction at Tredegar at the time of capture. The cart had 10-foot wheels and was welcomed by federal troops for hauling away heavy trophies after the fall of Richmond. When carrying an 8-inch columbiad over bad roads, the huge cart was drawn by twelve mules, attached to a siege limber, and one hundred and fifty men using drag ropes.[11]

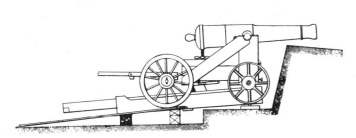

FIGURE: XI-19 IDENTIFICATION: Method of Lowering a Barbette, Front Pintle, Wood, Top Carriage from its Chassis. SOURCE: *Instruction for Heavy Artillery,* 1861.

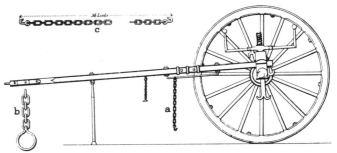

FIGURE: XI-20 IDENTIFICATION: Sling Cart. SOURCE: *Instruction for Heavy Artillery,* 1861. REMARKS: a. Cascabel Chain. b. Trunnion Ring. c. Sling Chain.

FIGURE: XI-21 IDENTIFICATION: Sling Cart. REMARKS: Sling Cart (left) in Fort Johnson, Charleston, S.C., after recapture in 1865. Non-standard, Confederate-made field limber at right.

FIGURE: XI-22 IDENTIFICATION: Confederate Sling Cart. REMARKS: This huge sling cart with 10-foot diameter wheels was built by the Confederates to handle the 12-inch columbiads under construction at Tredegar when Richmond was captured. The cart was used by the victorious Federals to carry away tophies such as this Brooke rifle.

240

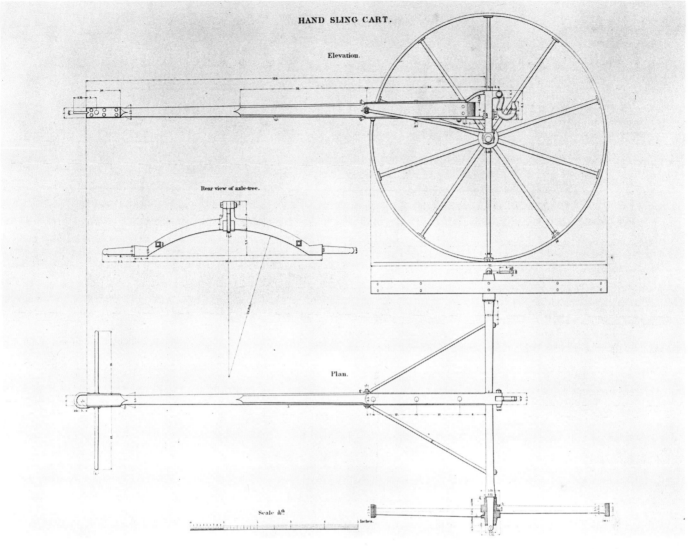

FIGURE: XI-23 IDENTIFICATION: Hand Sling Cart. SOURCE: Mordecai. REMARKS: Made of iron except for oak pole.

The standard two-wheel sling cart was often called the "large sling cart" to differentiate it from its smaller cousin, the hand sling cart (Fig. XI-23). Although similar in appearance, the smaller vehicle was made entirely of iron with exception of an oak pole. It was designed for short-distance conveyance of relatively light weapons and stores being normally restricted to 4,000 pounds maximum, although 24- and 32-pounder guns could be carried in an emergency. It was loaded in the same manner as the sling cart.

The casemate truck (Fig. XI-24) as the name indicates, was used to move weapons, carriages, and stores inside the casemates. It was a wood and iron vehicle with two 15-inch, barbette carriage traverse wheels in rear and a third in front that provided excellent maneuverability. Weapons could be loaded by casemate gin or lifting them on block scaffolds and positioning the truck beneath.

Also used for moving miscellaneous supplies were hand carts and store trucks (Fig. XI-24). The latter differed little from its civilian counterpart still found in warehouses today.

Gunpowder of the Civil War era was a combination of charcoal, saltpeter (potassium nitrate, or niter), and sulfur in the proportions 75-15-10 or 76-14-10 by weight.[12] Manufacturing processes varied between nations, between companies, and even between plants of the same firm, but the principal operations, as described in the Ordnance Manual,[13] involved pulverizing and thoroughly mixing the ingredients, pressing them into a cake, reducing the cake to grains, then glazing, drying, and dusting the grains.

A good grade of powder depended to a large extent on purity of raw materials. To ensure this, saltpeter was generally refined by leaching out impur-

241

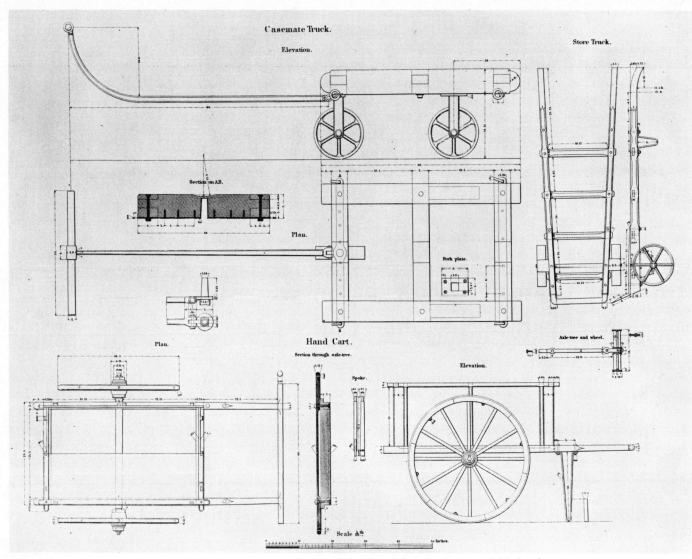

FIGURE: XI-24 IDENTIFICATION: Casemate Truck, Store Truck, and Hand Cart. SOURCE: Mordecai.

ities with water, sulfur by distillation, and charcoal by proper selection of wood, preferably willow or black alder, and care in its preparation. Refined saltpeter was often sufficiently fine for use when it arrived at the powder mill, but charcoal and sulfur had to be pulverized by rolling with bronze balls in large barrels, then mixed in proper proportion by rolling them together in still another barrel. The saltpeter could be added at this point in similar fashion or during the next process—the rolling mill.

This device consisted of twin cast iron cylinders rolling in a 9-foot diameter circular trough with a cast iron bottom. The cylinders were 6-feet in diameter, 18 inches wide on the face, and weighed about 8 tons each. They were followed by a wood scraper which kept the composition in the center of the trough. A charge of 75 pounds in some mills, 150 in others, was spread evenly around the trough and

moistened with 2 or 3 per cent water. Rolling started slowly, but soon picked up to eight or ten revolutions a minute and remained at this pace for approximately an hour per 50 pounds of charge. Water was added if the material appeared to be drying and by the end of the run this "mill cake" was thoroughly mixed and of a reddish brown color.

It was now sprinkled with water, spread in 2-inch thick layers between brass plates and subjected to heavy pressure for ten to fifteen minutes which reduced it to a hard cake about an inch thick. The cake was broken into small, angular pieces by bronze tooth rollers and separated by screens according to size. Several hundred pounds of this "grained" powder were placed in a glazing barrel and revolved for ten to twelve hours. The resulting product had lost its sharp angles and acquired a bright polish. It was now spread on sheets in a room under temperatures ranging from 140° to 160° for drying. Finally, it was sifted over fine mesh to remove dust and small particles, which could be reworked. The grains ended up brownish black or slate color, too hard for easy crushing between the fingers, irregular in shape and free of dust.[14] Standard sizes[15] were: musket, .03 to .06 inch; mortar, .06 to .10; cannon, .25 to .35, and mammoth, .60 to .90 inch.

Powder was packed 100 pounds to the barrel which left sufficient space for movement of the grains when the barrel was rolled periodically to prevent caking. Barrels were handled carefully in transportation being either boxed for rail shipment, or kept apart by straw and covered with tarpaulins when in wagons. For short distances, they were carried in hand barrows, not rolled—the occasional rolling to prevent caking being an entirely separate process, conducted carefully, a few barrels at a time.

Powder barrels stored in magazines of fortifications were stacked on their sides, usually three tiers high. Tops and bottoms, painted black, were stenciled in white on one end with the place and year of manufacture and kind of grain, and on the other with the year proved and proof range.[16] Magazines were well drained and ventilated, and customarily opened for airing in sunny weather. If despite precautions powder became damp, it could be spread out and dried with no deterioration provided absorption of moisture was less than 7 per cent. If more, the powder had to be returned to the factory for reworking.

Magazine sentinels were unarmed and anyone entering had to remove swords, canes, all metallic objects, and their shoes, any of which might cause a spark through striking a hard object, or static electricity. Loaded cartridge bags were often packed in powder barrels for storage and these and fixed ammunition were preserved in separate magazines if possible. Regulations prohibited keeping fireworks or shells in magazines with powder.

Magazines aboard ship were placed below the waterline for protection from enemy shot and ease of flooding in emergency. Seacocks, worked from the deck above, could flood magazines in case of fire. This impaired the fighting qualities of the vessel only during the period of actual flooding. Drains could quickly empty the water into the bilge below for pumping overboard and the room re-entered for use although an undesirable dampness no doubt lingered for some time. The powder, if properly stored, should survive magazine flooding undamaged since it was kept in watertight, copper tanks. These were of different capacity ranging from 50 to 200 pounds and

customarily held powder already packed in cartridge bags, each caliber to its own tank.

During action, the bags were handed out of the magazine to men who placed them in individual pass boxes similar to those described for service of a barbette piece. Empty boxes returned from the guns via a canvas chute, landing on wet swabs. Each was opened and knocked on a screen over a tub of water to ensure that no smoldering ember had inadvertently blown inside. Pass boxes were never taken into the magazine, even during practice. As on land, all personnel discarded metallic instruments and put on canvas shoes before entering the magazine. Shell rooms were separate from magazines, but also provided with means for flooding. Unloaded shells were stored in any dry, convenient spot, but not in the magazines or shell rooms.

Manufacture of cast iron and bronze cannon, excluding those made by the previously discussed Rodman process, involved four basic operations: molding, casting, cooling, and finishing.

Molding was a process of imbedding a model of the piece in sand held in a box, termed a flask, then withdrawing it to leave an imprint. Models or patterns were generally made of hardwood, although iron and copper were used on occasion. They were slightly larger than the desired weapon to allow for finishing and were separated into several parts for ease in handling. The model (Fig. XI-25) for small weapons, for instance, was usually divided into five

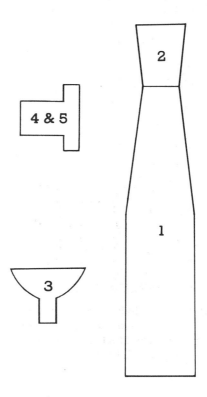

FIGURE: XI-25
IDENTIFICATION: Wood Pattern or Model for Manufacture of Cannon.
SOURCE: Benton, 1861.
REMARKS:
1. Body of the Piece.
2. Sprue or Dead-head.
3. Breech.
4 & 5. Trunnions.

sections: the breech, the body of the piece from base ring to neck, the sprue or deadhead which extended considerably beyond the muzzle, and two trunnions. Larger cannon often necessitated a further breakdown. Prior to use, the model was covered with a slip of cokewash—pulverized charcoal moistened with a clay-water solution—to prevent adhesion of sand. Hard, refractory sand proved best for molding and was moistened with water in which clay had been stirred to, in this case, increase its adhesive qualities. Flasks were made of iron separated into several pieces with flanges for bolts at strategic points to hold them together.

The process of molding differed between firms, but a general method consisted of bolting a section of the flask together, placing part of the model within, then adding sand gradually with constant tamping until the flask was filled. Dry sand was then sprinkled on top to prevent sticking when the next flask was attached and the process repeated. In this manner the tube, minus the breech section, could be fabricated up to the trunnions. These parts of the model were now affixed to the tube section and the flasks bolted around them (Fig. XI-26). The trunnion flask had a plate at the outer end which could be removed, sand packed around the pattern, and the plate replaced. The molding process continued with the remaining

sections of flask being bolted on until the sprue was completed.

The breech flask had plates bolted top and bottom. With the bottom closed, top open, the breech model could be inserted, chamber end down. Sand was then packed around it until the cascabel was covered, the top bolted on, and the flask turned over. Now the former bottom plate could be unbolted and the pattern lifted out.

In similar fashion patterns were withdrawn section by section from the tube and trunnion flasks. Repairs were made with molding sand to any parts damaged in the process, the entire impression given a thorough coating of cokewash and all parts placed in an oven for gradual drying. After removal from the oven, all flasks were bolted together and placed upright, breech down, in a large pit for casting.

Metal from several furnaces was pooled in a reservoir near the mold until a sufficient quantity was collected. Then the gate was knocked out and the metal flowed into a channel (Fig. XI-26) which had been formed inside the flasks at the same time and in similar fashion as the impression of the piece. The channel ran from top of the sprue down to connect at an angle with the breech in order to introduce metal at the bottom of the mold and let it rise gradually, for if poured in directly from the top, the fall would likely damage bottom and sides. The angled flow gave a rotary motion to the metal which was assisted by a workman with a long pine paddle continually stirring as the mold filled. This swirling effect kept extraneous matter, or scoria, out of the trunnion cavities and concentrated it in the center of the tube, where it would be removed later when the bore was cut, and also in the sprue. In addition to collecting a large part of the scoria, the sprue furnished extra metal to compensate for shrinkage during cooling and provided additional weight, believed necessary to compress the metal below as it cooled.

Cooling large masses created stresses and strains and in an effort to obviate this as much as possible by slow cooling, the flask was surrounded by sand at least as high as the trunnions. This was left in place for three days with a 24-pounder and proportionately longer as caliber increased. At the end of this period, the sand was removed, flask and casting hoisted from the pit, and the flask taken off. When nearly cold, sand caked around the casting was cleaned off and the piece was ready for finishing.

The rough casting was placed in a lathe and turned by power applied to the cascabel which had been cast in oblong shape to facilitate this step. The sprue was cut off at the muzzle face and a cutter

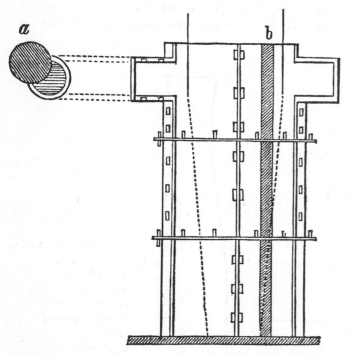

FIGURE: XI-26 IDENTIFICATION: Model with Trunnion Pieces attached emplaced in Mold or Flasks. SOURCE: Gibbon. REMARKS: a. End Plates of Trunnion Mold. b. Channel by which metal, poured from the top, was introduced at the bottom of the mold.

extending like a horizontal drill from a movable cart was pushed against the bore by weights and a series of cogwheels (Fig. XI-27). Often the first cutter was of small diameter and the hole was reamed to proper size in successive operations. A later method involved use of a tubular cutter. This left a core in the center which was broken out with wedges. If the piece was to be rifled, grooves were cut after proper diameter for the lands was attained. Since the piece revolved on its long axis during bore cutting, the exterior was finished to specifications except for the section between the trunnions which, of course, could not be reached and had to be dressed later by a planing machine. After boring, the weapon was placed in a trunnion lathe (Fig. XI-28) and turned around the axis of the trunnions which, with the rimbases, were now shaped to size. Before removal, the piece was positioned at the correct angle and the vent drilled.

The cascabel was not finished until after inspection and acceptance of the weapon by Army or Navy. This was merely a precaution on the part of the manufacturer so that in case of rejection for a minor measurement discrepancy, the cannon could be returned to the lathe for correction. If it passed all tests, finishing the cascabel was an easy matter.

Inspection was an involved process requiring an array of instruments for checking exact measurements of bore and other parts to insure that they fell within certain allowable tolerances. Brass, and often iron, cannon were then put through what was known as

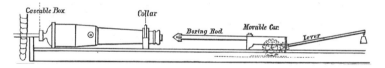

FIGURE: XI-27 IDENTIFICATION: One Method of Boring A Cannon. SOURCE: Simpson.

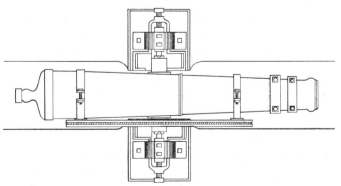

FIGURE: XI-28 IDENTIFICATION: Trunnion Lathe. SOURCE: Gibbon.

"water proof" to check for casting defects.[17] This was a hydraulic test in which the bore was filled with water, closed, and pressure applied. After removal of the water and drying, even hairline cracks showed as thin lines oozing moisture.

All pieces were subjected to "powder proof" —test firing under strict requirements which varied with caliber, but generally consisted of three rounds with charges roughly approximating the maximum used in service. In past years powder proof involved heavy overcharges, but the practice was discontinued since it only weakened the bore without proving that the piece would stand such strain in the future. If the cannon held together and no defects appeared, it received the inspector's stamp of approval—his initials literally stamped into the metal. Failure of a weapon to pass powder proof resulted in rejection of all made with that batch of metal and by the same process. Condemned cannon were stamped with the letters "XC" on the muzzle face. If rejected for erroneous dimensions that could not be rectified in the lathe, "XD" was added; if for powder proof "XP"; and for water proof "XW." Such markings on cannon found today, however, are extremely rare since most condemned weapons went back into the melting pot to be recast.

Before leaving the foundry, cannon were marked with various letters and numbers which, if properly interpreted, often provide considerable information on the history and even identification of the piece.

Army regulations prescribed one-inch figures on the muzzle face listing number of the piece, weight, year of fabrication, and initials of inspector and foundry. A large "U.S." was placed in the center of the tube roughly level with the trunnions, and the foundry number, in small figures, was stamped on the right rimbase above the trunnion. The rimbase number on certain weapons, particularly the larger Parrotts, was the same as the number on the muzzle face, but this similarity did not hold true for ordnance made by other founders.

The Navy substituted an anchor for the U.S. on the tube and required that foundry initials, weapon number, and weight be placed on the base ring. Caliber and year of fabrication went on the right trunnion face and the inspector's initials, prefaced by the letter "P" (Proved) on the left. The preponderance, in pounds, was marked on the upper jaw of the cascabel in half-inch figures and the foundry number, in addition to being on the right rimbase, was stamped on the end of the top cascabel jaw, the cascabel block, and the head of the pin. Rejected weapons were to have a "C" partially obliterating the anchor and founders were encouraged to destroy them.

Unfortunately, not all weapons were marked according to regulations, but the majority will have marks on muzzle or trunnion faces, tube or base ring, although often obscured by paint. Most cannon owners, including the federal government, take a dim view of promiscuous scraping since paint is needed as a preservative and for appearance, but assuming permission has been granted and paint has been removed to bare metal without revealing marks at the aforementioned points, examination of the base of the breech, cascabel, and tops and sides of sight masses may be rewarding. If the piece is thought to be a Blakely, the top of the tube between base ring and trunnions should be carefully examined. The rear top and face of Brooke or other Confederate banding should also be checked. The Confederates seem to have followed little overall system, but their markings generally will be found on muzzle or trunnion faces.

Interpretation of marks in most cases is not difficult. The date is self-explanatory. The weapon number is usually easy to pick out, but if high, may be confused with the weight although the latter is usually followed by the abbreviation for pounds (lbs). Weights of certain Navy weapons, as explained in Chapter I, English, and very ancient cannon are listed in hundredweights. Initials of various founders and inspectors will be found in the Appendices.

The art of fortification is far too complex to cover in its entirety within the few pages allotted here. However, a fundamental knowledge of the appearance of elements involved in both field and permanent works as well as some of the terms used may prove of value. Those readers interested in extensive study of the subject are referred to such books as D. H. Mahan's volume on field and permanent fortifications listed in the bibliography.

Webster's dictionary defines a fortification as ". . . a work or works erected to defend a place or position. . . ." To elaborate this concise description we could append the words of Mahan:[18]

"The means resorted to for . . . strengthening a position may be either those presented by nature, as precipices, woods, rivers, etc., or those formed by art as shelters of earth, stone, wood, etc.

"If the materials used are of durable character, and the position is to be permanently occupied, the works . . . receive the name of Permanent Fortification, but when the position is to be occupied only a short period or during the operations of a campaign, perishable materials as earth and wood, are mostly used and the works are denominated Temporary, or Field Fortification. . . ."

Permanent fortifications quite often were highly elaborate works of brick or stone with walls several feet thick and of such design as to make success of sudden assault against an alert garrison theoretically impossible. Yet despite complicated appearance, their basic elements were little different than those used in field defenses and may be reduced, in general, to the following forms: Right Line, Indented Line, Redan, Lunette, Priest Cap, Redoubt, Star Fort, and Bastioned Fort.

The *Right Line* was the simplest of field works and consisted merely of a straight trench with a mound of earth over which troops could shoot. Since men could only fire with facility straight ahead, it had virtually no flank defense and was useful primarily in conjunction with other forms—as a curtain, for instance, of a bastioned fort—or for short distances when the flanks were securely anchored on natural defenses such as wide rivers or marshes. However, it had the advantage of quick, easy construction and for its size required the smallest number of men to defend. Efforts to correct its deficiency and provide flank, in some cases rear, defense led to lines with various angular forms called "salients" when the point was toward the enemy, or "re-enterings" when toward the assailed. To resist weathering, ensure adequate space for troops inside, and provide better defense, salient angles were never less than 60°.

The *Cremaillere* or *Indented Line* (Fig. XI-29A) utilized both forms and was an improvement over the right line. Its salients (a) and re-enterings (b) offered a certain amount of flank defense, although not equal on both sides.

The *Redan* (Fig. XI-29B) could be a simple salient with two "faces" (ab) and (bc). The rear between (a) and (c), open in this case, was known as the "gorge." In permanent works the gorge was closed, generally elaborately fortified and often was the site of one of the fort's few openings, known as "outlets." Although the redan as a simple salient offered excellent fire to the flank, it had a blind spot or "sector without fire" directly in front. To correct this, the point, or "salient angle" was often flattened (Fig. XI-29C) to a short face (bc) termed a "pan coupe."

The *Lunette* (Fig. XI-29D) in addition to faces (bc,cd) had "flanks" (ab,de). It had similar defects to the redan, but was able to sweep with fire from the flanks terrain which might be poorly defended from the faces.

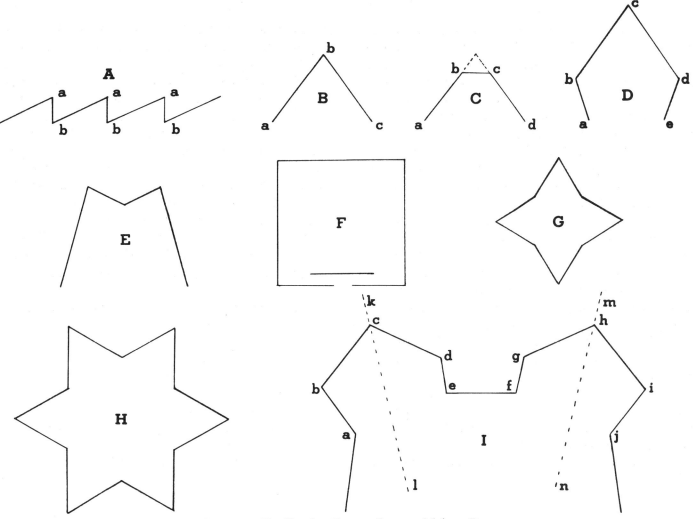

FIGURE: XI-29 IDENTIFICATION: Elementary Fortification Forms. SOURCE: Mahan. REMARKS:

B. Redan
    ab — Face
    bc — Face
    ac — Gorge
D. Lunette
    bc, cd — Faces
    ab, de — Flanks
H. Another form of Star Fort

A. Cremaillere or Indented Line
    a — Salients
    b — Re-Enterings
C. Redan with Pan Coupe (bc)
E. Priest Cap or Swallow Tail
F. Redoubt — in this case a Square. Traverse protects Outlet of Gorge.
G. Star Fort
I. Bastioned Fort
    ef — curtain
    abcde — Lunette
    fghij — Lunette
    kl, mn — Capitals

The *Priest Cap* or *Swallow Tail* (Fig. XI-29E) was seldom used as a detached work, but combined with a right or indented line to provide flank defense or cross fire in front.

The *Redoubt* was an enclosed work of polygonal form without re-entering angles. It differed from previous works which had open gorges and was used for all-round defense. The square (Fig. XI-29F) was the most common form due to ease of construction and its ability, when used in conjunction with others, to cover the line between by cross fire. All redoubts

had the same defects—the ditches were unprotected and the saliants left sectors without fire. Flattening the saliants with pan coupes helped little since it created additional saliants. The outlet of the gorge, which probably would have been closed by a heavy gate, was further protected by a mound of earth known as a "traverse."

The *Star Fort* could take many forms of which Figures XI-29G and H are but two. It was designed to correct the deficiencies of the redoubt, but was only partially successful since, if a regular polygon, "dead" angles unprotected by fire were found at the re-enterings. The star fort also had the inherent defect that occupying the same space as the redoubt, it afforded less interior area, yet required more troops to man. It also was more difficult to construct and consequently was ignored by the engineers unless forced to it by the nature of the terrain.

The *Bastioned Fort* (Fig. XI-29I) satisfied conditions of a well-rounded defense to a greater extent than any of the other works, but required considerably more time and effort to construct. The basic form could be a polygon of any number of sides, although the square and pentagon proved more popular in the field being easier to construct. Examination of the bastioned fort shows it to be nothing more than a right line, called a "curtain" (ef) in this case, flanked by lunettes. The imaginary lines (kl, mn) bisecting the salient angles were known as "capitals." Angles and lengths were carefully calculated to provide maximum coverage by fire and ideal lengths of bastioned fort sides were between 125 and 250 yards.

The sketch of a fortification from an overhead view was termed the "plan" or "trace." In addition, however, proper description also required a "profile." This was a side view (Fig. XI-30) outlining the various parts of the work, each with its specific name. Major divisions were the Rampart or Bulwark (abhi) topped by the Parapet (cdefgh), the Ditch (jklm), and the Glacis (nopqr).

The word parapet has taken on a somewhat misleading connotation through the years probably because of our lack of familiarity today with fortification terms. A field work quite often omitted the rampart and the entire mound of earth thrown up in rear of the ditch was the parapet. The description became erroneous, however, when used to denote the vaguely defined area encompassing the entire top of more extensive works. This was particularly true of stone or masonry fortifications that had only a low wall as a parapet to protect troops firing barbette cannon. The parapet protecting artillery positions was often known as an "epaulement."

Detailed parts of the work shown in profile are as follows:

Parade Slope (ab).

Terreplein (bc). Artillery was mounted on this section. It could fire over the parapet, in which case it was termed barbette, or as an "embrasure battery" firing through an opening cut in the parapet.

Banquette Slope (cd). This was a short,

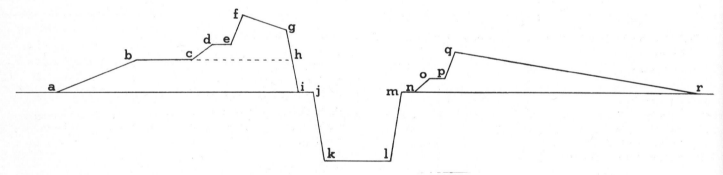

FIGURE: XI-30 IDENTIFICATION: Profile of Fortification. SOURCE: Mahan. REMARKS:

abhi — Rampart or Bulwark	cdefgh — Parapet
jklm — Ditch	nopqr — Glacis
ab — Parade Slope	bc — Terreplein
cd — Banquette Slope	de — Tread of the Banquette or simply Banquette
ef — Interior Slope	fg — Superior Slope
gi— Exterior Slope (if no Rampart, gh)	ij — Berm
jk — Scarp Wall	kl — Bottom of the Ditch
lm — Counterscarp Wall	mn — Covered Way
no — Glacis Banquette Slope	op — Banquette
pq — Interior Slope	qr — Glacis Slope
High points or Crests.	f — Interior Crest
g — Exterior Crest	j — Scarp Crest
m — Counterscarp Crest	q — Glacis Crest
Low points or Foot	c. Foot of Banquette Slope
e. Foot of Interior Slope	i. Foot of Exterior Slope (if no Rampart, h)
k. Foot of Scarp	l. Foot of Counterscarp
r. Foot of Glacis	

access slope. It could be replaced by steps if necessary to conserve space.

Tread of the Banquette (de), generally called simply the "banquette." This was the platform on which troops stood to fire.

Interior Slope (ef). A base one-third the height gave a degree of slope most convenient for men leaning against it to fire. Ideal vertical height was found to be 4 feet 3 inches.

Superior Slope (fg). This was slanted to protect by fire the crest of the counterscarp (m) of if not feasible due to size of the work, the crest of the glacis (q).

Exterior Slope (gi) (if no rampart, gh). It had the natural slope of the earth thrown up during construction. Attempts to make it steeper would invite destruction by enemy fire and consequent reduction in the thickness of the parapet.

Berm (ij). This narrow shelf was a defect of fortifications which gave the assailant a foothold on which to catch his breath before attempting the exterior slope. It was necessary, however, to throw the weight of the rampart and parapet rearward of the ditch to minimize danger of cave-in. It also formed a convenient spot for workmen to stand during construction. In firm soils the berm could be as little as 18 inches to 2 feet wide, but in soft ground it went up to 6 feet. Proper design required it to be 6 feet below the Exterior Crest (g) to prevent the enemy from firing at troops on the banquette.

Scarp Wall (jk). Its slope was dependent on the nature of the soil, but generally it was less steep than the counterscarp wall.

Bottom of the Ditch (kl). The ditch furnished earth for rampart and parapet and its size required a series of involved calculations. However, to present a respectable obstacle, a 6-foot depth and 20-foot width were considered minimum. On the other hand, 12 feet was about the maximum depth men equipped with picks and shovels could conveniently dig and still throw out the dirt.

Counterscarp Wall (lm).

Covered Way (mn). This provided concealed movement behind the glacis.

The *Glacis Banquette Slope* (no), *Banquette* (op), and *Interior Slope* (pq) duplicated those of the parapet.

Glacis Slope (qr). This was a very gradual slope to ground level providing an open field of fire from the banquette behind.

High points of a work were known as "crests," such as the Interior Crest (f), Exterior (g), Scarp (j), Counterscarp (m), and Glacis (q).

Low points were called the "foot," as Foot of the Banquette Slope (c), Interior Slope (e), Exterior Slope (i) (h if no rampart), Scarp (k), Counterscarp (l) and Glacis (r).

Two terms referred to the height of a work—"command" and "relief." The former was the height of the interior crest above ground level with 8 feet considered the minimum admitting of a reasonable defense. Relief was the height of the interior crest above the bottom of the ditch.

There were also a number of miscellaneous terms which the reader will find mentioned from time to time. Definitions of all would fill many pages, but the more common ones are as follows:

Traverse. A mound of earth or other substance placed between weapons or sections of a work to localize the effect of shell bursts on either position or as protection from enfilading or reverse fire.

Embrasure. As mentioned before, an embrasure was an opening in the parapet or epaulement for a weapon to fire through, or the opening in the casemate of a permanent fortification. The bottom of the embrasure was known as the "sole" and the sides "cheeks." The interior opening, known as the "mouth," was rectangular from 18 inches to 2 feet wide dependent upon caliber of the piece. It widened considerably to the exterior opening, the amount of slant being termed "splay." Casemate embrasures sometimes were splayed in two directions pinched toward the center, or "throat," in the form of a horizontal "X."

Merlon. The section of parapet between embrasures.

Mantlet. Cover for the mouth of an embrasure to provide protection from enemy fire as well as concealment. Mantlets could be made of iron, wood, heavy rope, or other material and were either hinged for removal while the piece fired or had an opening through which the muzzle could be inserted.

Revetment. A facing of stone, wood, sod, facines, gabions, sandbags, planks, or other material to sustain an embankment, particularly when its slope was steeper than natural.

Fascine. A bundle of twigs closely bound together. One size was 9 inches in diameter and 10 feet long, another, generally termed a "saucisson," 12 inches by 20 feet. Fascines were made on a "fascine horse," a trough formed by driving stout poles into the ground in a series of "X-like" figures set in a straight line about 18 inches apart. Twigs, ranging from little finger to thumb diameter were laid in the trough until a sufficient size bundle was attained. They were drawn tightly together by a "fascine choker" made of two 5-foot levers with a length of chain between, long enough to reach completely around the bundle of twigs. Thus held, they were bound tightly with "withes" or "gads" prepared from tough twigs, or by stout rope yarn.

Gabions. Cylindrical baskets, open at both ends, formed of twigs woven between stakes. They were about 2 feet in diameter and 2 feet 9 inches high and when placed in position, were filled with earth. Gabions reinforcing Fort Sumter are illustrated in Fig. II-7.

Chevaux de frise. A length of timber with pointed stakes driven through it to present a series of "X-shaped" spikes. Used to block a passage, particularly against cavalry.

Permanent fortifications were divided into "fortresses" and "forts," the former term designating a fortified town and the latter a work containing only a garrison. In either case, such extensive defenses required certain additional terms to describe their various parts. These are explained by Fig. XI-31, the plan of a "fortified front" or simply "front," a unit of a permanent work encompassing the section between two capitals.

The line enclosing the main part of a fort was called the "body of the place" or "enceinte" (A). Other parts were "outworks" if enveloped by the covered way; "detached" or "advanced works" if beyond it. The object of such additions was to lengthen the defense and force the enemy to gain possession of them before making a breach in the enceinte.

Principal outwork was one in the form of a redan (G) placed in front of the curtain. In the early days of fortifications, it had a crescent shape which gave it the name "demi-lune" or "half-moon." The name stuck despite later change in form and was used interchangeably with the more modern term "ravelin."

Re-entering (E) and salient (F) "places of arms" were areas in the covered ways convenient for assembling bodies of troops who were to act outside the work. Redoubts (M) were often erected in the places of arms to afford covering fire to members of the garrison returning after a sortie. If hotly pursued, they retired behind the redoubt, rather than into it,

to prevent the enemy from piling in on their heels.

The "tenaille" (O) was a small, low work between bastions designed to mask the curtain from enemy breaching batteries after he attained the crest of the glacis. It was deemed highly important since it forced the assailant to make the breach in a bastion face, rather than the curtain or bastion flank, and thus preserved the flanks for defense of the breach.

"Interior retrenchments," which had the same properties as redoubts, were often constructed within bastions and if high enough to command the exterior ground were called "cavaliers."

Communications of fortifications consisted of arched, underground outlets called "posterns" placed in retired, well-defended positions, interior ramps for moving heavy equipment, and stone stairs.

Seacoast forts had embrasures in the scarp wall and the artillery was protected in bomb-proof "defensive casemates," generally simplified to "casemates." They had arched, overhead covering, but were secure only against bombardment from the sea where pinpoint accuracy and close range were not to be feared. An unprotected scarp wall would stand only a short time against breaching batteries on land, however, so seacoast forts had to be protected by ditches and various works on sides where land attack was feasible.

Attack as well as defense was conducted according to established principles. Field works could often be carried by direct assault, but any permanent fortification worth constructing was safe against anything other than protracted siege.

The method "attack by regular approaches" had, like fortifications, its own terminology. Figure XI-32 illustrates siege of a permanent work by this method and the following is a brief description of the operation and explanation of certain major terms used.

The siege was divided into two parts. The first consisted of isolating the besieged by cutting off all communications and the second, the actual assault to gain possession of the work.

The first part, the "investment" was usually initiated by detaching a strong unit, probably cavalry, in advance of the besieging army to seize all avenues leading to the fort. While awaiting arrival of the main army, the investing forces usually stayed out of cannon range during the day, then moved in at night to form a continuous ring of sentinels. During this period, a complete reconnaissance was made of the work.

With arrival of the main body, camps were established in a circle around the fort just out of cannon range and a ring of continuous entrenchments —the "line of circumvallation"—thrown up to pre-

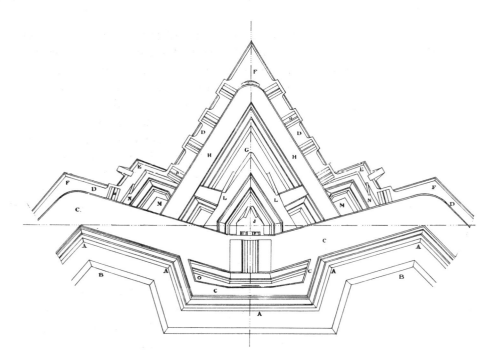

FIGURE: XI-31 IDENTIFICATION: Fortified Front or "Front". SOURCE: Mahan. REMARKS: Dcfincd as the unit between two capitals. A. Line enclosing main part of fort — The "Body of the Place" or Enceinte. B. Bastions. C. Main Ditch of the Enceinte. D. Bastion and Demi-Lune Covered Ways. E. Re-Entering Places of Arms. F. Salient Places of Arms. G. Demi-Lune. H. The Demi-Lune Ditch. J. The Demi-Lune Redoubt. L. The Ditch of the Demi-Lune Redoubt. M. The Redoubts of the Re-Entering Places of Arms. N. Ditch of the Redoubts. a. Traverse of the Covered Way. O. Tenaille.

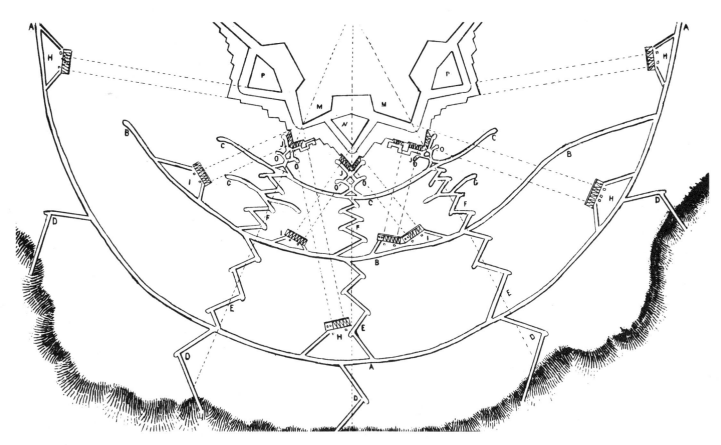

FIGURE: XI-32 IDENTIFICATION: Regular Siege Approaches. SOURCE: Halleck (also Mahan). REMARKS: AA — First Parallel. BB — Second Parallel. CC — Third Parallel. DD — Boyaux leading from Depots of the Trenches to the First Parallel. EE — Boyaux from First Parallel to Second Parallel. FF — Boyaux from Second Parallel to Third Parallel. GG — The Demi-Parallels. HH — Enfilading Batteries in First Parallel. II — Enfilading Batteries in Second Parallel. JJ — Batteries on Glacis. OO — Trench Cavaliers. MM — Bastions on the Front of Attack. N — Demi-Lune on Front of Attack. PP — Demi-Lunes of the Collateral Fronts.

vent aid from getting to the besieged. In conjunction with it, another line, generally detached works protecting such areas as camps and gun parks, was constructed to restrain excursions of the garrison. This was the "line of countervallation." Finally, all obstacles were removed to ensure quick movement of troops between camps if reinforcement of any point in the line became necessary.

Based on the reconnaissance, the second step was initiated. A suitable "point" or "front of attack" was selected for approaching the work and trenches started to provide shelter during the operation. The trenches were of two types, "parallels" and "boyaux." Both were ditches of uniform depth with parapets of the same height thrown up toward the work under attack.

The parallel was a long line of trench concentric with the fortification at the point of attack. Boyaux were simply communications trenches between parallels dug in zigzag shape to avoid enfilading fire. Artillery emplaced near the parallels silenced enemy fire as much as possible and troops were kept ready to beat off sorties against working parties.

The "first parallel," started or "opened" 600 yards from the most advanced salients, could usually be dug without too much annoyance from enemy fire. Work was normally at night and while underway on the first parallel, boyaux were initiated toward the position of the "second parallel" which was concentric with the first and a little less than 300 yards away.

Approaches were carried forward as the second parallel was constructed and since now the trenches were within musket range, workmen were normally replaced by engineers known as "sappers" who carried forward the trench or "sap" with the aid of a "sap roller," a large gabion stuffed with fascines which was inched forward to protect the sappers who worked behind it. Figure XI-33 shows a sap roller used on Morris Island during the siege of Battery Wagner which, although a field work, was successfully attacked by regular approaches during July-September, 1863, after direct assault failed.

During this part of the siege, the operation continued around the clock. The "third parallel" was opened 60 yards from the salient after taking the precaution of putting in "demi-parallels" between the second and third to protect the latter during construction. Now the assailants were within striking distance. The covered way of the demi-lune could be assaulted, a quick but often costly method, or the sap could be continued until 30 yards away. At this point, the trench was extended 15 or 20 yards left and right and mounds of earth 10 feet high, called "trench cavaliers," thrown up from the top of which plunging fire could be brought on the covered way to drive out the besieged.

When the defenders evacuated the covered way, the sap was extended to within 6 yards and a trench made entirely around it. This was known as "crowning the covered way" and led to the next step, erection of breaching batteries around the salient places of

FIGURE: XI-33 IDENTIFICATION: Sap Roller. REMARKS: Sap Roller at the head of the Flying Sap on Morris Island, S.C., 1863.

arms and the breaching of the demi-lune and bastion faces.

The besiegers then began operations to get at the breach, either by assault or a slower, surer method which involved building an underground gallery of framework and boards leading to the bottom of the ditch—termed "descent of the ditch." From here a sap was cut across the ditch and up the slope of the breach to its top where an encircling trench was dug—operations known as "passage of the ditch" and "lodgement of the breach."

This was the moment of truth for the garrison. Presumably during the preceding days or weeks, they had done everything possible by fire and sorties to disrupt or kill working parties, destroy enemy equipment and in general make the siege too costly to continue. When all failed and the lodgement of the breach was attained, the "customs of war" brought a carefully worded dispatch from the attacking commander. It usually cited the hopelessness of further resistance, commended the bravery of the defenders, hinted at kindly treatment for captives, and warned of the "effusion of blood" in the impending all-out assault.

Finally, it offered the garrison commander a standard choice—immediate capitulation, or "suffer the fate of those who are carried by storm."

NOTES

1. Henry L. Abbot, "Siege Artillery in The Campaigns Against Richmond With Notes on The 15-Inch Gun," *Professional Papers No. 14, Corps of Engineers*, 1867, pp. 89–91.
2. Edward Simpson, *A Treatise on Ordnance and Naval Gunnery*, 1862, p. 350.
3. J. G. Benton, *A Course of Instruction in Ordnance and Gunnery Composed and Compiled for Cadets of The United States Military Academy*, 1861, p. 433.
4. *Ibid.*, p. 431.
5. *Ordnance Manual for The Use of Officers of The United States Army*, 1861, pp. 32–33.
6. William Allan, "Reminiscences of Field Ordnance Service With The Army of Northern Virginia 1863–65," *Southern Historical Society Papers*, Vol. XIV, 1886, p. 141.
7. Abbot, *loc. cit.*
8. Q. A. Gillmore, *Engineer and Artillery Operations Against The Defenses of Charleston Harbor, 1863*, 1865, p. 281.
9. *Ordnance Manual*, 1861, *op. cit.*, pp. 136–137.
10. *Instruction for Heavy Artillery*, 1861, p. 225, lists siege limber which seems reasonable in view of the weight to be carried. The *Ordnance Manual*, 1861, *op. cit.*, p. 114, however, states field limber.
11. Abbot, *op. cit.*, p. 182.
12. *Ordnance Manual*, 1861, p. 239.
13. *Ibid.*, pp. 234–247.
14. Joseph Roberts, *Hand-Book of Artillery for The Service of The United States Army and Militia*, 1861, p. 86.
15. *Ordnance Manual*, 1861, p. 242.
16. Roberts, *op. cit.*, p. 88.
17. John Gibbon, *The Artillerist's Manual, Compiled From Various Sources and Adapted to The Service of The United States*, 1860, pp. 79, 82.
18. Dennis Hart Mahan, *A Treatise on Field Fortifications*, 1860, p. 1.

Chapter 12

Smoothbore Ammunition

IDENTIFICATION OF ARTILLERY PROJECTILES is a lengthy and varied subject that runs the gamut from obvious to obscure. Fortunately, however, they fall neatly into one of two categories—smoothbore or rifle—which not only simplifies the identification problem, but incidentally forms a convenient chapter arrangement confining the easier smoothbore varieties to this and the more complicated rifled types to the next. Fuses, vital accessories to both, are placed at the end of this chapter.

Smoothbores fired many forms of projectile: shot, shell, carcass, grape, canister, spherical case, chain, bar, and elongated shot. Each differed from the others and had its special function evolved through the years in furtherance of the ever-changing art of war.

Shot (Figs. XII-1 and 2), simplest and oldest of the lot, carried no explosive and were designed to cause death and destruction through sheer weight of impact. These solid, iron spheres were made in a wide variety of calibers and weights which, along with other forms of smoothbore ammunition, are listed in the Appendix. Identification is merely a matter of accurate measurement although diameter will be roughly one to two tenths of an inch less than the corresponding bore caliber. This is due to "windage" and a small tolerance permitted the manufacturer. Windage—the reduction necessary to allow free movement of the ball in the bore—varied from .09 to .16 inch and manufacturing allowance .04 to .06 inch. Rust and general ravages of time will also make a slight difference although the sum of all is inconsequential from the point of view of identification since there is sufficient difference between calibers to prevent confusing one with another.

The weight of shot may be calculated[1] by multiplying the cube of the diameter by .13268, but unless a slide rule is available, it's generally easier to find scales. However, the formula does come in handy for determining the "pounder" designation of ancient smoothbores which may not be of standard caliber. Care must be exercised to obtain as true a bore diameter as possible and to deduct an arbitrary tenth of an inch for windage. The result will not be precise, but close enough for identification.

As a rule, shot was designed for guns and columbiads, but also was prescribed for the Dahlgren smoothbores, one of which—15-inch—used both solid shot and a form called "cored shot." This projectile had a 5-inch hollow in the center made by casting the

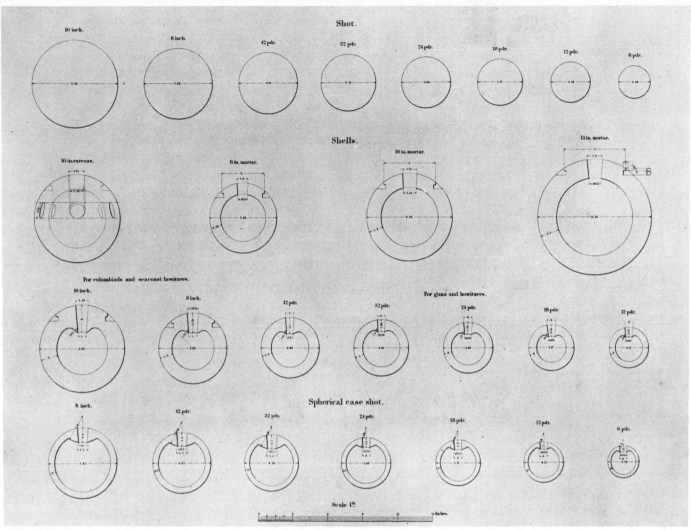

FIGURE: XII-1 IDENTIFICATION: Miscellaneous Shot, Shell, and Spherical Case. SOURCE: Mordecai.

FIGURE: XII-2 LOCATION: Fort Moultrie, S.C. IDENTIFICATION: Miscellaneous Shot. REMARKS: Left to Right: 11-Inch (Dahlgren), weight — 165 pounds. 10-Inch, weight — 127.5. 9-Inch (Dahlgren), weight — 88. 8-Inch, weight — 65. 7-Inch (42-Pounder), weight — 41.5.

256

ball around a core of sand which was knocked out after cooling through a small hole left in the surrounding wall. Unlike shell, which also was hollow, cored shot contained neither powder nor fuse. When fired the cavity was empty and to keep out water on ricochet, the entrance hole was plugged with a wood peg turned outward in the bore to prevent its being driven in by the blast of discharge.

The shot was to be used against masonry fortifications and although several reasons were advanced in Civil War texts for its peculiar design, the answer is still in doubt. Some officers believed the decrease in projectile weight, although relatively slight, reduced strain on the weapon which, it will be remembered from the chapter on Dahlgrens, was not trusted too far even by the inventor. Proponents of this theory held that 5-inch thick walls rendered the ball virtually indestructible and afforded sufficient weight to crush masonry. The projectiles did break on occasion, however, and solid shot were advised against ironclads. Other writers argued that the core assured a more uniform and solid product since thick castings had a tendency to crack. However, since conventional solid shot were made for both 15-inch Rodmans and Dahlgrens, this theory is a bit tenuous.

The cored shot illustrated in Figure XII-3 is in The Citadel Museum at Charleston. It was fired at Fort Sumter by one of the monitors during the Ironclad Attack of 7 April 1863, which resulted in the previously described sinking of the *Keokuk,* and was donated to the school some three weeks later by General Beauregard. Shortly before the evacuation of Charleston in 1865, this shot was sent with other relics to Columbia for safekeeping, but fell captive to General Sherman's army when the state capital was occupied. Forwarded to West Point as a war trophy, the projectile remained in the North until 1913 when it was returned to the South Carolina school.

Standard solid shot could be turned into incendiary projectiles by the simple expedient of heating. Such "hot shot" by the time of the Civil War had been largely superseded by shell, but fired from Fort Moultrie during the bombardment of 12-13 April 1861, they did an excellent job of burning down the wooden officers' quarters in Fort Sumter which filled the casemates with smoke and thereby hastened the surrender of Major Anderson.

Fort Moultrie's furnace, in which the shot were heated, is shown in Figure XII-4 along with certain implements including tongs for grasping a ball, and a three-handled ladle with which two men could carry red hot balls to the guns. These are probably 32-pounder shot which because of their weight neces-

FIGURE: XII-3 LOCATION: Citadel Museum, Charleston, S.C. IDENTIFICATION: 15-Inch Cored Shot. REMARKS: Weight — 400 pounds. Fired by an unidentified Federal monitor at Fort Sumter during the Ironclad Attack of 7 April 1863.

FIGURE: XII-4 IDENTIFICATION: Hot Shot Furnace. REMARKS 1861 view of hot shot furnace at Fort Moultrie, S.C. Shot which fired the officer's quarters and forced surrender of Fort Sumter 13 April 1861 were heated in this furnace. Note implements for handling hot shot.

sitated the more elaborate ladle. Light calibers, such as those used in the field, could be carried by a ladle consisting of a ring and a single handle (Fig. XI-4).

Furnaces of this type were built in most coastal fortifications and could hold more than sixty rounds on grates over the flame. It took about an hour and a quarter to bring cold projectiles to red heat, but additional 24-pounder shot could then be brought to proper temperature in twenty-five minutes, while 32- and 42-pounders took only a few minutes longer. Where no furnace existed, grates set over a hole in the ground and surrounded by iron plates served for heating shot as did the standard field forge in emergency.

Implements, in addition to those mentioned, included two iron pokers for stirring the fire, two iron forks for removing the shot (Fig. XI-4), a rasp to rub scale off those that had been overheated, an iron rake to remove cinders, a rammer with a circular iron plate at the end, slightly larger than the ball, to remove particles of clay wads from gun bores, and assorted tubs and buckets of water for cooling implements.

Despite the proximity of glowing iron to powder, hot shot could be fired safely if certain precautions were assiduously observed. In fact, they could cool in the bore without danger of setting off the charge. Paper or parchment cartridge bags, generally two, one inside the other, were used to prevent powder spilling in the tube. After careful ramming, a dry hay wad was inserted, then a wet hay or clay wad was rammed on top. Such wads were about a caliber in length and fully protected the powder. The piece was elevated slightly and the ball permitted to roll down against the wet wad. Another wet wad, this one about half a caliber in length, was rammed on top of the ball to hold it securely in place. If hay wads were used, steam often escaped through the vent. This, while disconcerting, created no danger, the Ordnance Manual states, but if prolonged would likely damage the powder.

Although ironclads were safe enough, wood ships were extremely vulnerable to hot shot which could ricochet several times on the water and still retain sufficient heat to accomplish their incendiary ends. Against such shipping, hot shot were fired with reduced charges to limit penetration to a depth of 10 or 12 inches. If shot buried deeper, combustion was curtailed through lack of air.

Shells, hollow spheres filled with powder, obviously could never be used as hot shot, but these projectiles, which combined incendiary and explosive properties, supplanted the heated ball. Shells could be fired by most forms of ordnance to achieve long-range destruction of men and equipment mainly through blast and fragmentation although there was also a limited potential from impact in cases where the projectile failed to explode.

With a few minor, but interesting, exceptions, shells divided into three categories: mortar, those for longer weapon generally called "common," and spherical case. Figure XII-1 shows sketches of Army projectiles of these types. Mortar shells, since they were fired with a light propellant which reduced the shock of discharge, had relatively thin walls of uniform dimension throughout. This resulted in a spherical interior of larger capacity than the thicker-walled common variety which was further reduced on the inside by reinforcement of the fuse hole. Case, although the walls were thinnest of all, were loaded with lead or iron balls which increased the weight.

Consequently, wall thickness is an excellent mode of identification, but one which presupposes that the fuse has been removed. Moreover, although a bent wire will give an approximate measurement of wall thickness, special equipment is required for accuracy. Without a hole in the projectile, this method is stymied, but it does lead to another mode of identification, equally good. Different wall thicknesses resulted in varied weights for common and mortar shells of similar caliber, differences sufficiently pronounced for identification purposes, particularly for 8- and 10-inchers (see Tables). Type of fuse, discussed later, is also a major identification aid.

Shells had to be handled with considerably more care than solid shot and one of the most important considerations was assurance that the fuse always faced outward when the projectile was seated at the bottom of the bore. Despite reinforcing in common shells and reduced propellant for mortars, the fuse created a weak spot in the shell casing and if turned toward the cartridge might be driven into the shell at discharge and the round exploded in the bore.

Long weapons obtained correct positioning by strapping the projectile to a cylindrical block of wood, hollowed to fit and known as a "sabot." The round thus strapped had an oblong shape and retained its position during loading and firing. Sabots were made of poplar, basswood, or pine and came in assorted shapes and sizes as evidenced by the selection (Fig. XII-5). Figure XII-6 shows the method of strapping and Figure XII-7, a strapped 6-pounder spherical case in the West Point collection.

When a cartridge was attached, the entire round was known as "fixed ammunition" (Fig. XII-8), a form generally restricted to light weapons. Heavier

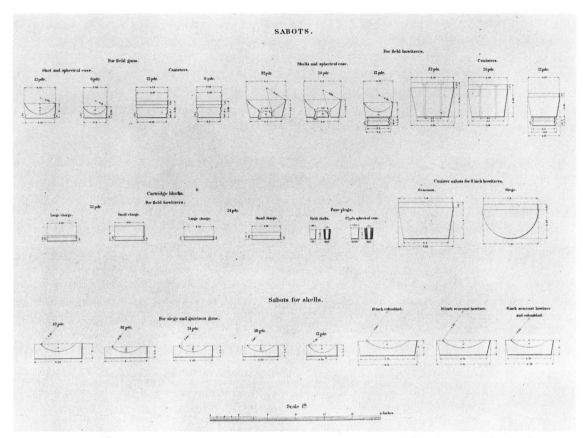

FIGURE: XII-5 IDENTIFICATION: Miscellaneous Sabots and Cartridge Blocks. SOURCE: Mordecai.

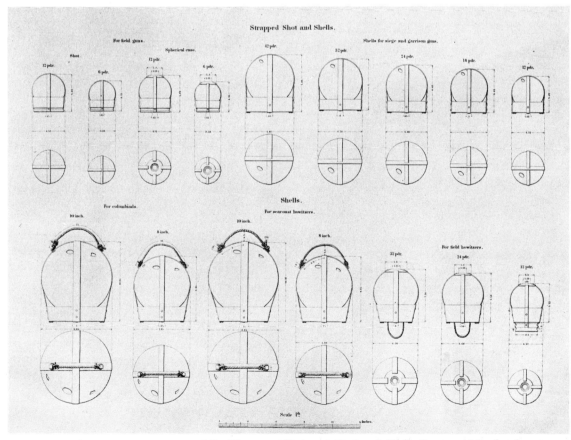

FIGURE: XII-6 IDENTIFICATION: Miscellaneous Strapped Shot and Shell. SOURCE: Mordecai.

FIGURE: XII-7 LOCATION: West Point, N.Y. IDENTIFICATION: 6-Pounder Spherical Case and Sabot. LENGTH: 5 inches.

FIGURE: XII-9 LOCATION: Charleston Museum, Charleston S.C. IDENTIFICATION: 13-Inch Mortar Shell. REMARKS: Early type of mortar shell with exterior "ears" on either side of the fuse hole (one broken in this case).

FIGURE: XII-10 LOCATION: Chickamauga-Chattanooga National Park. IDENTIFICATION: 8-Inch Mortar Shell. REMARKS: Interior "ears" (holes) cast on either side of fuse, a form used during the Civil War.

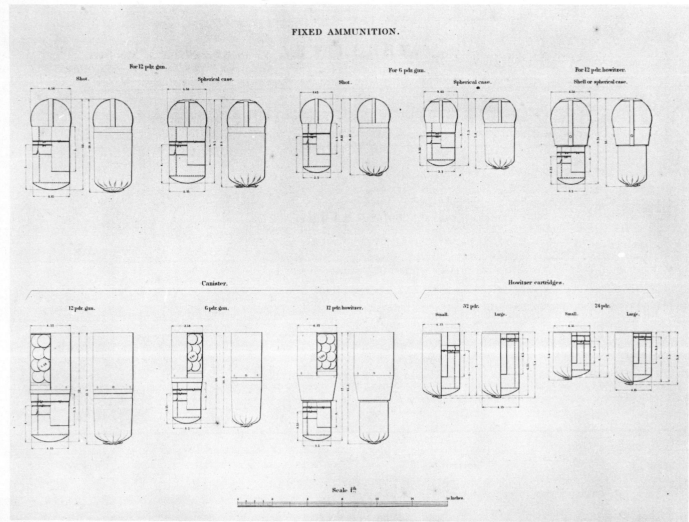

FIGURE: XII-8 IDENTIFICATION: Fixed Ammunition. SOURCE: Mordecai.

pieces utilized what is today known as "separate loading" ammunition in which cartridge and strapped projectile were inserted into the bore individually. Separate loading was also used with 24- and 32-pounder field howitzers, the cartridge attached to a form of sabot known as a "cartridge block" (Fig. XII-5). This device added rigidity to the cartridge and filled out the chamber flush with the bore where it rested against the sabot of the strapped projectile.

Mortar shells were often fired over the heads of friendly troops and sabots could not be used without risk of casualties. Therefore, some method had to be devised for easing the heavy shell—a 10-inch weighed roughly 88 pounds—into the bore and at the same time keep the fuse pointing outward. Initially this was accomplished by casting iron loops, known as "ears," on either side near the fuse hole to be used as handles. One of these rare projectiles, a 13-inch (Fig. XII-9), is in the Charleston Museum collection. One ear is missing, but the other will serve to illustrate the appearance.

Loop ears solved the loading problem but were difficult to manufacture and destroyed the balance of the projectile in flight, so they gave way to two small holes angled to leave a covering of the shell wall over much of their length (Fig. XII-10). Into these holes fitted the points of "shell hooks," iron implements resembling ice tongs (Fig. XI-1) and used in similar fashion.

The holes, although no longer having the appearance of ears, retained the name and, since they offered a convenient method of handling, were extended to many shells above 42-pounder even when sabots were used. This was not true of all, however, for certain large caliber projectiles, particularly Dahlgrens, are not so equipped. They were also left off the federal 24-pounder Coehorn shells in favor of fixed ammunition or a clumsy arrangement of tin strapping. On the other hand, the Confederates cast ears on some of their Coehorn shells, both 12- and 24-pounder, although whether this was standard practice for all has not been established.[2]

Mortar shells were also used in the 8-inch siege howitzer which had a chamber curved to fit the projectile and omitted the sabot for the same reason as the mortars.

Shells, although generally more effective than solid shot, utilized relatively low-yield black powder as an explosive. This deficiency resulted in low-order bursts which tore the shell into a small number of large fragments, deadly if they struck anyone, but far too few and widely scattered to obtain a high ratio of hits.

In an effort to remedy this defect, the Confederates cast the interior of some of their shells in polyhedral shape. The exterior remained the same, but inside instead of a smooth, curved surface, there were a number of flat faces which weakened the casing at their boundary lines and caused it to break into a specified number of segments after the fashion of a modern fragmentation grenade.

These "segmented" shells, called "polygonal cavity shells" by the Confederates, were used in the final Richmond campaign as well as other fronts for both long weapons and mortars.[3] The 12-pounder was a particularly popular caliber, but they also came in larger size, apparently solely for mortars. There were two types of interior design (Fig. XII-11) both with a dozen segments in 12-pounders. Figure XII-12 illustrates interior and exterior views of two segments and a pair that failed to separate.

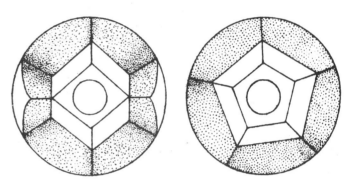

FIGURE: XII-11 IDENTIFICATION: Segmented Shells. SOURCE: Abbot. REMARKS: Two forms made by the South, each with a dozen segments in 12-pounder caliber. Called "Polygonal Cavity Shells" by the Confederates.

FIGURE: XII-12 LOCATION: Estes Collection, Mullins, S.C. IDENTIFICATION: Segmented Shell. REMARKS: Two segments and a pair that failed to separate.

FIGURE: XII-13 LOCATION: Fort Fisher, N.C. IDENTIFICATION: Segment, 13-Inch, U.S. Mortar Shell. REMARKS: Maximum diameter — 8 inches. Diameter across flat — 5.25 inches. Thickness — 3.1 inches.

FIGURE: XII-14 LOCATION: Fort Fisher, N.C. IDENTIFICATION: Segment, 13-Inch, U.S.Mortar Shell. REMARKS: Exterior of Fig. XII-13.

Abbot[4] mentions fragments of Confederate 4.62- and 8-inch spherical shells broken exactly on concentric inner and outer circles. These were found near Richmond, but similar fragments from 15-inch Dahlgrens fired by the Union fleet were reported at Fort McAlister, Georgia. Presumably they resembled the section of 13-inch mortar shell picked up at Fort Fisher (Figs. XII-13 and 14) which has an 8-inch outside diameter and is 5.25 across the flat inner surface. A similar specimen in the author's collection, from a 10-inch, measures 6 and 4 inches.

Reinforcement of shells with this "culot" of extra metal directly opposite the fuse hole is mentioned in at least one text of the era.[5] The theory behind it was twofold—to strengthen the casing against the shock of discharge and, since the extra weight tended to travel in front during flight, force the shell to land with fuse upright. However, eccentricity of the ball reduced accuracy and the device reportedly was not used in U.S. service—a belief disputed by Abbot as well as battlefield recoveries.

Federal efforts to increase the efficiency of shell brought experiments during the Richmond Campaign near the end of the war with two unusual types. Both seem to have been moderately successful, but since they were quite complicated would no doubt have been expensive to manufacture in quantity.

The Pevey was a single casting of two thick, concentric spheres connected by studs. The space between was filled through a hole in the outer shell with small, iron balls of musket size or with an incendiary composition. Then the hole was closed with lead. The projectile was solid around the fuse hole which led to the interior cavity filled with a bursting charge. Loaded with balls, 8- and 10-inch mortar rounds had weight comparable to ordinary shells of similar caliber. Several hundred tested over water or a dusty plain appeared to give about double the normal number of fragments, but it was felt that the iron balls, necessarily small due to the constricted space between the spheres, would be too light for practical work. Fragments (Fig. XII-15) are believed to be from one of these shells.

McIntyre's Repeating Shell (Fig. XII-16) worked on an entirely different principle. Two, sometimes three, shells of different size were cast. The outer separated into hemispheres and enclosed a smaller which was positioned in the center by studs. It also could be opened if a smaller shell was to be used inside. The inner shell, containing explosive and a time fuse, was placed inside the open halves of a larger shell, which was closed, and the opening between filled with powder. This shell also was fused and could be placed inside a third if necessary. Firing ignited the time fuse in the outer casing and a few seconds later exploded the powder between it and the next interior ball, breaking the case as in standard shell. The blast in turn ignited the fuse of the smaller shell and its explosion lit the third.

Only a few test samples, 10-inch triple and 24-pounder double-bursting mortar rounds, were fur-

FIGURE: XII-15 LOCATION: Fort Jackson, Savannah, Ga. IDENTIFICATION: Fragments, Pevey Shell (U.S.) REMARKS: see text for description.

FIGURE: XII-16 LOCATION: West Point, N.Y. IDENTIFICATION: McIntyre's Repeating Shell (U.S.). DIAMETER: 9-Inch. REMARKS: See text for description.

nished for experiments before Richmond in 1865 and since these were fired into Confederate lines, results were inconclusive. However, the projectiles did stand high propelling charges and generally gave the requisite number of bursts, either air, ground, or both.

Other experiments with the McIntyre proved the 24-pounder model, weighing about 18-pounds, could be fired successfully from field howitzers and that successive explosions gave the projectile great penetrating ability which might have made it valuable for exploding field magazines. The outer shell had a combination time and concussion fuse that ensured bursting if the projectile struck before explosion by the time element. However, since the concussion principle was somewhat similar to another form, it will be explained later in this chapter under the section on fuses. The illustrated projectile in the West Point collection apparently has a double-bursting capability and is listed in Military Academy records as a 9-inch.

Before leaving shells, the "carcass," an obsolete type that saw little if any service during the Civil War, is worth consideration on the basis of continued mention by writers rather than its dubious merit as a military weapon. It was dropped from the 1861 Ordnance Manual, but prominently listed by the 1841 book in various calibers from 12-pounder to 13-inch (see Tables).

The carcass (Fig. XII-1) was a common shell with three additional holes cast equidistant around the upper half and the same diameter as the fuse hole. Filled with an incendiary composition and fired at a flammable object, such as a wood building, it spewed forth burning liquid that was difficult to remove or extinguish. The incendiary material was generally either portfire or fire-stone cut into small pieces and moistened to liquid or paste for loading. Portfire was made from niter, sulfur, and mealed powder with a little antimony or steel filings often thrown in. Fire-stone included niter, sulfur, rosin, turpentine, tallow, and antimony. After the shell was filled with one or the other, plugs were inserted in all four holes until they met, then withdrawn when the filling hardened, and replaced with three strands of quick match long enough to protrude 2 or 3 inches and coiled on the inside until the projectile was needed. When fired, the quick match served as a fuse in each hole.

A carcass with only three holes (Fig. XII-17) was found at Fort Gadsden on the Apalachicola River near Sumatra, Florida, and probably dates from 1816 when the fort, held by renegade Indians and Negroes, saw action 27 July against United States troops in launches supported by two gunboats. The

battle, one of history's shortest, was opened by the fort which greeted the small fleet with a 32-pounder. The fifth round in reply from the gunboats—hot shot—touched off the magazine, sending the fort and defenders up in flame. There were thirty survivors of three-hundred in the fort. U.S. casualties were nil.

The carcass presumably was dumped overboard in 1818 when rubble was cleared for a new fort on the site ordered by General Andrew Jackson. The engineer, Lieutenant James Gadsden (1788-1858), gave his name to the fort and later to the "Gadsden Purchase." The projectile was found a few years ago by divers and is to be displayed in a fort museum. When deactivated, it was found to be loaded with a composition of pine pitch, or resin, and sulfur and is a 24-pounder with a weight, empty, of 15 pounds, a bit lighter than standard.

Common shell could also be loaded as carcass by placing the bursting charge in a flannel bag at the bottom and filling the remainder with incendiary composition. Four or five strands of quick match were inserted in the fuse hole. When fired, the shell burned as a carcass, then exploded.

Grapeshot, although listed in the 1861 Ordnance Manual for certain siege and seacoast weap-

FIGURE: XII-17 LOCATION: Fort Gadsden State Park, Sumatra, Fla. IDENTIFICATION: 24-Pounder Carcass. DIAMETER: Approximately 5.25. Holes, 1.12. WEIGHT: 15 pounds. REMARKS: Although diameter is somewhat small for 24-pounder (5.68) it is too large for 18-pounder (5.17). Weight is far closer to the 15.8 standard for 24-pounder than the 12.2 of the smaller caliber. The projectile has only three holes compared to four of regulation carcass (Fig. XII-1). It probably dates from about 1816 (see text).

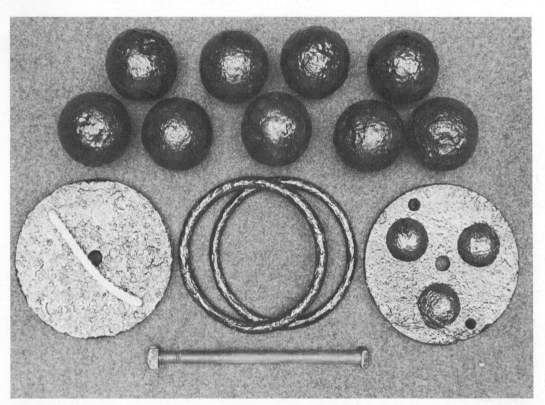

FIGURE: XII-18 LOCATION: Author's Collection. IDENTIFICATION: Elements of Stand of 32-Pounder Grape. DIAMETER: 6.4-Inch (assembled). REMARKS: Composite stand made up of modern rope and bolt, other elements of Civil War vintage found in the Charleston area. It contains one error — the "bottom" plate (right) is a top section with holes for the rope. The correct bottom plate omitted such holes and was recessed on the flat side for the bolt head.

FIGURE: XII-19 LOCATION: West Point, N.Y. IDENTIFICATION: Stand of 12-Pounder Grape.

ons, had been discontinued in field use several years before the war since it was felt canister could do a more efficient job.[6] Normally a "stand" of grape consisted of nine solid iron balls, top and bottom plates, two rings, a bolt, all of iron, and a rope handle on top. Figure XII-18 shows the elements of a stand of 32-pounder grape. Bolt and rope are modern, the remainder of Civil War vintage. This is a composite stand put together from individual pieces found at various locations in the Charleston area. It contains one error—the bottom plate is a duplicate of the top, as evidenced by the rope holes. These small holes were omitted in the correct bottom plate which had instead a recess in the flat side for the head of the bolt to keep it from turning when the nut was tightened at the top. Both top and bottom places were recessed to fit the balls which were arranged in three tiers held together by the iron rings and the bolt through the middle. Appearance of a complete stand is shown in Figure XII-19, a 12-pounder siege gun round at West Point. Figure XII-20 illustrates

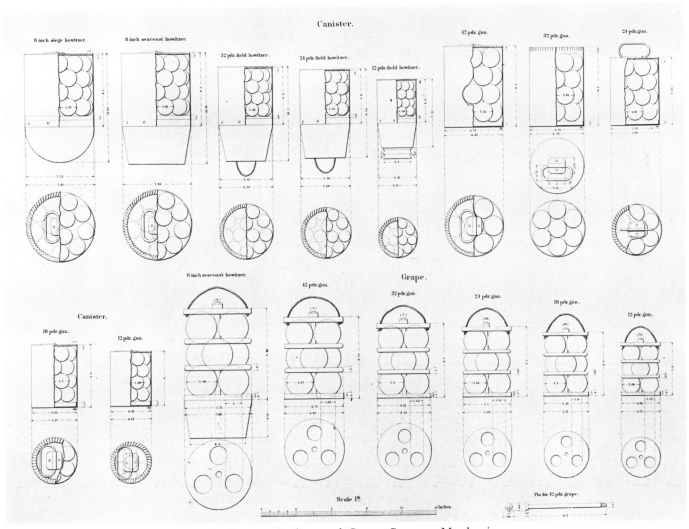

FIGURE: XII-20 IDENTIFICATION: Miscellaneous Canister and Grape. SOURCE: Mordecai.

drawings of grape and canister and Figure XII-21 a rare stand, apparently Confederate, in which iron bands replace the traditional rings.

The size of the balls used in Army grape differed for each caliber and were carefully calculated so that nine made the proper size projectile (see Tables). A selection of grape ranging up to 6-pounder shot which was used for the 8-inch is shown in Figure XII-22. Although nine balls were the traditional bolted stand, there was nothing mandatory about this number and the Confederates arranged smaller balls into three tiers of seven each in similar fashion to canister. One of these stands is dimly visible in an 1865 photograph (Fig. XII-23) of ammunition specimens collected at the Charleston Arsenal after the city's fall. The twenty-one balls are held by six vertical braces near the top and bottom plate rims and three bolts through the interstices equidistant from the center. Six similar coins placed around one in the center will illustrate the arrangement.

"Quilted" grape, an earlier form often used by the Confederates as well as the Federal Navy, could be made with almost any number of balls. It consisted of an iron bottom plate with a pin, sometimes a pipe, sticking up in the center like a bolt. Around this were piled the balls and the whole enclosed in canvas. The name was based on appearance of the stand after heavy twine had been stitched between the balls to hold them rigid. A quilted grape stand (Fig. XII-24) photographed by the Federals at Yorktown in 1862 seems to have six balls to a tier for a total of eighteen.

Sabots for grape could be loaded separately, screwed to the bottom plate, or attached by running a longer bolt through the wood before putting together the stand as illustrated for 8-inch grape in Figure XII-20. Although the 8-inch was the largest Army weapon listed for grape, the Navy used quilted grape for smoothbores through 11-inch (see Tables). The 15-inch was not specified for this ammunition, but there is evidence it may have been used in at least one instance.

During the Federal amphibious operation which placed troops on Morris Island 10 July 1863, a Union signal officer reported:[7] "I landed . . . and immediately opened communications with our fleet of monitors. They had a 15-inch gun trained on our party which they were about firing, when they perceived my flag. As the gun was loaded with grape shot, my signals must have saved our party a heavy loss. . . ." The officer, an infantryman, might well have been mistaken, and the piece been an 11-inch loaded

FIGURE: XII-21 LOCATION: Fort Jackson, Savannah, Ga. IDENTIFICATION: Stand of 32-Pounder Grape. REMARKS: Unusual specimen, believed to be Confederate, in which bands have taken the place of traditional rings.

FIGURE: XII-22 LOCATION: Author's Collection. IDENTIFICATION: Assorted Grape Shot. REMARKS: In order of descending diameter: 8-Inch grape — 3.36 inches. 42-Pdr. grape — 3.17 inches. 32-Pdr. grape — 2.87 inches. 24-Pdr. grape — 2.69 inches. (slightly oversize, should be 2.6-2.64). 12-Pdr. grape — 2.06 inches.

with grape, or a 15-inch with canister. However, he could also have been absolutely correct for use of grape in the 15-inch was entirely feasible and this may have been an isolated instance—perhaps a ship or squadron innovation.

FIGURE: XII-23 IDENTIFICATION: Collection of Confederate Ammunition at Charleston Arsenal, 1865. REMARKS: 1. Pinch-waist, elongated projectile for smoothbores. 2. Stand of grape with 21 balls. 3. Oval type, elongated projectile for smoothbores.

FIGURE: XII-24 IDENTIFICATION: Quilted Grape, Confederate. REMARKS: Quilted grape (lower left) and solid shot. Diameter undetermined, but probably 11-inch to go with Dahlgren of that caliber photographed in Yorktown defenses, 1862.

Although range of grape depended largely on size—the larger obviously traveling farther—300 to 600 yards was considered standard by the Army or 800 yards over hard, dry ground suitable for riochet.[8] The Navy believed grape inefficient against men of war beyond 150 yards, exposed personnel over 300 yards, and, from heavy weapons, against boats or massed men, more than 400 yards distant.[9]

Canister ranges were comparable to grape and since both left the tube in the form of a cone, too short range limited the area covered and too long gave excessive dispersion. This shotgun effect was particularly deadly from canister which used a larger number of balls and turned smoothbores into formidable weapons at optimum range.

Canister consisted of iron top and bottom plates over which were bent the ends of a cylinder formed from sheet tin. Inside were iron balls of calculated size for the caliber arranged in four tiers, the interstices solidly packed with sawdust to prevent the balls from moving. Six-pounder through 42-pounder guns had seven balls in each layer—one in the center surrounded by six. To leave room for the rivets of the handle, the center ball of the top tier was omitted giving a total of twenty-seven balls per round. With one exception, howitzer canister had twelve balls in each tier for a total forty-eight (see Tables). The exception

267

was mountain howitzer canister with thirty-seven lead musket balls to the tier or one hundred forty-eight. Effective range of mountain howitzer canister was limited to 300 yards. Figure XII-20 shows sketches of various caliber canister and Figure XII-25 a 32-pounder round at Fort Fisher which, since windage was secondary to ease in loading, is only 6.25-inch diameter.

If a sabot was used with canister, the bottom end of the tin cylinder was tacked to the wood instead of being crimped over the metal plate. When made up as fixed ammunition for field artillery, the ends of the cartridge bags were fitted over the sabots and tied.

Navy canister specified a 1.3-inch iron ball for all calibers except the 24-pounder boat howitzer, which also used a lead ball of the same diameter, and the 12-pounder boat howitzer having 1-inch lead or iron balls (see Tables).

In addition, the Navy seems to have used brass canister on rare occasions. A 1.125-inch ball of this metal has been found[10] on Edisto Island south of Charleston in a location where it could have been fired only by one of two vessels, but in view of their extensive armament, the weapon that fired it is open to conjecture. Various size iron and lead canister balls are illustrated in Figure XII-26.

"Spherical Case" or "Shrapnel" was developed by General Henry Shrapnel (1761-1842) of the British Army in an effort to extend the range of multi-shot projectiles such as grape and canister. It was first used by the British during the wars with Napoleon. "Case" as it was familiarly known, consisted of a thin-walled shell loaded with small lead or iron balls, a small bursting charge and a time fuse to explode it a calculated distance from the piece. Since the balls were not thrown out until explosion of the charge, case, in effect, extended the maximum range of canister without the dispersion normally associated with long distance.

Early case had a wood plug and paper fuse (Fig. XII-5), but by the Civil War era, the Bormann fuse, which will be described in more detail later, was generally used. This 5-second time fuse restricted maximum range to the distance the ball could travel during that period. It varied a bit depending on the weapon, but averaged about 1,200 yards. The bursting charge was sufficient only to rupture the shell and release the balls that continued along the trajectory with the momentum of the projectile. A larger charge would have increased velocity, but dispersed the balls too widely to be effective. Figure XII-27 shows a round of 12-pounder case with Bormann

FIGURE: XII-25 LOCATION: Fort Fisher, N.C. IDENTIFICATION: 32-Pounder Canister. DIAMETER: 6.25 inches. Balls, 2.06. LENGTH: 7.75 inches.

FIGURE: XII-26 LOCATION: Author's Collection. IDENTIFICATION: Miscellaneous Canister. REMARKS: In order of descending caliber. 24-Pdr. (or 8-Inch Siege Howitzer) — 1.84 inches; 18-Pdr. — 1.69 inches; 12-Pdr. (or 32-Pdr. Howitzer) — 1.50 inches; 24-Pdr. Howitzer (or many Navy calibers) — 1.30 inches; 12-Pdr. Howitzer — 1.08 inches; 24-Pdr. Navy Howitzer — 1.30 inches (lead); 12-Pdr. Mountain Howitzer — .69 inch (lead).

fuse, the most extensively used caliber, delivered in a load of dirt fill to a Charleston residence.[11] Drawings of this type projectile will be found in the section on fuses.

Early case was fabricated by loading the empty shell through the fuse hole with lead balls, pouring in powder which filtered down between, then fusing the projectile. This form proved unsatisfactory because the loose powder was ground fine by movement of the balls and the light charge was distributed over such a wide area inside the shell it often failed to rupture the casing properly.

To correct the deficiency, a mandrel was shoved through the fuse hole to the bottom of the shell, pushing the balls aside, and molten sulfur or rosin poured in around it. After the liquid hardened, the mandrel was withdrawn leaving a cavity which was filled with the bursting charge. This prevented the balls from moving thereby adding to the ballistic qualities of the projectile, reinforcing the walls against the shock of firing, and by confining the bursting charge made its action more consistent. Later it was found easier to dispense with the mandrel, fill the shell to the bottom of the fuse hole and, when the matrix material hardened, use a drill to bore through balls and sulfur to form the cavity.

Confederate case initially followed the Northern pattern, but construction problems with the Bormann fuse (q.v.) forced the South to revert to plug and paper fuse. A 12-pounder of this type (Fig. XII-28) is in the Fort Fisher collection. The plug is copper instead of wood and measures 1.5 inches in diameter. Near it is a ¾-inch filler hole which was closed with lead after insertion of the balls. Walls of standard 12-pounder case averaged .475-inch thick compared to .75 for those of common shell, or roughly a quarter inch difference. Even greater disparity is noted in 8-inch case and similar caliber mortar shell, 0.7 and 1.25-inch respectively. Lead musket balls of .69-inch diameter were used in U.S. Army case. This offers an excellent means of distinguishing them from shell, for the heavy lead balls brought the total weight to approximately that of similar caliber shot—noticeably heavier than shell (see Tables).

Although 8-inch is the largest caliber listed in the Ordnance Manual for spherical case, 10-inch mortar case—as mentioned in Chapter III—was tried experimentally in October 1863 at Fort Scott in the

FIGURE: XII-27 LOCATION: Author's Collection. IDENTIFICATION: 12-Pounder Spherical Case with Bormann Fuse. REMARKS: Fuse has been "cut" at just under 3 seconds, but failed to detonate the projectile. Quarter-inch hole in center was drilled during deactivation.

FIGURE: XII-28 LOCATION: Fort Fisher, N.C. IDENTIFICATION: 12-Pounder Spherical Case, Confederate. DIAMETER: 4.44 inches due to rust. Originally 4.52. REMARKS: Copper fuse plug 1.5-inch diameter with hole in center for paper time fuse. Nearby light section is a .813-inch diameter hole in the shell casing which was closed with lead after projectile was filled with balls.

Washington defenses. The shell was filled with 12-pounder iron canister balls, roughly 1.49-inch diameter, and a 2.5-pound bursting charge added loose as in the early days of case. The empty shell weighed 90 pounds and each of the twenty-seven balls 0.43 pound, a total weight of 104 pounds.

The Confederates, short of both lead and sulfur, tried filling case with small iron balls held in asphalt. The attempt is said to have proved a failure,[12] because of the lightness of the balls which often struck Federal gunners without inflicting injury, but was used nonetheless from 1863 until the surrender. Confederate case has also been found filled with conventional rifle bullets either alone or mixed with caliber .69 (.65-inch) balls.

The U.S. Navy also used a .65-inch lead ball for 12-pounder through 32-pounder case, .85-inch iron balls for 8 through 11-inch, and an even thousand 1-inch iron balls in 15-inch case. Although no mention has been found in Navy ordnance tables, the 12-pounder boat howitzer case, and perhaps others, may have utilized smaller lead balls interspersed with the standard diameter. A sketch later in this chapter of spherical case equipped with a Bormann fuse clearly shows different diameter balls and dredging off Fort Sumter has brought up hundreds of lead balls of varying diameter. These (Fig. XII-29) range from .31- to .69-inch and while several could be buckshot, the distance from the fort is beyond shotgun range and would indicate at least a tentative identification of balls from case.

"Chain" and "bar shot" were obsolete by the Civil War era although specimens of both may have been in ammunition inventories of coastal fortifications, left over from previous days. The former, as described in ordnance texts, was composed of hollow hemispheres connected by a short length of chain, folded inside, and the halves joined for firing. As the ball left the tube, the halves separated to the extent of the chain and went whirling in irregular flight toward the enemy. The segment of chain shot (Fig. XII-30) exhibited at Fort Sumter is a cruder, easily manufactured form originally made up of two 32-pounder shot, attached by a length of chain, stuffed one after the other down the tube for firing.

FIGURE: XII-30 LOCATION: Fort Sumter, S.C. IDENTIFICATION: 32-Pounder Chain Shot. REMARKS: Broken. Originally additional chain was linked to a duplicate ball.

Bar shot (Fig. XII-31) consisted of solid hemispheres connected by an iron bar. The illustrated segment was found at Fort Gadsden along with the previously described carcass and presumably had about the same history. It measures roughly 3.875 inches in diameter and, give or take a bit of rust, probably was intended for a 9-pounder. The rounded portion is only 2 inches thick and thus not a true hemisphere. The bar diameter is ½ inch.

Both chain and bar shot were designed primarily for use against rigging of sailing vessels where the scope of the spinning projectiles played hob with spars and lines that presented to standard shot a target more difficult to hit. Trajectories of both were highly erratic, however, which limited their use to close quarters.

FIGURE: XII-29 LOCATION: Author's Collection. IDENTIFICATION: Miscellaneous Balls for Spherical Case. REMARKS: Dredged from Charleston Harbor in the vicinity of Fort Sumter. From left in order of descending diameter, all lead: .69-Inch, .656, .625, .594, .563, .531, .469, .375, .344, and .316. Last is a Confederate, iron ball which varies in diameter from .625 to .687.

270

Although spheres were the normal load for smoothbores, elongated shot were tried on occasion, especially by the Confederates who had an abundance of smoothbores and a need for rifle-type projectiles capable of punching holes in ironclads. They experimented with several designs, but like most conversions, success was only partial. Two (Figs. XII-32 and 33) were oval shaped. One of the latter, in what seems to be 8-inch caliber, is illustrated in the 1865 Charleston Arsenal photograph (Fig. XII-23). Maury projectiles (Figs. XII-34, 35, and 36) reportedly were more successful. These three varieties, captured at Richmond, were made of chilled iron. Figure XII-34 is a 10-inch, the others 8-inch. The Charleston Arsenal picture (Fig. XII-23) also shows at left rear holding up the Blakely rifle band what appears to be still another form—a pinched waist type roughly resembling an "I."

In addition, there was the fascinating 100-pound "cylindrical conical" fused projectile with "soft metal base" found in the 8-inch siege howitzer, Model 1841, mentioned in Chapter II. This could have been an elongated shell for smoothbores with the base intended to reduce windage. However, since the nature of the engagement required heavy hitting power without corresponding increase in weapon weight, it is more likely some form of rifle projectile with time fuse was used. Such a shell would tumble with diminished accuracy, but at relatively short range this might be an acceptable loss, compared to the advantage it presented of more than doubling the 45-pound weight of spherical shell without the added transportation difficulties a heavy 8-inch rifle would entail.

Manufacture of shot and shell closely approximated the process used in casting cannon. Copper hemispheres were used instead of wood models, but the mold was formed in the same fashion as the

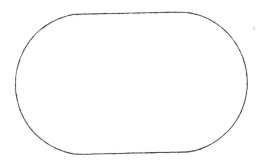

FIGURE: XII-32 IDENTIFICATION: Elongated Shot for Smoothbore, Confederate. WEIGHT: 25 pounds. SOURCE: Abbot.

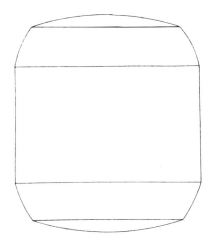

FIGURE: XII-33 IDENTIFICATION: Elongated Projectile for Smoothbores, Confederate. DIAMETER: 10-Inch. Weight — 211 pounds. Wrought Iron. SOURCE: Abbot. REMARKS: See Fig. XII-23.

breech section of cannon by reversing the flask, removing the bottom, and packing with sand. (Fig. XII-37). The illustration shows the flasks attached, but each was filled separately. The opening (d-a) held a wood handle while the sand was packed. It was then carefully removed, a metal cover affixed to the flask, and the mold of the half sphere turned over. The handle was screwed into (a) again, but from the inside, and used to lift out the copper model. The hole (d-a) was closed with sand if a solid shot was to be cast. The other half sphere was molded in similar fashion and the copper model removed. A stick was used to form the channel (b) which was cut through to the cavity at the "gate" (c) after the stick was removed. Both halves were given a coating of cokewash, sprinkled with dry sand at the joint to prevent sticking, and bolted together. When dried, the completed mold was ready for casting. Metal poured into the channel (b) flowed into the cavity at (c) and rose in the sinking head (e) which, upsidedown in the photograph, would, of course, be reversed for casting. After cooling, the

FIGURE: XII-31 LOCATION: Fort Gadsden State Park, Sumatra, Fla. IDENTIFICATION: 9-Pounder Bar Shot. DIAMETER: Hemisphere — 3.88. Bar — .5-inch. REMARKS: Broken. Orignial shot consisted of additional length of bar and a duplicate hemisphere.

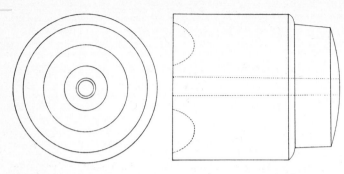

FIGURE: XII-34 IDENTIFICATION: Maury Projectile for Smoothbores, Confederate. DIAMETER: 10-Inch. Weight — 200 pounds. Chilled Iron. SOURCE: Abbot.

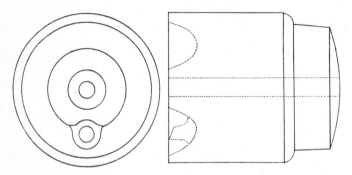

FIGURE: XII-35 IDENTIFICATION: Maury Projectile for Smoothbores, Confederate. DIAMETER: 8-Inch. Weight — 102 pounds. Chilled Iron. SOURCE: Abbot.

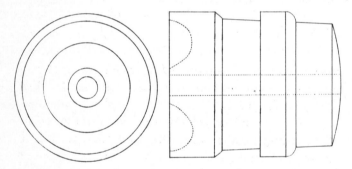

FIGURE: XII-36 IDENTIFICATION: Maury Projectile for Smoothbores, Confederate. DIAMETER: 8-Inch. Weight — 100 pounds. Chilled Iron. SOURCE: Abbot.

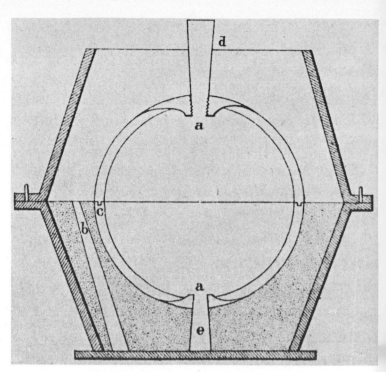

FIGURE: XII-37 IDENTIFICATION: Flask and Model for Manufacture of Shot and Shell. REMARKS: Top open for packing with sand. Flask was turned over for pouring. d - a — Wood Handle (a. was closed if shot to be cast); b — Channel; c — Gate from Channel to Shell Cavity (not cut in this case); e — Sinking Head (after flask was reversed for casting); (If shell was to be made, the core was affixed inside from a-d).

sinking head and gate were knocked off with a chisel and a number of balls were rolled together in a barrel for polishing.

The exterior of shells was made in the same manner, but the hole at the bottom, closed for shot, was left open to receive the stem of a "core." This was a ball of sand formed by compression in a spherical mold. The stem, or wire covered with sand, was shoved into the hole (d-a), the core being exactly centered in the shell cavity by gauges. Mold drying

and casting were the same as for shot. After the metal cooled, the sinking head and gate were removed and the core knocked out through the hole left by the stem, which also served later as the fuse hole.

After manufacture, shot and shell, like cannon, were subjected to rigid inspection. Both were visually examined for flaws in the metal, then checked by "ring gauges" (Fig. XII-38)—two for each caliber—to ensure correct diameter. One was from .02 to .03 inches larger than the true diameter of the ball, the other a similar amount less. In testing, the projectile had to pass through the larger and not through the smaller. It then had to roll without sticking through a "cylinder gauge," an iron tube of the same interior size as the larger ring gauge, to establish uniformity of diameter. Shot were also tested for strength or soundness by dropping them 20 feet onto an iron platform or rolling them from a similar height down an incline against an iron stop at the bottom.

Shells omitted this "test for strength," but faced further examination of dimension and soundness. Various calipers, with one arm bent to enter the fuse hole and another to touch the shell exterior (Figs.

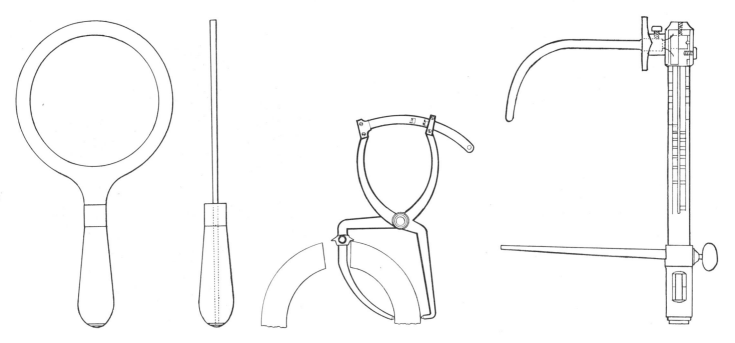

FIGURE: **XII-38** IDENTIFICATION: Ring Gauge. SOURCE: Gibbon. REMARKS: Used for inspection of shot and shell.

FIGURE: **XII-39** IDENTIFICATION: Calipers. SOURCE: Gibbon. REMARKS: Used by inspectors to measure thickness of 8- and 10-inch mortar shells.

FIGURE: **XII-40** IDENTIFICATION: Calipers. SOURCE: Gibbon. REMARKS: Used by inspectors to measure the thickness of sides in common shells.

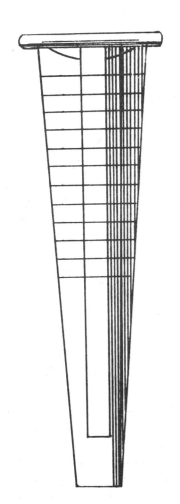

FIGURE: **XII-41** IDENTIFICATION: Fuse, Wood, Time.

XII-39 and 40) were used to check wall thickness while other instruments measured fuse hole diameter and thickness of metal at top and bottom. Finally, a plug was placed in the fuse hole for the nozzle of bellows and the shell immersed in a tub of water almost to the hole. Air was pumped in and any holes in the shell wall were revealed by bubbles. Shells rejected during inspection were marked by chipping out a piece of the fuse hole. Condemned shot were marked with an "X" near the gate.

Artillery fuses came in many shapes, sizes, materials, and methods of operation and this section is designed to give the reader a general knowledge of the main varieties with no pretense at complete coverage of the subject.

All, regardless of type, had a single aim—to explode a projectile at the proper time and place. But the method of accomplishing this goal differed considerably and divided fuses into four distinct categories: time, concussion, percussion, and combination of the first with either of the others.

The oldest and simplest form of fuse was the wood time fuse, initially designed for all shells and still used for mortars during the Civil War. It was a tapered wood "fuse plug" (Fig. XII-41) hollowed cylindrically from the top almost to the bottom and graduated on the outside with lines representing inches and, usually, tenths of inches. Powder was driven into the hollow part by drift and mallet until, packed

FIGURE: XII-42 LOCATION: Author's Collection. IDENTIFICATION: Fuse, Wood, Time. REMARKS: 10-Inch Mortar Shell. Fuse extends 6 inches inside shell and is bored for setting 2 inches from the top. This was the type shell and fuse which burst over Fort Sumter at 4:30 A.M. 12 April 1861 to signal the start of the Civil War.

FIGURE: XII-43 LOCATION: Author's Collection. IDENTIFICATION: Fuse, Wood, Time, Confederate. DIAMETER: Shell, 8-inch. Fuse — 1.3 inches. REMARKS: Paper fuse was inserted into wood case. Used in common shell.

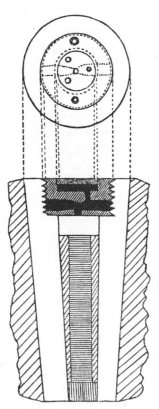

FIGURE: XII-44 IDENTIFICATION: Fuse, U.S. Seacoast. SOURCE: Gibbon. REMARKS: Brass fuse plug retained in shell by friction. Paper fuse. Note brass water cap with powder train at top and lead safety plug at bottom.

hard, it burned at a slow and fairly uniform rate. A small cup, left at the top, was primed with mealed powder moistened with whisky or alcohol to aid in ignition and the entire top covered with a waterproof cap on which the rate of burning, determined by experiment, was marked.

Prior to firing, the time of flight to the target was calculated and from this the length of fuse deduced. For instance, if the fuse burned at the rate of five seconds to the inch and the projectile would take ten seconds to reach the target, 2 inches of fuse were necessary. Since the marks started just under the cup, the fuse was cut off, or a hole bored through the wood case to the powder, at the proper spot and the plug was driven into the shell casing. The waterproof cap was removed before loading to permit the flame of the charge to lick around the ball and ignite the priming. The fuse burned during flight and, if properly set, was expected to explode the shell at the target.

That was a big "if," however, and one of the major problems with all fuses of this sort was irregularity of burning since it was almost impossible to drive the powder uniformly throughout. The fuse also had another defect in that when fired at long range, a large section of fuse extended into the shell and was subject to being snapped by the shock of discharge unless centered exactly along the axis of the bore.

Despite these faults, the wood fuse gave faithful service when a long time of flight was necessary. Figure XII-42 shows one of these wood fuse plugs, which were generally made of beech or ash, protruding from a 10-inch mortar shell found by the author. This was the same type shell and fuse that burst over Fort Sumter at 4:30 A.M. 12 April 1861 to signal the start of war. Although the illustrated projectile was probably fired two years later, the location where it was found indicates it came from a battery in the same general vicinity of that which fired the initial round. The fuse protrudes approximately half an inch which was about normal for mortar rounds.

The wood fuse required an array of implements (Figs XI-1 and 5) including a fuse setter for driving it into the shell, saws and drills for cutting or boring at the proper setting, and a fuse extractor, a complicated clamp and screw device for removing fuses when necessary to change the time of burning. These were largely eliminated by an improved model consisting of a wood plug, hollowed conically, into which a fuse of powder driven by mallet or machinery in a paper case could be inserted with the fingers just prior to firing. This form, designed mainly for long weapons, permitted use of fuses with varied rates of burning which could be altered still further by cutting. The plug was only two inches long and fitted almost entirely within the reinforced section of the shell wall thus obviating any chance of breakage during discharge. It also, since the fuse was separate, could be installed in the shell and left without danger. A slightly shorter variety, for field use, is illustrated in Figure XII-5.

Even this model had defects. Wood deteriorated with the years and there was no way to protect the flame if the projectile ricocheted on water, a particularly galling fault for seacoast or shipboard use. Consequently, some years before the outbreak of war, this form had been largely superseded by the more sophisticated United States Seacoast Fuse, but was resurrected by the South as an inexpensive substitute for long weapons as evidenced by its use in the 8-inch Confederate shell, Figure XII-43.

The seacoast model (Fig. XII-44), designed for columbiads and other heavy weapons, had a brass plug which fitted within the projectile wall and, like the wood fuses, was held in place by friction. The fuse proper, driven in paper, was made to burn ten, fourteen, or twenty seconds to the inch by varying the ratio of mealed powder to niter and sulfur and, for easy recognition, was colored yellow, green, or blue, respectively.

In addition to material of the fuse plug, the seacoast fuse differed from wood models in having the interior of the top threaded for a "water cap." This ingenious contrivance was a circular disk of brass having small holes filled with powder which took a circuitous course to the center and thence to the main powder of the fuse. Flame had no trouble following this course, but water, even under the pressure of ricochet, was prevented from entering. It was primed on top with mealed powder and strands of quick match. A lead safety plug, affixed to the bottom of the fuse plug, was heavy enough to prevent communication of flame to the charge from accidental ignition of the fuse and would even remain in place if the shell were dropped. However, the shock of firing dislodged the safety device and left the channel free for the flame to reach the bursting charge.

Water caps and safety plugs were also used in Navy fuses which, like the seacoast model, were made of metal, but differed in that they were threaded on the exterior and screwed into the shell. The fuse proper was driven in a paper case and although five seconds was considered standard, gunners also had a choice of three and a half, seven, ten, fifteen, and twenty seconds with further change available by cutting. A lead patch or cover, removed before firing, protected the priming from moisture during storage.

The representative selection of Navy fuse plugs in Figure XII-45 are all brass types dating from 1857

FIGURE: XII-45 LOCATION: Estes Collection, Mullins, S.C. IDENTIFICATION: Miscellaneous Selection of U.S. Navy Fuse Plugs. REMARKS: All are marked "Ord. D." (Ordnance Department), anchor, and dates ranging from 1857 to 1864. Top diameters roughly 1.3-inch, shanks approximately 0.8. All are brass with exception of zinc adapter (light color) on an 1862 model. Note small water cap.

to 1864 and marked with the Navy anchor. The small, round object is a water cap removed from one of them. The extra collar on one of the center models is zinc, although brass was often used, and presumably is an adapter to make the plug fit a different projectile from the intended type. A section of 15-inch Dahlgren shell in a Fort Fisher exhibit (Fig. XII-46) shows twin Navy fuse plugs still in the fragment. Two, often three fuses set at different times permitted a quick choice for gunners, the protective cover being left on the fuse, or fuses, not used.

Parrott and Dyer time fuses for rifled projectiles were similar in appearance, consisting of metal plugs threaded on the exterior and hollowed conically for paper fuses which operated in the same fashion as those previously discussed. The Parrott (Fig. XII-47) is threaded its entire length, but others for these projectiles were threaded part way, narrowing abruptly to approximately half the former diameter in similar fashion to one of the Parrott percussion types in a later illustration. This permitted a relatively long fuse, but let the plug rest on a circular shelf of metal near the bottom of the shell's fuse cavity. Parrotts examined by the author were made of zinc although brass probably was used in early models.

Spherical case and shell for light weapons, particularly Navy 12- and 24-pounder howitzers and Army field weapons, used an excellent time fuse invented by a Belgian Army officer about 1840, but retained as a state secret until late in the decade. This Bormann time fuse, although graduated by quarters to five and a half seconds, was generally called a five-second fuse and in United States service was

FIGURE: XII-47 LOCATION: Estes Collection, Mullins, S.C. IDENTIFICATION: Parrott Time Fuse. REMARKS: Zinc.

considered among the most reliable of all. Made of lead and tin in equal parts, the complete fuse was 1.65 inches in diameter and .45-inch thick. Figure XII-48 shows one of these fuses on a strapped 12-pounder spherical case and a cutaway view of the same projectile which, incidentally, illustrates the previously mentioned varied size lead balls.

Beneath the time markings was a horizontal powder train formed in horseshoe shape. Cutting through the thin metal at any mark exposed the train to the flame of discharge. It burned at a uniform rate in both directions, but one route ended in a blind alley just beyond the five and a half-second mark. The other, at zero, communicated with a cylindrical powder magazine, or booster, in the center which flashed into the bursting charge below through a small hole in a plug, or adapter, beneath the fuse. These plugs, two sizes of which are shown with a fuse for comparison in Figure XII-49, were made of brass, as illustrated, or iron. Their function was solely to form a solid base for the fuse which, due to its soft metal construction, might be driven into the shell by setback at discharge.

A major feature of the Bormann fuse was the horseshoe train formed of powder compressed by machinery into a channel of the fuse body and hermetically sealed beneath the top. As a result, the powder was driven vertically, yet burned horizontally thereby eliminating the layer effect in other time fuses which contributed heavily to irregular performance. Since there was no communication with the air until cut, Bormann fuses had a high safety factor for storage or handling and in addition to their normal time role, could turn case into canister by the simple

FIGURE: XII-46 LOCATION: Fort Fisher, N.C. IDENTIFICATION: Fragment of 15-Inch Dahlgren Shell with 2 U.S. Navy Fuse Plugs.

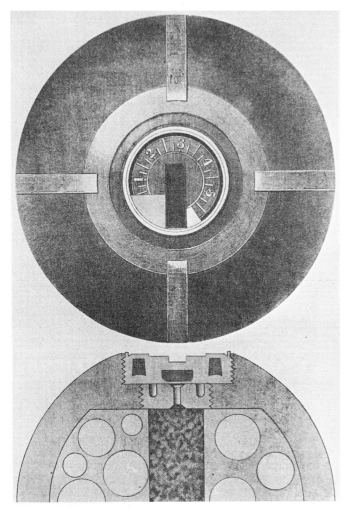

FIGURE: XII-48 IDENTIFICATION: Fuse, Time, Bormann. SOURCE: Ordnance Instructions for the U.S. Navy, 1866. REMARKS: Standard fuse for 12-Pounder Spherical Case such as this. Note adapter in cutaway drawing. Also various diameter balls. Circle around fuse with four straps affixed projectile to sabot.

FIGURE: XII-49 LOCATION: Estes Collection Mullins, S.C. IDENTIFICATION: Bormann Time Fuse and 2 Adapters. DIAMETER: Fuse, 1.63-Inch, Zinc. Large Adapter, 1.63-Inch, Brass. Small Adapter, 1.06-Inch, Brass. REMARKS: Note fuse has been "cut" at 2 seconds. Either adapter, depending on the type of shell, was used to strengthen the soft-metal fuse against the shock of firing. (See Fig. XII-48).

expedient of cutting directly into the booster which exploded the projectile at the muzzle, or be used as shot by not cutting the fuse at all.

Although highly successful when produced by precision equipment in the North, the Bormann fuse was a miserable failure in the South. Confederate Bormanns sent to the field in 1861 were discouragingly inefficient for, according to General Alexander:[13] "Fully four-fifths of the shell exploded prematurely and very many of these in the gun. . . ." The trouble was in the bond of metal under the horseshoe powder train. The shock of firing loosened the seal and flame communicated directly with the magazine. Various attempts were made to correct the evil with white lead, putty, or leather under the fuse, but success was only partial and an Ordnance Bureau

circular,[14] Christmas Eve, 1862, ordered manufacture of the Bormann fuse discontinued and fuse plugs and paper fuses substituted. However, much of the old ammunition remained in the field and artillerymen were still plagued with the inferior Bormanns as late as Gettysburg.

Failure of shells to explode was a constant irritation to the Confederates, particularly rifle projectiles in which the copper cup, when forced into the rifling, cut off access of the discharge flame to the fuse. Notches cut in the cup were little help, but an ingenious contrivance known as the "McEvoy Fuse Igniter" seems to have been quite successful. The device (Fig. XII-50) comprised a hollowed wood cylinder (b) containing a friction primer (c) encased in lead (d) and hung from a wire (f). Pressed on the end of a paper fuse, the flash of the friction primer, set off by inertia of discharge, ignited the fuse. Somewhat similar was a Confederate fuse (XII-51) which had a friction primer attached to a lead bullet. Rotation of the shell in the rifling threw off the bullet, igniting the primer thus activating the time element.

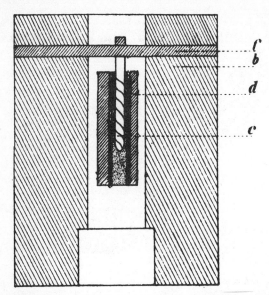

FIGURE: XII-50 IDENTIFICATION: McEvoy Fuse Igniter, Confederate. SOURCE: Abbot. REMARKS: b. Hollowed Wood Cylinder; c. Friction Primer; d. Lead Casing; f. Wire.

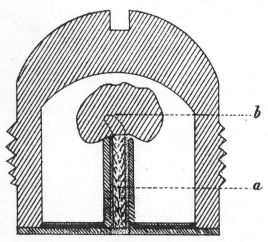

FIGURE: XII-51 IDENTIFICATION: Bullet-Type Igniter, Confederate. SOURCE: Abbot. REMARKS: Centrifugal force of rotating rifle projectile hurled lead bullet (b) from its mount drawing friction primer (a) and igniting time fuse attached below.

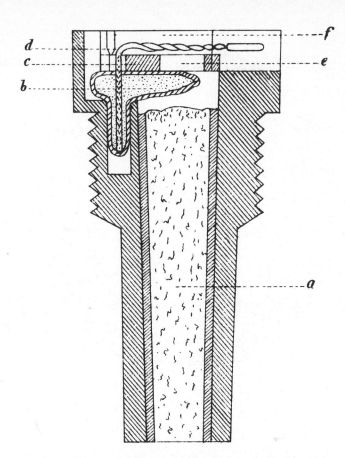

FIGURE: XII-52 IDENTIFICATION: Fuse, Adams, (U.S.). SOURCE: Abbot. REMARKS: Inserted in 6-Pounder Spherical Case for use as a hand grenade which could be thrown 100 feet and scattered fragments 200 feet. a. Common Time Fuse (short-burning type); b. Friction Primer; c. Iron disk; d. One of four lead shoulders securing (c); e. Control hole to permit escape of gas; f. Cavity for primer. Covered with paper cap until ready for use.

The United States also used a time fuse ignited by friction primer. The Adams (Fig. XII-52) was an ignition device invented by J. S. Adams for hand grenades, not artillery ammunition, but is included here since the projectile was 6-pounder spherical case. A lanyard fired the primer when the shell was thrown, the time element of the fuse delaying the burst sufficiently to protect the thrower.

Although various types of time fuses were standard for years in the world's armies and navies, artillerymen dreamed and experimented with ways to burst spherical shell at the moment of impact. This offered obvious advantages over time which, although the best method available, was far from efficient requiring precision of operation far beyond manufacturing and gunnery capabilities of the era.

At first glance, the problem of exploding a shell at impact didn't appear insurmountable—any explosive that could be set off by a sudden jar would do the trick. But to be successful, it also had to survive the shock of discharge, and a fuse that would burst on target with reliability and yet be "bore safe" to protect cannoneers was a far tougher problem. It was further complicated by the nature of the projectile—round. This necessitated a fuse that would work regardless of its position at the moment of impact, an accomplishment of no mean proportion.

These three basic factors—activation on impact, bore safety, and reliability regardless of position—

when linked with such prosaic requirements as simplicity and cost of manufacture, kept inventors busy but a long way from rich. Efforts were channeled along two main lines, "concussion" and "percussion," which for purposes of this book will be given the somewhat arbitrary definitions as follows:

Concussion fuses, like time models, were ignited at discharge and retained the fire until impact when a built-in device allowed the flame to communicate with the bursting charge.

Percussion fuses were inert during flight, but created flame on impact to explode the charge.

Percussion fuses for spherical projectiles were generally complicated and unsuccessful. Most types involved use of a sensitive fulminate set off by a piece of metal slamming against it at impact. One form, a British model, used small, metal cylinders in channels. The cylinders were held during firing by wires which sheared on impact to let a cylinder slide forward and strike the fulminate. The various channels were so arranged that the ball could hit on any of six equidistant points and find a cylinder in direct line. However, the further away from a direct line the impact point moved, the less reliable was the fuse. Moreover, it was expensive, complicated, and, despite the wires, not entirely bore safe.

Concussion fuses, although far from perfect, offered more promise. Moderately successful types depended on glass tubes, that protected the charge from flame until shattered when the shell landed, or zinc, which had the peculiar property of becoming brittle when heated. In all cases, the tubes were embedded in driven powder. This reinforced and protected them during firing, but burned away in flight to leave them standing fragilely alone. Burning powder in the zinc model heated the metal to the point where by impact time it had become sufficiently brittle to shatter and open a channel to the bursting charge.

Best of all concussion fuses seems to have been the Splingard which, like the Bormann, was developed in Belgium and retained as a state secret from its invention about 1830 until 1850. The Splingard (Fig. XII-53) was driven in a paper case which had been previously treated with ammonium sulfate to make it fireproof. Most of the case was filled with normal, slow-burning fuse composition and the remainder with a quicker type topped with mealed powder for priming. After driving, a small cone-shaped hollow was bored from the bottom almost to the end of the slow-burning section. This was

sealed with a coat or two of varnish to protect the powder, then filled with plaster of Paris. Just before the plaster hardened, a needle pierced most of its length in the center, care being taken to avoid going entirely through to the powder. When completed, this left a tiny hollow enclosed, except at the bottom, by plaster supported by fuse composition. A wood plug (Fig. XII-54) was lined on the interior at top with a ring of cork, giving added stability to the fuse during discharge, and had a small step near the bottom on which the fuse, pushed in by finger pressure, rested. The plug, which had a strip of gauze pasted to the bottom to prevent powder of the charge from entering, could be emplaced well in advance, and the fuse inserted just prior to firing.

In operation, the fuse composition protected the plaster cone at discharge, but, ignited by the flame, soon burned away sufficiently to leave the plaster standing without support. At impact, it shattered and the flame swept through the tiny hollow in the still protected part of the plaster to the bursting charge. If the entire composition was consumed before impact, the Splingard operated as a normal time fuse. The device gave excellent performance and European experiments in 1850 with an 11-inch mortar resulted in 204 rounds out of 224 bursting at impact, 13 shortly after striking when the fuse composition had burned down to the charge, and 3 prematurely. The rest were duds, due mainly to the fuse failing to ignite.

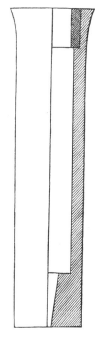

FIGURE: XII-53 IDENTIFI-CATION: Fuse, Splingard, Concussion, Belgian. SOURCE: Gibbon.

FIGURE: XII-54 IDENTIFI-CATION: Fuse Plug, Splingard, Concussion, Belgian. SOURCE: Gibbon.

The McIntyre shell, mentioned previously, had a concussion fuse (Fig. XII-55) similar to the Splingard in operation. Inside the plaster, however, the McIntyre had a brass tube with one end open to the charge and the other closed by a brass stopper held in place by plaster and the fuse composition. After the powder burned away, the plaster shattered on impact releasing the brass stopper and opening the channel through the brass tube to the bursting charge.

The advent of rifled artillery suddenly solved problems of detonation on impact. Since the projectile, theoretically at least, landed on its nose, a simple fulminate cap would explode the round on striking and could easily be made bore safe by protecting it during discharge. Time fuses were also used with rifled artillery and during the early days, which included. the Civil War era, were often more efficient than percussion. But in the long run, the ability to detonate a projectile at the moment of impact by this method is, in the author's opinion, one of the major advantages of rifled artillery and one that has been largely overlooked by writers preoccupied with improvements in range and accuracy, or increased weight of bursting charge.

Initially, United States experiments at West Point involved a nipple attached to a piece of metal over which a common percussion cap was placed (Fig. XII-56). Dropped into the projectile before firing and a metal head piece screwed on, the cap remained back during firing and flight, but slammed forward at impact to explode against the head piece and send flame down the center channel to the bursting charge.

Later fuses were more sophisticated, including devices to assure reliability and safety, but most, in the last analysis, were little more than complex versions of this basic West Point model. An early Parrott (Fig. XII-57) was similar to the basic fuse, but with a slightly different shaped plunger which, however, still apparently had no device for holding it safely during discharge. The head piece, like that of the basic fuse, screwed into the projectile. Two later Parrotts (Fig. XII-58) were similar, but were now self-contained. The plunger was filled with powder to serve as a booster and the head piece, or screw cap, went into the fuse plug instead of the projectile.

Parrott used several methods for holding the plunger away from the screw cap during discharge. One consisted of a hollow cylinder of soft metal supported by two small projections resting on a ring near the front end of the plunger. At impact, the projections were broken by the plunger which passed

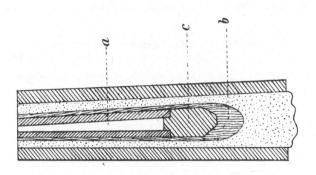

FIGURE: XII-55 IDENTIFICATION: Fuse, McIntyre, U.S. SOURCE: Abbot. REMARKS: a. Hollow Brass Cylinder; b. Plaster of Paris; c. Brass Stopper.

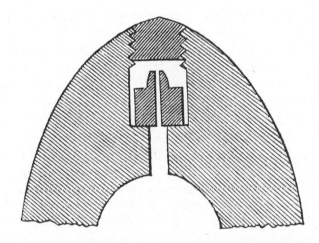

FIGURE: XII-56 IDENTIFICATION: Fuse, Percussion, Experimental. SOURCE: Gibbon. REMARKS: Model used in early experiments at West Point.

through the soft metal cylinder and exploded against the screw cap.[15] Another method involved two metallic prongs designed to be wrenched off by rotation during the first few moments of the projectile's flight. The metal, however, was found to be too stiff and artillerymen discovered that removing the device just before firing improved performance without materially diminishing bore safety. A third type, apparently not particularly successful, had a wood washer fitted over the nipple and designed to be broken by the shock of impact. Parrott shells with percussion fuses used by federal forces on Morris Island against Fort Sumter

gave excellent results when they hit a vertical wall, but
were likely to ricochet without exploding when landing in piles of masonry or rubbish.[16]

The United States Tice fuse is termed a concussion model by Abbot, but according to the previously
mentioned definition, would fall into the percussion
category. Made of metal, the device (Fig. XII-59)

had a cylinder (a) which on firing snapped two
safety pins (b) that let the compressed spring (c)
shove the long brass tube (d) up to the head of the
fuse. This withdrew protection from around a glass
vial of liquid fulminate (g) which had been further
guarded by the cork (f) held down by the pin (e).
At impact, the loose shot smashed the glass exploding
the fulminate which set off the booster (h), and,
blowing out the base (i), set off the charge.

The Tice was tested successfully near Richmond
in November, 1864, with Berney's incendiary composition in a modified Parrott, long, 6.4-inch projectile. No mention has been found of the Tice being
used with spherical shell, but it seems one of the few
percussion models that might be capable of this service. However, the rolling action of the ball in flight
might smash the vial while the rotation of a rifled
projectile would tend to hold the shot against the side
of the fuse and away from the vial until impact.
Incidentally, the Tice, especially in fired ammunition,

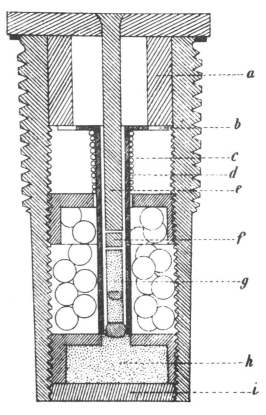

is obviously a sensitive fuse and any shell so armed should be treated with marked respect. A specimen at Fort Jackson, Savannah, Georgia (Fig. XII-60) has been photographed at an angle to illustrate appearance of the top. The brass device is in almost issue condition and still "hot."

The Absterdam fuse resembled the Parrott, but the plunger and nipple were held back by a small, hollow cone of lead attached at its apex to the bottom of the plunger. The base of the cone extended through a hole in the center of a metal plate covering the bottom of the fuse and was flared to hold it secure. Impact tore the plunger loose and drove it against the nose piece. Despite a cushion of oakum between nose piece and cap, the Absterdam gave a high percentage of prematures and was considered dangerous.

The Hotchkiss percussion fuse (Fig. XII-61) had a metallic case closed at the front by a flat screw cap with a small "V"-shaped anvil on the inner side. The fulminate was affixed to the nipple on a lead plunger retained prior to firing by a thin wire anchored in a tapered lead safety plug closing the base of the fuse like a cork. Setback at discharge sheared the wire and dropped the safety plug into the shell clearing a passage for the flame and leaving the plunger free to drive the cap into the anvil at impact. The fuse is generally found in Hotchkiss shells (Chapter XIII). The anvil apparently was considered unnecessary by some artillerymen since it has been filed off the illustrated fuse.

James percussion fuses, used with this inventor's shells (Chapter XIII), resembled the early Parrott. A loose plunger holding the fulminate cap was dropped into the nose of the shell and a brass or iron head piece screwed on top. Inertia held the plunger back during firing and it drove forward at impact.

Two types of Schenkl fuses were available, percussion and combination. Figure XII-62 illustrates two brass percussion models differing slightly in size and appearance, but identical in operation. Inside was the familiar iron plunger, with nipple and cap, retained during firing by a small screw—shown as a hole in the side wall below the threads—which sheared at impact. An additional safety feature was the nose piece (above left fuse) which had a small hollow on one side, as illustrated, and was flat on the other. During storage, the indented side was turned inward so that the cap, even if the plunger broke loose, would find no anvil to strike. Just before firing, the nose piece was reversed which placed the flat side face down for the cap to hit. Both sides of the nose piece were slotted for a screwdriver.

FIGURE: XII-60 LOCATION: Fort Jackson, Savannah, Ga. IDENTIFICATION: Fuse, Tice, Percussion, U.S.

FIGURE: XII-61 LOCATION: Bartleson Collection, Charleston, S.C. IDENTIFICATION: Fuse, Hotchkiss, Percussion, U.S. REMARKS: Removed from 3-Inch Hotchkiss shell. Disassembled to show fuse body, bottom; cap, left, and plunger with safety wire and lead plug, top.

FIGURE: XII-62 LOCATION: Estes Collection, Mullins, S.C. IDENTIFICATION: Fuse, Schenkl, Percussion, U.S. REMARKS: Two slightly different forms of Schenkl percussion fuse with cap removed from one.

FIGURE: XII-63 LOCATION: Estes Collection, Mullins, S.C. IDENTIFICATION: Fuse Plugs, Confederate, Miscellaneous. REMARKS: All copper or copper alloy. Time models with exception of two with rounded, slotted tops.

FIGURE: XII-64 LOCATION: Estes Collection, Mullins, S.C. IDENTIFICATION: Fuse, Percussion, Confederate. REMARKS: Breakdown of one of the percussion fuses in Fig. XII-63. Note hole in threads of fuse near top which held a safety pin, or wire.

An array of copper and copper alloy Confederate fuses is shown in Figure XII-63. These are time models with the exception of two percussion types at the bottom with slotted tops—for ease in screwing them into the projectiles. Figure XII-64 is a breakdown of one of these fuses. The plunger was inserted from the base and the round piece, with a center hole for the flame flanked by two wrench holes, screwed in to hold it. The plunger was held back by a safety wire inserted through the small hole in the side of the fuse body, which was off-center to miss the cap but meet the shoulder of the plunger. An identical fuse was removed from a 6.4-inch Brooke shell at Fort Fisher and a more elongated form (Fig. XII-65) from a similar caliber Mullane. Both projectiles are discussed in Chapter XIII.

All metallic Confederate fuses thus far seen by the author have been copper or copper alloy, but whether or not this can be considered an infallible rule must await additional evidence.

Combination fuses, by the fact of their dual nature, were more complicated than single types and ranged from the fairly complex Sawyer to the British Armstrongs termed by Abbot[17] ". . . so complicated and costly as to be curiosities. . . ."

The Sawyer (Fig. XII-66) consisted of a metal fuse plug (a) which screwed into the lead coating of the Sawyer shell, extended for this purpose, and contained a ring of fulminate (b) that, in case the time element failed, was crushed on impact against

FIGURE: XII-65 LOCATION: Fort Fisher, N.C. IDENTIFICATION: Fuse, Percussion, Confederate. REMARKS: Copper fuse, plunger, and plug removed from 6.4-Inch Mulane shell. Wire, modern, is attached to identification tag.

the iron nose of the shell. The opening for the time element was closed by a cork until ready for use. The time fuse, kept separate until ready for loading, was composed of a brass cylinder (c) open at both ends and pierced by four rows of small holes (h) of which two rows are shown in the drawing. The holes were

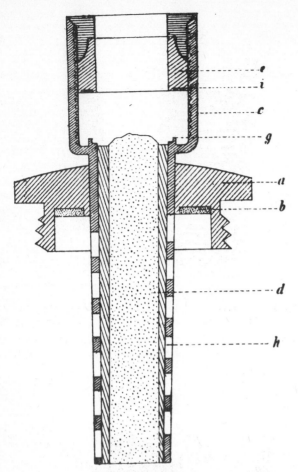

FIGURE: XII-66 IDENTIFICATION: Fuse, Sawyer, Combination, U.S. SOURCE: Abbot. REMARKS: a — Fuse Plug; b — Ring of Fulminate; c — Time Fuse Case (brass cylinder); d — Paper Fuse; e — Brass and Lead Plunger; g — Iron Ring; h — Four Rows of Holes (2 shown); i — Ring of Fulminate (for igniting time element by crushing against (g) on setback at discharge.

placed to mark quarter seconds on the seven-second paper fuse (d) contained within the case, and the proper one was bored with a gimlet for setting. Since the flash of discharge had a difficult time getting past the rifling, the fuse was ignited by a fulminate ring (i) at the bottom of the lead plunger (e) held in place by the roughened interior of the brass case. The shock of firing shoved the fulminate down on the iron ring (g) to ignite the time element. Limited testing of the fuse proved it a good one, according to Abbot.

Somewhat more intricate was the Schenkl combination fuse (Fig. XII-67) composed essentially of a fuse plug, standard fuse composition, and a fuse rotator. The hollow plug (k) was graduated on the top from zero to nine seconds. It screwed into the fuse hole and differed from ordinary plugs by being closed at the bottom, but pierced by a series of small

holes beginning near the middle of the plug where it entered the shell cavity and extending in a curved line nearly around the plug from left to right. The fuse proper (l) of ordinary time fuse composition was contained in the metallic case (m) pierced by small holes like the fuse plug, but running in the opposite direction. The time element was ignited by a percussion cap (h) covered with highly flammable treated cotton in the space (i) which was struck by the iron plunger (a) after the soft metal pin (b) had been broken by inertia of the discharge. The plunger was held secure by the safety pin (g) which was removed before firing.

The rotator, made up of the remaining parts, screwed into the plug and was held securely by two dowels (n). It was kept in place by the latch pin (e) which fitted into any of twenty holes in the top of the fuse plug of which two are shown. By raising the latch spring (c) the pin was lifted and the rotator turned to the proper setting marked by an arrow on the side of the rotator, which could be aligned with any number on the fuse plug top. The figures were set so that when the fuse composition had burned the requisite number of seconds, the hole it had reached in the metallic fuse case would be opposite the corresponding hole in the fuse plug which let fire to the bursting charge. If the shell struck before the fuse burned down, the impact gave the rotator a quick turn and admitted flame immediately to the charge.

Abbot[18] found the soft-metal fuse melted in seven or eight seconds hastening the time of explosion, a defect he felt could be remedied by using brass. He also noted a number failed to ignite, a fact he blamed on the pin (b) being made too strong. The fuse came from the factory with a canvas band wrapped around the top (Fig. XII-68) to protect the rotator.

Armstrong fuses were beautifully made, precision pieces of equipment that came in two models, percussion and combination. The percussion (Fig. XII-69) had a lead plunger (a) containing a cavity (b) filled with a booster charge and, on the forward end, a wood cylinder (c) loaded in the center (d) with fulminate. A safety pin (e), removed just before firing, held the plunger as well as four small lead projections resting against the lower part of the brass ring (f) and similar to the two marked (e) in Figure XII-70.

At impact, the plunger broke the lead projections and struck the fulminate against the steel needle, or anvil (g). A rubber washer (h) assured close contact between fuse and projectile. The fulminate was covered at top by a thin, circular sheet of brass

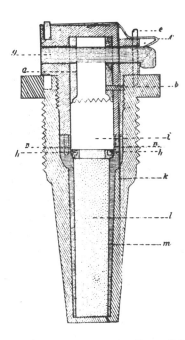

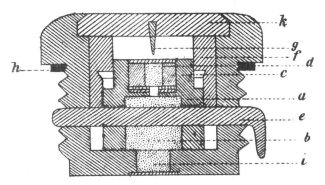

FIGURE: XII-69 IDENTIFICATION: Fuse, Armstrong, Percussion, British. SOURCE: Abbot. REMARKS: a — Lead Plunger; b — Booster (powder); c — Hollow Wood Cylinder; d — Fulminate; e — Safety Pin; f — Brass Ring; g — Steel Needle or Anvil; h — Rubber Washer; i — Quick Burning Composition; k — Circular Top.

FIGURE: XII-67 IDENTIFICATION: Fuse, Schenkl, Combination, U.S. SOURCE: Abbot. REMARKS: a — Iron Plunger; b — Soft Metal Pin; c — Latch Spring; e — Latch Pin; g — Safety pin; h — Percussion Cap; i — Flammable Treated Cotton; k — Fuse Plug; l — Time Fuse Composition; m — Metallic Case; n — Dowels.

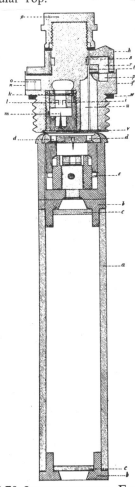

FIGURE: XII-68 LOCATION: Fort Jackson, Savannah, Ga. IDENTIFICATION: Fuse, Schenkl, Combination, U.S. REMARKS: Unused fuse protected by canvas strip around top which was removed prior to insertion in shell. Length 3 inches. Diameter, top, 1.13; wider portion below, 1.5. Marked "Pat. July 18, 1862, 10 Sec".

FIGURE: XII-70 IDENTIFICATION: Fuse, Armstrong, Combination, British. SOURCE: Abbot. REMARKS: a — Iron Case; b — Brass Caps; c — Leather Disks; d — Holes in Percussion Fuse (2 shown of 4); e — Lead Projections (2 shown of 4); f — Surface for Pasting Paper Band Graduated in Burning Time; g — Clamping Cap; h — Arrow (not shown); i — Brass Ring; k — Safety Wire; l — Fulminate Bedded in Fuse Composition; m — Steel Needle or Anvil; n — Escape Hole for Flame; o — Exposed End of Fuse Composition; p — Ring of Fuse Composition; r — Quick Composition; s — Ring of Quick Composition; t — Duct; u — Chamber; v — Brass Sheet; w — Rubber Washer.

and at bottom by paper and two rubber rings. Central holes in the rubber and in a thin lead plate supporting the cylinder let flame to the booster (b) which was separated by paper from the cavity (i) containing a quick-burning composition hermetically sealed at the bottom by a thin sheet of brass. The importance of protecting the interior of the fuse from dampness was so highly stressed that the circular top (k) was held in place by crushing the surrounding brass upon it thus making it necessary to destroy the fuse in order to inspect it. The fuse contained some seventeen parts, in contrast to half that in most U.S. models, and was packed individually, surrounded by oakum, in a tin box.

The Armstrong combination fuse (Fig. XII-70) for segmented shell, was an ingenious contrivance employing percussion bursting and ignition devices as well as the time element. This marvel of complication came to the field packed in two containers—percussion fuse and booster in one and the percussion igniter and time fuse in the other—for use separately or together.

The booster was a powder-filled, iron case (a) covered at the ends by identical brass caps (b) closed with leather disks (c). Either end could be inserted into the shell cavity to eliminate mistakes in loading. The percussion fuse on top of the booster was similar to that already described, but has been turned 90° so that the safety pin is facing the viewer. It differed from the other primarily in omission of threads, since it fitted down in the shell cavity, and addition of four holes at top (d) to admit flame to the booster from the time fuse above.

The brass time element and percussion ignition device screwed into the shell on top of the other fuse and booster. At discharge, the brass ring (i) sheared the brass safety wire (k) and shoved fulminate bedded in fuse composition (l) down on the steel needle (m), also surrounded by fuse composition. Flame passed through the hollow plunger and out a passage terminating in an escape hole (n). On the way it passed the exposed end (o) (drawn in elevation) of a ring of fuse composition (p) (drawn in section) which encircled the top of the plug in similar fashion to the Bormann. The ring burned to the index (h) where it ignited a quick composition (r) firing another ring (s) (drawn in section) that communicated through the duct (t) to the chamber (u). A hole down the center of the chamber permitted instant ignition throughout, driving out the soldered circular sheet of brass, (v) and continuing through one of the four holes in the top of the percussion fuse to the booster.

The time element could burn four seconds and was graduated in twentieths of a second on a printed paper pasted around the circumference of the fuse plug on a line at (f). By loosening the clamping cap (g), a rotary motion could be given the index piece (shown in section) which had an arrow at (h); the arrow could be pointed to the desired mark on the time scale and held in place by tightening the clamping cap.

Heavy black lines on the sketch denote rubber washers and, like the percussion fuse, all openings were carefully sealed against moisture to the point where the device had to be cut apart for examination.

The Confederates, and possibly the U.S., had at least one form of base fuse which was inserted in the rear of the shell, but operated in similar fashion to nose percussion types.

A post-war U.S. model, made by Hotchkiss, had a brass case roughly resembling a modern smallarms cartridge in shape and containing priming composition. The front end was threaded inside and closed by a screw cap. The rear had threads outside and was screwed into the shell base until the flange rested flush against the iron.

Inside the case was a movable lead plunger with roughened sides to hold it secure against all but heavy shock. The plunger contained a brass firing pin embedded in the lead, the point barely covered. Setback at discharge compressed the lead sufficiently to expose the end of the pin which, when the plunger slid forward at impact, detonated the priming composition, blowing out a soft plug in the screw cap at front and exploding the charge.

Navy demolition experts disarming Fort Sumter ammunition came across a Confederate Mullane which also had a base fuse. The Mullane, described in the following chapter, had a brass cup at the base affixed by a heavy iron screw. In this case, the base fuse was inserted in place of the screw in a projectile which had all the exterior earmarks of a solid bolt and apparently was intended for defense against ironclads where a base fuse might have permitted a bit more penetration before exploding than the front model.

Unfortunately, the fuse was not preserved and the only photograph is too poor for reproduction. However, it seems to have roughly resembled the point detonating fuse in Figure XII-64. Made of copper or copper alloy, the exterior end, or base in this case, was flat rather than domed and presumably was slotted like the nose model. The plunger was similar, but operated in reverse direction against the screw cap at the bottom which, like the nose fuse, must have had a small hole for the flame and side holes for a wrench. The safety pin, if present, would have been near the screw cap necessitating removal before insertion into the shell. The plunger probably was held to the rear by inertia and rammed against the screw cap at impact. Whether this was an experimental or issue fuse has not been determined. However, examination of Fort Sumter projectiles has turned up no more of this type.

Moisture, with its damaging effect on black powder, was a constant annoyance and various methods were devised to protect both fuse and charge in the shell from dampness. One (Fig. XII-71) was a simple brass plug with a square wrench hole in the top which sealed the shell cavity until replaced by a fuse prior to firing. The illustrated plug is a type used in Whitworth projectiles, discussed in the next chapter.

In closing, it must be reiterated that other fuses were employed by both sides, but the foregoing were the major forms and give a general idea of the methods used to detonate projectiles.

FIGURE: XII-71 LOCATION: Estes Collection, Mullins, S.C. IDENTIFICATION: Fuse Plug for Whitworth Shell, British. REMARKS: Brass plug protected charge in shell during shipment and storage. It was removed and discarded for insertion of fuse just prior to firing.

NOTES

1. *Ordnance Manual for The Use of Officers of The United States Army,* 1861, p. 37.
2. Henry L. Abbot, "Siege Artillery in The Campaigns Against Richmond With Notes on The 15-Inch Gun," *Professional Papers No. 14, Corps of Engineers,* 1867, p. 31.
3. *Ibid.*
4. *Ibid.,* p. 50.
5. John Gibbon, *The Artillerist's Manual, Compiled From Various Sources and Adapted to The Service of the United States,* 1860, p. 163.
6. *Ibid.,* p. 345.
7. *Official Records,* Series I, Vol. 28, Part 1, p. 340.
8. Gibbon, *op. cit.,* p. 269.
9. J. B. Brandt, *Gunnery Catechism as Applied to The Service of Naval Ordnance,* 1864, p. 92.
10. Collection of John Bartleson, Charleston, S.C.
11. The projectile, concealed in a truck-load of dirt, was dumped in the yard of Dr. Albert Cannon and found by his daughter, Josephine, and a cousin, Frank Jervey Ball, Jr.—a rather fascinating combination of last names to turn up such a find. Despite judicious checking, no pinpoint location could be established from where the dirt originally came.
12. William LeRoy Broun (sic), "The Red Artillery, Confederate Ordnance During The War," *Southern Historical Society Papers,* Vol. XXVI, 1898, p. 370; Abbot, *op. cit.,* p. 28.
13. E. P. Alexander, "Confederate Artillery Service," *Southern Historical Society Papers,* Vol. XI, 1883, p. 104.
14. Circular, 24 December 1862, signed by J. Gorgas, Colonel, Chief of Ordnance, Richmond, Va., *General Orders from Adjutant and Inspector General's Office, C. S. Army from January 1862 to December 1863,* p. 235.
15. Q. A. Gillmore, *Engineer and Artillery Operations Against The Defenses of Charleston Harbor, 1863,* 1865, p. 151.
16. *Ibid.*
17. Abbot, *op. cit.,* p. 113.
18. *Ibid.,* p. 171.

Chapter 13

Rifle Projectiles

RIFLE PROJECTILES OFFER the most difficult identification problem of all Civil War artillery, yet in many respects the most fascinating. Both sides entered the conflict with more enthusiasm than knowledge in this new field and inventors gave their minds free rein to turn out a bewildering barrage of shot and shell, leaving today's collectors an intriguing puzzle to which many of the answers may never be learned.

The main types, particularly federal, are not too difficult. Since thousands were used, they are prevalent today and, being relatively successful, were discussed and illustrated in contemporary texts. Moreover, Northern models were manufactured by only a few firms under fairly strict specifications which led to consistency in appearance. But even in the North numerous experimental projectiles were tested, turned down by the Ordnance Department, then discarded and forgotten, except for occasional specimens that turn up to delight, yet plague collectors.

Identification of Confederate models is much tougher. Many were manufactured by relatively small shops that made little attempt to meet specific standards other than caliber and were not above adding a few ideas of their own. Since the field was new, particularly in the early stages of the conflict, officers and civilians entered their brainchildren, duly cast

them and tried them out—often in combat, on the theory that the best way to test any projectile was against the enemy. Later, when the mill wheels of war began to grind finer, experiment continued under government auspices in an effort to develop improved models that might tip the balance a bit in the South's favor. These types were often novel in design and might have been promising had the Confederacy possessed sufficient manufacturing capability to back up its inventors.

Fortunately for collectors, many of the best projectiles of both sides failed to explode and an even higher percentage of experimentals were duds. This has left a surprising number available for study, although they are widely dispersed in public and private collections, and, with a few exceptions, not particularly well catalogued or identified.

Undoubtedly the first serious collector of Civil War ammunition, and perhaps the most successful, was General Abbot. The general, of course, had one advantage over modern hobbyists—he didn't have to hunt. The collection came to him just as fast as the Confederates could fire, and it was merely a matter of having his men pick up anything unusual. At the end of the war, Abbot sketched the specimens and his publication, listed in the bibliography, is a basic source of Confederate types, although it included only those found in the Richmond, Petersburg, and Fort Fisher areas and, consequently, omitted a few models used farther west and south. He later donated the collection to the Military Academy Museum at West Point where much of it still reposes, as evidenced by the number of photographs in this section furnished by that museum.

Unfortunately, although he was an avid collector, the general's interest was largely professional and Confederate projectiles were valued only so far as their design might provide improvement in U.S. models. Names of the different types were either unavailable to the general or considered unimportant, and his book, although invaluable, is not the prime source of information it might have been.

General Gillmore also sketched a number of Confederate projectiles, but he too omits identifying names. However, a member of General Gillmore's command was not so unmindful of future generations and took the trouble to chalk the names on a small but diversified collection captured at the evacuation of Charleston and exhibited at the Arsenal. There are a number of photographs of these projectiles, fortunately arranged to feature various specimens. In Figure XIII-1, and in Figure XII-23, a different view of the same scene, the names of many projectiles are visible with the aid of a magnifying glass. Not all, since measurements are lacking, can be reconciled with existing rounds, but many fall into this category and our unknown benefactor's labors are a valuable, though limited, source of identification. Newspapers and letters are often another source since both openly extolled the merits of new inventions without regard to enemy intelligence agents, and through such documents the writer has been able to identify several rounds, particularly one previously known only as a "pointed projectile," which can now be established as the product of a Charlestonian named Quinlivan.

However, even with recourse to all sources, the subject of rifle projectile identification still poses many questions, so the following pages will include shot and shell of established authenticity as well as a few that must be labeled either "tentative" or "unknown," but are listed since all are interesting. Perhaps the future will bring firm identification.

Rifle projectiles generally took the name of their inventor and were made in numerous calibers as well as varied forms including solid, shell, case, and canister. They differed mainly in methods of providing rotation, a major problem in muzzle-loaders since the round had to slip easily into the bore, yet follow the twist of the rifling as it was expelled.

FIGURE: XIII-1 IDENTIFICATION: Miscellaneous Confederate Ammunition. REMARKS: A different arrangement of ammunition shown in Fig. XII-23 collected in 1865 at the Charleston, S. C., Arsenal.

Almost every inventor had a slightly different way of achieving this, but all types can be consolidated into seven major categories, a method preferable to that of Abbot, who set up ten classes for Confederate models alone.

1. The largest and most successful category consisted of projectiles having an iron, brass, copper, or lead cup or ring affixed to the base.
2. Projectiles with lead or paper covering extending from a third to half-way up a splined projectile and squeezed into the grooves on firing.
3. Projectiles made in two parts with a soft metal band between, which was forced into the grooves when the parts were shoved together at discharge.
4. Projectile and bore shaped to fit.
5. Projectiles with flanges to follow the grooves in the bore, or grooves in the projectile to fit the lands.
6. Projectiles with a thin covering of soft metal over the entire shell, which was driven into the rifling at discharge.
7. Miscellaneous.

U.S. projectiles fell into all but Category 4 and the major types consisted of Parrott (1), Schenkl (2), Dyer (2 and 7), Hotchkiss (1 experimental, tentative, and 3 standard), Absterdam (1), Sawyer (5 and 6), and James (2).

Early 2.9- and 3.67-inch Parrott projectiles had a wrought iron cup similar to Confederate rounds developed by Read, with whom Parrott was associated prior to the war. However, this form was found unsatisfactory and later Parrott projectiles were of two types—the indented brass cup (Fig. XIII-2), an early form for up to 6.4-inch rifles, and a flat variety in which the brass was cast flush around the projectile base (Fig. XIII-3). Gear-like indentations in the base prevented the brass from turning.

Parrott shells were made in all calibers of his rifles from 2.9- to 10-inch and were generally similar in appearance, although short and long models were made for 6.4- and 8-inch. Bolts also fit all calibers

and in most cases came in two flat-nose varieties—one with a rounded ogive, the other with a marked step to the flat surface. A complete collection of all calibers would run from thirty-five to forty specimens and is unavailable in a single location. Consequently, a random sampling from collections of the author and the National Park Service in the Charleston area, with one, a 3-inch, from Atlanta,[1] is shown in Figures XIII-4-6.

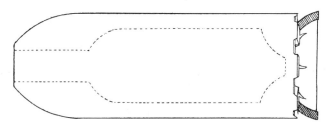

FIGURE: XIII-2 CATEGORY 1. IDENTIFICATION: Parrott, 3.67-Inch, Shell, U.S. WEIGHT: 16.5 pounds. SOURCE: Abbot. REMARKS: 20-Pounder. Brass cup, open type.

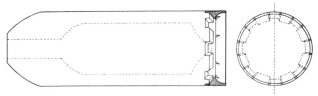

FIGURE: XIII-3 CATEGORY 1. IDENTIFICATION: Parrott, 4.2-Inch, Shell, U.S. WEIGHT: 25 pounds. SOURCE: Abbot. REMARKS: 30-Pounder. Brass ring sabot.

FIGURE: XIII-4 LOCATION: Author's Collection. CATEGORY 1. IDENTIFICATION: Miscellaneous Parrott Shells and Bolts, U.S. REMARKS: Left to right:
3-Inch (10-Pounder) Shell. Length — 8.4. Weight — 9.
3.67-Inch (20-Pounder) Shell. Length — 10.4. Weight — 18.
4.2-Inch (30-Pounder) Shell. Length — 11.9. Weight — 25.
4.2-Inch (30-Pounder) Bolt. Length — 9.4. Weight — 30.
3.67-Inch (20-Pounder) Bolt. Length — 8.6. Weight — 20.
Note: 4.2-Inch Bolt in unfired condition. All sabots brass.

FIGURE: XIII-5 LOCATION: Fort Moultrie, S.C. CATEGORY 1. IDENTIFICATION: Miscellaneous Parrott Shells, U.S. REMARKS: Left to right:
10-Inch (300-Pounder). Length — 22.8. Weight — 250, (approximate).
10-Inch (300-Pounder). Length — 22.5 (includes .25-inch nut in base similar to that on 8-inch of Fig. XIII-10). Weight — 250 (approximate).
8-Inch (200-Pounder, Navy 150). Length — 20. Weight — 137 (shell recoverd from salt water and probably has sustained an estimated 13-pound weight loss).
8-Inch (200-Pounder, Navy 150). Length — 16.9 (includes .5-inch nut as in Fig. XIII-10). Weight — 138.
6.4-Inch (100-Pounder). Length — 18.5. Weight — 90.
6.4-Inch (100-Pounder). Length — 15.8. Weight — 74.
Note: Both 10-inch and one 8-inch unfired. Other 8-inch has thrown off its brass ring. Smaller 6.4-inch is badly rusted and has sustained an approximate 6-pound weight loss. Sabots all brass.

FIGURE: XIII-6 LOCATION: Fort Moultrie, S.C. CATEGORY 1. IDENTIFICATION: Miscellaneous Parrott Bolts, U.S. REMARKS: Left to right:
10-Inch (300-Pounder). Length — 16.5. Weight — 222 (cored).
8-Inch (200-Pounder). Length — 14.8. Weight — 150.
6.4-Inch (100-Pounder). Length — 13.25. Weight — 95.
Note: Brass, ring-type sabots.

The raised nose, such as illustrated by the 10-inch bolt, is chilled iron and was designed for punching ironclads, although this specimen was fired at the masonry of Fort Sumter. It is cored, but unlike the 15-inch Dahlgren of the preceding chapter, was cast without a hole to the core. Black founder's sand poured out when an identical round at Sumter was drilled some years ago in the mistaken belief that it might have been loaded. Some 6.4- and 8-inch with chilled heads probably also were cored, but since such rounds are seldom drilled, this has not been definitely established. A drilled 6.4-inch in the writer's possession is not.

Washington Navy Yard has two 12-inch Parrott bolts, 23.5 inches long, with chilled heads that likely were made for testing one of the three 15-inch Dahlgrens (Chapter V) bored to 12-inch and rifled in three different forms—including Parrott. The flush-type, brass rings show marks of 17 lands and grooves.

The indented cup (see Fig. XII-57 and 4.2-inch bolt in (Fig. XIII-4) was used in the belief that it would be more easily forced into the grooves by light charges. However, the flat type, made with metal overhanging the base of the shell a fraction of an inch, was sufficient to "start" the ring even in light projectiles. The metal was made flush with the base of heavier rounds, but gunners were advised to start the brass in two or three places with a cold chisel if several rounds were erratic.

Two 4.2-inch Parrotts (Fig. XIII-7) illustrate shells which did and did not take the grooves. That at the left was fired into Charleston from Morris Island and shows almost perfect rifling marks. The other has marks so faint they are almost invisible and doubtless the shell tumbled in flight.

Parrott projectiles were also modified to fire incendiary materials by casting the interior with a partition which separated the cavity into two compartments. The top section held a small bursting charge loaded through the fuse hole. The bottom was packed through a hole in the base with cotton then filled with liquid incendiary composition and the hole closed with a copper washer and bolt.

Abbot tested[2] a number of long, 6.4-inch Parrotts modified (Fig. XIII-8) to fire Berney's incendiary composition. Each shell held 6 pints of the secret material which, to judge from the way it burned, contained turpentine and petroleum. It ignited, so the inventor said, at 120°. Fired at wood houses within the Confederate lines, a conflagration ensued each time a shell burst within a building.

Flemming's composition, also secret, was tested

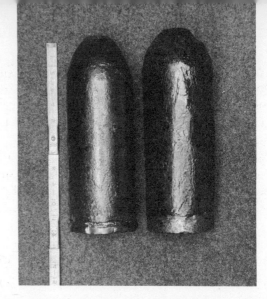

FIGURE: XIII-7 LOCATION: Author's Collection. CATEGORY 1. IDENTIFICATION: Parrott, 4.2-Inch, Shells, U.S. Length — 11.875 and 11.75. REMARKS: Note brass rings. Rifling marks, excellent on one are barely discernable on the other which probably tumbled in flight.

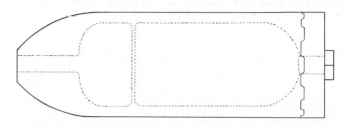

FIGURE: XIII-8 CATEGORY 1. IDENTIFICATION: Parrott, 6.4-Inch, Incendiary Shell, U.S. SOURCE: Abbot. REMARKS: Parrott "Long" shell cast with two compartments and bolt hole in base to accommodate Berney's incendiary composition. Top cavity held a small bursting charge and the bottom 6 pints of incendiary material. The bolt was removed for loading. Ring-type, brass sabot.

in March, 1865[3] against log palisading. The projectile (Fig. XIII-9) was a 4.2-inch modified Parrott differing only slightly from the previous model. It held only a pint of liquid and failed to ignite the logs unless leaves or other dry material were present. Abbot felt it was useless for the purpose, but might be better against houses or shipping, especially if a larger shell were used.

Various types of incendiaries were tried against Charleston from both the celebrated Swamp Angel and Morris Island guns. Whether these were modified or standard projectiles has not been determined, but a few 8- and 10-inch shells have been found with bolts protruding from the bases. One of the illustrated 10s and an 8-inch (Fig. XIII-10) have standard cavities with no compartments and a normal fuse hole in the nose. Whether the bolt indicates intended use as an incendiary is problematical, but unless this was the case, the reason is not apparent and most 8- and 10-inchers do not have it. Even without compartments, loading incendiaries through the base makes a certain amount of sense, for a small bursting charge would collect near the fuse when the shell was upended for packing with incendiary material through the base. If incendiary action was not desired, the projectile, bolt in place, presumably could be filled with powder and used as standard shell.

A disconcerting tendency toward premature bursts in large caliber Parrotts was attributed by the inventor[4] to the bursting charge rasping against the rough sides of the projectile at the moment of discharge. He advised coating the interior with lacquer or varnish. This did diminish the number of prematures although it did not eliminate them entirely. In addition, a number of projectiles in the Charleston area, both Parrott and Schenkl, which were fired by Parrott rifles, held a double charge.

One consisted of powder mixed with an unidentified substance, which was poured into the projectile until the cavity was about half filled and then permitted to harden into a solid mass. The second charge, normal black powder, was placed on top. Apparently by making roughly half the cavity solid, movement of the remaining powder was limited and the rasping action reduced. The right 4.2-inch in Figure XIII-7 had such a charge although badly damaged by moisture. Both black powder and composition in the 8-inch Schenkl (Fig. XIII-11), however, were in excellent condition and burn well today despite their age—vivid reminders that Civil War projectiles still may be dangerous.

Schenkls,[5] were a common U.S. projectile, but are rare in this caliber. It seems to have been used

FIGURE: XIII-10 LOCATION: Author's Collection. CATEGORY 1. IDENTIFICATION: Parrott, 8-Inch, Shell, U.S. Length — 17.3 (includes .3 of nut). Weight — 137. REMARKS: Unfired, excellent brass ring. Nut may indicate a form of incendiary shell although cavity is that of standard shell, see text.

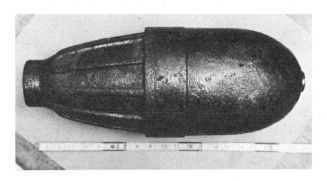

FIGURE: XIII-11 LOCATION: Author's Collection. CATEGORY 2. IDENTIFICATION: Schenkl, 8-Inch, Shell, U.S. Length — 20. Weight — 125. REMARKS: 10 ribs. Contained double charge, see text. Papier-mâché sabot.

primarily, if not entirely, by the Navy. The Schenkl illustrated was found near Charleston. Based on caliber and location, it must have been fired in the summer of 1864 by the USS Lehigh. The Lehigh with another monitor, the Montauk, and several lesser craft gave one of the forts quite a pummeling. But sand fortifications were difficult to destroy and the work today is still in excellent condition. Since the Montauk was armed with 15- and 11-inch Dahlgrens and the Lehigh with a 15-inch Dahlgren and an 8-inch Parrott, the projectile had to have come from the Lehigh.

At least three other Schenkl calibers, all fired by the Navy, have been found in the Charleston area—6.4-inch (Fig. XIII-12, 4.2-inch, and the quite rare 5.1-inch for Admiral Dahlgren's rifle (Fig. XIII-13). Deactivation of one 5.1-inch revealed twenty-eight brass percussion caps mixed with the

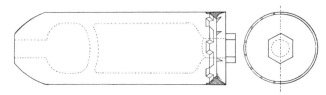

FIGURE: XIII-9 CATEGORY 1. IDENTIFICATION: Parrott, 4.2-Inch, Incendiary Shell, U.S. SOURCE: Abbot. REMARKS: Parrott shell cast with two compartments and bolt hole in base for firing Flemming's incendiary composition. Top cavity held a small bursting charge, the bottom one pint of incendiary material loaded through bolt hole. Ring-type, brass sabot.

FIGURE: XIII-12 LOCATION: Private Collection, Charleston, S.C. CATEGORY 2. IDENTIFICATION: Schenkl, 6.4-Inch, Shell, U.S. Length — 16.75. REMARKS: 8 ribs. Papier-maché sabot.

FIGURE: XIII-13 LOCATION: Author's Collection. CATEGORY 2. IDENTIFICATION: Schenkl, 5.1-Inch, Shell, U.S. Length — 14. Weight — 35. REMARKS: Six ratchet-shaped ribs. Papier-maché sabot.

powder.[6] However, since reliability of caps under such circumstances would have been extremely uncertain—and thus far the phenomenon has been noted in only a single round—they probably became mixed with the powder inadvertently or were dropped in surreptitiously by a federal sailor in a mistaken attempt to add to the shell's destructiveness.

The Schenkl falls into Category 2 having a papier-maché covering extending throughout the conical portion. This was jammed into the grooves at discharge and prevented from slipping by the ribs, or splines, of the projectile. The papier-maché disintegrated into powder, making the Schenkl ideal for firing over the heads of friendly troops. A West Point 7-inch with part of the sabot still attached (Fig. XIII-14) probably was intended for testing in the 7-inch wrought iron Ames gun in 1864 or for a rifled 42-pounder.

The number of ribs in Schenkls varied considerably. Abbot listed an early variety (Fig. XIII-15) with six ribs, later types (Figs. XIII-16 and 17), with seven, and another form (Fig. XIII-18) with six shaped like ratchets. The previously illustrated 8-inch

has ten and the 6.4- and 5.1-inch six ribs, the latter ratchet-shaped. Exterior appearance also differed a bit as did interior cavity design.

The Schenkl was made for standard U.S. rifle calibers in shell, case, canister, and, occasionally, shot. It was extensively used in the 3-inch Ordnance and 4.5-inch siege rifles. Abbot[7] felt the Schenkl—when in good condition—out-performed the Parrott. However, the papier-maché sabot was often made of inferior quality paper which was detrimental to performance. It was also subject to swelling from moisture and then could not be loaded. Attempts were

FIGURE: XIII-14 LOCATION: West Point, N.Y. CATEGORY 2. IDENTIFICATION: Schenkl, 7-Inch, Shell, U.S. Length — 12.1. REMARKS: 9 ribs. Papier-Maché Sabot partially torn to show ribs.

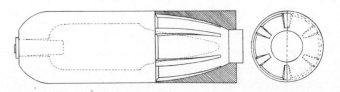

FIGURE: XIII-15 CATEGORY 2. IDENTIFICATION: Schenkl, 4.2-Inch, Shell, U.S. Weight — 24. SOURCE: Abbot. REMARKS: Papier-maché sabot.

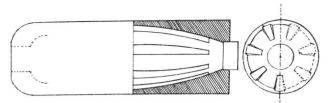

FIGURE: **XIII-16** CATEGORY 2. IDENTIFICATION: Schenkl, 3-Inch, Shell, U.S. Weight — 9.2. SOURCE: Abbot. REMARKS: Papier-maché sabot.

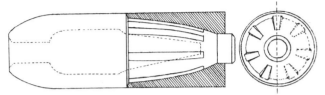

FIGURE: **XIII-17** CATEGORY 2. IDENTIFICATION: Schenkl, 3-Inch, Shell, U.S. Weight — 7.8. SOURCE: Abbot. REMARKS: Papier-maché sabot.

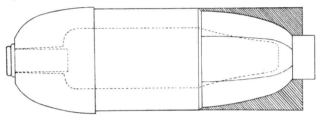

FIGURE: **XIII-18** CATEGORY 2. IDENTIFICATION: Schenkl, 4.5-Inch, Shell, U.S. Weight — 26. SOURCE: Abbot. REMARKS: 6 ratchet-shaped ribs. Papier-maché sabot.

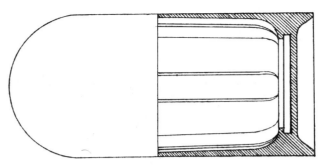

FIGURE: **XIII-19** CATEGORY 2. IDENTIFICATION: Dyer, 4.5-Inch, Shot, U.S. Weight — 31. SOURCE: Abbot. REMARKS: Lead sabot cast upon base and rear half of projectile.

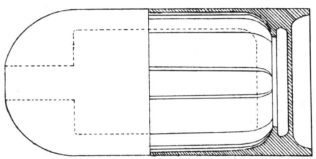

FIGURE: **XIII-20** CATEGORY 2. IDENTIFICATION: Dyer, 4.5-Inch, Shell, U.S. Weight — 23. SOURCE: Abbot. REMARKS: Lead sabot cast upon base and rear half of projectile.

made to correct the latter deficiency by covering it with a thin layer of zinc, but without marked success. As a consequence, thousands of rounds were condemned and the projectile's reputation suffered.

The peculiar shape of the Schenkl makes it among the easiest of U.S. projectiles to recognize and identification can be confirmed by the brass fuse stamped with the name of the maker, J. P. Schenkl, as well as the patent date.

Dyer projectiles went through several model changes, the product of continued experimentation by their inventor, General Alexander Brydie Dyer (1815-1874), who in 1864 became chief of the U.S. Ordnance Department. One, a Category 2 type (Figs. XIII-19 and 20), was used extensively in 4.5-inch siege rifles during the Richmond Campaign. The lead sabot of this model extended about half-way up the iron body which was ribbed to prevent slipping.

A Category 7 Dyer (Fig. XIII-21), which made its appearance just after the war, had a lead cup grooved to facilitate expansion into the rifling. It was greatly improved by addition of the time fuse and igniter shield developed at the Washington Arsenal and stamped with the inventor's name and date, "Taylor, 1865." The shield, placed over the nose of the projectile, funneled the flame of discharge directly to the ignition holes in the fuse.

Dyer also is said to have invented the Category 7 shell with polyhedral interior (Fig. XIII-22). Like the Confederate segmented spherical shell, it was intended to break into a specified number of fragments. The sabot consisted of soft metal fins sweated onto the body of the projectile in position to be squeezed into the rifling.

The Hotchkiss projectile, made by Hotchkiss and Sons of New York and one of the leading types

FIGURE: XIII-21 LOCATION: West Point, N.Y. CATEGORY 7. IDENTIFICATION: Dyer, 3-Inch, Shell, U.S. REMARKS: Late model Dyer. Lead sabot. Time fuse and igniter shield marked with the inventor's name, "Taylor" and patent date, April 11, 1865.

FIGURE: XIII-22 LOCATION: West Point, N.Y. CATEGORY 7. IDENTIFICATION: Dyer, 3.67-Inch, Shell, U.S. Length — 6.25. REMARKS: Polyhedral cavity designed to aid fragmentation. Fin-like lead sabot was sweated to shell base and forced into rifling at discharge.

of field ammunition throughout the war, was designed in 1855, but ignored by the Ordnance Department until the start of hostilities, which brought about large and continued orders for shot, shell, case, and canister, the latter unrifled. Various calibers up to 12-inch were produced, but by 1864 larger sizes were proscribed, except for testing, in the belief they caused excessive strain on the bore. However, field calibers, particularly 3- and 3.67-inches, were considered excellent ammunition, even winning praise from the vitriolic Wiard who prescribed the shot, shell, and case for his rifles.

The Hotchkiss falls into Category 3 and was composed of three parts—a cast iron body, cast iron cup, and a lead band between (Figs. XIII-23 and 24). Discharge forced the cup forward squeezing the lead into the rifling. Pressure of the cup against the body of the shell prevented slipping of the band which was covered on the exterior with greased canvas. Time fuse shell and case generally had longitudinal grooves which permitted access of the discharge flame to the fuse and reduced strain by providing a certain amount of windage. Three is the usual number, but some large calibers had 5 and a few none. Grooves normally, but not always, were absent on shot such as that in Figure XIII-25 found at Manassas. The round is stamped "Hotchkiss, Pat. 1855," and the date of manufacture, though difficult to read, seems to be May 14, 1861. This type of marking is traditional with U.S. Hotchkiss rounds and is an aid in distinguishing them from Confederate copies.

Figure XIII-26 illustrates an unfired Hotchkiss case in the West Point collection and Figure XIII-27 a fired case which broke open, but failed to explode, now displayed in the National Park Museum at Chancellorsville. It is 4.5-inch and roughly 10 inches long, the West Point specimen 3 and 6.75 inches.

The huge projectile in Figure XIII-28 is listed on Washington Navy Yard records as a 12-inch, 600-pound Hotchkiss shot, but judging from the pro-

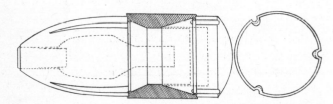

FIGURE: XIII-23 CATEGORY 3. IDENTIFICATION: Hotchkiss, 3.67-Inch, Shell, U.S. Weight — 19. SOURCE: Abbot. REMARKS: Separate cast iron cup squeezed lead band around center into the rifling.

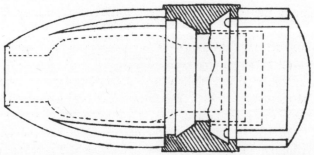

FIGURE: XIII-24 CATEGORY 3. IDENTIFICATION: Hotchkiss, 3-Inch, Shell, U.S. Weight — 9. SOURCE: Abbot. REMARKS: Separate cast iron cup squeezed lead band around center into rifling.

FIGURE: XIII-25 LOCATION: Manassas, Va. CATEGORY 3. IDENTIFICATION: Hotchkiss, 3.67-Inch, Shot, U.S. Length — 7.25. REMARKS: Separate cast iron cup squeezed central lead band into rifling at discharge. Bottom is marked: "Hotchkiss, Pat. 1855, May 14, 1861."

FIGURE: XIII-27 LOCATION: Chancellorsville, Va. CATEGORY 3. IDENTIFICATION: Hotchkiss, 4.5-Inch, Case, U.S. REMARKS: Broken nose of projectile shows lead balls in matrix. Separate cast iron cup squeezed lead band into rifling at discharge.

FIGURE: XIII-26 LOCATION: West Point, N.Y. CATEGORY 3. IDENTIFICATION: Hotchkiss, 3-Inch, Case, U.S. Length — 7. REMARKS: Separate cast iron cup squeezed lead band into rifling at discharge. Note one of three grooves to permit access of flame to time fuse.

FIGURE: XIII-28 LOCATION: Washington Navy Yard, D.C. CATEGORY 1 (tentative, see text). IDENTIFICATION: Hotchkiss, 12-Inch, U.S. Length — 24. REMARKS: Listed on Navy Yard records as 600-Pounder Hotchkiess Shot. However, in view of protuberance in the nose, which may be a form of fuse plug, and 5 grooves in the side, the projectile may be a shell, see text.

297

truding plug at the top, could be a shell. The plug presumably protects a cavity for either a fuse or lifting eye. If the former, the round doubtless is a shell and the five parallel grooves along the side are designed to let flame to the time train. If the cavity held a lifting eye during manufacture or for insertion prior to loading, the grooves were intended to reduce the strain by providing windage. Since the grooves are not slanted, they were not expected to fit the lands—as did the Rodman 12-inch (Fig. XIII-29)—and the projectile likely had a Category 1, rear sabot. Its caliber and presence at the Navy Yard would indicate it was made for one of the experimental 15-inch Dahlgrens bored to 12 inches and rifled.

The Rodman, also located at the Navy Yard, is probably one of twenty-five which the major reported sending to Fort Monroe for use in his 15-inch, bored to 12 and rifled. These rounds, he told the Senate Committee[8] ". . . have grooves cut in them so that they are locked with the gun and cannot get out without rotating. . . ." The shot weighs about 600 pounds and has 7 grooves, slanted to conform to the twist of the rifling. Rodman's method of grooving the projectile to fit the lands places the projectile in Category 5. However, this is an unusual form for this category which normally involves projectiles flanged to fit the grooves. The round is listed out of context for comparison with the Hotchkiss, for the 12-inch Rodmans, sent to Monroe with a similar number of 8-inch, must be considered experimental projectiles and not general issue.

Specimens of Absterdam projectiles are far from prevalent in today's collections although more than 60,000 shot, shell, and case were purchased by the federal government.[9] Field calibers were 3-, 4.2- and 4.5-inch, but there is also record of Absterdam shot and shell being used to test a 7-inch wrought iron Ames rifle at Bridgeport, Connecticut in the fall of 1864. No performance data has been found on the 3-, or 4.2-inch, but Abbot considered the 4.5 ". . . an utter failure . . ." since 144 tumbled out of 209 tested.[10] The 7-inch also had a miserable record. Of four rounds fired, the single shell went to pieces in the bore and flight of shot, which weighed 119 pounds 8 ounces, was erratic.[11]

The Category 1 Absterdam (Fig. XIII-30) had a lead sabot prevented from slipping by the grooves in the projectile base. "Bourrelets," machined ridges encircling the projectile, front and rear, helped center the round in the bore. They are unusual in U.S. ammunition although many Confederate projectiles had iron bands cast as an integral part of the body.

A 4.5-inch shell at West Point (Fig. XIII-31)

weighs 32.5 pounds and has characteristic saw cuts in the cup rim to facilitate expansion. One of these narrow grooves is dimly visible above the point of the small notch. Saw cuts in the sabot seem to be a mark of the Absterdam and may be used to differentiate the late model Absterdam (Fig. XIII-32), introduced in 1864, from the Parrott which it closely resembles.

Sawyer projectiles were made in several calibers, but the main testing seems to have been with 5.862- and 3.67-inch. Abbot[12] reported the larger size performed well until the gun, which had been fired extensively at Fort Monroe, exploded and put an end to the tests. The ten rounds fired, however, were serviceable.

The 5.862-inch Sawyer (Fig. XIII-33) had six flanges to follow the grooves of the rifling relegating it to Category 5. A thin coating of lead was cast over the flanged section to reduce wear on the bore and at the same time eliminate windage. Figure XIII-34 is a 5.862-inch Sawyer shell found at Fort Monroe and probably one of those intended for testing the same rifle which Abbot later burst.

FIGURE: XIII-29 LOCATION: Washington Navy Yard, D.C. CATEGORY 5. IDENTIFICATION: Rodman, 12-Inch, Shot, U.S. REMARKS: Listed on Navy Yard records as 600 pound Rodman shot. Probably it was designed for the 15-Inch Rodman cast and bored to 12-inch rifle and tested at Fort Monroe. Note 7 slanted grooves designed to fit the lands.

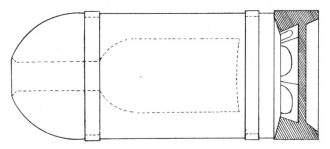

FIGURE: **XIII-30** CATEGORY 1. IDENTIFICATION: Abster-dam, 4.5-Inch, Shell, U.S. Weight — 32.5. SOURCE: Abbot. REMARKS: Lead sabot. Two narrow rings, or bourrelets, of lead cast on body of projectile.

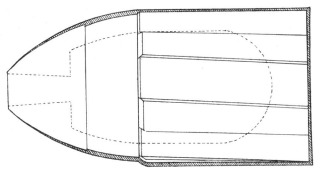

FIGURE: **XIII-33** CATEGORY 5. IDENTIFICATION: Sawyer, 5.862-Inch, Shell, U.S. Weight — 41. SOURCE: Abbot. RE-MARKS: Lead-coated flanges fit grooves of the bore.

FIGURE: **XIII-31** LOCATION: West Point, N.Y. CATEGORY 1. IDENTIFICATION: Absterdam, 4.5-Inch, Shell, U.S. Length — 10.75. Weight — 32.5. REMARKS: Lead sabot. Note saw cut in sabot base and two lead rings, or bourrelets, cast on body of projectile.

FIGURE: **XIII-34** LOCATION: Fort Monroe, Va. CATEGORY 5. IDENTIFICATION: Sawyer, 5.862-Inch, Shell, U.S. Length — 10. REMARKS: Lead-coated flanges fit grooves of the bore.

FIGURE: **XIII-32** LOCATION: West Point, N.Y. CATEGORY 1. IDENTIFICATION: Absterdam, 3-Inch, Shell, U.S. Length — 8.75. Weight — 12. REMARKS: 1864 model. Brass sabot. Note three of six saw cuts in base.

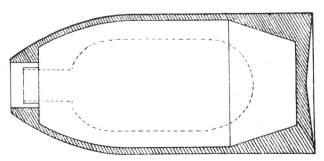

FIGURE: **XIII-35** CATEGORY 6. IDENTIFICATION: Sawyer, 3.67-Inch, Shell, U.S. Weight — 13.2. SOURCE: Abbot. RE-MARKS: Lead covering was forced into rifling at discharge.

Eighty-one out of one hundred and five caliber 3.67 Sawyers took the grooves successfully, but many lost their sabot in flight, Abbot recalled.[13] This projectile (Fig. XIII-35) was quite different from the larger size and utilized the Category 6 principle of coating the entire projectile with soft metal which expanded into the rifling at discharge. The covering of a West Point specimen (Fig. XIII-36) has been sectionalized to show the iron shell within.

There is a possibility that the projectile in Figure XIII-37 is an experimental 3.67-inch Sawyer shot. Rust prevents accurate measurement, but the round seems to be a scant 3.6-inch which would leave sufficient room for the covering. General resemblance to the Sawyer is strong and splines on the boattail would improve performance by preventing the covering from slipping. The round was recovered at Fort Monroe along with the 5.862-inch, lending weight to the theory while lack of recoveries elsewhere minimizes chances of its being Confederate. However, identification pending additional evidence is strictly tentative. Both rounds are preserved at Monroe's Casemate Museum.

At the beginning of the war, the North began rifling existing smoothbores to fit a projectile developed by General James, inventor of the rifle which bears his name. Most James projectiles fitted rifled smoothbore calibers, 6- through 42-pounder as well as his 3.8-inch rifles, but a small number of 5.1-, 8- and 12-inch rounds were also made, apparently for test purposes. James shot were generally considered to be double the weight of similar caliber spheres—a 42-pounder (7-inch) James weighing 84 pounds, for instance. However, exact weights shaded these figures a bit and the 42-pounder averaged 81.25 pounds. Shells were considerably lighter, the same caliber weighing about 64 pounds.

James made shot, shell, and canister and his projectiles were highly praised at the beginning of the war, giving good service to General Gillmore in the bombardment of Fort Pulaski where specimens such as the 5.8-inch (Fig. XIII-38) are uncovered every now and then during excavation work. Although later U.S. ammunition was infinitely superior and the James fell into disrepute, judged in the light of its time, it probably was a better projectile than detractors would have us believe.

The general made two models, both in Category 2, operating on the principle of a lengthy soft-metal covering being forced into the grooves and prevented from slipping by ribs. They differed widely in appearance with the earlier, Type 1, being considerably more common today.

The Type 1 James consists of a cast iron body shaped like a football with a cage of slanted iron ribs starting near the middle and extending beyond the lower end. The soft-metal covering was composed of light tin plate over a layer of lead with greased canvas

FIGURE: XIII-36 LOCATION: West Point, N.Y. CATEGORY 6. IDENTIFICATION: Sawyer, 3.67-Inch, Shell, U.S. Length — 8.3. REMARKS: Sectionalized to show lead covering over cast-iron projectile.

FIGURE: XIII-37 LOCATION: Fort Monroe, Va. CATEGORY 6. IDENTIFICATION: Sawyer (tentative) 3.67-Inch, Shell. Length — 8. REMARKS: Note ribbed boattail. See text.

FIGURE: XIII-38 LOCATION: Fort Pulaski, Ga. CATEGORY 2. IDENTIFICATION: James, 5.82-Inch, Shell, U.S. Length — 11.25. REMARKS: Unfired round. See text for operation. Type 1.

FIGURE: XIII-39 LOCATION: West Point, N.Y. CATEGORY 2. IDENTIFICATION: James, 3.8-Inch, Shot, U.S. Length — 8.75. Weight — 14. REMARKS: Type 1 James sectionalized to show soft-metal covering iron ribs.

FIGURE: XIII-40 LOCATION: Tradd St. Pharmacy, Charleston, S.C. CATEGORY 2. IDENTIFICATION: James, 7-Inch, Shot, U.S. Length — 12.9. REMARKS: Photographed at angle to illustrate rib cage. ten openings.

FIGURE: XIII-41 LOCATION: Vicksburg, Miss. CATEGORY 2. IDENTIFICATION: James, 3.8-Inch, Shot, U.S. Length — 7.68. REMARKS: Type 2 James. Portion of lead covering remains between several of the eight ribs.

wrapped and sewed around the outside. Gases of discharge entered the open center of the cage and expanding through openings between the ribs, forced the soft-metal into the grooves, the greased canvas serving to lubricate the rifling. Figure XIII-39 is a West Point 3.8-inch, or 14-pounder, James shot with half the soft metal removed to show the method of operation. A beautiful 7-inch specimen (Fig. XIII-40) found in the Charleston area illustrates the arrangement of the cage.

James later found the openings were unnecessary and a simpler arrangement of eight wide ribs worked as well or better. One of these Type 2 projectiles, a 3.8-inch shot (Fig. XIII-41) in the Vicksburg National Military Park collection, still retains part of the lead covering. Operation was about the same as Type 1 in that gases of discharge entered between the ribs and forced the soft metal into the rifling.

U.S. inventors turned out a number of projectiles which were tested by the government and either condemned or used only to a limited extent. Specimens of some of these have been preserved, others are only names pending discovery and identification. Admiral Dahlgren in connection with gun design, carried out lengthy experimentation on ammunition, but his projectile seems to have received relatively little use while Parrotts and Schenkls were rammed through his tubes.

301

Two 3.4-inch Dahlgrens—also known as JAD projectiles—are in the West Point collection. The shell (Fig. XIII-42) with lead sabot weighs 11 pounds, 5 ounces, and the shot (Fig. XIII-43) with sabot missing, 8 pounds. Both shot and shell are rare today and the few specimens of the latter observed have been "blind shells" containing black sand instead of powder, held in place by a copper plug in the fuse hole. Four shallow flanges are cast on the body, but since the 3.4-inch JAD was intended for the rifled boat howitzer which has 12 grooves, this caliber probably rode the lands and the Category 1 lead sabot imparted twist.

This did not hold true for larger calibers, however, for Lieutenant Simpson[14] in 1862 described a 150-pounder (7.5-inch) Dahlgren shell as ". . . cylindro-conical in form and made of cast iron with leaden base; projections to fit the grooves are cast on the front or iron portion of the cylinder. . . ." The lieutenant's description leaves little room for argument and relegates the 150-pounder—and probably other large calibers—to Category 5. The lead, while doubtless aiding the projectile to follow the grooves, would have had the primary role of reducing windage.

General Abbot, in addition to his propensity for collecting ammunition, turned his mind to invention and produced the Category 7 projectile (Fig. XIII-44) listed on West Point records as 3.5 inches in diameter and about 6.5 long. The shot apparently had a band of soft metal or other material which fitted into the groove near the middle. Small holes, visible in the groove, indicate that pressure from the discharge gases flowing through them expanded the band into the rifling.

Although Wiard adopted Hotchkiss shot, shell, and case for his rifles, he developed an ingenious canister which neither scarred the lands nor picked up the rifle motion to scatter widely as it left the bore—twin faults that discouraged use of common canister in rifles.

Wiard's projectile (Fig. XIII-45) was composed of a cast iron case in sections (c), loaded with shot and held together by wire. All sections were rounded leaving no sharp edges to abrade the bore. They were connected by the wire (E) extending from the hook (e) in end-casting (R) to projections (g) in the end-casting (A). Also at (g) were small holes which allowed discharge gases to enter the projectile. The strain sheared the bolt (e), made weak for this purpose, and stretched the canister longitudinally. Pressure against the sides dropped as the case extended thus minimizing the tendency to expand against the rifling which caused the twist in common canister.

Cochran, developer of the previously described breechloader also designed ammunition including the 3.67-inch flanged shot (Fig. XIII-46). Twin copper rings forced into the rifling by pressure against the iron base plate place the Cochran in Category 7, for although operation was similar to that of the Category 3 Hotchkiss, the rings are near the base of the projectile and the iron plate is an integral part of the shot, not separate. The flanges were designed for stabilization in flight and were not intended to enter the grooves of the bore.

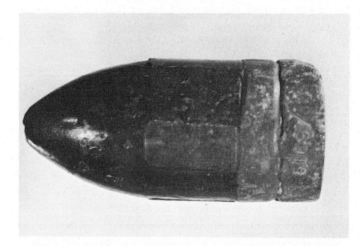

FIGURE: XIII-42 LOCATION: West Point, N.Y. CATEGORY 1. IDENTIFICATION: Dahlgren, 3.4-Inch, Shell, U.S. Length — 7.75. Weight — 11.3. REMARKS: "Blind Shell" filled with black sand and fuse hole permanently closed with copper plug. Lead sabot. Flanges intended to ride lands, not enter grooves. See text.

FIGURE: XIII-43 LOCATION: West Point, N.Y. CATEGORY 1. IDENTIFICATION: Dahlgren, 3.4-Inch, Shot, U.S. Length — 7.25. Weight — 8 (without sabot). REMARKS: Lead sabot missing.

FIGURE: XIII-44 LOCATION: West Point, N.Y. CATEGORY 7. IDENTIFICATION: Abbot, 3.67-Inch, Shot, U.S. Length — 6.5. REMARKS: Projectile measures 3.5-inch diameter, but presumably was designed for a 3.67-inch rifle. Note holes in central groove which permitted discharge gases to expand band of unidentified material into the rifling.

FIGURE: XIII-46 LOCATION: West Point, N.Y. CATEGORY 7. IDENTIFICATION: Cochran, 3.67-Inch, Shot, U.S. Length — 7.5. REMARKS: Diagonally flanged shot. Copper rings sabot.

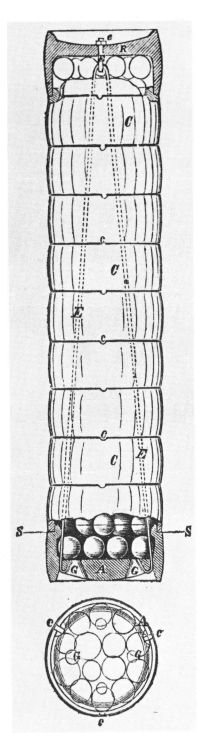

FIGURE: XIII-45 IDENTIFICATION: Wiard, Canister, U.S. SOURCE: Wiard's System of Field Artillery, 1863. REMARKS: C — Cast iron sections of case; E — Wire; e — Hook; R — End casting, front; A — End casting, base; G — Projections to hold wire, also holes; S — Joint. Note: Although fired from Wiard Rifles, projectile was designed not to pick up the rifle motion or scar the lands.

303

Stafford sub-caliber projectiles for use against ironclads offered the armor-punching capabilities of a small diameter bolt fired from a large caliber rifle on somewhat the principle of a hammer driving a nail. The projectile seems to have been made in several forms, but the drawing (Fig. XIII-47) will show the method of enclosing the bolt in a casing of wood affixed to a Category 1 brass sabot at rear. Upon striking armor, the bolt smashed through while the wood casing was left in splinters on the outside.

Stafford also made shell (Fig. XIII-48) on the same principle with an unusual side fuse. However, the bursting charge was necessarily small. Two 6.4-inch Staffords at West Point are shown in Figure XIII-49. That at left has a wood body enclosing a 4.5-inch steel bolt, and a steel base plate behind the brass sabot. The other has iron enclosing the bolt, but operates in similar fashion. Holley[15] mentions a sub-caliber projectile weighing 70 pounds and consisting of 4.62 inch steel bolt encased in wood with a brass sabot being fired from a 6.4-inch Parrott at West Point September 5, 1862. The round, presumably a Stafford, penetrated 6 inches of wrought iron plate backed by logs.

Stafford also made an 8-inch model for we find Admiral Dahlgren[16] in July 1863 ordering monitors in the South Atlantic Blockading Squadron to load 8-inch Parrotts at night with "Stafford projectiles" in case Confederate ironclads appeared. An unidentified Stafford projectile (Fig. XIII-50) utilized a Category 1 sabot which depended on friction of the rim of the brass cup forced over the projectile base to prevent slipping on discharge. According to Holley,[17] this form was used in Stafford's "new" projectile.

The Dimick, brainchild of Horace E. Dimick, had a soft-metal cup at rear and belonged in Category 1. It was mentioned[18] along with the Dyer and Dahlgren as possible ammunition for the 3-inch Ordnance Rifle during early discussion of that weapon, but seems to have lost out to the Dyer along the way.

Three other U.S. projectiles tested, but probably never put in service, were the Hersey, Mann, and Gillmore. All were used during trials of the 7-inch wrought iron Ames rifle at Bridgeport, Connecticut, in October 1864,[19] but data to determine their appearance is tantalizingly insufficient. Four Hersey shot of 111 and 112 pounds "went well," according to the testing board, but each lost a "small piece" in flight. Two Hersey sub-caliber shot, weighing 115 and 117 pounds, were also fired, but the trajectory was erratic. Five Mann shot, each weighing 96 pounds, gave irregular flight.

General Gillmore, who was a member of the testing board, also tried four of his own shot. The first, weighing 122 pounds 8 ounces and having "copper 1-inch thick," which presumably refers to the type sabot, went irregularly. The second, 121 pounds 8 ounces, with .75-inch copper, "went well." Two others, each weighing 124 pounds 4 ounces, "went slightly irregularly," but even so one gave a range of 8,270 yards.

Confederate rifle ammunition is a particularly difficult subject since few records have survived and identification must be based partially on supposition, much of it open to argument. Take the case of Dr. Read, whose rifles were described in Chapter IX and was mentioned earlier in this section as a pre-war associate of Parrott. Read patented a Category 1 soft-metal sabot projectile as early as 1856 and continued making ammunition for the Confederacy during the war. His method was to place the cup in a mold and cast the projectile around it, giving a general appearance as in Figure XIII-51. Read started with wrought iron for the cup, later used copper and occasionally even lead—presumably with a modified casting process. But should he receive credit for all Confederate projectiles falling within Category 1? Some writers, General Alexander for one, would argue in the affirmative on the basis of prior patent, but for purposes of today's hobbyists, it would be misleading.

FIGURE: XIII-47 CATEGORY 1. IDENTIFICATION: Stafford, Sub-Caliber Shot, U.S. SOURCE: Holley. REMARKS: Wood covering iron or steel bolt. Brass sabot.

FIGURE: XIII-48 CATEGORY 1. IDENTIFICATION: Stafford, Sub-Caliber Shell, U.S. SOURCE: Holley. REMARKS: Wood covering iron shell. Note side fuse. Brass sabot.

FIGURE: XIII-49 LOCATION: West Point, N.Y. CATEGORY 1. IDENTIFICATION: Stafford, 6.4-Inch, Sub-Caliber Shot, U.S. REMARKS: Left — Wood covering 4.5-inch hollow steel cylinder. Steel base plate with brass sabot. Length — 21. Right — Steel faced shot. Brass sabot. Length — 21.25.

FIGURE: XIII-50 CATEGORY 1. IDENTIFICATION: Stafford's "New Projectile," U.S. SOURCE: Holley. REMARKS: Brass sabot. Friction of sabot rim forced over projectile base prevented slipping at discharge.

number developed by other designers who used his principle, all projectiles with the cup attached by the method illustrated will be called Reads unless a different inventor is known or extra devices for holding the cup have been added.

A 3.67-inch, wrought iron cup (Fig. XIII-52) is a common form and, like most Reads, seems to have been used mainly in field and siege calibers. Figure XIII-53 is a copper cup Read at West Point and Figure XIII-54 another differing in exterior appearance which came from the previously illustrated (Fig. I-33) banded 24-pounder in the Charleston area. The entire tube of the weapon is filled with these projectiles solidly wedged by rust. This, the outermost shot, apparently fell out and was later found in the gun position.

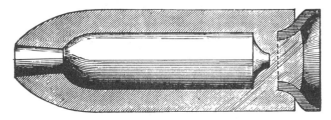

FIGURE: XIII-51 CATEGORY 1. IDENTIFICATION: Read, Shell, Confederate. SOURCE: Holley. REMARKS: Typical construction. Cast iron projectile, soft metal (wrought iron, copper, occasionally lead) cup.

FIGURE: XIII-52 LOCATION: Estes Collection, Mullins, S.C. CATEGORY 1. IDENTIFICATION: Read, 3.67-Inch, Shell, Confederate. Length — 9.25. REMARKS: Wrought iron cup.

Differences between Confederate projectiles, even of the same type, indicate that Southern foundries were quite casual with specifications and often incorporated their own ideas. Perhaps these should be classed as model changes, but sufficient data is lacking to warrant this separation and a general lumping together by class will make identification somewhat easier. Consequently, at the risk of cheating Dr. Read of a few rounds and probably giving him credit for a

Abbot attributed a large number of projectiles to Read and those which conform to the previous description follow in Figures XIII-55 through 68.

Three Reads in the West Point and Estes collections (Figs. XIII-69 through 71) are similar 3-inch rounds roughly 7.5 inches long, yet close examination will show that each has peculiarities separating it from the others, one even having a small lug cast on the ogive. Another type with similar protuberance is shown in Figure XIII-72. The bracket is quite rare and its purpose has invited considerable speculation, including fuse wrench lug, rammer stop, and purchase to facilitate holding the shell in a lathe, inadvertently left on after turning.[20] Possible evidence that the lug remained by mistake is found in the exceptionally fine Fort Jackson 3-inch (Fig. XIII-73) which seems almost identical to Figure XIII-69, but with the bracket omitted.

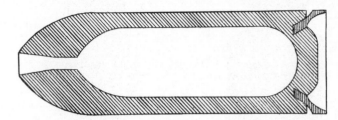

FIGURE: XIII-55 CATEGORY 1. IDENTIFICATION: Read, 4.2-Inch, Shell, Confederate. Weight — 26. SOURCE: Abbot. REMARKS: Wood fuse plug. Wrought iron cup.

FIGURE: XIII-53 LOCATION: West Point, N.Y. CATEGORY 1. IDENTIFICATION: Read, 5.3-Inch shot, Confederate. Length — 7.5. REMARKS: Copper Cup.

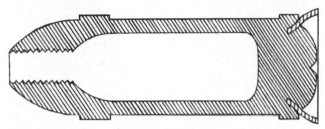

FIGURE: XIII-56 CATEGORY 1. IDENTIFICATION: Read, 3-Inch, Shell, Confederate. Weight — 8. SOURCE: Abbot. REMARKS: Wrought iron cup.

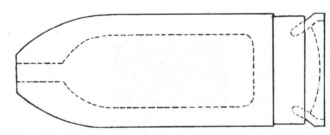

FIGURE: XIII-57 CATEGORY 1. IDENTIFICATION: Read, 3-Inch, Shell, Confederate. Weight — 8. SOURCE: Abbot. REMARKS: Wrought iron cup.

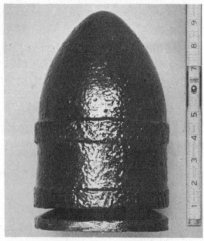

FIGURE: XIII-54 LOCATION: Author's Collection. CATEGORY 1. IDENTIFICATION: Read, 5.82-Inch, Shot, Confederate. Length — 9. Weight 40.5. REMARKS: Copper cup. One of several similar projectiles used to plug rifled 24-pounder (Fig. I-33).

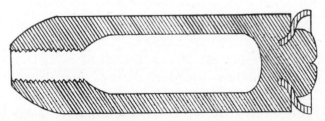

FIGURE: XIII-58 CATEGORY 1. IDENTIFICATION: Read, 3-Inch, Shell, Confederate. Weight — 10. SOURCE: Abbot. REMARKS: Wrought iron cup.

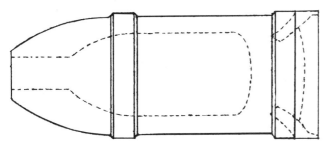

FIGURE: XIII-59 CATEGORY 1. IDENTIFICATION: Read, 3-Inch, Shell, Confederate. Weight — 7. SOURCE: Abbot. REMARKS: Copper ring.

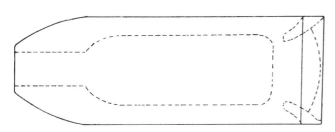

FIGURE: XIII-60 CATEGORY 1. IDENTIFICATION: Read, 3-Inch, Shell, Confederate. Weight — 9. SOURCE: Abbot. REMARKS: Copper ring.

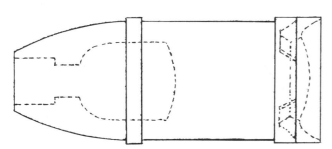

FIGURE: XIII-61 CATEGORY 1. IDENTIFICATION: Read, 3-Inch, Shell, Confederate. Weight — 6.8. SOURCE: Abbot. REMARKS: Copper ring flush with rear bourrelet.

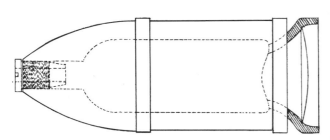

FIGURE: XIII-62 CATEGORY 1. IDENTIFICATION: Read, 4.62-Inch, Shell, Confederate. Weight — 29. SOURCE: Abbot. REMARKS: Copper cup.

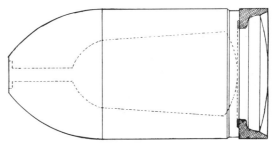

FIGURE: XIII-63 CATEGORY 1. IDENTIFICATION: Read, 7-Inch, Shell, Confederate. Weight — 91. SOURCE: Abbot. REMARKS: Copper ring.

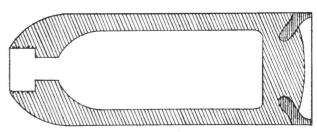

FIGURE: XIII-64 CATEGORY 1. IDENTIFICATION: Read, 3.67-Inch, Shell, Confederate. Weight — 14.5. SOURCE: Abbot. REMARKS: Copper ring.

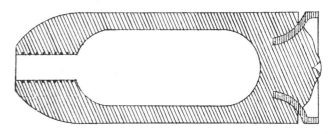

FIGURE: XIII-65 CATEGORY 1. IDENTIFICATION: Read, 3.67-Inch, Shell, Confederate. Weight — 17.7. SOURCE: Abbot. REMARKS: Wrought iron cup.

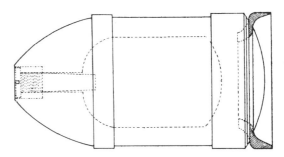

FIGURE: XIII-66 CATEGORY 1. IDENTIFICATION: Read, 6.4-Inch, Shell, Confederate. Weight — 59. SOURCE: Abbot. REMARKS: Wrought iron cup. Copper ring to receive fuse plug.

FIGURE: XIII-67 Category 1. Identification: Read, 6.4-Inch, Shell, Confederate. Weight — 58. Source: Abbot. Remarks: Wrought iron cup. Wood fuse plug.

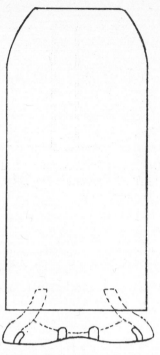

FIGURE: XIII-68 Category 1. Identification: Read, 3.67-Inch, Shot, Confederate. Weight — 19.5. Source: Abbot. Remarks: Wrought iron cup.

FIGURE: XIII-69 Location: West Point, N.Y. Category 1. Identification: Read, 3-Inch, Shell, Confederate. Length — 7.5. Remarks: Copper cup. Note lug cast on ogive.

FIGURE: XIII-71 LOCATION: Estes Collection Mullins, S.C. CATEGORY 1. IDENTIFICATION: Read, 3-Inch, Shell, Confederate. Length — 7.5. REMARKS: Copper cup. Copper time fuse plug similar to smallest model in Fig. XII-63, miscellaneous Confederate fuse plugs.

FIGURE: XIII-70 LOCATION: West, Point, N.Y. CATEGORY 1. IDENTIFICATION: Read, 3-Inch, Shell, Confederate. Length — 7.375. REMARKS: Copper cup.

FIGURE: XIII-72 LOCATION: West Point, N.Y. CATEGORY 1. IDENTIFICATION: Read, 3-Inch, Shell, Confederate. Length — 9. Weight — 12. REMARKS: Copper cup.

FIGURE: XIII-73 LOCATION: Fort Jackson, Savannah, Ga. CATEGORY 1. IDENTIFICATION: Read, 3-Inch, Shell, Confederate. Length — 7.3. REMARKS: Copper cup. Threaded copper fuse adapter.

The West Point Read (Fig. XIII-74) has been sectionalized to show the cup and the ogive curve is widened to form a bourrelet in similar fashion to the Fort Jackson specimen (Fig. XIII-75) which has a rear bourrelet in addition. Crude casting is evident in the West Point shot (Fig. XIII-76) and although the Citadel shell (Fig. XIII-77) reveals better workmanship, the copper cup was affixed at a noticeable slant.

Excellent rifling marks are visible on the 6.4-inch shot (Fig. XIII-78) in the Vicksburg National Military Park collection. Gillmore reported the same type used at Charleston. Figure XIII-79 is a 3.67-inch shot with Read type cup, but paint obscures whether it is iron or copper. The base projects beyond the cup and tapers sharply. A 4.5-inch with copper cup (Fig. XIII-80) has a fuse protected by a removable nose piece.

FIGURE: XIII-74 LOCATION: West Point, N.Y. CATEGORY 1. IDENTIFICATION: Read, 3-Inch, Shell, Confederate. Length — 7.4. Weight — 10. REMARKS: Copper ring partially removed to illustrate construction. Copper fuse plug.

FIGURE: XIII-76 LOCATION: West Point, N.Y. CATEGORY 1. IDENTIFICATION: Read, 3.8-Inch, Shot, Confederate. Length — 8. REMARKS: Copper cup. Projectile may have been intended for captured 3.8-inch James.

FIGURE: XIII-75 LOCATION: Fort Jackson, Savannah, Ga. CATEGORY 1. IDENTIFICATION: Read, 3.67-Inch, Shell, Confederate. Length — 11.1. REMARKS: Copper cup.

FIGURE: XIII-77 LOCATION: The Citadel, Charleston, S.C. CATEGORY 1. IDENTIFICATION: Read, 3.5-Inch, Shell, Confederate. Length — 9. REMARKS: Thin copper cup projects about .75-inch beyond base of shell. Note marked slant of joint.

Figure XIII-81 of three West Point projectiles—a Confederate Parrott flanked by two Reads—emphasizes the general resemblance of Confederate Parrotts to many of the Alabama doctor's projectiles. Consequently, for identification purposes, only those which have the external appearance of U.S. Parrotts and similar gear-like indentations around the base to prevent the cup from slipping, will be classed as Confederate Parrotts.

The indentations are clearly visible in the previous illustration and are also evident in Figures XIII-82 and 83. These specimens were collected by Abbot

FIGURE: **XIII-80** LOCATION: West Point, N.Y. CATEGORY 1. IDENTIFICATION: Read, 4.5-Inch, Shell, Confederate. Length — 7.5. REMARKS: Copper cup. Fuse protected by removable copper nose piece.

FIGURE: **XIII-78** LOCATION: Vicksburg, Miss. CATEGORY 1. IDENTIFICATION: Read, 6.4-Inch, Shot, Confederate. Length — 8. REMARKS: Copper ring.

FIGURE: **XIII-81** LOCATION: West Point, N.Y. CATEGORY 1 (all). IDENTIFICATION: Left to right:
Read, 4.62-Inch, Shell, Confederate.
Length — 12. Weight — 29. Copper cup.
Parrott, 4.2-Inch, Shell, Confederate.
Length — 12. Copper ring with gear-like indentations.
Read, 3.67-Inch, Shell, Confederate.
Length — 10 (excluding fuse). Weight — 17.7. Copper cup, copper fuse plug.

FIGURE: **XIII-79** LOCATION: West Point, N.Y. CATEGORY 1. IDENTIFICATION: Read, 3.67-Inch, Shot, Confederate. Length — 5.6. REMARKS: Metal of cup is obscured by paint, but probably is copper.

and illustrate a change in shape of large-caliber Confederate Parrotts made during the Richmond Campaign in a successful effort to improve their ballistic qualities by shortening the projectile.[21] A bolt (Fig. XIII-84) has a copper sabot attached in approximately the same way as do the 4.2-inch shells (Figs. XIII-85 and 86) which have a marked exterior resemblance to similar caliber U.S. Parrotts.

Abbot[22] felt the form of copper cup in the 4.2-inch Confederate Parrott (Fig. XIII-87) was

". . . decidedly more successful than that of Parrott. The projectile was often thrown into our batteries and some captured samples were fired from a 30-pounder Parrott at the enemy. So far as we could judge, it was free from the three greatest faults to which this system is liable, viz: failing to take the grooves, throwing off the ring, and chipping off dangerous fragments from the base of the shell. The troublesome use of the cold chisel for starting the ring is also avoided. In my judgment, this pattern ought to be thoroughly tested with a view to use in our own service. . . ."

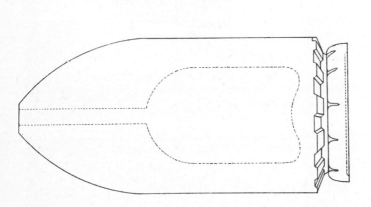

FIGURE: **XIII-82** CATEGORY 1. IDENTIFICATION: Parrot, 8-Inch, Shell, Confederate. Weight — 145. SOURCE: Abbot.

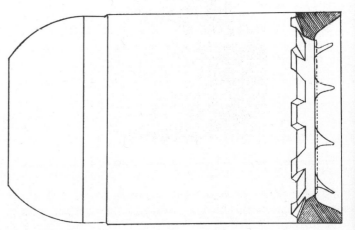

FIGURE: **XIII-84** CATEGORY 1. IDENTIFICATION: Parrott, 8-Inch, Bolt, Confederate. Weight — 153. SOURCE: Abbot. REMARKS: Copper ring.

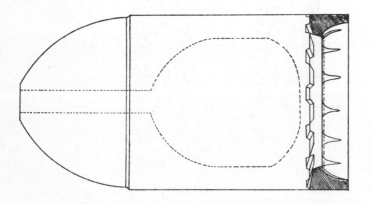

FIGURE: **XIII-83** CATEGORY 1. IDENTIFICATION: Parrott, 8-Inch, Shell, Confederate. Weight — 131. SOURCE: Abbot. REMARKS: Copper ring. Captured at Tredegar Iron Works, Richmond, Va.

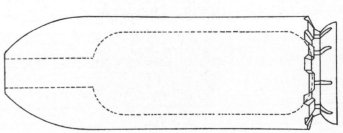

FIGURE: **XIII-85** CATEGORY 1. IDENTIFICATION: Parrott, 4.2-Inch, Shell, Confederate. Weight — 25. SOURCE: Abbot. REMARKS: Copper ring.

per cup bolted to the base of the projectile and prevented from slipping by three dowels cast either on the projectile base or the cup. Mullanes generally were restricted to large calibers,[24] but the little 2.25-inch shell at Chancellorsville National Military Park (Fig. XIII-88) falls into this category and has dowels on the projectile. The missing cup may have resembled the copper plate in the exploded view (Fig. XIII-89) of a West Point 3-inch.

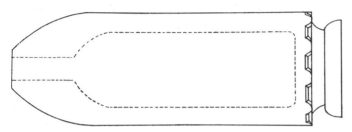

FIGURE: XIII-86 CATEGORY 1. IDENTIFICATION: Parrott, 4.2-Inch, Shell, Confederate. Weight — 25. SOURCE: Abbot. REMARKS: Missing ring was copper.

FIGURE: XIII-88 LOCATION: Chancellorsville Va. CATEGORY 1. IDENTIFICATION: Mullane, 2.25-Inch, Shell, Confederate. Length — 4.25. REMARKS: Originally had copper plate attached by center bolt and prevented from turning by three projections on base of shell.

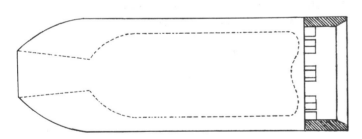

FIGURE: XIII-87 CATEGORY 1. IDENTIFICATION: Parrott, 4.2-Inch, Shell, Confederate. Weight — 26. SOURCE: Abbot. REMARKS: Copper ring, wood fuse plug. Abbot considered the ring arrangement of this type projectile superior to that of the U.S. Parrott.

General Alexander believed the next type should be called a Read since its inventor was refused papers by the Confederate Patent Office on the grounds of infringement on the doctor's principle.[23] However, since cup and method of attachment differ markedly from the previously advanced definition of a Read, the generally accepted identification of "Mullane" seems more appropriate.

Classed in Category 1, the Mullane had a cop-

FIGURE: XIII-89 LOCATION: West Point, N.Y. CATEGORY 1. IDENTIFICATION: Mullane, 3-Inch, Shell, Confederate. Length — 7.75 (including projections). REMARKS: Copper base plate, washer and bolt.

More conventional Mullanes (Figs. XIII-90 through 100) consisted of a heavy copper cup with dowels that entered corresponding holes in the projectile base. A great deal of copper was used in this type of round—up to 8 pounds in large calibers—and whether it was worth the expenditure is somewhat doubtful.

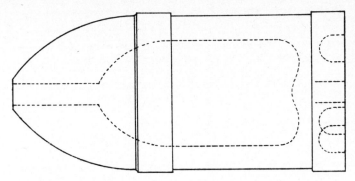

FIGURE: XIII-92 CATEGORY 1. IDENTIFICATION: Mullane, 7-Inch, Shell, Confederate. Weight — 92. SOURCE: Abbot. REMARKS: Copper cup missing.

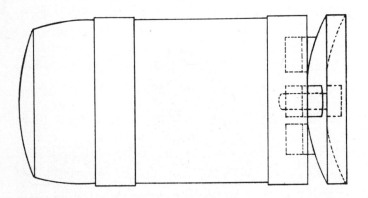

FIGURE: XIII-90 CATEGORY 1. IDENTIFICATION: Mullane, 7-Inch, Bolt, Confederate. Weight — 122. SOURCE: Abbot REMARKS: Rope lashing was between copper cup and base of projectile.

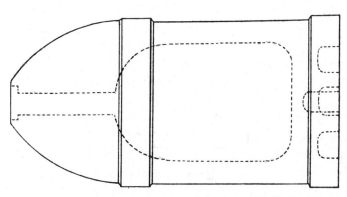

FIGURE: XIII-93 CATEGORY 1. IDENTIFICATION: Mullane, 6.4-Inch, Shell, Confederate. Weight — 58. SOURCE: Abbot. REMARKS: Copper cup missing.

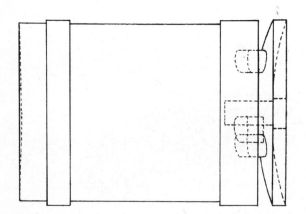

FIGURE: XIII-91 CATEGORY 1. IDENTIFICATION: Mullane, 7-Inch, Bolt, Confederate. Weight — 95. SOURCE: Abbot. REMARKS: Rope lashing between copper cup and base of projectile.

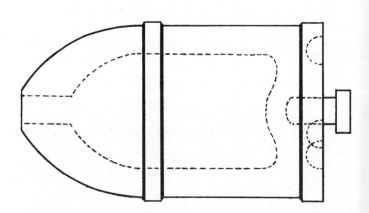

FIGURE: XIII-94 CATEGORY 1. IDENTIFICATION: Mullane, 4.62-Inch, Shell, Confederate. Weight — 21.5. SOURCE: Abbot. REMARKS: Copper cup missing.

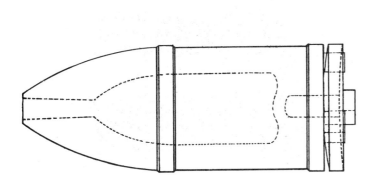

FIGURE: **XIII-95** CATEGORY 1. IDENTIFICATION: Mullane, 4.62-Inch, Shell, Confederate. Weight — 28. SOURCE: Abbot. REMARKS: Copper cup.

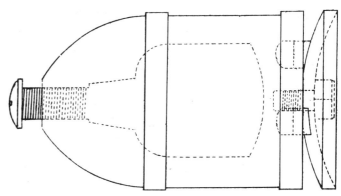

FIGURE: **XIII-98** CATEGORY 1. IDENTIFICATION: Mullane, 6.4-Inch, Shell, Confederate. Weight — 58. SOURCE: Abbot. REMARKS: Tarred rope lashing (missing) was between copper cup and projectile base. Copper percussion fuse.

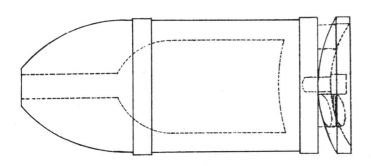

FIGURE: **XIII-96** CATEGORY 1. IDENTIFICATION: Mullane, 5.82-Inch, Shell, Confederate. Weight — 57.5. SOURCE: Abbot. REMARKS: Copper cup.

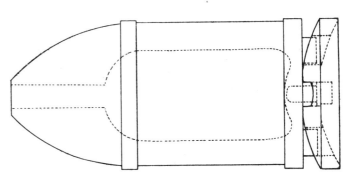

FIGURE: **XIII-99** CATEGORY 1. IDENTIFICATION: Mullane, 6.4-Inch, Shell, Confederate. Weight — 76. SOURCE: Abbot. REMARKS: Tarred rope lashing (missing) was between copper cup and projectile base. Shell was found at Fort Fisher, N.C.

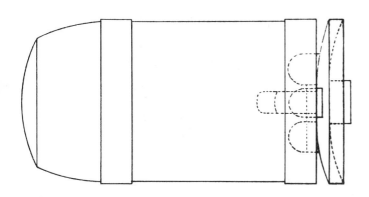

FIGURE: **XIII-97** CATEGORY 1. IDENTIFICATION: Mullane, 6.4-Inch, Bolt, Confederate. Weight — 91. SOURCE: Abbot. REMARKS: Tarred rope lashing (missing) was between copper cup and projectile base.

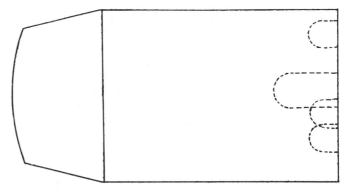

FIGURE: **XIII-100** CATEGORY 1. IDENTIFICATION: Mullane, 4.62-Inch, Bolt, Confederate. Weight — 32. SOURCE: Abbot. REMARKS: Copper cup missing.

Figure XIII-101 is a 6.4-inch shot believed to contain a small-diameter, chilled iron or steel rod in the center for punching ironclads, and Figure XIII-102 a bolt of the same caliber. Both are solid and the different terminology is based on whether the nose is rounded or flat, although the terms were loosely used and often interchanged. Both rounds originally had a brown substance, apparently grease or tallow for lubricating the bore, between cup and projectile base, but this was removed in an effort to bare the dowels. It still conceals the dowels of a 3.67-inch shot (Fig. XIII-103) which also has a heavy copper washer between cup and bolt. In addition to tallow, Abbot found several types employed a tarred rope lashing designed to control chipping.

Fort Fisher has an excellent 6.4-inch specimen (Fig. XIII-104) which holds the copper percussion fuse illustrated in the previous chapter.

The bolt—called a shot by the producer—(Fig. XIII-105) found at the Richmond Naval Laboratory had a steel plate in front and the following note pasted to it: "Steel banded shot (134 lbs) to be fired from VIII-inch rifled guns of 15,000 lbs weight against ironclad ships with a charge of 18 pounds of powder." It was signed "N.H. Van Zandt, Lieut. C.S. Navy," from headquarters of the "Chief of Bureau, Ord. and Fleet, Richmond." This was one of the forms that had a rope lashing between cup and base.

FIGURE: XIII-102 LOCATION: Author's Collection. CATEGORY 1. IDENTIFICATION: Mullane, 6.4-Inch, Bolt, Confederate. Length — 9.25. Weight — 61. REMARKS: Copper cup.

FIGURE: XIII-103 LOCATION: West Point, N.Y. CATEGORY 1. IDENTIFICATION: Mullane, 3.67-Inch, Shot, Confederate. Length — 7.5. REMARKS: Copper cup and washer. Tallow between cup and base of projectile.

FIGURE: XIII-101 LOCATION: Author's Collection. CATEGORY 1. IDENTIFICATION: Mullane, 6.4-Inch, Shot, Confederate. Length — 11.5. Weight — 68. REMARKS: Copper cup. Believed to have chilled iron or steel rod in center for punching ironclads.

FIGURE: XIII-104 LOCATION: Fort Fisher, N.C. CATEGORY 1. IDENTIFICATION: Mullane, 6.4-Inch, Shell, Confederate. Length — 13. REMARKS: Copper cup. Copper percussion fuse illustrated in Fig. XII-65. Copper fuse adapter screwed into shell.

Evidence that the Mullane postdated the Read— Alexander said it came to the field in 1862—is shown in Figures XIII-106 and 107, two rounds captured at Fort Harrison. In the former, a wrought iron, Read cup was replaced by the copper Mullane form and in the latter a copper ring was removed in favor of the doweled cup.

Ammunition collectors are reminded that certain Mullanes, as described in Chapter XII, may have the appearance of bolts, but be shells equipped with a base fuse. The warning might also be extended to the ratchet base, or "Brooke," for although none of this type has been reported, the round seems readily adaptable to its use.

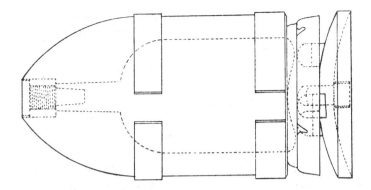

FIGURE: XIII-107 CATEGORY 1. IDENTIFICATION: Mullane, 6.4-Inch, Shell, Confederate. Weight — 60. SOURCE: Abbot. REMARKS: Condemned copper ring removed and replaced by copper cup of Mullane form. Tarred rope lashing (missing) was between cup and shell base. Copper fuse adapter. Captured at Fort Harrison.

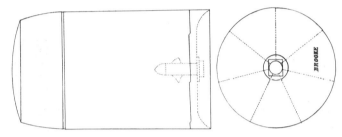

FIGURE: XIII-108 CATEGORY 1. IDENTIFICATION: Brooke, 8-Inch, Bolt, Confederate. Weight — 157. SOURCE: Abbot. REMARKS: Brooke's name stamped on copper cup.

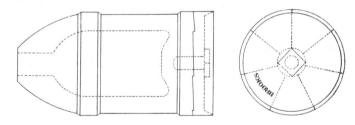

FIGURE: XIII-109 CATEGORY 1. IDENTIFICATION: Brooke, 7-Inch, Case, Confederate. Weight — 91. SOURCE: Abbot. REMARKS: Copper cup stamped with Brooke's name, misspelled. Time fuse with double plug for insertion of balls. Projectile appears readily adaptable for use as shell.

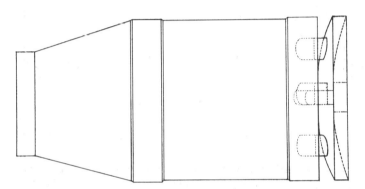

FIGURE: XIII-105 CATEGORY 1. IDENTIFICATION: Mullane, 8-Inch, Bolt, Confederate. Weight — Listed by Abbot as 136, but in note attached to projectile as 134. SOURCE: Abbot. REMARKS: Copper cup, steel plate on nose. See text for accompanying note.

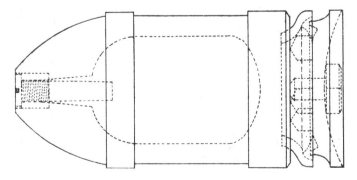

FIGURE: XIII-106 CATEGORY 1. IDENTIFICATION: Mullane, 6.4-Inch, Shell, Confederate. Weight — 64. SOURCE: Abbot. REMARKS: Wrought iron cup of original Read shell replaced by copper cup of Mullane type. Projectile captured at Fort Harrison.

Projectiles with a copper cup bolted, like the Mullane, to the base, but with a series—usually seven, occasionally six—of slanted indentations resembling shallow ratchets are attributed by most hobbyists to Brooke. Justification for the belief is based primarily on two 7-inch projectiles (Figs. XIII-108 and 109), picked up by Abbot during the Richmond Campaign, which had Brooke's name, albeit misspelled in one case, stamped on the copper cup. Moreover, the projectile was used extensively with Brooke guns and in this connection was often called in the Official Records a "ratchet service bolt."[25] Consequently, all such rounds, for the sake of uniformity, will be arbitrarily assigned to Brooke unless future evidence proves one or more the product of another inventor.

General Abbot, who acquired a fair number of different type ratchet base projectiles, illustrates one (Fig. XIII-110) which could fall into this category. The round is stamped with the initials "Lt. R.D.M."

and "RNOW." These presumably stand for Lieutenant Robert D. Minor who was commander of the Richmond Naval Ordnance Works. Perhaps the round should be called a "Minor," but since no corroborative evidence has been found that the lieutenant was an inventor and since the initials of a government facility are also present—often the case in gun marking—it seems more logical to call the shell a Brooke, manufactured under Minor's supervision.

Another in the Abbot collection (Fig. XIII-111) was an extremely long shell with extensive

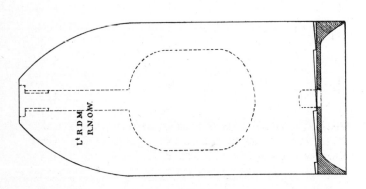

FIGURE: XIII-110 CATEGORY 1. IDENTIFICATION: Brooke, 7-Inch, Shell, Confederate. Weight — 100. SOURCE: Abbot. REMARKS: Copper cup. Ogive stamped with initials of Lt. Robert D. Minor, commander of the Richmond Naval Ordnance Works.

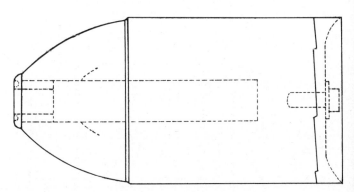

FIGURE: XIII-112 CATEGORY 1. IDENTIFICATION: Brooke, 7-Inch, Case, Confederate. Weight — 94. SOURCE: Abbot. REMARKS: Copper cup with iron washer. Copper fuse plug with leather washer. Tin tube for bursting charge soldered to fuse plug.

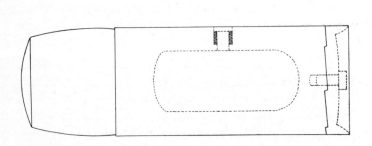

FIGURE: XIII-111 CATEGORY 1. IDENTIFICATION: Brooke, 7-Inch, Shell, Confederate. Weight — 169. SOURCE: Abbot. REMARKS: Copper cup. Heavy weight of metal in front and side fuse indicates projectile was designed for punching ironclads.

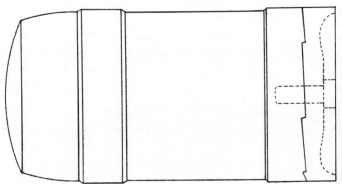

FIGURE: XIII-113 CATEGORY 1. IDENTIFICATION: Brooke, 7-Inch, Bolt, Confederate. Weight — 120. SOURCE: Abbot. REMARKS: Copper cup.

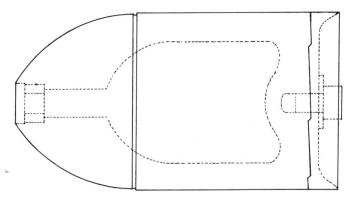

FIGURE: **XIII-114** CATEGORY 1. IDENTIFICATION: Brooke, 8-Inch, Shell, Confederate. Weight — 117. SOURCE: Abbot. REMARKS: Copper cup with iron washer.

metal in front of the cavity and an unusual side fuse. Found at Richmond, it was evidently designed for punching ironclads.

Case is seldom seen with ratchet sabot, but one of these rare projectiles (Fig. XIII-112), a 7-inch, has a copper cup strengthened by an iron washer around the bolt. A copper fuse plug with leather washer was used, and the bursting charge was contained in a tin tube soldered to the plug.

Additional varieties acquired by Abbot are shown in Figures XIII-113 through 118.

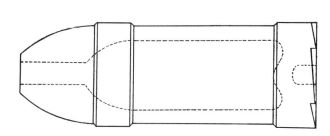

FIGURE: **XIII-115** CATEGORY 1. IDENTIFICATION: Brooke, 4.2-Inch, Shell, Confederate. Weight — 25. SOURCE: Abbot. REMARKS: Copper cup missing.

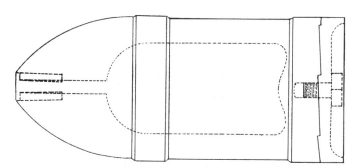

FIGURE: **XIII-117** CATEGORY 1. IDENTIFICATION: Brooke, 7-Inch, Shell, Confederate. Weight — 95.5. SOURCE: Abbot. REMARKS: Copper cup. One specimen found at Richmond marked "Anderson Rifle, 7"."

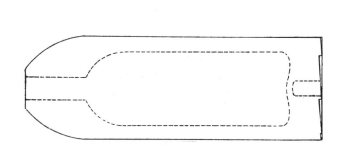

FIGURE: **XIII-116** CATEGORY 1. IDENTIFICATION: Brooke, 4.2-Inch, Shell, Confederate. Weight — 24.5. SOURCE: Abbot. REMARKS: Copper cup missing.

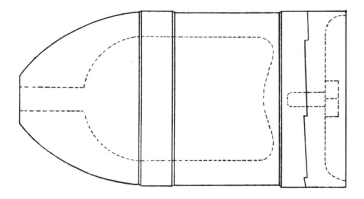

FIGURE: **XIII-118** CATEGORY 1. IDENTIFICATION: Brooke, 7-Inch, Shell, Confederate. Weight — 73. SOURCE: Abbot. REMARKS: Copper cup.

A 4.62-inch shell with a copper fuse (Fig. XIII-119) and 6.4-inch bolt (Fig. XIII-120) are missing sabots, but may be identified by the ratchet base as in Figure XIII-121 of the latter round.

An unfired 7-inch shell (Fig. XIII-122) in the Washington Navy Yard collection marked "Fort Fisher," shows the tight joint between cup and projectile base.

FIGURE: XIII-121 LOCATION: Author's Collection CATEGORY 1. IDENTIFICATION: Brooke, 6.4-Inch, Bolt, Confederate. REMARKS: Base of Fig. 120 showing appearance of ratchets.

FIGURE: XIII-119 LOCATION: Estes Collection, Mullins, S.C. CATEGORY 1. IDENTIFICATION: Brooke, 4.62-Inch, Shell, Confederate. Length — 8. REMARKS: Copper cup missing. Copper fuse plug.

FIGURE: XIII-120 LOCATION: Author's Collection. CATEGORY 1. IDENTIFICATION: Brooke, 6.4-Inch, Bolt, Confederate. Length — 9. Weight — 64. REMARKS: Copper cup missing.

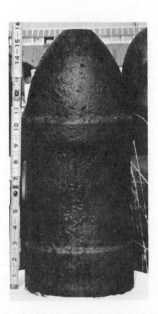

FIGURE: XIII-122 LOCATION: Washington Navy Yard, D.C. CATEGORY 1. IDENTIFICATION: Brooke, 7-Inch, Shell, Confederate. Length — 15.75. REMARKS: Copper cup painted black. Note close joint. Projectile listed as captured at Fort Fisher, N.C. in 1865.

320

Abbot believed the Mullane was superseded by the ratchet base since the doweled form was used at the siege of Yorktown, but in later engagements the ratchet base was fired from 7-inch Brooke rifles. This may well have been the case although old stocks of Mullane ammunition no doubt remained in service until expended.[26] Certainly, the ratchet base was preferred by artillerymen for we find specific requests for it in Confederate ammunition requisitions.[27]

The name "Tennessee Sabot" or "Tennessee Shell" also crops up on occasion in reference to either Mullane or Brooke projectiles, but unfortunately it is difficult to determine which. Abbot[28] applied the term to ratchet base. Alexander[29] said "Tennessee Shell" and Mullane were synonymous. The Official Records mention "Tennessee Sabot" but fail to define the projectile, so it appears six of one, half a dozen of the other with perhaps a slight edge in favor of the Mullane since Alexander, as a Confederate, should have known the colloquial terms for his own ammunition better than Abbot.

Writing in 1883, General Alexander stated:[30] "The first rifle shells [used in the field by the Confederacy] were Burton and Archer. Both had a leaden ring or sabot . . . and [in 3-inch caliber] differed by about two pounds in weight. . . ." They were supposed to take a slightly different charge, he recalled, but generally were used indiscriminately. "Later they were found to be utterly worthless. . . never took the grooves . . . innacuracy was excessive . . . and not one shell in 20 exploded. . . . Their manufacture was discontinued in 1862. . . ."[31]

Wise[32] echoed Alexander's statements reporting that Longstreet 18 July 1861 around Blackburn's Ford fired 310 rounds of the new Burton and Archer projectiles which were entirely ineffective ". . . although most favorable reports were made about it by the inexperienced officers who conducted the fire. . . ." In a footnote Wise mentions that competent tests a few weeks later proved the projectiles were worthless and their manufacture was discontinued. They tumbled, he said, and had no range. From this evidence, it appears that the Burtons and Archers were of little value, but neither Alexander nor Wise gives us much to go on for identification.

Shells at Chancellorsville (Fig. XIII-123) without sabot and at West Point (Fig. XIII-124) in unfired state have been identified as Archers as well as the shot in Figure XIII-125 which has a narrower lead band and in the Abbot drawing (Fig. XIII-126) with rounded base. All are 3-inch caliber and although it stretches the definition a bit, are assigned to Category 2 on the basis of indentations in the iron

FIGURE: XIII-123 LOCATION: Chancellorsville, Va. CATEGORY 2. IDENTIFICATION: Archer, 3-Inch, Shell, Confederate. Length — 5.6. REMARKS: Lead sabot missing.

FIGURE: XIII-124 LOCATION: West Point, N.Y. CATEGORY 2. IDENTIFICATION: Archer, 3-Inch, Shell, Confederate. Length — 5.6. REMARKS: Lead sabot formerly covered with canvas.

FIGURE: XIII-125 LOCATION: West Point, N.Y. CATEGORY 2. IDENTIFICATION: Archer, 3-Inch, Shot, Confederate. Length — 6. Weight — 8. REMARKS: Lead sabot.

321

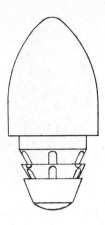

FIGURE: XIII-126 CATEGORY 2. IDENTIFICATION: Archer, 3-Inch, Shot, Confederate. Weight — 8. SOURCE: Abbot. REMARKS: Lead sabot missing.

FIGURE: XIII-128 LOCATION: Fort Morgan, Ala. CATEGORY 7. IDENTIFICATION: Burton, 6.4-Inch, Shell, Confederate. Length — 11.4. REMARKS: Lead sabot missing.

designed to serve the purpose of splines. They probably were the invention of Bellona Foundry's Junius L. Archer, but this has not been definitely established.

James H. Burton, superintendent of armories for the Confederacy, is credited with developing the following six Category 7 projectiles—in which the lead was prevented from slipping solely by friction—although Figures XIII-129 through 131 may be English Blakelys.

Figure XIII-127 is an Abbot drawing of 3.3-inch case and Figure XIII-128 a shell at Fort Morgan, Alabama, of similar design, but 6.4-inch. Function of the small teat at the base of each projectile has not been determined. The sabot attached in similar fashion, but without the grooves, as that of the 6.4-inch shell (Fig. XIII-129) and 4.2 (Fig. XIII-130), which were recovered in the Charleston area and, as previously mentioned, may be Blakelys.

FIGURE: XIII-129 LOCATION: Author's Collection. CATEGORY 7. IDENTIFICATION: Burton (tentative), 6.4-Inch, Shell, Confederate. Length — 10.5. Weight — 45. REMARKS: Part of lead sabot still attached. Projectile may be a British Blakely.

FIGURE: XIII-130 LOCATION: UDC Museum, Charleston, S.C. CATEGORY 7. IDENTIFICATION: Burton (tentative), 4.2-Inch, Shell, Confederate. Length — 7.75. REMARKS: Lead sabot missing. May be British Blakely.

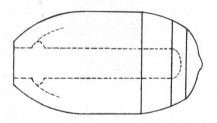

FIGURE: XIII-127 CATEGORY 7. IDENTIFICATION: Burton, 3.3-Inch, Case, Confederate. Weight — 11.5. SOURCE: Abbot. REMARKS: Lead sabot missing.

Abbot lists Figure XIII-131 as 3.67-inch, indicating Burton design. However, the shell, which has a slightly different base and one of the most intriguing interiors of all ammunition, was captured with a 3.6-inch Blakely and probably should be placed in that category. The Manassas 3-inch (Fig. XIII-132) has been identified as Burton despite the short sabot. Four grooves theoretically assured access of flame to the time fuse.

The Category 2 projectile (Fig. XIII-133) for lack of a better name is identified as a Confederate Schenkl. It was a 2.25-inch experimental round with brass sabot apparently designed for the Confederate mountain rifle.

FIGURE: XIII-133 LOCATION: West Point, N.Y. CATEGORY 2. IDENTIFICATION: Schenkl, 2.25-Inch, Shell, Confederate. Length — 8. REMARKS: Experimental Confederate round identified as a Schenkl solely on the basis of appearance. Brass sabot.

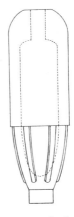

FIGURE: XIII-134 CATEGORY 2. IDENTIFICATION: Schenkl, 4.2-Inch, Shell, Confederate (tentative). Weight — 24.5. SOURCE: Abbot. REMARKS: Projectile was fired by Confederates into Union lines. However, based on appearance and measurement, Abbot felt it was a U.S. Schenkl dud fitted with a copper fuse plug and some sort of sabot for the return flight.

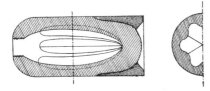

FIGURE: XIII-131 CATEGORY 7. IDENTIFICATION: Burton (tentative), 3.67-Inch, Shell, Confederate. Weight — 14.5. SOURCE: Abbot. REMARKS: Abbot, who records all rifled ammunition in terms of smoothbore caliber, lists this shell as 6-pounder diameter, or 3.67. On the basis of this and sabot arrangement, it has been identified tentatively as a Burton. However, the projectile was captured with a 3.6-inch Blakely rifle and the author feels it probably should be relegated to the Blakely category.

FIGURE: XIII-132 LOCATION: Manassas, Va. CATEGORY 7. IDENTIFICATION: Burton, 3-Inch, Shell, Confederate. Length — 7.4. REMARKS: Lead sabot, note grooves to permit access of discharge flame to time fuse.

Abbot records another projectile (Fig. XIII-134) with considerable hesitancy as a Confederate Schenkl. When thrown into Union lines near Richmond, it had a copper fuse and presumably some sort of Southern sabot to fire it. However, appearance and measurement were identical to early U.S. 4.2-inch Schenkls, some of which had been fired at the Confederates, and since only a single round was discovered, indications are it was merely a U.S. dud fitted with fuse and sabot and fired back.

The Confederates imitated Hotchkiss (Category 3) ammunition, some of it so closely (Figs. XIII-135 and 136) that Abbot hinted they might have been made for, rather than by, the Confederacy. He pointed out that absence of patent marks and calibers not used in federal service were the main exterior differences and added:[33] "Where or how they obtained

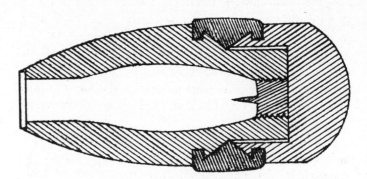

FIGURE: XIII-137 CATEGORY 3. IDENTIFICATION: Hotchkiss, 3-Inch, Shell, Confederate. Weight — 9.3. SOURCE: Abbot. REMARKS: Lead band. Purpose of point on inner plug not determined.

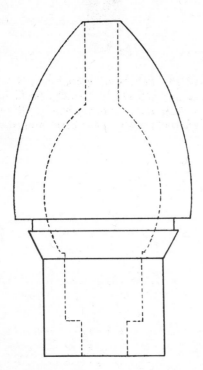

FIGURE: XIII-135 CATEGORY 3. IDENTIFICATION: Hotchkiss, 5.3-Inch, Shell, Confederate. Weight — 24. SOURCE: Abbot. REMARKS: Lead band and cast iron cup to squeeze it into rifling are missing.

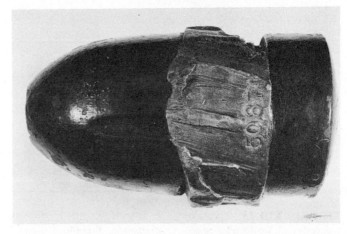

FIGURE: XIII-138 LOCATION: West Point, N.Y. CATEGORY 3. IDENTIFICATION: Hotchkiss, 3.4-Inch, Shell, Confederate. Length — 6.5. REMARKS: Actual diameter, about 3.31, indicates 3.4-inch weapon. However, measurements of 100-year-old ammunition often are not precise and projectile could have been fired by a 3.5-inch. Form of rifling on lead band tends toward the latter.

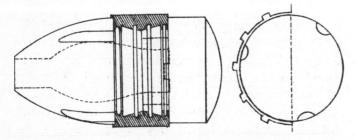

FIGURE: XIII-136 CATEGORY 3. IDENTIFICATION: Hotchkiss, 3.3-Inch, Shell, Confederate. Weight — 9.5. SOURCE: Abbot. REMARKS: Wrapped with wire beneath lead band.

their supply is open to conjecture. . . ." There is one additional identification mark—brass fuses for federal models instead of copper.

Figure XIII-137 also resembled the U.S. Hotchkiss, but close examination will reveal differences and the interiors of all three Confederate models varied widely from the federal.

Figure XIII-136 had horizontal grooves on the body of the shell wrapped with wire embedded in the lead. One of these projectiles (Fig. XIII-138) shows the grooves at right where the lead has been stripped.

The Gorgas shot, which operated on the Hotchkiss principle, was the invention of the Confederate Chief of Ordnance. The 4-inch, Category 3 projectile (Fig. XIII-139) had a lead band in the middle which was driven into the rifling at discharge.

FIGURE: XIII-140 LOCATION: McLeod Collection, Charleston, S.C. CATEGORY 1. IDENTIFICATION: Quinlivan, 7-Inch, Shot, Confederate. Length — 13.5. REMARKS: Central bolt hole surrounded by three others indicates a Mullane copper cup was used.

FIGURE: XIII-139 LOCATION: West Point, N.Y. CATEGORY 3. IDENTIFICATION: Gorgas, 4-Inch, Shot, Confederate. Length — 10. Weight — 20. REMARKS: Lead band.

All are identical projectiles designed for 7-inch rifles and measuring 13.5 inches long without sabot. A center bolt hole surrounded by three equidistant openings indicate a Category 1, Mullane type cup with three dowels was used, and, incidentally, sustains the assumption that one inventor's principle was utilized by others.

A 7-inch found at Fort Fisher (Fig. XIII-141) is tentatively identified as a Quinlivan on the basis of

Michael Quinlivan, mentioned in Chapter IX as having a hand in forging the Cameron Rifle, has been identified by the writer as the inventor of the pyramidal shot in Figure XIII-140. According to the inventor's obituary in a Charleston newspaper 20 January 1909, the Quinlivan was a "steel pointed shot" which was used against the *USS Keokuk* in the federal Ironclad Attack 7 April 1863. The article probably erred in calling the shot steel—indications are it was wrought iron, a far more logical material at this stage of the war.

Four rounds have survived in Charleston, two in private hands and two at the Charleston Museum.

FIGURE: XIII-141 LOCATION: West Point, N.Y. CATEGORY 7. IDENTIFICATION: Quinlivan (tentative), 7-Inch, Shot, Confederate. Length — 13. Weight — 98. REMARKS: Identification based on general appearance. Method of providing rotation involved routing out the base of the wrought iron projectile to leave a thin wall which was squeezed into the rifling at discharge. Shot was captured at Fort Fisher, N.C.

appearance, although the form of sabot places it in an entirely different category—No. 7. Abbot illustrates the same 98-pound projectile in Figure XIII-142. The sabot was formed by routing out the base to leave a thin wall of metal which could be forced into the grooves at discharge. According to Abbot, this type was peculiar to the Confederacy and projectiles, regardless of shape and size, were always solid and made by welding wrought iron bars together then shaping them on a lathe.

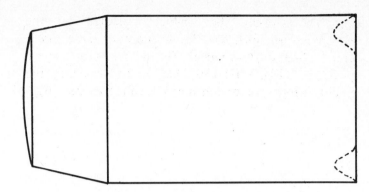

FIGURE: XIII-143 CATEGORY 7. IDENTIFICATION: 4.62-Inch, Wrought Iron Bolt, Confederate. Weight — 40.5. SOURCE: Abbot. REMARKS: Routed out base. Smallest caliber of the type found by Abbot.

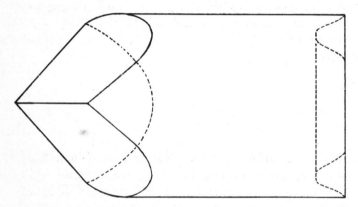

FIGURE: XIII-142 CATEGORY 7. IDENTIFICATION: Quinlivan (tentative) 7-Inch, Shot, Confederate. Length — 13. Weight — 98. SOURCE: Abbot. REMARKS: Sketch of round in Fig. XIII-141, now at West Point. Wrought iron projectile with routed out base.

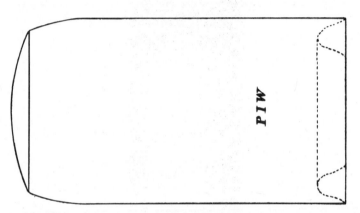

FIGURE: XIII-144 CATEGORY 7. IDENTIFICATION: 6.4-Inch, Wrought Iron Bolt, Confederate. Weight — 95. SOURCE: Abbot. REMARKS: Routed out base. Initials "PIW" believed to be those of Petersburg Iron Works.

Projectiles with routed out bases were costly to manufacture, but several types were made by the Confederacy. Five (Figs. XIII-143 through 147) were illustrated by Abbot who said that in Figure XIII-143 was fired into federal lines from Fort Clifton on the Appomattox River. Those in Figures XIII-144 and 145 bear the initials "PIW" which are believed to stand for Petersburg Iron Works where the bolts were made. A wrought iron round at Fort Sumter (Fig. XIII-148) is badly rusted, but seems to have an interior base somewhat more rounded than those in the drawings.

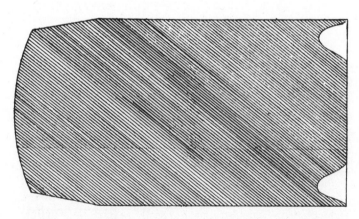

FIGURE: XIII-145 CATEGORY 7. IDENTIFICATION: 7-Inch, Wrought Iron Bolt, Confederate. Weight — 120. SOURCE: Abbot. REMARKS: Routed out base. Abbot stated this round was marked with the initials "PIW" (Petersburg Iron Works) but neglected to mention where. Projectile was fired by Confederate fleet in James River.

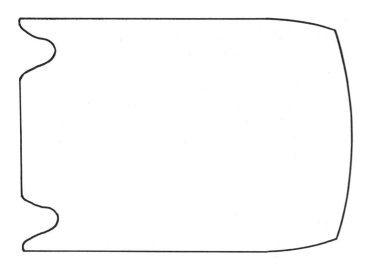

FIGURE: XIII-146 CATEGORY 7. IDENTIFICATION: 6.4-Inch, Wrought Iron Bolt, Confederate. Weight — 75. SOURCE: Abbot. REMARKS: Routed out base.

FIGURE: XIII-148 LOCATION: Fort Sumter, S.C. CATEGORY 7. IDENTIFICATION: 6.4-Inch, Wrought Iron Bolt, Confederate. Length — 12. REMARKS: Routed out base.

FIGURE: XIII-147 CATEGORY 7. IDENTIFICATION: 8-Inch, Wrought Iron Bolt, Confederate. Weight — 177. SOURCE: Abbot. REMARKS: Routed out base. Note cupped section in nose of projectile.

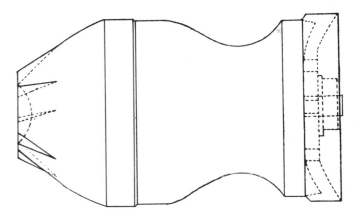

FIGURE: XIII-149 CATEGORY 1. IDENTIFICATION: 6.4-Inch, Curved Bolt, Confederate. Weight — 61.5. SOURCE: Abbot. REMARKS: Copper cup with three small dowels, iron washer, square-head nut.

Three types of curved bolts (Figs. XIII-149 through 151), with an hourglass figure reminiscent of the '80s, were found at Richmond and obviously designed for punching ironclads. Copper cups on these Category 1 rounds were attached by iron bolts. Hexagonal nuts headed the second and third which were reinforced by a square iron washer beneath, the cup further strengthened by three small dowels. These would tend to classify the bolts as a Mullane type. However, the dowels were too small to be more than secondary and the prime method of preventing slippage was by the outer rim of the cup being forced over the beveled base of the projectile—a method, it will be recalled, used by Stafford in his "new" projec-

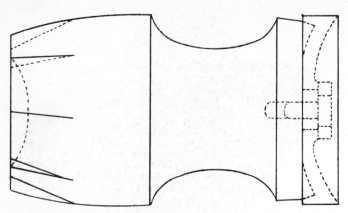

FIGURE: XIII-150 Category 1. Identification: 6.4-Inch, Curved Bolt, Confederate. Weight — 70. Source: Abbot. Remarks: Copper cup, square iron projection and iron screw with hexagonal nut.

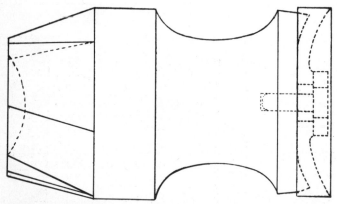

FIGURE: XIII-151 Category 1. Identification: 6.4-Inch, Curved Bolt, Confederate. Weight — 67. Source: Abbot. Remarks: Copper cup, square iron projection, and iron screw with hexagonal nut.

FIGURE: XIII-152 Location: West Point, N.Y. Category 1. Identification: 6.4-Inch, Curved Bolt, Confederate. Length — 11. Weight — 70. Remarks: 8 diagonal ribs to top. Copper cup. Similar to Fig. XIII-150.

tile. A specimen (Fig. XIII-152) of the bolt diagramed in Figure XIII-150 is in the West Point collection.

An 8-inch conical projectile (Fig. XIII-153) is identified as a Harding solely on the basis of the 1865 photograph of Confederate ammunition collected at the Charleston Arsenal (Fig. XIII-1). The words "Harding Bolt" (shot, according to definition) are identifiable on the round which is in line between the second torpedo from the left and the breech of the 12.75-inch Blakely rifle which was illustrated in Chapter VIII displayed at West Point.

Harding ammunition is mentioned several times in the Official Records, particularly in connection with the banded Model 1844 columbiads in which 215-pound Harding projectiles failed generally to take the grooves and with 16-pound charges "broke up." In a similar 10-incher, they disintegrated with 15-pound charges. However, whether these rounds were similar to the illustrated projectile is questionable since no less than ten specimens in the Arsenal photograph are marked with the name "Harding," most apparently Category 1 types with copper sabot of Read or perhaps Parrott form. However, one, just behind the conical Harding's base, is somewhat similar in shape, but appears to be longer and to have a thicker base.

The Arsenal photograph, in addition to the Hardings, has four Blakely projectiles, several Brookes, elongated projectiles for smoothbores, a couple of Whitworths, Parrott, stand of grape,

FIGURE: XIII-153 Location: West Point, N.Y. Category 7. Identification: Harding, 8-Inch, Shot, Confederate. Remarks: Copper ring extends beyond base of projectile.

328

Prestons, and an excellent assortment of torpedoes. These devices, which today would be called mines, are outside the province of this book, but are worth mentioning since they serve as excellent reference points in identifying various projectiles.

The wasp-waisted variety, at right, in Figure XIII-1, is a floating torpedo which, in the water, had the larger compartment upright and probably just awash as it drifted with the tide. Pressure on the prongs at top activated the firing mechanism.[34] Moving left, the two upright types, which resembled large shells, are raft (also called shell) torpedoes. Four castings at the base held bolts with which they were attached to the ends of long timbers hooked together by cross pieces in the shape of an open raft. One end of each timber was secured to the bottom, the other, with torpedo attached, was allowed to float upward to a predetermined depth below the surface and was held there by a line and anchor. Set in a shallow channel, these torpedoes with percussion fuse in the nose were a decided menace to shipping. A specimen in Charleston today measures 11.5 inches in diameter, 22.5 inches long.

The next five are varied types of barrel torpedoes, in simplest form a wooden keg with pointed wood ends to supply buoyancy as well as a streamlined configuration to reduce drag from the current. Anchored at varying depths, barrel torpedoes were formidable obstacles and sank a fair number of Federal vessels.

They were also used as land mines and numbers of these "torpedoes" as they were still called, buried in the sands of Morris Island impeded siege approaches to Battery Wagner. That nearest the raft torpedoes is a crude form with a sharp, but poorly cut, end. The next is equipped for at least four pressure detonating devices, such as percussion fuses, to increase chances of successful operation. The Arsenal picture of the previous chapter (Fig. XII-23) shows one end of this torpedo is missing. The last three are similar and equipped for single detonators.

Four fascinating small projectiles in that photograph bear a "Preston" label—three looming indistinctly behind the crudely made barrel torpedo, the fourth at right of the nearest raft torpedo between a slim Whitworth shell and a 7-inch Brooke bolt.

Preston shells came from the factory with a metal cover over the fuse and were flanged to fit the rifling, a characteristic which relegates them to Category 5. They are reported in 4.2- and 3.75-inch calibers, both of which seem to be in the picture. The larger type has three projections cast on the ogive that show clearly in the West Point 4.2-inch (Fig.

XIII-154). Since they are omitted from a similar caliber shot (Fig. XIII-155), are too short to reach the rifling, and would be unnecessary in such a small shell for lifting, they may be some sort of anti-ricochet device to trip the projectile if it hit on the side forcing it to pivot and strike the fuse.

FIGURE: **XIII-154** LOCATION: West Point, N.Y. CATEGORY 5. IDENTIFICATION: Preston (Blakely), 4-Inch, Shell, Confederate. Diameter — Across flats, 4. Across flanges, 4.2. Length — 8.6. REMARKS: See text. Probably made in England.

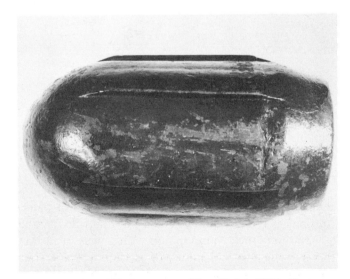

FIGURE: **XIII-155** LOCATION: West Point, N.Y. CATEGORY 5. IDENTIFICATION: Preston (Blakely), 4-Inch, Shot, Confederate. Diameter — Across flats, 4. Across flanges, 4.2. Length — 8. REMARKS: See text. Probably made in England.

The name "Preston" has been used thus far to conform with the photographic identification. However, despite this strong evidence, the author feels the name is erroneous, a belief admittedly founded more on supposition than proof and one to which other ammunition collectors may be irrevocably opposed.

A cross-section of the larger projectile, illustrated in General Gillmore's book of operations in the Charleston area (Fig. XIII-156) shows the shell has six ratchet-shaped splines, or flanges, which obviously fitted into the grooves of the rifle. But what rifle? Both U.S. and Confederate 4.2-inch Parrotts had

FIGURE: XIII-156 CATEGORY 5. IDENTIFICATION: Preston (Blakely), 4-Inch, Shell, Confederate. Diameter — Across flats, 4. Across flanges, 4.2. Length — 8.75 (estimated). SOURCE: Gillmore. REMARKS: See text. Probably made in England.

straight-type rifling which certainly wouldn't work, and the Confederate hook-slant "Brooke" form generally had 7 lands and grooves.

In fact Confederate lists of weapons in the Charleston area as well as a federal report[35] of pieces captured at the city's fall include but one rifle capable of handling such ammunition. This was a 4-inch Blakely which specifications of British weapons (see Appendix) shows was rifled 6 x 6. Normally, of course, a 4.2-inch shell can't be rammed successfully through a 4-inch tube, but it can when the projectile is erroneously measured across flanges—which fitted

into the grooves—and the bore across lands. In this case, the diameter of the main body of the shell represents the lands and is the anticipated 4 inches, give a fraction for windage.

Similarly, the so-called 3.75-inch actually measures a shade under 3.5 across the body. There were no 3.75-inch rifles of any sort in Charleston, but several 3.5-inch Blakelys are reported that could fire this projectile with facility.

Digging further into Confederate inventories at Charleston,[36] we find a listing of "4-inch Blakely shell," "4-inch Blakely grape," and "4-inch Blakely canister," but not a single mention of the name "Preston." Smaller ammunition is not listed by name.

Why then, one wonders, did the Federals who collected the specimens clearly stencil them "Preston"? Was the name, perhaps, marked on one or more of the rounds? If so, it falls into place as made by the Fawcett-Preston Co., of Liverpool. As described in Chapter VIII, this company manufactured Blakely rifles and its name is often found stamped alone on weapons which for identification purposes are termed Blakelys. It will be recalled that at least one of these pieces was listed by its Union captors as a "Fawcett-Preston" rifle, yet the Confederates who used them traditionally refer to the weapons as Blakelys.

The fuse is a simple type composed of a striker with nipple for the cap. On impact the striker crushed the cap against the metal covering which doubled as the anvil. The same fuse has been found in other Blakely ammunition and may be seen on English Whitworths in the Charleston Arsenal photograph. Flanges, although unusual in rounds this small, are customary for large Blakely ammunition and the author feels these projectiles should be catalogued under that category, but has listed them out of context in deference to the identification they have carried for a hundred years.

Experimental models of any ordnance, although they often never see service, are always intriguing and the three, possibly four, shot which follow are not only highly unusual, but illustrate Confederate attempts to reproduce the guiding principle of a feathered arrow in artillery ammunition.

First of these extremely rare projectiles is known as "Confederate Winged Shot." Only one round seems to have survived, a 3.5-inch (actual diameter) with hinged metal "wings" which folded into the closed position (Fig. XIII-157) for firing and extended (Fig. XIII-158) after the round left the bore. It probably was an attempt to achieve a rifle effect from the 6-pounder (3.67-inch) smoothbore.

FIGURE: XIII-157 LOCATION: West Point, N.Y. CATEGORY 7. IDENTIFICATION: 3.5-Inch (actual), Winged shot, Confederate. Length 9. REMARKS: "Wings" folded. Experimental. Projectile probably was designed to achieve a rifle effect from the 6-pounder (3.67-inch) smoothbore.

FIGURE: XIII-159 LOCATION: West Point, N.Y. CATEGORY 7. IDENTIFICATION: 3-Inch, Flanged Shot, Confederate. Length — 8.25. REMARKS: Experimental. Flanges did not enter rifling.

FIGURE: XIII-158 LOCATION: West Point, N.Y. CATEGORY 7. IDENTIFICATION: 3.5-Inch (actual), Winged Shot, Confederate. Length — 9. REMARKS: Same as Fig. XIII-157, "wings" extended. Experimental. Projectile probably was designed to achieve a rifle effect from the 6-pounder (3.67-inch) smoothbore.

FIGURE: XIII-160 LOCATION: West Point, N.Y. CATEGORY 7. IDENTIFICATION: 4.5-Inch, Flanged Shot, Confederate. Length — 14.75. REMARKS: Lead and wood sabot unattached to projectile. Three large flanges which did not enter rifling. Experimental.

Another, a 3-inch (Fig. XIII-159), had narrow diagonal flanges, and the third (Fig. XIII-160), three large diagonal flanges. This model, a 4.5-inch, was equipped with a wood and lead sabot for firing, but apparently it was not attached to the shot which went its separate way in the air. The fourth projectile (Fig. XIII-161) while not definitely established as Confederate, probably was another Southern experiment. It is 6.4-inch diameter, about 20 inches long and appears to be a shot unless the base, which could not be examined, is equipped with a fuse.

FIGURE: XIII-161 LOCATION: Washington Navy Yard, D.C. CATEGORY 7. IDENTIFICATION: 6.4-Inch, Winged Shot, Confederate (tentative). Length — 19.6. REMARKS: Believed to be Confederate, experimental.

The Confederates also developed many different shot and shell, which, although not common types, were none the less employed in the field. Several have lead, rear sabots prevented from slipping by various ribs or indentations in the projectile base and often, unless the sabot is missing or sectioned, are extremely hard to identify. Abbot lists five of this kind. That in Figure XIII-162 has a splined, curved base and typical Confederate bourrelet cast in the body of the shell. The Figure XIII-163 specimen has a split bourrelet to permit passage of the flame to the fuse. The base is angular instead of curved and has six narrow indentations.

The example in Figure XIII-164 has four straight projections which served the same function as the bourrelet and permitted even better access for the flame. The base is curved and has five splines. Soaped yarn was wrapped in the junction between lead sabot and shell. This and the previous shell are similar in principle and were captured together at Fort Harrison.

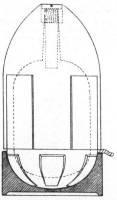

FIGURE: XIII-164 CATEGORY 1. IDENTIFICATION: 6.4-Inch, Shell, Confederate. Weight — 58. SOURCE: Abbot. REMARKS: Lead sabot, soaped rope yarn at junction with shell base. Copper ring to receive fuse plug. Wide flanges serve same function as bourrelet.

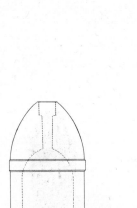

FIGURE: XIII-162 CATEGORY 1. IDENTIFICATION: 7-Inch, Shell, Confederate. Weight — 111. SOURCE: Abbot. REMARKS: Lead sabot.

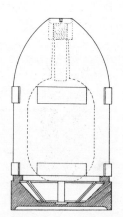

FIGURE: XIII-163 CATEGORY 1. IDENTIFICATION: 6.4-Inch, Shell, Confederate. Weight — 60. SOURCE: Abbot. REMARKS: Lead sabot. Copper adapter to receive fuse plug. Note split bourrelet. Captured at Fort Harrison.

Cross-shaped cuts in the bottom of the curved base prevented slippage in the 3-inch shell (Fig. XIII-165) and base indentations performed a similar function for the West Point shot (Fig. XIII-166).

The preceding projectiles would fall into Category 1. However, the 3.67-inch shell shown in Figure XIII-167 had such an extensive lead sabot that it should be relegated to Category 2 although grooves, rather than splines, controlled slippage. The threaded nose piece was screwed down on a percussion fuse prevented from premature detonation by a metal safety pin.

An iron base plate in the 3.67-inch shot in Figure XIII-168 drove the lead into the grooves. Interior arrangement, if any, in the 3-inch (Fig. XIII-169) to prevent its lead sabot from slipping has not been determined. Both are in Category 7.

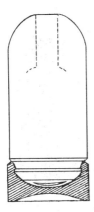

FIGURE: XIII-165 CATEGORY 1. IDENTIFICATION: 3-Inch, Shell, Confederate. Weight — 8. SOURCE: Abbot. REMARKS: Lead sabot prevented from slipping by cross-shaped indentations in projectile base. Lead fuse plug. Shell is unclassified, but may be a Burton.

FIGURE: XIII-168 LOCATION: West Point, N.Y. CATEGORY 7. IDENTIFICATION: 3.67-Inch, Shot, Confederate. Length — 5.6 REMARKS: Iron base plate drove lead band into grooves of rifling at discharge.

FIGURE: XIII-166 LOCATION: West Point, N.Y. CATEGORY 1. IDENTIFICATION: 3-Inch, Shot, Confederate. Length — 7.25. REMARKS: Missing sabot presumably lead.

FIGURE: XIII-169 LOCATION: West Point, N.Y. CATEGORY 7. IDENTIFICATION: 3-Inch, Shot, Confederate. Length — 6.25. REMARKS: Lead sabot. Interior arrangement undetermined.

FIGURE: XIII-167 LOCATION: West Point, N.Y. CATEGORY 2. IDENTIFICATION: 3.67-Inch, Shell, Confederate. Length — 6.5. REMARKS: Probable lead sabot. Threaded nose piece screwed down over percussion fuse.

A double-pointed 3-inch (Fig. XIII-170) is Category 7 rather than 3 since the opening of the band at rear as well as smaller diameter of the body indicates the metal was pushed into the grooves by gas pressure rather than squeezing of one iron part against another in Hotchkiss fashion. Since the band is considerably wider than the body, it presumably was designed for a breechloader.

FIGURE: XIII-170 LOCATION: West Point, N.Y. CATEGORY 7. IDENTIFICATION: 3-Inch, Shot, Confederate. Length — 9. Weight — 11. REMARKS: Copper band, open at rear to permit access of discharge gases. Presumably intended for breechloader.

FIGURE: XIII-171 LOCATION: The Citadel, Charleston, S.C. CATEGORY 1. IDENTIFICATION: 3.5-Inch, Shell, Confederate. Length — 7.13 REMARKS: Lead sabot. Belived to be Confederate-made shell for Blakely rifle.

Figure XIII-171 shows a 3.5-inch lead sabot round in The Citadel collection which appears to be in Category 1 although the arrangement under the band has not been determined. It was discovered during landscaping of private grounds near Columbia, South Carolina and is a Confederate-made projectile designed for use in a Blakely rifle.

An experimental Category 7 round which probably saw little if any field service utilized a sabot made of rope. It was neatly coiled around an indented portion of the iron body from the base to approximately mid-section and driven into the rifling at discharge.

The British-developed Pattison also seems to have been largely experimental although at least one specimen made its way to this country and the West Point Museum (Fig. XIII-172). Flanges place the projectile in Category 5. Windage was reduced by a leather collar, missing in the illustrated shot, which wrapped around the indented portion of the body. The projectile is mentioned here because of its novelty, not its value to the war effort.

British projectiles, like the guns they fed, were used in such limited quantity by the North that to all intents they may be considered part of the Southern war chest. Armstrongs, Blakelys, and Whitworths flowed into the Confederacy through the blockade, but specimens today are quite rare and generally found only in museum or very large private collections.

FIGURE: XIII-172 LOCATION: West Point, N.Y. CATEGORY 5. IDENTIFICATION: Pattison, 2.5-Inch, Shot, British. Length — 6.9. REMARKS: Flanged. Leather (missing) covered indented section to reduce windage.

Armstrong projectiles were made for use in either of two systems, compression or shunt. The former, designed for breechloaders, consisted of an iron body slightly smaller than the bore wrapped with a coating of lead to make the round oversize. Too large for front loading, the projectile had to be inserted at the rear where discharge pressure compressed the lead into the rifling.

Abbot illustrates one of these Category 6 compression shells (Fig. XIII-173) which was fired into his Dutch Gap batteries in 1864. The dentil-like openings are grooves encircling the body. This is evident in Holley's sketch (Fig. XIII-174) of an Armstrong shot with a thinner lead coating. A 3-inch shell at West Point (Fig. XIII-175) resembles the Abbot type.

Armstrong's celebrated segmented shell, which could be used as shot, case, or canister, was sketched by Abbot (Fig. XIII-176) from a projectile found at Richmond. Designed for the battery of Armstrong muzzle-loaders it arrived too late for Confederate use. The Category 5 shunt projectile consisted of a thin cast iron body enclosing segment-shaped pieces

FIGURE: XIII-175 LOCATION: West Point, N.Y. CATEGORY 6. IDENTIFICATION: Armstrong, 3-Inch, Compression Shell, British. Diameter — 3.25. Length — 8.5. REMARKS: Lead covering. Breechloader.

FIGURE: XIII-173 CATEGORY 6. IDENTIFICATION: Armstrong, 3-Inch, Compression Shell, British. Weight — 12.3. SOURCE: Abbot. REMARKS: Lead covering. Breechloader. Fired into U.S. Dutch Gap batteries near Richmond in summer of 1864.

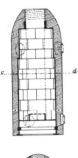

FIGURE: XIII-176 CATEGORY 5. IDENTIFICATION: Armstrong, 3-Inch, Segmented Shunt Shell, British. Weight — 10. SOURCE: Abbot. REMARKS: Sixty encased fragments. Six brass studs. Could be used as case, canister, or solid.

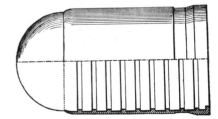

FIGURE: XIII-174 CATEGORY 6. IDENTIFICATION: Armstrong, Compression Shot, British. SOURCE: Holley. REMARKS: Caliber not listed. Lead covering. Breechloader.

of the same metal—sixty in this case—put together to form a cylindrical cavity in the center for the charge. The exterior received a very thin coating of lead which was permitted to trickle between the segments binding them firmly when hard.

Equipped with the expensive Armstrong combination fuse, the round could be set to burst on target by percussion, in the air by time, near the mouth of the piece as canister, and, by leaving off the percussion element and setting the time at zero, as solid shot. A specimen in the West Point Museum (Fig. XIII-177) is a 3-inch. Common 3-inch Armstrong shunt shells had triple rows of three brass studs instead of two as in the shorter, segmented model. Figure XIII-178 is an Abbot drawing and Figure XIII-179 a 3-inch at West Point.

Larger Armstrongs increased the number of studs per row—as in the 6.4-inch (Fig. XIII-180) which has three rows of six—or both studs and rows as in the sectionalized 10-inch (Fig. XIII-181) at the Naval Academy Museum. This huge projectile has ten rows of five. The interior arrangement, featuring a central channel, would indicate the round is a form of shrapnel although the purpose of the nose cavity—which might or might not have held powder—is puzzling and has not been definitely determined.

Another peculiar form of Armstrong is that in Figures XIII-182 and 183, the former an 8-inch at West Point that probably came from Fort Fisher where the Academy's beautiful 8-inch Armstrong rifle was used. The latter is a 10-inch at the Washington Navy Yard. This type of shell, for shells they are despite lack of fuse, was far ahead of its time being a forerunner of today's "shaped charge" for armor piercing.

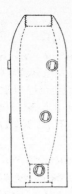

FIGURE: XIII-178 CATEGORY 5. IDENTIFICATION: Armstrong, 3-Inch, Shunt Shell, British. Weight — 10. SOURCE: Abbot. REMARKS: Companion to Segmented Shell so only two types of ammunition need be carried. Nine brass studs.

FIGURE: XIII-179 LOCATION: West Point, N.Y. CATEGORY 5. IDENTIFICATION: Armstrong, 3-Inch, Shunt Shell, British. Length — 9.4. REMARKS: Nine brass studs.

FIGURE: XIII-177 LOCATION: West Point, N.Y. CATEGORY 5. IDENTIFICATION: Armstrong, 3-Inch, Segmented Shunt Shell, British. Length — 7.38. REMARKS: Six brass studs. Could be used as case, canister, or solid.

FIGURE: XIII-180 LOCATION: Washington Navy Yard, D.C. CATEGORY 5. IDENTIFICATION: Armstrong, 6.4-Inch, Shunt Shell, British. Length — 15.5. REMARKS: Eighteen brass studs (covered with paint).

FIGURE: XIII-181 LOCATION: Annapolis, Md. CATEGORY 5. IDENTIFICATION: Armstrong, 10-Inch, Shunt Case, British. Length — 20. REMARKS: Forty brass studs. Purpose of nose cavity undetermined.

Abbot's sketch (Fig. XIII-184) of an 8-inch found at Fort Fisher, shows the design with six rows of five studs each on the exterior and a relatively small interior cavity closed by a threaded iron cap. The bursting charge was contained in a woolen bag to help insulate the powder from heat and could have been loaded at the factory, or shipped separately and inserted just before firing. The projectile, intended exclusively for armor piercing, was exploded by heat generated from friction of the projectile driving through an ironclad's side. This method of detonating a projectile was unusual, but by no means unique since Whitworth utilized the same principle in one of his shells.

FIGURE: XIII-182 LOCATION: West Point, N.Y. CATEGORY 5. IDENTIFICATION: Armstrong, 8-Inch, Armor-Piercing Shunt Shell, British. Length — 15.5. REMARKS: Detonated by friction, see text. 30 brass studs.

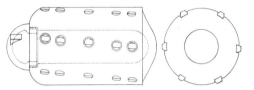

FIGURE: XIII-184 CATEGORY 5. IDENTIFICATION: Armstrong, 8-Inch, Armor-Piercing Shunt Shell, British. Weight — 145. SOURCE: Abbot. REMARKS: Detonated by friction. Note thin nose walls for shaped-charge feature.

FIGURE: XIII-183 LOCATION: Washington Navy Yard, D.C. CATEGORY 5. IDENTIFICATION: Armstrong, 10-Inch, Armor-Piercing Shunt Shell, British. Length — 17.5. REMARKS: Detonated by friction, see text. Forty brass studs.

The "modern" feature of the Armstrong was the overall design. Sides were purposefully very thick to resist the action of the bursting charge, so also the rounded base. But the nose was thin, designed to be crushed during passage through the iron. The short delay to build sufficient heat to set off the charge, enabled the shell to poke its forward part through the iron before explosion—channeled forward in the direction of minimum resistance—ripped through the wood backing of the vessel's iron side and sprayed splinters of wood and iron along the decks. The lugs on top aided in unscrewing the cap to insert or inspect the bursting charge. Benton[37] called these projectiles "blind" shells. However, since they were loaded with powder rather than sand, the word is dangerously misleading and "armor-piercing" seems more appropriate.

A final Armstrong is the 8-inch shot (Fig. XIII-185) captured with the 8-inch rifle now at West Point. Lack of sabot indicates the projectile was designed for very short range firing against ironclads where the rifled motion would not be necessary.

Blakely projectiles are of three general types, lead sabot, flanged, and copper cup.

The first rifled shots fired in combat in America came from the 3.5-inch Blakely described in Chapter VIII and one of these, picked up by Captain Truman Seymour of Major Anderson's command, was forwarded to the Military Academy where today it is a rare item in the West Point ammunition collection. The shot (Fig. XIII-186) has a mangled base which indicates it tumbled in flight and perhaps was not the outstanding success proclaimed by both sides. It is 3.4 inches in diameter, 6.5 inches long, and weighs 12 pounds 4 ounces. The lengthy lead sabot would place it in Category 7. Another Blakely shot (Fig. XIII-187) roughly the same caliber, but 5.88 inches long, illustrates the type sabot, unfired.

The Blakely name is tentatively ascribed to the West Point shells (Figs. XIII-188 and 189) which apparently have the same type lead sabots as well as form of fuse noted in certain Whitworths and the previously described 4- and 3.5-inch Blakelys (and/or Prestons). The 2.4-inch Category 7 shot (Fig. XIII-190) has been called an experimental Confederate round but seems to be a Blakely although what piece fired it is open to question.

Blakely's larger rifles normally used flanged, Category 5 projectiles similar to the 4- and 3.5-inch Blakely (Preston) rounds, but an exception is the 6.4-inch shell which lodged in the rudder post of the *Kearsarge.* The oval-shaped projectile definitely established as coming from a 100-pounder Blakely aboard the *Alabama,* measures about 13 inches long. A marked step, similar to that of the Schenkl, sepa-

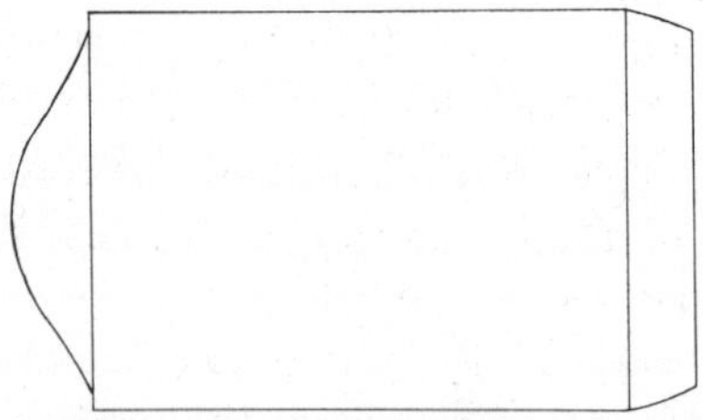

FIGURE: XIII-186 LOCATION: West Point, N.Y. CATEGORY 7. IDENTIFICATION: Blakely, 3.5-Inch, Shot, British. Diameter — 3.4. Length — 6.5. Weight — 12.25. REMARKS: Lead sabot. Fired against Fort Sumter during the initial bombardment April 12–13, 1861 from a 12-pounder Blakely, the first rifled cannon to be fired in America during combat.

FIGURE: XIII-187 LOCATION: West Point, N.Y. CATEGORY 7. IDENTIFICATION: Blakely, 3.5-Inch, Shot, British. Length — 5.88. REMARKS: Lead sabot. Listed as shot, but indentation on ogive could indicate removable nose piece of a shell.

FIGURE: XIII-188 LOCATION: West Point, N.Y. CATEGORY 7. IDENTIFICATION: Blakely (tentative, see Preston), 3-Inch, Shell, British. Length — 6.5. REMARKS: Lead sabot. With the possible exception of Type 10, caliber fits no known Blakely. However, such projectiles could have been used in various other Confederate rifles. Note brass fuse and cover.

FIGURE: XIII-185 IDENTIFICATION: Armstrong, 8-Inch, Shot, British. Weight — 157. SOURCE: Abbot. REMARKS: Captured with 8-inch Armstrong rifle at Fort Fisher, N.C. Projectile had no sabot and was intended for close-range firing against ironclads where the rifled motion would be unnecessary.

rates the forward section from the rear and is indicative of a lead sabot retained by friction alone without benefit of splines. The fuse is missing, but the front appears to have projections on the ogive similar to the specimen illustrated by Gillmore.

FIGURE: XIII-189 LOCATION: West Point, N.Y. CATEGORY 7. IDENTIFICATION: Blakely (tentative, see Preston), 3.5-Inch, Shell, British. Length — 8.6. REMARKS: Lead sabot sectioned to show base of projectile. Note brass fuse cover.

FIGURE: XIII-190 LOCATION: West Point, N.Y. CATEGORY 7. IDENTIFICATION: Blakely, 2.4-Inch (actual), Shot, British. Length — 5. REMARKS: Believed to be a Blakely, but what piece fired it is open to conjecture.

FIGURE: XIII-191 CATEGORY 7. IDENTIFICATION: Blakely, 6.4-Inch, Shell, British. Length — 13 (approximate). SOURCE: *Battles and Leaders,* Vol. 4. REMARKS: Shell fired by *CSS Alabama* into rudder post of *USS Kearsarge.* The projectile, still lodged in the rudder post, today is displayed at the Historical Display Center, Washington Navy Yard. Sabot missing, but presumed to have been lead.

The shell today, with its charge drawn, is still embedded in the post where it landed more than a century ago. A prized exhibit at the Washington Navy Yard Historical Display Center, it is covered with heavy wire mesh which prevents quality photographs, but the sketch (Fig. XIII-191) from *Battles and Leaders of the Civil War* will give a rough idea of its appearance.

Flanges also provided rotation for Blakely shot and shell (Figs. XIII-192 and 193) found at Fort Fisher with an 8-inch Blakely rifle which, in the words of Abbot:[38] ". . . was the most efficient of the Confederate armament and was taken marked by our shot and stained by the blood of its cannoneers. . . ."

The Charleston Arsenal photograph shows four rounds for the pair of 12.75-inch Blakely rifles in that city. At left are two shells and nearby two bolts. Although the lettering on only one shell is visible in this view, other photographs show that both were marked: "600-pdr. Blakely shell, made in Charleston, S.C." At the top of one is the number 454 which doubtless is the correct weight. The bolts are marked: "600-pdr. Blakely shot, Charleston, S.C." which would indicate they came with the rifles although the shells were cast locally. The shell without marking has a band, probably copper, a few inches up from the base which must have been designed to decrease windage.

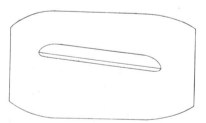

FIGURE: XIII-192 CATEGORY 5. IDENTIFICATION: Blakely, 8-Inch, Shot, British. Weight — 168. SOURCE: Abbot. REMARKS: Three iron flanges.

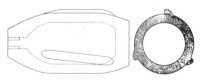

FIGURE: XIII-193 CATEGORY 5. IDENTIFICATION: Blakely, 8-Inch, Shell, British. Weight — 114. SOURCE: Abbot. REMARKS: Three iron flanges.

Four rounds for the huge Blakelys are today at Washington Navy Yard, of which two are shown in Figure XIII-194. The shot is identical to that in the 1865 picture, but the shell has lugs (one broken) cast on the nose, which may have been used in loading, and hence differs from the Charleston rounds and probably was made in England.

The Category 1 copper cup Blakely (Fig. XIII-195) is identified by Holley[39] as being made by the Blakely Ordnance Co. and elsewhere in England for use with Blakely and Brooke rifles.

"The expanding copper cup (c) is secured to the base of the shot, whatever its size, by a single tap bolt and is prevented from revolving on the shot by being compressed by the powder gas against projections cast, or in the case of steel shot, planed on the base of the shot. The space (e) is filled with tallow to lubricate the gun. The small, soft metal studs (a) are greater in number than the grooves of the gun so that however the shot is put in, some of the studs will bear on the lands and hold up or center the point of the shot. The engraving shows a 21-lb. shot for an 18-pdr. . . ."

This seems to be a ratchet base projectile similar to the Brooke with exception of the cup curving outward, like the Mullane, instead of fitting flush, and with addition of the bourrelet studs. Despite its intended use in the Brooke, lack of recoveries indicates it was not imported in quantity, if at all.

Like the Armstrong, a Blakely shot without

FIGURE: XIII-195 CATEGORY 1. IDENTIFCATION: Blakely, 5.3-Inch, Shot, British. Weight — 21. SOURCE: Holley. REMARKS: Copper cup, probably ratchet base similar to the Brooke.
a — Studs, in greater number than the grooves of the rifling in order to always bear on the lands.
c — Expanding copper cup.
e — Space between cup and shell base filled with tallow.

sabot (Fig. XIII-196) was found at Fort Fisher and obviously was intended for close range practice against ironclads. In addition to established models, the South supplied its Blakelys, particularly field calibers, with locally made projectiles.

FIGURE: XIII-194 LOCATION: Washington Navy Yard, D.C. CATEGORY 5. IDENTIFICATION: Blakely, 12.75-Inch, Bolt and Shell, British. Length: Bolt (left) — 20. Shell — 23. REMARKS: Four iron flanges. One of lifting lugs on shell is broken. These projectiles were designed for the 12.75-inch Blakely rifles at Charleston, see text.

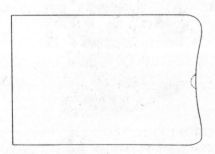

FIGURE: XIII-196 IDENTIFICATION: Blakely, 8-Inch, Bolt, British. Weight — 145. SOURCE: Abbot. REMARKS: Captured at Fort Fisher, N.C. Projectile had no sabot and was intended for close-range firing against ironclads where the rifled motion would be unnecessary.

Whitworth projectiles fall into Category 4 having hexagonal sides machined to fit the bore, and were made in both long and short models for various calibers as evidenced by the selection in Figure XIII-197.

Figure XIII-198 shows a 6.4-inch armor piercing shell, a 5-inch common shell, and the remains of a 5-inch bolt fired by the Naval Battery on Morris Island against Fort Sumter in 1863. The AP shell was detonated by friction generated as it passed through an ironclad's side on the same principle as the Armstrong, without, however, the Armstrong's "shaped charge" feature.

The diagram (Fig. XIII-199) shows two Whitworth AP shell models. That at left and, cutaway, center has a percussion fuse. The other is a friction type like the previously described 6.4-inch. Both were loaded through the threaded base, the charge probably packaged in flannel—merely a convenience in the fused model, but necessary for the other where, as in the Armstrong, cloth insulated the powder against heat sufficiently to delay explosion while the shell penetrated.

FIGURE: XIII-197 Location: West Point, N.Y. Category 4. Identification: Whitworth, British, (left to right): 2.75-Inch, Shell, Length — 11.25. 2.75-Inch, Bolt, Length — 8.75. 2.75-Inch, Shot, Length — 9. 2.15-Inch, Shell, Length — 9. 2.15-Inch, Shot, Length — 7. Remarks: Projectile and bore shaped to fit.

FIGURE: XIII-199 Category 4. Identification: Whitworth, Armor-Piercing Shells, British. Left and (cutaway) center — percussion fuse type. Right — friction model. Source: Holley. Remarks: Projectile and bore shaped to fit. a — body of shell. b — fuse. c — base loading plug.

FIGURE: XIII-198 Location: West Point, N.Y. Category 4. Identification: Whitworth, British (left to right): 6.4-Inch, Armor-Piercing Shell, Length — 16.75. 5-Inch, Shell, Length — 15.9. Removable nose piece. 5-Inch, Bolt, broken against Fort Sumter in 1863. Remarks: Projectile and bore shaped to fit.

The blockade runner *Modern Greece,* chased ashore near Fort Fisher by the Federals, has given up a large number of artifacts to divers including the 6.4-inch Whitworth shell and 2.75-inch (short) shot, photographed together (Fig. XIII-200) for comparison of size. When examined, the projectiles were under treatment at the Fort Fisher Preservation Laboratory. Weight of the larger round is 105 pounds, indicating a possible slight loss from salt-water immersion since a similar Whitworth (Fig. XIII-201) found after capture of Fort Fisher, weighed 110 pounds.

Figure XIII-202 illustrates as English 2.75-inch Whitworth with an adequate powder chamber. A similar caliber, Confederate imitation (Fig. XIII-203) had a small cavity which could contain only enough explosive to break the shell into two or three pieces. It was one of many expedients that, inadequate for the job, left Confederate artillerymen plagued by inferior ammunition and equipment—a chronic frustration which no amount of courage or ability could overcome.

In leaving ammunition, a word of warning for the collector. Shells, regardless of type, were designed for but one purpose—to kill. They may look innocuous, but many are still capable of fulfilling their destiny despite the years. Black powder deteriorates little with age and is extremely sensitive to shock or heat. Consequently, Civil War projectiles should never be retained in collections without deactivation and this is a specialty better left to professionals in the Armed Forces. Demolition experts often crack shells with a shaped charge which at best leaves a gaping hole or several large pieces. If the powder is "hot," nothing remains but fragments. In either case, the prospect from a collector's point of view, is discouraging.

A better method is employed by the Navy's Explosive Ordnance Disposal Unit No. 2 formerly at the Charleston S.C. Navy Yard and now stationed near Norfolk, Virginia. Figure XIII-204 shows one of the unit's rigs—basically an electric drill anchored to a frame. The shell, in this case the previously illustrated 8-inch Schenkl, is clamped to a movable platform and shoved against the drill bit by a hydraulic jack beneath. Ground wires carry off any electrical leaks and a stream of water plays on the bit continuously to minimize heat. The entire operation is performed remotely. Operators of drill switch and jack are protected by a bunker and observe progress of the drill through mirrors. After the bit breaks into the cavity, the powder is thoroughly soaked with water, the shell upended and the fuse drilled in similar fashion. The projectile is then taken to a nearby dock and the powder washed out with a hose. The job is messy, but safe and only a small hole or two mars the specimen which from then on is perfectly harmless.

FIGURE: XIII-200 LOCATION: Fort Fisher, N.C. CATEGORY 4. IDENTIFICATION: Whitworth, British: 6.4-Inch, Shell, Length — 21.25, Weight — 105. 2.75-Inch, Shot, Length — 9.13. REMARKS: Projectile and bore shaped to fit. Note fuse plug removed from 6.4-inch.

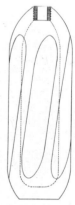

FIGURE: XIII-201 CATEGORY 4. IDENTIFICATION: Whitworth, 6.4-Inch, Shell, British. Weight — 110. SOURCE: Abbot. REMARKS: Projectile and bore shaped to fit. Abbot lists this shell as 7-inch. However, that is the diameter between edges and the correct caliber, measured between flats, is 6.4.

FIGURE: XIII-202 CATEGORY 4. IDENTIFICATION: Whitworth, 2.75-Inch, Shell, British. Weight — 9.5. SOURCE: Abbot. REMARKS: Projectile and bore shaped to fit.

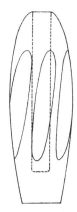

FIGURE: XIII-203 CATEGORY 4. IDENTIFICATION: Whitworth, 2.75-Inch, Shell, Confederate copy. Weight — 12.1. SOURCE: Abbot. REMARKS: Projectile and bore shaped to fit. Note inadequate cavity.

FIGURE: XIII-204 LOCATION: Charleston, S.C. IDENTIFICATION: Shell deactivation. REMARKS: Rig devised by the Navy's Explosive Ordnance Disposal Unit No. 2. See text for description.

NOTES

1. Courtesy of Tom Dickey, Atlanta, Ga.
2. Henry L. Abbot, "Siege Artillery in The Campaigns Against Richmond With Notes on The 15-Inch Gun," *Professional Papers No. 14, Corps of Engineers,* 1867, p. 97.
3. *Ibid.*
4. *Official Records,* Series I, Vol. 35, Part 2, p. 143, letter from Parrott to Maj. Gen. J. G. Foster, 21 June 1864.
5. The name, as pointed out in Chapter IX, often will be found spelled "Schenkle." The spelling used here is taken from the brass fuse in the projectile.
6. The author is indebted for information on the caps to John Bartleson of Explosive Ordnance Disposal Unit No. 2 (U.S.N.), Charleston, S. C., who deactivated the round.
7. Abbot, *op. cit.,* pp. 93–95.
8. Reports of committees of the U.S. Senate, 2nd session, 38th Congress, "Heavy Ordnance," p. 104, testimony T. J. Rodman, 6 February 1864.
9. Col. Berkeley R. Lewis, Ordnance Corps, USA (Ret.), *Notes on Ammunition of The American Civil War, 1861–1865,* 1959.
10. Abbot, *op. cit.,* p. 96.
11. Reports of committees of the U.S. Senate, *op. cit.,* pp. 151–166.
12. Abbot, *loc. cit.,* p. 97.
13. *Ibid.,* pp. 96–97.
14. Edward Simpson, *A Treatise on Ordnance and Naval Gunnery,* 1862, p. 426.
15. Alexander L. Holley, *A Treatise on Ordnance and Armor,* 1865, pp. 702–703.
16. *Official Navy Records,* Series I, Vol. 14, pp. 384–385.
17. Holley, *op. cit.,* p. 490.
18. *Official Records,* Series III, Vol. 1, pp. 295–296.
19. Reports of committees of the U.S. Senate, *op. cit.,* pp. 154–166.
20. The lathe theory, to which the author subscribes, has been advanced by Mr. Sydney C. Kerksis of Atlanta, Ga., who has noticed in a number of such shells that the lug was originally present, but knocked off—presumably by the manufacturer.
21. William LeRoy Broun (sic), "The Red Artillery, Confederate Ordnance During The War," *Southern Historical Society Papers,* Vol. XXVI, 1898, p. 372.
22. Abbot, *op. cit.,* p. 101.

23. E. P. Alexander, "Confederate Artillery Service," *Southern Historical Society Papers*, Vol. XI, 1883, p. 106 footnote.

24. Abbot, *op. cit.*, pp. 102–103.

25. *Official Navy Records*, Series I, Vol. 21, p. 877, letter 11 February 1864 from Selma, Ala.: ". . . in proving a rifled and banded VII-inch with 16 lbs. powder and 111-pound ratchet service bolt. . . ."

26. Mr. Kerksis has informed the author that he has found a 6.4-inch Mullane at Mobile, Ala., which was fired by the Confederate Navy in April 1865.

27. *Official Records*, Series I, Vol. 28, Part 2, p. 242, request of 29 July 1863 from Charleston, S. C., to R. M. Cuyler, Macon, Ga.: "Please send me rifle projectiles for 24, 32 and 42-pounders with ratchet sabots at once if possible. . . ."

28. Abbot, *op. cit.*, pp. 103–104.

29. Alexander, *op. cit.*, p. 106.

30. *Ibid.*

31. Mr. Kerksis, to whom the author is indebted for much of the material on Burtons and Archers, states that one form of the latter was still being manufactured in 1863.

32. Jennings Cropper Wise, *The Long Arm of Lee*, 1915, Vol. 1, p. 128.

33. Abbot, *op. cit.*, p. 107.

34. W. R. King, *Torpedoes, Their Invention and Use From The First Application of The Art of War to The Present Time*, 1866.

35. *Official Records*, Series I, Vol. 35, Part 2, p. 386. Q. A. Gillmore, "Supplementary Report to Engineer and Artillery Operations Against The Defenses of Charleston Harbor, 1863," *Professional Papers No. 16, Corps of Engineers, U.S.A. Supplement*, 1868.

36. *Official Records*, Series I, Vol. 35, Part 2, p. 387.

37. J. G. Benton, *A Course of Instruction in Ordnance and Gunnery Composed and Compiled for Cadets of The United States Military Academy*, 1875, p. 556.

38. Abbot, *op. cit.*, p. 107.

39. Holley, *op. cit.*, p. 476.

Chapter 14

Conclusion

THIS SECTION, IN STRICT SENSE, should be a summary. However, since the definition seems to be more honored in the breach than in observance, the path away from conformity will be followed and these few pages devoted to rockets which utilized certain elements discussed in preceding chapters, yet stand alone as specialized munitions.

Military rockets were of two types—signal and war. The former, familiar fireworks models with paper case guided by a stick strapped to the side, need no further explanation. War rockets, however, were more sophisticated and merit brief discussion. Two principal varieties were available—Congreve and Hale—both developed in England, but differing markedly in method of guidance.

Sir William Congreve (1772-1828) began experimenting with rockets about 1804 and while his products saw little if any service during the American Civil War, they had been employed by the British in this country during the War of 1812—particularly against Fort McHenry, which gave us our National Anthem—and in later years by our government on a test basis.

The Congreve (Fig. XIV-1) consisted of a warhead—shot, shell, or carcass usually—attached to a sheet iron case filled with propellant composed of niter, sulphur, and charcoal. Since a high rate of burning was desired, the propellant was hollowed in the center through much of its length to expose more area to the flame, the cavity being known as the "bore." The rear opening of the case was closed with a metal disk pierced by a threaded central hole surrounded by five smaller orifices. A 7- to 9-foot stick (in light calibers) screwed into the central hole for guidance and the propelling gases escaped through the surrounding holes.[1]

These rockets, mainly 6- to 12-pounders, although made as large as 300, were generally fired from a tube on a tripod stand which could be adjusted for elevation (Fig. XIV-2). They also could be laid on the ground and several touched off together by quick match. If the ground was smooth, they traveled near the surface for 100 to 150 yards, then, in the words of a contemporary writer[2] ". . . they rise more or less, become deflected and rush about in a most destructive manner. . . ."

The stick was a decided inconvenience and was eliminated during the 1840s by William Hale whose rocket resembled the Congreve superficially, but operated on an entirely different principle. Hale's first

345

successful model had a warhead of shot or shell attached to a sheet metal case which, like the Congreve, was closed at the rear by a metal disk pierced by a large central hole and surrounding orifices. However, Hale's rocket dispensed with the stick and the central aperture emitted the propellant gases. The small vents let gas escape at a tangent which imparted a rotary motion to the rocket, thus stabilizing it in flight in the same manner as a rifled projectile.

Hale rockets in this form were employed by our forces during the Mexican War, license for their production having been purchased from the inventor in 1847 after extensive trials the previous year. About 2,000 subsequently were produced at Washington Arsenal in 2.5- and 3.5-inch caliber, and they were considered equal or superior to the Congreve.[3]

In 1855 Hale moved the rotation orifices forward, placing three vents at the base of the head (Fig. XIV-3). This was the model specified in the ordnance manuals[4] for use during the Civil War although there is evidence the older type may also have been used.[5] Two calibers were authorized, but the method of measurement leads to confusion in contemporary texts. Official[6] rocket diameters were 2 and 3 inches—measured inside the case. However, many, if not most, officers measured them like conventional ammunition and recorded exterior diameters of 2.25 and 3.25 inches for exactly the same weapons.

Regardless of measurement method, the smaller was about 15 inches long and weighed 6 pounds, the larger 16.9 inches and either 14 or 16 pounds depending on which text[7] is believed. Warheads were shot, shell, and case and ranges at 47° were 1,760 and 2,200 yards respectively. A specimen of the 2-inch (Fig. XIV-4) is in the West Point collection.

About 1858[8] Hale again moved the holes—this time rearward to the center of gravity—and reduced them to two (Fig. XIV-5), but whether this type was used during the war in this country is problematical.

The inventor also developed a "U-shaped" tube for firing rockets aboard ship where the back-blast was an uncomfortable companion. The rocket was touched off in one leg of the "U" headed inboard with the initial blast pointed overboard. The missile moved down the tube and, since no stick was involved, made the curve at the bottom and was released out the other leg toward the enemy with diminished back-blast.

In describing the apparatus, the writer,[9] somewhat skeptically, remarked that no one had experienced a broadside from such tubes, but that he would like to do so ". . . from a convenient distance."

Rockets apparently were used very little by ei-

ther side during the Civil War. However, occasional mention is found in the Official Records with perhaps the most extensive employment being by U.S. forces in the Charleston area during 1864, but with little marked success.[10]

FIGURE: XIV-1 IDENTIFICATION: Congreve War Rocket. SOURCE: Benton. REMARKS: Guidance by stick attached at rear.

FIGURE: XIV-2 IDENTIFICATION: Congreve Rocket Launcher. SOURCE: Scoffern (*Projectile Weapons of War*).

FIGURE: XIV-3 IDENTIFICATION: Hale War Rocket. SOURCE: Benton. REMARKS: Introduced in 1855. Rotation orifices in head.

a — Bore and Vent.
b — Recess in base of head.
c — Tangential vents (three).
d — Head, solid in this case.

FIGURE: XIV-5 IDENTIFICATION: Hale War Rocket. SOURCE: Benton. REMARKS: New type with two rotation orifices at center of gravity. Shell.

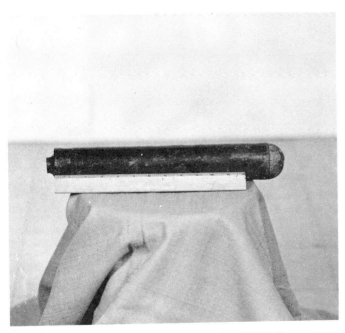

FIGURE: XIV-4 LOCATION: West Point, N.Y. IDENTIFICATION: Hale War Rocket, 2-Inch. Exterior Diameter — 2.25. Length — 15. Weight — 6. REMARKS: See text.

1. Congreve first tried strapping the stick to the side of the case, but soon moved it to the central position.
2. John Scoffern, *Projectile Weapons of War and Explosive Compounds*, 1859, p. 173.
3. *Ibid.*, pp. 183–187.
4. *Ordnance Manual for The Use of Officers of The United States Army*, 1861, p. 314–315. *Ordnance Manual for The Use of Officers of The Confederate States Army*, 1863, pp. 299–300.
5. *Official Records*, Series I, Vol. 35, Part 2, pp. 60–61, letter from Brig. Gen. A. Schimmelfennig 18 April 1864 requesting 3,000 "2.5-inch" Hale rockets "old construction with rotation holes in the rear and a 4-second fuze (sic). . . ."
6. *Ordnance Manual*, 1861, loc. cit., pp. 314–315; *Ordnance Manual* (Confederate 1863), *loc. cit.*, pp. 299–300.
7. Ordnance Manual, 1861, *loc. cit.*, p. 315 specifies weight 14 pounds. J. G. Benton, *A Course of Instruction in Ordnance and Gunnery Composed and Compiled for Cadets of The United States Military Academy*, 1861, p. 98, states the weight as 16 pounds.
8. John Scoffern, *New Resources of Warfare*, 1859, pp. 56–57; Benton, 1861, *op. cit.*, p. 94 footnote.
9. Scoffern, *Projectile Weapons, op. cit.*, p. 180.
10. *Official Records*, Series I, Vol. 35, Part 2, pp. 60–61, 91, 101.

Bibliography

Henry L. Abbot, "Siege Artillery in The Campaigns Against Richmond With Notes on The 15-Inch Gun," *Professional Papers No. 14, Corps of Engineers,* Washington, D.C.: Government Printing Office, 1867. (Also, New York, D. Van Nostrand, 1868.)

Alabama Genealogical Register, (Handsboro Miss.) Vol. III, No. 4 (December, 1961).

E. P. Alexander, "Confederate Artillery Service, "*Southern Historical Society Papers,* (Richmond, Va.) Vol. XI (1883).

William Allan, "Reminiscences of Field Ordnance Service With The Army of Northern Virginia 1863–65," *Southern Historical Society Papers,* (Richmond, Va.) Vol. XIV (1886).

Appleton's Cyclopaedia of American Biography, New York: D. Appleton & Co., 1895.

Francis Bannerman & Sons, *60th Anniversary Catalogue,* (New York, 1925).

J. C. Barnard, *Notes on Sea Coast Defense Consisting of Sea Coast Fortification, The Fifteen-Inch Gun, and Casemate Embrasures,* New York: D. Van Nostrand, 1861.

J. C. Barnard and W. F. Barry, *Report of The Engineer and Artillery Operations of The Army of The Potomac From Its Organization to The Close of The Peninsular Campaign,* New York: D. Van Nostrand, 1863.

Edward Barrett, *Gunnery Instructions Simplified for The Volunteer Officers of The U.S. Navy,* New York: D. Van Nostrand, 1862.

Battles and Leaders of The Civil War, (4 Vols.) New York: Century & Co., 1887.

Edwin C. Bearss, *Hardluck Ironclad, The Sinking and Salvage of The Cairo,* Baton Rouge, La.: Louisiana State University Press, 1966.

Edwin C. Bearss, "The Vicksburg River Defenses and The Enigma of Whistling Dick," *Journal of Mississippi History,* (Jackson, Miss.) Vol. XIX (January 1957).

Carl M. Becker, "Miles Greenwood," *For The Union, Ohio Leaders in The Civil War,* Columbus, Ohio: Ohio State University Press, 1968.

S. V. Benet, *Organization of The Ordnance Department and The Reasons for Separation From The Line of The Arm,* (Washington, 1874).

J. G. Benton, *A Course of Instruction in Ordnance and Gunnery Composed and Compiled for Cadets of The United States Military Academy,* New York: D. Van Nostrand, 1861.

J. G. Benton, *A Course of Instruction in Ordnance and Gunnery Composed and Compiled for Cadets of The United States Military Academy,* New York: D. Van Nostrand, 1875.

William E. Birkhimer, *Historical Sketch of The Organization, Administration, Materiel and Tactics of The Artillery, United States Army,* Washington: James J. Chapman, 1884.

James Leander Bishop, *History of American Manufacturers, 1609–1860,* (2 Vols.) Philadelphia, Pa.: Young & Co., 1864.

J. B. Brandt, *Gunnery Catechism as Applied to The Service of Naval Ordnance,* New York: D. Van Nostrand, 1864.

William LeRoy Broun (sic), "The Red Artillery, Confederate Ordnance During The War," *Southern Historical Society Papers,* (Richmond, Va.) Vol. XXVI No. 1 (1898).

D. Alexander Brown, *Grierson's Raid,* Urbana Ill.: University of Illinois Press, 1962.

Calendar of Confederate Papers, Preliminary Report of Southern Historical Manuscripts Commission, (Richmond, Va., 1908).

Eugene B. Canfield, *Notes on Naval Ordnance of The American Civil War 1861–1865,* (Washington) American Ordnance Association (1960).

The Charleston Daily Courier (Civil War Newspaper), Charleston, S.C.

The Charleston Mercury (Civil War Newspaper), Charleston, S.C.

J. Webster Cochran, *Improvements in Ordnance, Firearms and Projectiles,* New York: J. W. Orr, 1860.

Jack Coggins, *Arms and Equipment of The Civil War,* New York: Doubleday & Co., 1962.

Complete Army and Navy Register of The U.S. 1776–1887, New York: Thomas H. S. Hamersly, 1888.

The Confederate Veteran, (Nashville, Tenn.) Vol. XVI (1908).

Sir William Congreve, *A Treatise on The General Principles, Powers and Facility of Application of The Congreve Rocket System as Compared With Artillery,* London: Longman, Rees, Orme, Brown, and Green, 1827.

Auguste Paul Cooke, *A Text-Book of Naval Ordnance and Gunnery Prepared for Use of The Cadet Midshipmen of The United States Naval Academy,* New York: John Wiley & Son, 1880.

Samuel Wylie Crawford, *The Genesis of The Civil War, The Story of Sumter 1860–61,* New York: L. Webster & Co., 1887.

George W. Cullum, *Biographical Register of The Officers and Graduates of The U.S. Military Academy at West Point, N.Y.,* (3 Vols.) Cambridge, Mass.: Houghton, Mifflin & Co., 1891.

J. A. Dahlgren, *Boat Armament of The U.S. Navy,* Philadelphia, Pa.: King & Baird, 1856.

J. A. Dahlgren, *Shells and Shellguns,* Philadelphia, Pa.: King & Baird, 1856.

Madeleine Vinton Dahlgren, *Memoir of John A. Dahlgren, Rear Admiral, USN,* Boston: James R. Osgood & Co., 1882.

Madeleine Vinton Dahlgren, *The Petition to The National Government of Madeleine Vinton Dahlgren, Widow of The Late Rear Admiral Dahlgren, Submitting Her Claim Asking for Compensation for The Adoption and Use by The United States Navy of Certain Inventions of The Late Rear Admiral Dahlgren Relating to Ordnance,* Washington, D.C.: Gideon Brothers, 1872.

Dictionary of American Biography, New York: Charles Scribner's Sons, 1928.

Dictionary of National Biography, London: Smith, Elder & Co., 1888.

Abner Doubleday, *Reminiscences of Forts Sumter and Moultrie in 1860–61,* New York: Harper & Brothers, 1876.

Sir Howard Douglas, *A Treatise on Naval Gunnery,* London: John Murray, 1860.

Sir Howard Douglas, *Observations on Modern Systems of Fortification,* London: John Murray, 1859.

Sir Howard Douglas, *On Naval Warfare With Steam,* London: John Murray, 1860.

Encyclopedia Americana, (30 Vols) New York: Americana Corporation, 1946.

Encyclopaedia Britannica, Chicago Ill.: Encyclopaedia Britannica, Inc., including editions 1771, 1878, 1881, 1946.

James Q. Erwin, "Notes on The Coehorn Mortar," *The Military Collector and Historian,* Journal of the Company of Military Historians, (Washington, D.C.) Vol. XIII (Summer 1961).

Field Manual, Confederate States of America, Ordnance Bureau, (Richmond, Va.) (July, 1862).

Lamar Fontaine, *My Life and Lectures,* New York: Neale Publishing Co., 1908.

General Orders From Adjutant and Inspector General's Office, Confederate States Army From January 1862 to December 1863, Prepared From Files of Headquarters Department of South Carolina, Georgia and Florida, Columbia, S.C.: Evans and Cogswell, 1864.

General Orders From Adjutant and Inspector General's Office, Confederate States Army From January 1864 to July 1864, Prepared From Files of Headquarters Department of South Carolina, Georgia and Florida, Columbia, S.C.: Evans and Cogswell, 1864.

General Orders, Adjutant General's Office, U.S. War Department, Washington, D.C.: 1861, 1866, 1867.

John Gibbon, *The Artillerist's Manual, Compiled From Various Sources and Adapted to The Service of the United States,* New York: D. Van Nostrand, 1860.

William Gilham, *Manual for Instruction of Volunteers and Militia of The United States,* Philadelphia, Pa.: Charles DeSilver, 1861.

William Gilham, *Manual for Instruction of Volunteers and Militia of The Confederate States,* Richmond, Va.: West and Johnston, 1861, (Revised and enlarged, 1862).

Q. A. Gillmore, *Engineer and Artillery Operations Against The Defenses of Charleston Harbor, 1863,* New York: D. Van Nostrand, 1865.

Q. A. Gillmore, "Supplementary Report to Engineer and Artillery Operations Against The Defenses of Charleston Harbor, 1863," *Professional Papers No. 16, Corps of Engineers, U.S.A. Supplement,* New York: D. Van Nostrand, 1868.

S. James Gooding, *An Introduction to British Artillery in North America,* Ottawa, Ontario: Museum Restoration Service, 1965.

William A. Gordon, *A Compilation of Registers of The Army of The United States From 1815 to 1837 Inclusive,* Washington, D.C.: James C. Dunn, 1837.

Josiah Gorgas, "Contributions to The History of The Confederate Ordnance Department," *Southern Historical Society Papers,* (Richmond, Va.) Vol. XII (1884).

William Greener, *Gunnery in 1858, Being a Treatise on Rifles, Cannon and Sporting Arms,* London: Smith, Elder & Co., 1858.

F. W. Hackley, *A Report on Civil War Explosive Ordnance,* Indian Head, Md.: U.S. Naval Propellant Plant, 1960.

H. Wager Halleck, *Elements of Military Art and Science, or Course of Instruction in Strategy, Fortification (and) Tactics of Battles,* New York: D. Appleton & Co., 1861.

Lewis R. Hamersly, *The Records of Living Officers of The U.S. Navy and The Marine Corps With a History of Navy Operations During The Rebellion of 1861–65 and a List of Ships and Officers Participating in The Great Battles,* Philadelphia, Pa.: J. B. Lippincott & Co., 1870. Also, later editions, New York: L. R. Hamersly Co., 1884, 1898, 1902.

Harper's Weekly, A Journal of Civilization, (weekly newspaper) New York.

James C. Hazlett, five articles published in indicated issues of *The Military Collector and Historian,* journal of The Company of Military Historians, Washington, D.C.:
"False Napoleons," Vol. XIV (Summer 1962).
"The Napoleon Gun, Its Origin and Introduction into American Service," Vol. XV (Spring 1963).
"The Federal Napoleon," Vol. XV (Winter 1963).
"The Confederate Napoleon Gun," Vol. XVI (Winter 1964).
"The Napoleon Gun, Markings, Bore Diameters, Weights, Costs," Vol. XVIII (Winter 1966).

The Hebe Skirmish Centennial and The Fort Fisher Visitor Center Groundbreaking Program August 24, 1963, Wilmington, N.C.: (August, 1963).

Francis B. Heitman, *Historical Register of Officers of The Continental Army During The War of The Revolution, April 1775 to December 1783,* Washington, D.C.: Government Printing Office, 1893.

Francis B. Heitman, *Historical Register and Dictionary of The United States Army From Its Organization 29 September 1789 to 2 March 1903,* (2 Vols.) Washington, D.C.: Government Printing Office, 1903.

Alexander L. Holley, *A Treatise on Ordnance and Armor,* New York: D. Van Nostrand, 1865.

U.S. House of Representatives Document No. 99, 2nd session, 40th Congress, 1867–68, Washington, 1868.

Instruction for Field Artillery, Horse and Foot, Baltimore, Md.: Joseph Robinson, 1845.

Instruction for Field Artillery, Philadelphia, Pa.: J. B. Lippincott, 1860. Also, 1862.

Instruction for Heavy Artillery, Charleston, S.C.: Evans and Cogswell, 1861. Also, Washington, D.C.: Government Printing Office, 1863.

Colonel Jebb, *Jebb's Treatise on Attack and Defense,* London: William Clowes & Sons, 1857.

H. Paul Jeffers, "Mr. Griffen's Gun," *Civil War Times Illustrated,* Gettysburg, Pa., Vol. III, No. 7 (November, 1961).

John Johnson, *The Defense of Charleston Harbor 1863–65,* Charleston, S.C.: Walker, Evans and Cogswell, 1890.

John Johnson, unpublished collected papers, 1862–1906, in the collection of the South Carolina Historical Society, Charleston, S.C.

W. R. King, *Torpedoes, Their Invention and Use From The First Application of The Art of War to The Present Time, For Use of The Officers of The Corps of Engineers,* Washington, D.C.: 1866.

H. Lallemand, *A Treatise on Artillery,* Vol. I, New York: C. S. Van Winkle, 1820.

Frank Leslie's Illustrated Newspaper, New York.

Berkeley R. Lewis, *Notes on Ammunition of The American Civil War, 1861–1865,* (Washington) American Ordnance Association (1959).

List of The Officers of The Navy of The United States and The Marine Corps From 1775 to 1900, New York: L. R. Hamersly & Co., 1901.

Dennis Hart Mahan, *A Treatise on Field Fortifications,* New York: John Wiley, 1860.

Dennis Hart Mahan, *Summary of The Course of Permanent Fortifications and of The Attack and Defense of Permanent Works for The Use of Cadets of The U.S. Military Academy,* Charleston, S.C.: Evans and Cogswell, 1862. (Confederate edition.)

Albert Manucy, *Artillery Through The Ages,* Washington, D.C.: U.S. Government Printing Office, 1949.

Alfred Mordecai, *Artillery for The United States Land Service,* Washington, D.C.: J. and G. S. Gideon, 1849.

F. C. Morgan, *Handbook of Artillery Materiel,* London: William Clowes & Sons, 1886.

John Muller, *A Treatise of Artillery for Use of The Royal Academy of Artillery,* London, 1757 (first edition). Also, reprint of the 3rd edition, 1780, Ottawa, Ontario, Museum Restoration Service, 1965.

The News and Courier, (daily newspaper), Charleston, S.C.

The War of The Rebellion, A Compilation of The Official Records of The Union and Confederate Armies, (Generally known as the *Official Records,* the set consists of 127 books divided into four series of 70 volumes, many of one or more "parts." In addition there is a comprehensive index and an atlas of maps and illustrations. It was published in Washington, D.C., Government Printing Office, at varying dates between 1880 and 1901.

Official Records of Union and Confederate Navies in The War of The Rebellion, (31 Vols. including index) Washington, D.C.: Government Printing Office, varying dates between 1894 and 1927.

Ordnance Instructions for The Confederate States Navy, London: Saunders, Otley & Co., 1864.

Ordnance Instructions for The United States Navy, Part I, "Relating to The Preparation of Vessels of War for Battle;" Part II, "The Equipment and Manoeuvre of Boats and Exercise of Boat Howitzers;" Part III, "Ordnance and Ordnance Stores," Washington, D.C.: Government Printing Office, 1864 and 1866.

Ordnance Manual for The Use of Officers of The United States Army, Washington, D.C.: J. and G. S. Gideon, 1841.

Ordnance Manual for The Use of Officers of The United States Army, Washington, D.C.: Gideon & Co., 1850.

Ordnance Manual for The Use of Officers of The United States Army, Philadelphia, Pa.: J. B. Lippincott & Co., 1861 and 1862.

Ordnance Manual for The Use of Officers of The Confederate States Army, Charleston, S.C.: Evans and Cogswell, 1863.

Foxhall A. Parker, *The Naval Howitzer Afloat,* New York: D. Van Nostrand, 1866.

Robert Parker Parrott, *Ranges of Parrott Guns and Notes for Practice,* New York: D. Van Nostrand, 1863.

J. N. Paulding, *The Cannon and Projectiles Invented by Robert Parker Parrott,* New York, 1879.

Taylor Peck, *Round Shot to Rockets, A History of The Washington Navy Yard and The U.S. Naval Gun Factory,* Annapolis, Md.: United States Naval Institute, 1949.

Harold L. Peterson, *Notes on Ordnance of The American Civil War, 1861–1865,* Washington, D.C.: American Ordnance Association, 1959.

Photographic History of The Civil War, Francis Trevelyan Miller, editor in chief, (10 Vols.) New York: Review of Reviews Co., 1911.

Geo. W. Rains, "History of The Confederate Powder Works," address delivered before the Confederate Survivors Association 26 April 1882, (Augusta, Ga.) (1882).

Register of The Commissioned and Warrant Officers of The Navy of The Confederate States to 1 January 1864, Richmond, Va.: MacFarlane & Fergusson, 1864.

Regulations for The Army of The Confederate States 1863, Richmond, Va.: West and Johnston, 1863.

Reports of committees of the U.S. Senate, 2nd session, 38th Congress, 1864–65, Report No. 142, "Heavy Ordnance," Washington, D.C.: Government Printing Office, 1865.

Reports of committees of the U.S. Senate, 3rd session, 40th Congress, 1868–69, Report No. 266, "Experiments in Heavy Ordnance," Washington, D.C.: Government Printing Office, 1869.

Joseph Roberts, *Hand-Book of Artillery for The Service of The United States Army and Militia,* New York: D. Van Nostrand, 1861.

Alfred Roman, *The Military Operations of General Beauregard, 1861–65,* (2 Vols.) New York: Harper & Brothers, 1884.

J. Thomas Scharf, *History of The Confederate States Navy From Its Organization to Surrender of Its Last Vessel,* Albany, N.Y.: Joseph McDonough, 1894.

John Scoffern,, *New Resources of Warfare,* London: Longman, Brown & Co., 1859.

John Scoffern, *Projectile Weapons of War and Explosive Compounds,* London: Longman, Brown & Co., 1859.

Edward Simpson, *A Treatise on Ordnance and Naval Gunnery,* New York: D. Van Nostrand, 1862.

Walter W. Stephen, "The Brooke Guns of Selma, Alabama," *Alabama Historical Quarterly,* (Montgomery, Ala.) Vol. 20, No. 3 (Fall 1958).

Lynall Thomas, *Rifled Ordnance,* New York: D. Van Nostrand, 1864, (first American edition from the fifth English).

Louis de Tousard, *Elements of Artillery,* Vol. III, Philadelphia, Pa.: C. and A. Conrad & Co., 1809.

Daniel Treadwell, *On The Construction of Improved Ordnance as Prepared in a Letter to The Secretaries of War and of The Navy and The Chiefs of The Bureaus of Engineers and Ordnance of The United States,* Cambridge, Mass.: Welch, Bigelow & Co., 1862.

Daniel Treadwell, "On The Construction of Hooped Cannon, Being a Sequel to a Memoir on The Practicability of Constructing Cannon of Great Caliber," *Memoirs of The American Academy of Arts and Sciences,* (Boston, Mass.) (1864).

Cary S. Tucker, "Virginia Military Institute Cadet Battery Guns," *The Military Collector and Historian,* Journal of The Company of Military Historians, (Washington, D.C.) Vol. XIII (1961).

James H. Ward, *Elementary Instruction in Naval Ordnance*

and Gunnery, New York: D. Van Nostrand, 1861.

Laura Singleton Walker, *History of Ware County, Georgia,* Macon, Ga.: The J. W. Burke Co., 1934.

Jac Weller, "The Confederate Use of British Cannon," *Civil War History,* (Iowa City, Iowa) Vol. III, No. 2 (June 1957).

Norman Wiard, *War Pamphlets,* (New York) (All 1863 unless otherwise indicated):

Memorial of Norman Wiard to The Senate and House of Representatives In Congress Assembled, to be Accompanied by Eight Pamphlets Entitled:

    I. "Great Guns, The Cause of Their Failure and The True Method of Constructing Them."
    II. "Wiard's System of Field Artillery."
    III. "Marine Artillery As Adapted for Service on The Coast and on Inland Waters. . . . Invented and Adapted by Norman Wiard."
    IV. "The Manufacture of Small Arms at Home Versus Their Purchase Abroad."
    V. "Ships, Rams and Forts."
    VI. "Proposals for Great Guns, a Letter to The Secretary of War by Norman Wiard."
    VII. "Experiences of a Contractor."
    VIII. "Review in Detail of The Annual Report of The Chief of The Navy Ordnance Bureau," (1862).

Norman Wiard, "Inefficiency of Heavy Ordnance in This Country and Everywhere and About Parrott and Other Hooped Guns," (Washington) (1865).

George Will and J. C. Dalton, *The Artillerists Handbook of Reference,* London: William Clowes & Son, 1879.

John L. Wilson, *Abstract of a System of Exercise and Instruction of Field Artillery and The Exercise of Heavy Artillery in Battery and Some Directions for The Laboratory Together With The Sword Exercise of The Artillerist, for The Use of The South Carolina Militia,* Charleston, S.C.: A. E. Miller, 1834.

Jennings Cropper Wise, *The Long Arm of Lee, or The History of The Artillery of The Army of Northern Virginia,* (2 Vols.) Lynchburg, Va.: J. P. Bell Co., 1915.

Glossary

(NOTE: Letters or numbers in parentheses will be found in the illustration)

ASTRAGAL

Small, convex molding, roughly half-circle, which, with a fillet on either side, is found in place of a chase ring (6) on various weapons, predominantly bronze.

AXIS OF A PIECE

Central line of the bore.

BAND

See Reinforcing Band.

BASE LINE

Line traced around the gun in rear of the vent.

BASE RING

Projecting band of metal adjoining the base of the breech (3) and connected with the body of the gun by a concave molding.

BASE OF THE BREECH

Rear surface of the breech (d), also (B-C).

BORE

All the part bored out including the chamber, if present, and the junction of the bore with the chamber.

BORE DIAMETER

Diameter of the opening, generally measured for convenience at the muzzle face. A few weapons will be found in which the bore is flared and in these bore diameter must be measured a few inches inside. See Caliber.

BORE LENGTH

The entire length inside the tube, including chamber if present. This measurement was of more value to ancient ordnance men than modern hobbyists since the bores of most cannon today are filled with paper, leaves, empty beer cans, bird nests, and, occasionally, becs. An approximation of bore length can be made from muzzle face to vent along the top of the tube, but this may be as much as 4 or 5 inches off due to slant of the vent and location where it joins the bore.

BREECH

Mass of solid metal behind the bottom of the bore extending to the cascabel (B-D). Formerly considered the mass of metal from bottom of the bore to the base of the breech (C-D).

BREECH SIGHT MASS

Block of metal cast on the base of the breech just in rear of the base ring of certain Navy weapons which forms a support for the breech sight. See Reinforce Sight Mass.

BREECHING LOOP

Rounded piece of metal extending from the base of the breech to the cascabel knob of many older cannon such as the Model 1821 32-pounder. Although the loop was designed to hold breeching tackle aboard ship, many of these guns were also used by the Army.

BUSHING

Metal piece, usually about an inch in diameter, through which a hole for the vent had been drilled. The normal vent of the weapon, which was subject to erosion by the gases of discharge, was reamed out and threaded to receive the bushing. In bronze cannon, the bushing, also called a Vent Piece, was of wrought copper.

CALIBER

Diameter of the bore. It was expressed in inches—7-inch, or in the weight of its spherical shot—42-pounder.

CASCABEL (Older spelling cascable)

Technically (A-C) consisting of the knob (a), neck (b), fillet (c), and base of the breech (d). Today the term is loosely used, as in this book, to designate the section (A-B) and includes knob, neck and, if present, the fillet. The cascabel has several forms other than the one illustrated.

CASCABEL BLOCK

Small block of metal which could be removed from the rear of certain types of Navy cascabels for insertion of breeching tackle, then replaced. It was retained in position by a Cascabel Block Pin, often reduced to Cascabel Pin.

CASCABEL BLOCK PIN

See Cascabel Block.

CAVETTO

Concave molding in which the curve is usually a quarter circle. The lip of a number of weapons was cavetto molding (9).

CHAMBER

A smaller diameter section of the bores of some weapons. It contained the powder charge. There are three main types:

Cylindrical Chamber—Shaped like a smaller diameter bore at the bottom of the main bore. The base may be rounded or square. Used generally in howitzers.

Conical Chamber—(Also called Gomer Chamber after its inventor). Shaped like the frustum of a cone. Normally used for mortars.

Spherical Chamber—Consists of a sphere joined to the bore by a small diameter cylinder, or may be oval shaped with one end open to the bore. Used in very early mortars. It developed greater force than the other types, but was likely to break projectiles and was difficult to clean. By the Civil War, it was no longer used.

CHASE

Conical part of the piece in front of the reinforce (F-G).

CHASE RING

Band at the front end of the chase (6). In bronze weapons often replaced by astragal and fillets.

CLEVIS

U-shaped iron shackle which fitted the hole, or eye, of the ear of a mortar for lifting. See Ear.

CONICAL CHAMBER

See Chamber.

CYLINDRICAL CHAMBER

See Chamber.

DISPART

Difference of the semi-diameters of the base ring and the swell of the muzzle or muzzle band. Of value in sighting a piece, but of purely academic interest today.

DOLPHIN

See Handles.

EAR

Lug of metal with a hole in it cast on some mortars, such as the Model 1861 15-inch, as an aid in lifting. It was generally fitted with a clevis, a U-shaped iron shackle with a removable pin closing the open end, for attachment of a rope or chain. The hole in the ear was known as the "Eye." Also: Circular rings of metal cast equidistant from the fuse of very early mortar shells to assist in loading. Later the holes which replaced them retained the name "Ears."

ECHINUS

A quarter-round molding. Muzzle moldings of the 6-pounder field gun, Model 1839 consist of an echinus, a fillet, and a cavetto.

EYE

Hole in the ear of a mortar. See Ear.

FACE

A plane surface. Generally qualified as Muzzle Face (10) or Trunnion Face (4). Used alone, muzzle face is usually meant.

FILLET

A narrow, flat molding often used in connection with others such as the junction of the swell of the muzzle and lip of many weapons (9). Also, with an astragal, on the chase near the neck of some weapons.

FIRST REINFORCE

See Reinforce.

GOMER CHAMBER

See Chamber.

GROOVES

See Rifling.

HANDLES

Flat rings cast on certain bronze weapons such as the 24- and 32-pounder field howitzers. They were placed over the center of gravity to facilitate lifting and in the early days, when guns were heavily ornamented, often were cast to resemble dolphins and hence became known by this name. The handle of the mortar is called an "ear."

KNOB

See Cascabel.

LANDS

See Rifling.

LENGTH OVERALL

Total length of the piece from muzzle face to extreme tip of cascabel (A-H). Certain Civil War era texts, particularly Navy, exclude the cascabel and consider length the distance from muzzle face to rear of the base ring (C-H).

LINE OF METAL

See Natural Line of Sight.

LIP

Casual term for outer unit of muzzle molding, generally cavetto in form, and usually backed by a fillet.

LOCK

Device for firing a cannon. See Chapter XI.

LOCK PIECE

Block of metal cast on the tube at the outer opening of the vent to facilitate attaching a lock to the weapon (2). Note: The illustration shows both top and side elevation of the lock piece.

MUZZLE

Mouth, or opening of the bore.

MUZZLE BAND

A band, or ring, which takes the place of the muzzle swell in such weapons as field howitzers.

MUZZLE FACE

See Face.

MUZZLE SIGHT

Generally a leaf sight screwed into the top of the muzzle swell, or band, for use as a forward aiming point.

MUZZLE SWELL

The largest part of the piece in front of the neck (8).

NATURAL ANGLE OF SIGHT

Angle which the Natural Line of Sight makes with the Axis of a Piece. Today of academic interest only.

NATURAL LINE OF SIGHT

Line from the highest point of the base ring to the highest point on the swell of the muzzle. Also called the Line of Metal.

NECK

Smallest part of the piece in front of the chase (7). Also, narrowest part of the cascabel (b).

OGEE

Form of molding used on very ancient weapons often to join a reinforce ring with the next reinforce.

POINT BLANK RANGE

The distance from the muzzle of the piece to that point in a shot's trajectory where it cuts the prolongation of the Natural Line of Sight a second time.

PREPONDERANCE

The excess weight of the part of a piece in rear of the trunnions over that in front. It is measured on a balance, the point of support at the rear of the base ring, the weapon being suspended freely on the axis of its trunnions.

RATCHET

One of a number of indentations cut in the base of the breech of certain weapons, including the U.S. Model 1861 columbiads, for use in setting elevations.

RECESS

A section of reduced diameter of certain howitzers, such as the 32-pounder field model, between base ring and about midway to the trunnions.

REINFORCE

The thickest part of the body of the gun, in front of the base ring. If there is more than one reinforce, that which is next to the base ring is called the First Reinforce (D-E), the other (E-F), the Second Reinforce.

REINFORCE BAND

See Reinforce Ring, also Reinforcing Band.

REINFORCING BAND

Heavy ring or band of metal affixed over the breech area of rifled weapons to provide additional strength.

REINFORCE RING

Narrow ring of metal at junction of first and second reinforce, similar in appearance to the chase ring (6). In very ancient weapons this was generally joined to the next reinforce by an ogee molding. Also called Reinforce Band, a term which became confusing with the introduction of rifled cannon which often had one or more Reinforcing Bands.

REINFORCE SIGHT

Sight on the second reinforce. Certain weapons, particularly Navy that had to fire through ports which tended to break muzzle sights or large Army weapons, had the front sight in this position.

REINFORCE SIGHT MASS

Block of metal on the second reinforce just in front of the axis of the trunnions of certain weapons which forms a base into which the reinforce sight is screwed. This is the Navy term for the appendage; the Army called it a Reinforce Sight Piece. Both generally abbreviated the names to Sight Mass and Sight Piece. See Breech Sight Mass.

REINFORCE SIGHT PIECE

Block of metal cast on top of the tube near the axis of the trunnions to serve as a base into which a sight is screwed. See illustration Model 1861, U.S. columbiad. The Navy referred to this appendage as a Reinforce Sight Mass. Also called Sight Piece.

RIFLING

A method of imparting rotation to a projectile as it moved through the bore. There were several systems of rifling, all composed of indentations called "grooves" and raised portions, "lands."

RIMBASE

Shoulder at the base of a trunnion (5).

RIMBASE SIGHT

Small sight, generally leaf type, screwed into the top of the rimbase or in a bracket cast thereon. Often termed "trunnion sight" although technically this is a misnomer.

SECOND REINFORCE

See Reinforce.

SHELL

Shallow indentation around the vent of very ancient cannon used to hold the priming. At first this was cast and ornamented in the form of a seashell, later reduced generally to a simple rectangle. No longer used by the Civil War era. Also a form of projectile.

SIGHT

Device to guide the eye in aiming. There were various types including breech, reinforce, rimbase, muzzle, tangent scale, and pendulum hausse.

SIGHT MASS

See Reinforce Sight Mass.

SIGHT PIECE

See Reinforce Sight Piece.

SPHERICAL CHAMBER

See Chamber.

TRUNNIONS

Two cylinders generally near the center of gravity of a piece by which it is supported on its carriage (4).

TRUNNION SIGHT

See Rimbase Sight.

VENT

Tube (11) leading from the top of the barrel to the bore or chamber for use in igniting the charge. In Civil War era U.S. weapons it was usually .2-inch diameter. Also see Lock Piece.

VENT ASTRAGAL AND FILLETS

Molding consisting of an astragal and two fillets encircling the tube at the vent. This form of ornamentation was seldom used after the 1820s. Similar to chase astragal and fillets which remained in use on certain weapons.

VENT MOLDING

See Vent Astragal and Fillets

VENT PIECE

See Bushing.

WINDAGE

The difference between the diameter of the bore and that of the projectile.

24-Pounder Siege and Garrison Gun.
AC – Cascabel
        a. – Knob
        b. – Neck
        c. – Fillet
        d. – Base of Breech
BC – Base of Breech
CD – Breech
DE – First Reinforce
EF – Second Reinforce
FG – Chase
No. 1. – Bottom of Bore
     2. – Lock Piece
     3. – Base Ring
     4. – Trunnions
     5. – Rimbases
     6. – Chase Ring
     7. – Neck
     8. – Swell of Muzzle
     9. – Lip and Fillet
    10. – Face
    11. – Vent

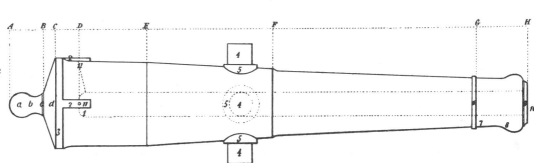

Initials of inspectors and manufacturers are found on most weapons and the following lists will be an aid in identification. However, by no means all names are known today and while the lists are believed to be reasonably complete, presumably certain individuals and firms are missing. Conversely, although an effort has been made to eliminate smallarms inspectors and others on duty unconnected with cannon, doubtless names have been included of a few individuals who performed other ordnance chores.

Weapons made after 1832 were inspected by Ordnance Department personnel, but this was not always the case in prior years. According to Birkhimer (See Bibliography), the following inspected cannon during the indicated periods:

1798 (approximately)–1802—Col. Louis de Tousard.

1802–1812—Colonels commanding the Regiment of Artillerists.

1812–1821—Ordnance Department (organized in 1812) personnel.

1821–1832—The Ordnance Department was merged back into artillery in the reorganization of 1821, and cannon inspection was performed by artillery officers during this period—often the same men who had been in the Ordnance Department.

1832– —Ordnance Department personnel. (There is reason to believe artillerymen on ordnance duty who did not transfer to the newly reorganized department may have finished out their tours into 1833).

APPENDIX B

Inspectors and Manufacturers

Following are lists of Army and Navy inspectors. Dates designate known (or assumed, "a") periods of ordnance duty. However, officers familiar with inspection procedures no doubt were placed on short tours of inspection service considered too insignificant to be mentioned in biographies and registers from which the lists were compiled († indicates probable additional years).

James S. Abeel—1829.
Isaac Austin Adams—1827, 1829.
Thomas Boylston Adams—1833–35.
Robert Anderson—1829, 1831–33.
William Anderson—1816.
Samuel B. Archer—1822.
Richard Bache—1833–35.
Nehemiah Baden—1813–21.
Thomas J. Baird—1827.
James Baker—1813–19.
Rufus L. Baker—1813–54.
George Thatcher Balch—1851–65.
Oliver O. Bangs—1816.
James Bankhead—1830.
Francis Noel Barbarin—1834–36.
Joshua Barney—1826–27.
Alfred Beckley—1829–33.
William Hayward Bell—1826–30, 1832, 1833–35.
Stephen Vincent Benet—1849–91.
James Gilchrist Benton—1842–81.
Horace Bliss—1833.
George Bomford—1810–11a, 1812–48.
John Rudolph Bowes—1820.
James Andrew John Bradford—1833–61.
William Pinckney Buchanan—1820–21.
Joseph Buckley—1820.

Adelbert Rinaldo Buffington—1861–1901.
Martin Burke (also listed as Burk)—1834–36.
John G. Butler—1864–88†
Thomas L. Campbell—1815a.
Clemens C. Chaffee—1862–67.
John A. Chambers—1827–28.
John Childe (also listed as Child)—1829–33.
Sylvester Churchill—1826.
Clifton Comly—1863–89†
James H. Cooke—1828–32.
Henry Knox Craig—1832–63 (also probably between 1821 and 1832).
Silas Crispin—1850–89.
William Crozier—1881–1901†
James Dalliba (also listed as Dalaby)—1813–21.
William B. Davidson—1815–21.
James Low Dawson—1819–21.
John Chetwood deHart—1816–18.
William Chetwood deHart—1816–21.
Julius Adolphus deLagnel—1826–27, 1831–32, 1836.
Alexander Brydie Dyer—1838–74.
John Rufus Edie—1861–74.
John Farley—1829.
Joseph P. Farley—1861–87†
Josiah Horace Vincent Field—1863–64.
Daniel Webster Flagler—1861–99.
Abram C. Fowler—1826–28.
Josiah Gorgas—1841–61 (Chief of Confederate Ordnance Department 1861–65).
John Edwin Greer—1867–87†
Peter V. Hagner—1838–81.
Edward Harding—1829–55.
Jeremiah D. Hayden—1816–21.
Frank Heath—1874–86†
Daniel S. Herring—1833–34.

Richard M. Hill—1861–76.
John Hills—1815–22, 1827–32, 1832–35a.
John B. Hobkirk—1818.
Joshua Howard—1831–34.
Benjamin Huger—1832–61. (Confederate inspector of ordnance 1862–65).
James R. Irwin—1829.
Francis L. Jones—1832–33.
Christopher Keiser—1813–19.
John A. Kress—1865–66.
Theodore Thaddeus Sobieski Laidley—1842–82.
Richard Lee Bland—1829–32.
Thomas C. Legate—1830–32.
Thomas Beasly Linnard—1830–33.
James Livingston—1815–18.
Joseph Lorenzo Locke—1831–33.
Mann Paige Lomax—1838–42 (possibly prior to 1838).
Allen Lowd—1827–28.
Stephen Carr Lyford—1861–85.
David Alexander Lyle—1874–99†.
William C. Lyman—1813–19.
Julian McAllister—1848–87.
John R. McGinness—1863–89†.
James Simmons McIntosh—1818–21.
George W. McKee—1863–88†.
Thomas Patrick McMahon—1816–18.
Matthew J. Magee—1816–18.
William Seton Maitland—1827–30.
Henry S. Mallaroy (also listed as Mallory)—1834.
John H. Margart—1812–21.
Thomas Martin—1817–21, 1826–29.
William Maynadier—1828–71.
Charles Mellon—1829.
Henry Metcalfe—1869–86†.
Otho E. Michaelis—1865–66.
James Monroe—1823–26.
Alfred Mordecai—1823–61.
Alfred Mordecai (son of above)—1861–87†.
William Walton Morris—1827–28.
Charles C. Morrison—1879–89†.
Charles F. Morton—1814–21.
John Morton—1812–21.
Jasper Myers—1865–66.
George Nauman—1823–24, 1831–35, 1859–60.
Joseph S. Nelson—1816–21.
William S. Newton—1822–23, 1826, 1834–37.
William Palmer—1831–32, 1834–35.
Francis H. Parker—1865–66.
Robert Parker Parrott—1834–36 (See Manufacturers).
M. A. Patrick—1827.
Charles Pettigru—1833–35.
John Walter Phillips—1815–21.
Frank H. Phipps—1865–66.

Martin L. Poland—1865–66.
Richard C. Pomeroy—1814–21.
William Prince—1864–80.
George D. Ramsay—1835–70.
George Douglas Ramsay Jr.—1863–78.
Joseph H. Rees—1814–21.
James W. Reilly—1863–88†.
Robert D. Richardson—1813–21.
Louis A. Rigail—1818–21.
William W. Rigal—1815–18.
Samuel Ringgold—1826–31, 1835–36.
Thomas Lee Ringgold—1840–51.
James Wolfe Ripley—1832–63.
Charles F. Rockwell—1865–66.
Thomas J. Rodman—1841–71.
Stephen Van Rensselaer Ryan—1830–31.
John Benjamin Scott—1821–22, 1835–38.
James Simonson—1815–26.
Raphael Cummings Smead—1828–32.
Stansbury Smith—1841–44.
Walter Smith—1819, 1829–32.
William S. Smoot—1865–66.
Howard Stockton—1864–71.
Thomas Emery Sudler—1820–21.
John Symington—1815–62.
John C. Symmes—1849–60.
George Talcott—1813–21, 1821–31a, 1832–51.
George H. Talcott—1836–54.
Charles Thomas—1819–21.
John W. Thompson—1816–21.
William A. Thornton—1829–66.
Daniel D. Tompkins—1820–28, 1833.
Danforth H. Tufts—1834–36.
Daniel Tyler—1826, 1828–33.
Edwin Tyler—1813–19.
David Van-Ness—1826, 1829–32.
Benjamin Chew Vining—1818–21.
David Hammond Vinton—1822–23, 1825–26, 1831–33.
Richard Dean Alden Wade—1832–33.
William Wade—1813–22.
Decius Wadsworth—1802–05, 1812–21.
Louis A. de Barth Walbach (initials L.A.B.W.)—1835–53.
Benjamin Walker—1819–21.
Charles Ward—1816–21, 1826, 1834.
John MacRae Washington—1827–33.
Washington Wheelwright—1821–22, 1826–33.
Robert Henry Kirkwood Whitely—1834–36, 1838–75.
James M. Whittemore—1861–86†.
Wolvert Ecker Williams—1815–24.
John Williamson—1835–49.
Amos Woodward—1819–21.
Abram R. Woolley—1812–21.
William J. Worth—1832–38.

INSPECTORS — NAVY

John J. Almy—1868–69.
John H. Aulick—1834a, 1840a, 1846a, 1851.
Charles A. Babcock—1866.

Oscar C. Badger—1858, 1861a, 1864–66.
Charles H. Baldwin—1864–67.
Edward Barrett—1866.

John M. Berrien—1862–64.
Daniel L. Braine—1866–67.
Randolph K. Breese—1868–69a.
Overton Carr—1852–54, 1864–65a.
Ralph Chandler—1868.
John S. Chauncey—1840–43, 1847–50.
George H. Cooper—1857.
Johnston B. Creighton—1866–67.
John A. Dahlgren—1847–63, 1868–70.
William H. Dana—1866.
Henry K. Davenport—1859–60.
Edward Donaldson—1865.
Thomas Aloysius Dornin—1847–48, 1856.
Earl English—1866.
Robley D. Evans—1867.
Donald M. N. Fairfax—1859, 1868–69.
Samuel R. Franklin—1868–69.
John R. Goldsborough—1864–65, 1868–69.
Joseph F. Green—1853–54, 1861, 1866–68.
Theodore F. Greene—1866.
James A. Greer—1869.
Francis S. Haggerty—1861–66.
Andrew A. Harwood—1843–52, 1859–61, 1862–63a.
Francis J. Higginson—1876–78a.
Robert Bradley Hitchcock—1850–52, 1854–55a, 1856–57, 1861, 1864–65.
Henry K. Hoff—1864–67.
Henry L. Howison—1866, 1869.
Timothy Atwater Hunt—1856–59, 1862–67.
Duncan N. Ingraham—1855–60. (Joined Confederacy in 1861).
John Irwin—1864.
William N. Jeffers—1862–65.
Catesby ap Roger Jones—1853, 1854–60a. (Joined Confederacy 1861).
Edmund Lanier—1866–67.
Joseph B. Lanman—1845–46.

John Madigan—1864.
George A. Magruder—1845–46, 1855.
Matthias C. Marin—1864–65, 1867–68.
Joseph D. Marvin—1867.
William Mitchell—1862–64.
Madison J. R. Mullany—1856–58, 1861–62, 1866–68.
J. W. A. Nicholson—1863.
Somerville Nicholson—1856–57, 1869.
P (Proved or Proof)—Found on most Navy weapons, often immediately preceding initials of inspectors, ie: "PJAD" (Proved—John A. Dahlgren). In older weapons, Pf is usually used.
Austin Pendergrast—1858, 1869.
George H. Perkins—1870.
Thomas S. Phelps—1857–58.
Cicero Price—1853.
Walter W. Queen—1862–63, 1865–66.
William Reynolds—1870.
Stephen C. Rowan—1850–53, 1858–61.
John H. Russell—1857–60, 1864, 1866.
Gustavus H. Scott—1848–49, 1851.
Alexander A. Semmes—1866–68.
William B. Shubrick—1833–37, 1852.
Fabius Stanly—1864.
Oscar F. Stanton—1862, 1865.
George A. Stevens—1861.
Cornelius K. Stribling—1834–35.
William Rogers Taylor—1853–55, 1857–59, 1861, 1866–67.
Edward R. Thompson—1858–60.
Egbert Thompson—1859–60.
Thomas Turner—1854–57, 1868.
John H. Upshur—1852, 1856–57.
Alexander Scammell Wadsworth—1825–29, 1841–50.
William C. West—1863.
Edward P. Williams—1864–65, 1867–69.
Henry A. Wise—1854–69.
Jonathan Young—1864.

MANUFACTURERS — U. S.

Cyrus Alger	Founder of Cyrus Alger & Co. (q.v.).	tials "S.B.F." (South Boston Foundry) occasionally may be found on cannon, but the signature is traditionally "C.A. & Co., Boston, Mass." or, rarely, "C. Alger & Co., Boston, Mass."
Cyrus Alger & Co.	Cyrus Alger, who during the War of 1812 furnished the government with shot and shell, in 1817 started South Boston Iron Company which at an early date was known locally as Alger's Foundry and later became Cyrus Alger & Co. The Massachusetts firm was a leading cannon manufacturer and when Cyrus died in 1856, leadership was assumed by his son, Francis, who piloted the company until his death in 1864. During the war, both Army and Navy were supplied with large numbers of weapons. The ini-	
		Francis Alger	President, Cyrus Alger & Co. (q.v.) 1856–64.
		A. M. Co.	Ames Manufacturing Co. (q.v.).
		Ames Co. Founders	Ames Manufacturing Co. (q.v.).
		Horatio Ames	Inventor and owner of a foundry at either Salisbury or Falls Village, Conn. for production of his own weapons.
		James Tyler Ames	(1810–1883), headed Ames Manufacturing Co. 1847–74.
		Ames Mfg. Co.	Ames Manufacturing Co. (q.v.).

Ames Manufacturing Co.	Cannon foundry at Chicopee (Springfield) Mass. operated by Nathan Peabody Ames and his brother James Tyler Ames. Between 1836, when the firm which had been organized in 1834 began casting cannon, and Nathan's death in 1847, weapons were marked "N.P.Ames, Founder, Springfield, Mass." After this date, when the younger brother became president, marks were "Ames Co., Founders, Chicopee, Mass.", "Ames Mfg. Co., Chicopee, Mass.", or "A.M.Co." With exception of certain weapons discussed in Chapter IX, products of this company were brass.
Nathan Peabody Ames	(1803–1847). President of Ames Manufacturing Co. (q.v.) 1834–47.
Joseph Reid Anderson	(1813–1892). Owner of J.R.Anderson & Co., better known as Tredegar Foundry (q.v.). A more extensive biography will be found in Chapter VII.
J. R. Anderson & Co.	See Tredegar Foundry.
A. P. W.	One of the many trademarks of Fort Pitt Foundry (q.v.). Possibly initials of a foundry co-owner named Wade.
Dr. Junius L. Archer	Owner of Bellona Foundry (q.v.).
B. A.	Bellona Arsenal (q.v.).
Bellona Arsenal	Military post garrisoned by a battery of U.S. artillery; said to have been established 1816–17. It was 14 miles above Richmond, adjacent to Bellona Foundry (q.v.) and served as a facility for repair and fabrication of smallarms and other munitions. It presumably also received and stored cannon produced for the government at the nearby foundry. May also have been called Bellona Foundry Arsenal (B.F.A.).
B.F.	Bellona Foundry (q.v.). Builder's Foundry (q.v.).
Bellona Foundry	Cannon foundry near Richmond operated in 1819, and probably earlier, by Maj. John Clark who still owned the firm in 1836. Clark sold it later (probably in the early 1840s) to Dr. Junius L. Archer. Under both owners the company was a major supplier of weapons for the U.S. and state governments. Initials "B.F." will be found coupled with those of Clark, but in early weapons written "I.C." rather than "J.C." in the same manner as those of Gen. John Mason of Columbia Foundry (q.v.). Whether Clark shifted to "J," as did Mason, in the 1830s has not been

	determined. Weapons will be found marked "I.C. & Co. B.F." and "I.C.B.F." at least until 1830 and thereafter probably with "J" substituted for "I." After purchase by Archer, cannon were marked "J.L. A. B.F." (See Confederate listing for wartime operations.)
B.F.A.	Bellona Foundry Arsenal (assumed). See Bellona Arsenal.
Builder's Foundry	Technically Builder's Iron Foundry, but apparently known generally by the shorter name. Providence, R.I., firm operated by Zechariah Chafee which cast ammunition and heavy iron cannon during the war.
C.A. & Co.	Cyrus Alger & Co. (q.v.).
Zechariah Chafee	Operator of Builder's Foundry (q.v.).
John Clark	Owner of Bellona Foundry (q.v.).
Col. Found.	Abbreviation of Columbia Foundry (q.v.) found on an eprouvette cast in 1816.
Columbia Foundry	Established in 1801 at Georgetown (D.C.) by Henry Foxall. He sold the firm in 1815 to Gen. John Mason who manufactured iron cannon for the government until 1841. Initials "C.F." are generally coupled with Mason's in one of two forms, "I.M." or "J.M." "I" was the early method of making a "J" and has been found with "C.F." on weapons dated 1821 and 1828 and with "Col. Found." in 1816. "C.F. J.M." is stamped on guns of 1836 and since Webster's Dictionary began separating the two letters in 1828, Mr. Mason seems to have followed suit between this date and 1836.
Eagle Iron Works	Cincinnati, Ohio, firm headed by M. Greenwood (q.v.)
F.P.	Fort Pitt. See Fort Pitt Foundry.
F.P.F.	Fort Pitt Foundry (q.v.).
Fort Pitt Foundry	Pittsburg, Pa., manufacturer of iron cannon, particularly during the war when as the holder of Rodman's patents, this firm turned out large numbers of weapons by this process. It was founded in 1814 by Joseph McClurg and seems to have had a number of owners and co-owners over the years including Joseph and Alexander McClurg, Charles Knap, and men of the last names Totten, Rudd, and Wade. This resulted in a hodgepodge of names and initials including the following:

> F.P.—Fort Pitt.
> McC., Pitt—McClurg, Pittsburg.
> F.P.F., KR` & Co.—Fort Pitt Foundry, Knap, Rudd & Co.

McC. & W., or McC.W. & Co.— McClurg and Wade.

McP & W, P.P.F.—Unidentified. The "W" probably is Wade.

A.P.W.—Unidentified. Possibly Wade's initials.

Fort Pitt, Pa.

K.& T., or K.T.& Co.—Assumed initials of Knap and Totten.

K.& W., or K.W.& Co.—Assumed initials of Knap and Wade.

Knap & Co.—Assumed.

Henry Foxall — Columbia Foundry (q.v.) owner 1801–15.

M. Greenwood
or
M.G. Cin.O. — Miles Greenwood (1807–85) owner of the Eagle Iron Works at Cincinnati, Ohio, which produced a number of bronze field weapons 1861–62.

Hinckley — Hinckley, Williams & Co. (q.v.).

HNH & Co. — Henry N. Hooper & Co. (q.v.).

Henry N. Hooper & Co. — Foundry at Boston, Mass., which during the war produced limited numbers of brass and iron weapons as well as a 3-inch experimental rifle said to be made of German silver.

I.C. B.F. or I.C. & Co. B.F. — John Clark, Bellona Foundry (q.v.).

I.M. — John Mason of Columbia Foundry (q.v.).

J.C. B.F. or J.C. & Co. B.F. — Assumed initials of John Clark, Bellona Foundry (q.v.) after substitution of "J" for "I."

J.L.A. — Junius L. Archer, owner of Bellona Foundry (q.v.).

J.M. — John Mason, owner of Columbia Foundry (q.v.).

J.R.A. or J.R.A. & Co. — Joseph Reid Anderson or his firm. Initials are generally coupled with "T.F.," Tredegar Foundry (q.v.).

Charles Knap — Owner, Fort Pitt Foundry (q.v.).

KR & Co. — Knap, Rudd & Co. See Fort Pitt Foundry.

Knap & Totten — See Fort Pitt Foundry.

McC. Pitt. — McClurg, Pittsburg. See Fort Pitt Foundry.

Alexander McClurg — Owner, Fort Pitt Foundry (q.v.).

Joseph McClurg — Owner, Fort Pitt Foundry (q.v.).

McC. & W. — McClurg and Wade. Fort Pitt Foundry (q.v.).

McManus — See Scott Foundry.

McP & W., P.P.F. — See Fort Pitt Foundry.

Marshall & Co., St. Louis, Mo. — A few brass cannon have been found with the name of this firm stamped on the trunnions.

John Mason — Proprietor of Columbia Foundry (q.v.).

Nimick — See Singer-Nimick & Co.

N.W. — Norman Wiard (q.v.).

N.Y.C., O.F. — Unidentified. Presumably a New York City foundry which made weapons designed by Norman Wiard (q.v.). Possibly John O'Donnell.

O.F. — Unidentified founder, possibly John O'Donnell. See Norman Wiard.

Robert Parker Parrott — (1804–1877). Supt. West Point Foundry 1836–67. Inventor of Parrott Rifle. See West Point Foundry. Also, Inspectors, Army.

Phoenix Iron Company — Phoenixville, Pa., firm which began manufacturing wrought iron cannon in 1855 and during the war produced the 3-inch Ordnance Rifle.

P.I.Co. — Phoenix Iron Co. (q.v.).

Portland Co. — Portland, Maine, firm operated by J. Sparrow. It is listed as manufacturing heavy weapons during the war—apparently in relatively limited numbers.

Revere Copper Co. — Manufacturer of brass weapons, especially Napoleons.

S.B.F. — South Boston Foundry. See Cyrus Alger & Co.

Scott Foundry — Reading, Pa., foundry apparently organized after the war began by Seyfert, McManus & Co. of Reading which had been in operation since 1836. Scott Foundry cast heavy iron weapons such as the 15-inch Rodman under an arrangement with Fort Pitt Foundry for use of the patented interior cooling process. Weapons are marked "S.F." which often is easily confused with initials of the inspector.

Seyfert, McManus & Co. — See Scott Foundry.

S.F. — Scott Foundry (q.v.).

Singer-Nimick & Co. — Pittsburg, Pa., firm which in 1862 manufactured a small number of cast steel 3-inch rifles on the Ordnance Rifle pattern. The name is stamped on the trunnions.

South Boston Foundry — See Cyrus Alger & Co.

J. Sparrow — Proprietor of Portland Co. (q.v.).

T.F. — Tredegar Foundry (q.v.).

Totten — One of the co-owners of Fort Pitt Foundry (q.v.).

Daniel Treadwell — Produced a few weapons of his own design during the 1840s.

Tredegar Foundry — Major weapons manufacturer for U.S. and state governments 1848–61, and for the Confederacy during the war. Owned by Joseph Reid Anderson. Markings may be "J.R.A. & Co.," but more likely "T. F.," generally without Anderson's initials prior to the war and with them on Confederate pieces. The firm also was called Tredegar Iron Works,

West Point Foundry	but Tredegar Foundry was by far the most commonly used name. Cold Springs, N.Y., establishment operated by Robert Parker Parrott 1836–67. The company produced most types of iron ordnance until the war, then concentrated primarily on production of Parrott Rifles invented by the owner. Most cannon are plainly marked with the foundry initials "W.P.F." and also the owner's "R.P.P."
West Point Foundry Arsenal	Initials of this facility have been found on weapons and presumably, like Bellona Arsenal (q.v.) it served as a receiving and storage depot for government weapons made at West Point Foundry.
W.P.F.	West Point Foundry (q.v.).
W.P.F.A.	West Point Foundry Arsenal (q.v.).
Norman Wiard	Inventor of the Wiard Rifles, other weapons, carriages and ammunition. Rifles are usually marked "N.W." and "N.Y.C., O.F." thought to be initials of a New York City foundry. The New York Public Library has informed the author that Trow's Business Directory of the City for 1863–64 and 1865–66 lists but one iron founder with the initial "O"— John O'Donnell—and there is a possibility the mysterious "O.F." may stand for O'Donnell's Foundry.
Hinckley, Williams & Co.	Boston, Mass., firm produced cannon for the Navy during the war.

MANUFACTURERS, INSPECTORS — CONFEDERATE

The following Confederate listing was compiled from the Official Records and other sources believed to be reliable. However, available information is scant and such factors as inclusive dates of service, location, and type duty often not recorded. Consequently, the names of many individuals who served in ordnance, but may never have inspected cannon, are no doubt included while other, bonafide inspectors may have been overlooked.

All—Army, Navy, and manufacturers—have been listed together alphabetically and initials are recorded only where they differ from those normally to be expected from the name.

A.D.B.	See A. M. DeBree.
A.F.	See Augusta Foundry and Machine Works.
Joseph Reid Anderson	Owner of J. R. Anderson & Co. at Richmond, variously known as Tredegar Iron Works and Tredegar Foundry (q.v.). After a brief period of field service, he was brought back to Richmond and supervised the firm throughout the remainder of the war. See U.S. listing and Chapter VII. Note: Initials on Confederate weapons are easily confused with J.L.A. (Junius L. Archer of Bellona Foundry).
R. Snowden Andrews	Major, artillery, apparently on ordnance duty at Richmond.
Dr. Junius L. Archer	Owner of Bellona Foundry. His initials are always coupled with those of the foundry and if indistinct may be confused with Joseph Reid Anderson of Tredegar Foundry.
Atlanta (Ga.) Arsenal	Commanded by Col. Moses Hanibal Wright.
Atlanta Naval Ordnance Works	Commanded by Lt. D. P. McCorkle.
Augusta (Ga.) Arsenal	Upon approach of the enemy, machinery was moved about June, 1864, to Augusta, Ga. Made projectiles and ordnance stores primarily. Commanded by Col. George Washington Rains.
Augusta Foundry and Machine Works	Commanded by Col. George Washington Rains. Manufactured cannon, projectiles and had a very extensive powder works. Initials on cannon "A.F." (Augusta Foundry), often linked with those of Rains.
Briscoe G. Baldwin	Captain in Ordnance Department.
John G. Barnwell	Major, artillery, on duty with Ordnance Department as an inspector.
Baton Rouge (La.) Arsenal	Closed due to approach of the enemy.
Bellona Arsenal	See U.S. listing. Wartime activities of this Richmond, Va., facility have not been determined. However, at least one weapon has been found stamped with the initials "B.A." and dated 1864.
Bellona Foundry	See U.S. listing. During the war was a major supplier of cannon. Initials will be found linked to those of the owner, Junius L. Archer, and also Richard M. Cuyler, superintendent of Macon Arsenal, who seems to have inspected certain weapons at Bellona during periods of 1863–64.
Bennett & Surges	New Orleans firm. Made a few heavy iron cannon and brass field pieces just prior to fall of the city in April, 1862.

Addison G. Brenizer	Captain commanding Salisbury Arsenal (q.v.).
T. M. Brennan	Nashville, Tenn., company which made iron cannon.
Briarfield Arsenal	Selma, Ala., facility cast a few field weapons before being turned over to the Navy and becoming the Selma Naval Ordnance Works under Cmdr. Catesby ap Roger Jones.
John Mercer Brooke	Chief of the Office of Ordnance and Hydrography and inventor of the Brooke Rifle. He graduated from the U.S. Naval Academy and served in the U.S. Navy until joining the Confederacy in 1861.
William LeRoy Brown	Lieutenant colonel commanding the Richmond Arsenal.
Bujac & Bennett	New Orleans smallarms maker who had installed machinery and started casting heavy weapons when the city fell in April, 1862.
James H. Burton	Arrived from England shortly before the war and worked at Tredegar Foundry. Later was lieutenant colonel in charge of the Macon Armory. Inventor of the Burton shell (Chapter XIII).
Cameron & McDurmit	See Cameron, Taylor & Johnson.
Cameron, Taylor & Johnson	Charleston, S.C., firm which made a very limited number of wrought iron guns. Also known as Cameron & McDurmit, or Phoenix Iron Works.
Charleston (S.C.) Arsenal	Commanded by Maj. J. T. Trezevant.
Charlotte (N.C.) Naval Ordnance Works	Commanded by Chief Engineer Ramsay. Manufactured carriages, projectiles, and other munitions for the Navy.
F. L. Childs	Major commanding Fayetteville Arsenal and Armory.
John Clark	New Orleans manufacturer of a few brass weapons.
H. P. Cochran	Lieutenant in the Ordnance Department.
Columbus (Ga.) Arsenal	Confederate States Arsenal, Columbus. Ga. Commanded by Maj. Frederick Clinton Humphreys.
Columbus Naval Iron Works	Technically Confederate States Naval Iron Works, Columbus, Ga. This was the Columbus Iron Works Co., established in 1853 and taken over by the government during the war. It produced at least one weapon, a 2.75-inch breechloader.
Richard M. Cuyler	Commander Macon Arsenal. His initials are also found on a few Bellona Foundry weapons and a Bel-

	ona Arsenal piece indicating that he may have inspected weapons at those facilities.
F.B.Deane Jr. & Son	Lynchburg, Va., firm which made shot, shell, and a number of light caliber weapons, probably iron 24-pounder siege and garrison howitzers.
A. M. DeBree	Joined U.S. Navy 1841 and C.S. Navy Aug. 1862. Stationed at Tredegar as assistant inspector of ordnance 1862 to 1 Oct. 1863 when he became commander of the Richmond Naval Ordnance Works. He apparently used initials "A.D.B.," generally prefaced by "P" (Proved).
J. A. DeLagnel	Lieutenant colonel in Ordnance Department at Richmond and inspector of arsenals.
Charles Dimmock	West Pointer. Resigned U.S. Army 1836 to become civil engineer, and served in the Virginia militia. Became brigadier general in Confederate service in charge of Ordnance Department of Virginia. Died October, 1863.
W.S.Downer	Superintendent Richmond Armory and Clarksville Harness Shops.
J.M.Eason Bros.	Charleston firm operated by J. M. and T.D.Eason.
? Eggleston	Lieutenant in charge of Naval Ordnance Works, New Orleans, La.
Etowah Works, Ga.	Probably Etowah Iron Works. Operated by Quinby & Robinson (q.v.). Made shot and shell.
Archibald B. Fairfax	Navy inspector of ordnance. Rifled and banded a number of 32-pounders captured at Norfolk Navy Yard.
Fayetteville (N.C.) Arsenal & Armory	North Carolina facility commanded by Maj. F. L. Childs.
John M. Gibbs	Transferred to Office of Ordnance and Hydrography in 1864.
Josiah Gorgas	(1818–1885). Chief of Confederate Ordnance Department with rank of brigadier general. See Inspectors, Army, for federal service.
James Harding	Captain at Charleston Arsenal. He is believed to have invented the various types of "Harding" projectiles used in the Charleston area. See Chapter XIII.
William James Hubard	(1807–1862). Artist, silhouettist, sculptor, and scientist. Became interested in making bronze castings of Houdon's marble statue of Washington and from 1853 to 1860 devoted most of his time and finances to this end. At the start of war, he converted his foundry near Richmond to production of brass cannon and by fall, 1861, was furnishing weapons

to state and Confederate governments. In addition, he began experiments with powder which resulted in his death the following February from accidental explosion of a shell. Hubard apparently made only the rough casting and his weapons were finished in the Richmond machine shops of Thomas Sampson and James Pae. Brass field pieces have been found marked with Hubard's initials coupled with the "S & P" of Sampson and Pae and in rare instances with an additional, unidentified "W.F."

R.K.Hudgins	Captain in Ordnance Department.
Benjamin Huger	After failure in field commands, was made inspector of ordnance. See Inspectors, Army, for U.S. service.
Frederick Clinton Humphreys	Major commanding Columbus Arsenal.
Duncan N. Ingraham	Chief Confederate Naval Ordnance, Construction and Repair for a very brief period. Then commander naval forces in South Carolina waters. See Inspectors, Navy, for federal service.
Catesby ap Roger Jones	Commander Naval Ordnance Works at Selma, Ala., a major producer of Brooke Rifles. His initials "C. ap. R. J." often found on these weapons. See Inspectors, Navy, for federal service. Also, Chapter VII for more extensive biography.
Beverly Kennon	Commander Naval Ordnance Works at New Orleans prior to Lt. Eggleston.
John Knepps	Believed to have been a civilian inspector at Macon Arsenal.
Elliott Lacey	Civilian inspector of ordnance at Tredegar Foundry.
Leeds & Co.	New Orleans firm which apparently made a single 8-inch columbiad, which burst, and from then on produced brass field calibers until fall of the city in April, 1862.
Little Rock (Ark.) Arsenal	Closed by approach of the enemy.
James G. McCluskey	Stationed at Richmond Naval Ordnance Works.
A. W. McConnell	Believed to be inspector with Quinby & Robinson at Memphis, Tenn.
D. P. McCorkle	Lieutenant in command of Naval Ordnance Works at Atlanta. Joined U.S. Navy in 1841 and Confederate Navy June, 1861.
Charles A. McEvoy	Stationed at Richmond in Office of Ordnance and Hydrography.
Macon (Ga.) Armory	Commanded by Lt. Col. James H. Burton.
Macon Arsenal	Commanded by Col. R. M. Cuyler (q.v.). Made both brass and iron

	weapons including a few 8-inch columbiads. Initials "M.A." generally coupled with "R.M.C."
George Minor	Commander in Charge, Office of Ordnance and Hydrography.
John C. Minor	Stationed at Richmond, Office of Ordnance and Hydrography.
Robert D. Minor	Lieutenant commanding Richmond Naval Ordnance Works until 1 Oct. 1863.
Montgomery (Ala.) Arsenal	Commanded by Maj. C. G. Wagner.
Mount Vernon Arsenal	Mount Vernon, Ala.
William H. Murdaugh	Ordnance duty at Norfolk Navy Yard.
Nashville (Tenn.) Arsenal	Closed by approach of the enemy.
Noble Bros. & Co.	Rome, Ga., foundry cast bronze and iron field calibers.
Henry Clay Pate	Petersburg, Va., lawyer said to be designer of 3.13-inch Pate, Tappey and Lumsden Revolving Cannon.
Petersburg Iron Works	Produced shot and shell, in at least one case (Chapter XIII) stamped with the initials "P.I.W."
Phoenix Iron Works	See Cameron, Taylor & Johnson.
Quinby & Robinson	Memphis, Tenn., firm made brass field calibers. Also listed as owners of Etowah Works, Ga. (q.v.).
George Washington Rains	Colonel commanding Augusta Arsenal, Augusta Powder Mills, and Augusta Foundry and Machine Works (q.v.). Initials "G.W.R." are generally coupled with "A.F." (Augusta Foundry).
[?] Ramsay	Chief Engineer in charge of Naval Ordnance Works, Charlotte, N.C.
A. B. Rand Bros.	Vicksburg, Miss., firm manufactured field calibers. Weapons usually stamped "A.B.R.Bros. V.Burg. Miss."
Thomas S. Rhett	Colonel in Ordnance Department and inspector of ordnance.
Rice & Wright	Florence, Ala., company reported to have made a number of 24-pounder howitzers, probably iron, siege and garrison models.
Richmond (Va.) Armory	Supervised by W. S. Downer.
Richmond Arsenal	Commanded by Lt. Col. William LeRoy Brown.
Richmond Naval Ordnance Works	Commanded at various times by Lt. J. M. Brooke, Lt. R. D. Minor, Lt. A. M. DeBree, and R. B. Wright. Initials "R.N.O.W." have been found on projectiles.
S.	See Selma Naval Ordnance Works.
Salisbury (N.C.) Arsenal	Received this name 29 August 1864. Previously known as the Govern-

	ment Foundry, Blacksmith Shops and Laboratory at Salisbury, or "Salisbury Foundry." Made projectiles. Commanded by Capt. Addison G. Brenizer.
Sampson & Pae	Richmond machine shop which finished weapons cast by William James Hubard (q.v.).
Selma (Ala.) Arsenal	Commanded by Lt. Col. J. L. White.
Selma Naval Ordnance Works	Commanded by Cmdr. Catesby ap Roger Jones and one of the most important foundries in the Confederacy. Produced Brooke Rifles for the Navy although many wound up in Army service. Variously called "Selma Foundry," "Selma Cannon Foundry," and "Naval Gun Foundry and Ordnance Works, Selma, Ala." Initial usually found on weapons, however, is "S" followed by the gun number in most cases. Both are much smaller than traditional marks (quarter-inch or so) and very difficult to spot. See Chapter VII.
T. A. Sengstack	Believed to have been an ordnance inspector at Macon Arsenal.
[?] Simms	Lieutenant listed as assistant to C. ap R. Jones at Selma Naval Ordnance Works.
Skates & Co.	Mobile, Ala., firm which rifled a number of heavy pieces and produced field calibers.
E. [?] Smith	Major in Ordnance Department at Richmond.
Stansbury Smith	Artillery captain on duty with Ord-

	nance Department. See Inspectors, Army, for U.S. service.
E. T.	Unidentified ordnance inspector at Macon Arsenal.
Tappey and Lumsden	Petersburg, Va., firm. Producer of revolving cannon designed by Henry Clay Pate (q.v.).
Texas Arsenal	San Antonio, Texas. Closed due to encroachment of the enemy.
Tredegar Foundry	Foremost cannon manufacturer in the South. Also known as J. R. Anderson & Co. or Tredegar Iron Works. Initials "T.F." or "J.R.A.& Co." See Manufacturers, U.S.
J.T.Trezevant	Major in command of the Charleston Arsenal.
N. H. Van Zant	Lieutenant at Selma Naval Ordnance Works and later supervised manufacture of carriages, projectiles and other materiel at Charleston.
C. G. Wagner	Major commanding Montgomery Arsenal.
J. L. White	Lieutenant colonel commanding Selma Arsenal.
S. Wolfe & Co.	New Orleans firm which at the surrender in April, 1862, had manufactured two mortars and was making other heavy weapons.
Moses Hanibal Wright	Ordnance officer at Nashville, Tenn. Assigned as colonel commanding Atlanta Arsenal in July, 1863.
R.B.Wright	Civilian superintendent of Richmond Naval Ordnance Works during temporary absence of Lt. R.D. Minor about November, 1864.

British Marks

British ordnance marking is an extensive field and no pretence is made here to comprehensive coverage. The few manufacturers and devices which follow include only those commonly found on weapons used in this country and known or suspected producers of ordnance supplies imported during the war.

Sir W.G.Armstrong & Co.	Founded in 1859 by Sir William George Armstrong as Elswick Ordnance Co., Newcastle-on-Tyne, to manufacture his rifles solely for the government. With rearmament complete and withdrawal of government support in 1862, Elswick was merged with other interests into Sir W.G.Armstrong & Co. Since the British government jealously guarded its ordnance, probably no Armstrongs bearing the Elswick brand were imported, and those found in

	America will be marked on the trunnions "Sir W.G.Armstrong & Co."
Blakely Ordnance Co.	London firm which manufactured Blakely Rifles, presumably late in the war.
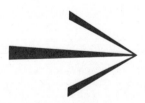	The Broad Arrow. This device generally is found on the upper surface near the breech of all cannon made for the British government and even projectiles, such as solid shot recovered from battle sites of the Revolution and War of 1812.
John Brown & Co.	Sheffield firm asked by the Confederacy for prices on 8-inch smoothbores, carriages and ammunition and may have supplied any or all of these items.
William Butcher Jr. & Co.	Sheffield firm asked for prices on 8-inch smoothbores, carriages, and

Elswick Ordnance Co.	See Sir W. G. Armstrong & Co.

ammunition and may have furnished any or all of these items.

| Elswick Ordnance Co. | See Sir W. G. Armstrong & Co. |

Fawcett, Preston & Co. Liverpool firm manufactured Blakely Rifles. Generally found stamped on top of the tube about midway between breech and trunnions.

George Forrester & Co. Liverpool company which made Blakely Rifles. "Forrester & Co." is found stamped on trunnions.

G. R. Georgius Rex. Monograms of George II (1727–1760) and George III (1760–1820). In each case the device, in raised metal, was cast atop the tube generally on first or second reinforce. It consists of an intertwined "G.R." in script with a crown above. Generally there is an arabic "2" or "3" intertwined with the top left loop of the "G." In brass weapons the device of George III is enclosed in a circular "Garter" bearing the motto of the order "Honi Soit Qui Mal Y Pense" (Shamed be he who thinks evil of it).

T. & C. Hood Apparently made cannon and projectiles for the Confederacy.

Low Moor Produced rifles for Blakely. Name is stamped in this fashion on trunnions although full name seems to have been Low Moor Iron Co.

Manchester Ordnance & Rifle Co. See Whitworth Ordnance Co.

Mersey Steel & Iron Co. Liverpool firm asked by Confederacy for prices on 8-inch smoothbores, carriages, and ammunition and may have supplied any or all of these items.

Tudor Rose Outline of rose, surmounted by a crown, raised on tubes of early 18th Century British weapons.

Whitworth Ordnance Co. Manufacturer of rifles invented by Sir Joseph Whitworth. Based on trunnion marks, the firm changed names during the war for an 1861 specimen is stamped "Whitworth Ordnance Co., Manchester" and another piece, dated 1864, is marked "Manchester Ordnance & Rifle Co."

NOTES FOR FOLLOWING SECTION

Statistics for this section, insofar as possible, have been compiled from ordnance manuals and equally reliable sources. If unrecorded in ancient texts, information has been obtained from existing weapons.

Abbreviations are as follows (Lengths and diameters in inches and tenths, weights in pounds and tenths):

B—Bronze
BL—Breechloader
BLR—Breech-Loading Rifle
BS—Broadside
BT—Boat
C—Confederate
CS—Cast Steel
Cwt—Hundredweight (112 lbs.)
D—Deck
E—Estimated
Exp—Experimental
F—Field
GS—German Silver
I—Cast Iron
In—Inch
M—Model
ML—Muzzle-Loader

MLR—Muzzle-Loading Rifle
Mt—Mountain
N—Navy
NA—Not Applicable
P—Pivot
Pdr—Pounder
R—Rifle
Range—Number of yards to first graze with stated elevation, charge and projectile. Not necessarily maximum range.
SS—Semi-Steel
S—Steel
SB—Smoothbore
SC—Seacoast
S&G—Siege & Garrison
T—Turret
TT—Tentative
v—Length muzzle face to vent. Other bore lengths measured inside of tube and include chamber if present.
W—Wood
WI—Wrought Iron
Wt—Weight
__x__Number of lands and grooves of rifled weapons.

Tables of Statistics

(Please see notes at foot of page 365.)

APPENDIX C

GUNS: CHAPTER I

Type Weapon	Category	Metal	Bore Diameter	Bore Length	Length Overall	Trunnion Diameter	Trunnion Length	Weight	Charge (Pounds)	Elevation	Projectile	Range (Yards)	Photo Number	Remarks
6-Pdr. M 1819	F	I	3.67	62E	71.25	3.67	3	—	—	—	—	—	I-3	Termed "Walking Sticks" due to length.
6-Pdr. M 1831E	F	I	3.67	47.5v	59	3.67	3	—	—	—	—	—	I-4	
6-Pdr. M 1838	F	B	3.67	51.38	59.5E	3.67E	—	—	—	—	—	—	—	Designed for Horse Artillery.
6-Pdr. M 1839	F	B	3.67	57.5	65.6	3.67	2.8	880	1.25	—	—	—	—	Also listed as M 1840.
6-Pdr. M 1840 (Modified) Exp.	F	I	3.67	57.5	65.6	3.67	2.4	821	—	—	—	—	I-5	Made of Swedish Iron.
6-Pdr. M 1841	F	B	3.67	57.5	65.6	3.67	2.8	884	1.25	5° 4°	Shot Case	1523 1200	I-1	Standard U.S. Model of the Civil War.
6-Pdr. M 1841 (Standard piece rifled).	F	B	3.67 15 x 15	57.5	65.6	3.67	2.8	884*	1.25	5°	Shell 12 lb.	1700	—	*Wt. diminished slightly by rifling, but not listed.
6-Pdr. M 1848	F	B	3.67	44	51.5	2.8	2.5	462	—	—	—	—	I-7	Cadet Gun.
6-Pdr. — C.	See statistics on Confederate 6-pounders with photographs, Chapter I.													
6-Pdr. M 1861E, C.	F	I	3.67	62.45	70.71	3.67	2.75	910	—	—	—	—	—	Used, but not permanently adopted.
9-Pdr. M 1831E	F	I	4.2	—	—	4.2	—	—	—	—	—	—	—	
9-Pdr. M 1836	F	B	4.2	66.1v	77	4.2	3.12	1350E	—	—	—	—	I-14	Handles over center of gravity.
12-Pdr. M 1819	F	I	4.62	71.6	—	—	—	—	—	—	—	—	—	
12-Pdr. M 1831E	F	I	4.62	—	—	—	—	—	—	—	—	—	—	Termed 12-Pdr. Cannon (light) to differentiate from S & G pieces.
12-Pdr. M 1836	F	B	4.62	74	85	4.62	3.1	—	—	—	—	—	I-15	
12-Pdr. M 1839	S & G	I	4.62	103.4	116	4.62	4.5	3590	—	—	—	—	I-18	
12-Pdr. M 1840	F	B	4.62	74	85	4.62	3.5	1800	—	—	—	—	—	
12-Pdr. M 1841	F	B	4.62	74	85	4.62	3.5	1757	2.5	5° 3°30'	Shot Case	1663 1200	I-16	After 1857 termed 12-Pdr. "Heavy."
12-Pdr. M 1857	F	B	4.62	61	69.5	4.2	3.25	1187	—	—	—	—	I-19	With handles. Napoleon No. 1. Made in 1857
12-Pdr. M 1857 (Modified)	F	B	4.62	62.5v	72.15	4.2	3.25	1232E	—	—	—	—	I-20	With handles.
12-Pdr. M 1857 (Modified)	F	B	4.62	63.6	72.15	4.2	3.25	1227	2.5 2.5 2.0	5° 3°45' 3°45'	Shot Case Shell	1680 1135 1300	I-21	Standard U.S. Napoleon of the Civil War
12-Pdr. C.	F	B	4.62	Measurements of Confederate Napoleons conform generally to U.S. Model 1857 (modified), but may vary between foundries. See text, Chapter I, and photograph I-22.											
12-Pdr. M 1864 C. Iron Napoleon	F	I	4.62	63.6	72	4.2	3.4	1250	—	—	—	—	I-24	Breech banded.
18-Pdr. M 1839	S & G	I	5.3	108.5	123.25	5.3	4.75	4913	4.5	5°	Shot	1592	I-29 I-31	
24-Pdr. M 1819	SC	I	5.823	108.17	123.95	5.823	5	5500	—	—	—	—	I-35	No lock piece or chase ring.
24-Pdr. M 1839	S & G	I	5.82	108	124	5.82	5	5790	6	5°	Shot	1901	I-29 I-32	Also called M 1840 with weight 5,600.
32-Pdr. M 1821TT	N*	I	6.4	104E	121.5	6.4	6.5	6720	—	—	—	—	I-37	*Later used in forts.

32-Pdr. M 1829	SC	I	6.4	107.59	125.2	6.41	6	7531	—	—	—	—	I-39	
32-Pdr. M 1840	SC	I	6.4	107.6	125.2	6.4	6	7100	—	—	—	—	—	
32-Pdr. M 1841	SC	I	6.4	107.6	125.7	6.4	6	7200	8	5°	Shot	1922	I-41	Standard U.S. Army model of the Civil War.
32-Pdr. M. 1841	N	I	6.4	90.75	106	6.4	5.5	—	—	—	—	—	I-42 I-43	Straight muzzle.
32-Pdr. M.1845, 42 cwt.	N	I	6.4	90.75E	106.4E	6.4	5.5	4761*	6	5°	Shot	1756	I-44	*Average of 6 guns.
32-Pdr. M.1846, 27 cwt.	N	I	6.4	68.4E–70	80E–81.6	5.82	5	3024	4	5°	Shot	1469	I-46	Only gun with chamber.
32-Pdr. M.1846, 33 cwt.	N	I	6.4	75.04–75.1	91.83–91.89E	6.4	5.5	3696	4.5	5°	Shot	1598	I-46	Also called 32 cwt.
32-Pdr. M.1847, 42 cwt.	N	I	6.4	90.5–92.05	105–108	6.4	5.5	4704	6	5°	Shot	1756	I-45	
32-Pdr. M.1846, 46 cwt.	N	I	6.4	97.2	115.69	6.4	5.5	5152	7	—	—	—	—	
32-Pdr. M.1846, 51 cwt.	N	I	6.4	104	121.08	6.4	5.5	5712	7	—	—	—	I-47	
32-Pdr. M.1846, 57 cwt.	N	I	6.4	107.9	125.34	6.4	6	6384	9	5°	Shot	2731	I-48	"Long 32-Pounder."
32-Pdr. of 4500 Lbs, M.1864. — See Dahlgrens & Shellguns, Chapter V.														
42-Pdr. M.1821 TT	N	I	7	101.5v	121	7	6.5	7870	—	—	—	—	I-52	
42-Pdr. M.1831	SC	I	7.018	109	129.4	7.018	6.5	8688	—	—	—	—	I-53	No chase ring. Raised Lock Piece.
42-Pdr. M.1840	SC	I	7	110	129	7	6.5	8300	—	—	—	—	—	
42-Pdr. M.1841	SC	I	7	110	129	7	6.5	8465	10.5	5°	Shot	1955	I-54	First type. No lock Piece.
42-Pdr. M.1841	SC	I	7	110	129	7	6.5	8465	10.5	5°	Shot	1955	I-51	With Lock Piece. Standard U.S. piece. Suppressed 9 Feb. 1861.
64-Pdr. M.1849, 106 cwt.	N	I	8	124.2	140.95	—	—	11872	12	—	—	—	I-55	Also listed as 105 cwt.

125-Pdr. (10-Inch) — See Dahlgrens & Shellguns. Chapter V.

HOWITZERS CHAPTER II

Type Weapon	Category	Metal	Bore Diameter	Bore Length	Length Overall	Trunnion Diameter	Trunnion Length	Weight	Charge (Pounds)	Elevation	Projectile	Range (Yards)	Photo Number	Remarks
12-Pdr. M 1836	F	B	4.62	50.50	58.6	3.67	2.8	785	—	—	—	—	—	Substantially the same as M.1841.
12-Pdr. M 1839	F	B	4.62	47F.	55.5	3.67	2.8	700E	—	—	—	—	—	Experimental, only a few made.
12-Pdr. M 1841	F	B	4.62	50.50	58.6	3.67	2.8	788	.75	5° 3°45'	Shell Case	1072 1050	II-1	Standard field model of the Civil War.
12-Pdr. M 1841	Mt	B	4.62	30.91	37.21	2.7	2.25	220	.5	5° 4°30'	Shell Case	1005 800	II-6	
12-Pdr. M 1862 C.	F	I	4.62	56.8	64.4	3.67	3	850	—	—	—	—	II-2	Not considered permanently adopted.
24-Pdr. M 1819E	F	I	5.82	31E	39.25	3.5	3.5	—	—	—	—	—	II-17 II-18	
24-Pdr. M 1841	F	B	5.82	61	71.2	4.2	3.25	1318	2 2.5	5° 3°50'	Shell Case	1322 1200	II-3	With handles.
24-Pdr. C.	F	B	5.82	61	71.2	4.2	3.25	—	—	—	—	—	II-4	Without handles.
24-Pdr. C.	F	I	5.82	—	—	—	—	—	—	—	—	—	—	Reported but no statistics available.
24-Pdr. M 1844	S & G	I	5.82	58	69	4.62	3.25	1476	2	5°	Shell	1322	II-8 II-9	
32-Pdr. M 1844	F	B	6.4	71	82	4.62	3.5	1920	2.5 3.25	5° 3°45'	Shell Case	1504 1200	II-5	With handles.
8-Inch. M 1841	S & G	I	8	43.12	61.5	5.82	5	2614*	4	12°30'	Shell	2280	II-10	*Wt. 1861 Manual. 1841 Manual lists 2650.
8-Inch. M 1841 C.	S & G	I	4.62R	—	61.5	5.82	5	—	—	—	—	—	—	Experimental rifle made by Confederates
8-Inch. M 1861	S & G	I	8	46.5	60	5.82	5	2550	4	—	—	—	II-11	

HOWITZERS CHAPTER II (Continued)

Type Weapon	Category	Metal	Bore Diameter	Bore Length	Length Overall	Trunnion Diameter	Trunnion Length	Weight	Charge (Pounds)	Elevation	Projectile	Range (Yards)	Photo Number	Remarks
8-Inch. M 1841	SC	I	8	93	109	6.4	6	5740*	8	5°	Shell	1800	II-12	*Wt. 1861 Manual. 1841 Manual lists 5800
10-Inch. M 1841	SC	I	10	105.5	124.25	8	7.5	9500	12	5°	Shell	1650	II-13	

MORTARS CHAPTER III

Type Weapon	Category	Metal	Bore Diameter	Bore Length	Length Overall	Trunnion Diameter	Trunnion Length	Weight	Charge (Pounds)	Elevation	Projectile	Range (Yards)	Photo Number	Remarks
6-Pdr.	S & G	W	3.67	—	—	—	—	—	—	—	—	—	—	Field expedient, see Chapter III.
12-Pdr. U.S. & C.	S & G	W	4.62	—	—	—	—	—	—	—	—	—	III-20	Field expedient, see Chapter III.
12-Pdr. C.	S & G	I	4.62	—	—	—	—	—	—	—	—	—	—	Confederate "Coehorn."
24-Pdr. C.	S & G	I	5.82	—	—	—	—	—	—	—	—	—	III-2E	Confederate "Coehorn."
24-Pdr. Coehorn	S & G	B	5.82	13.07	16.32	2.75	2.5	164	.5	45	Shell	1200	III-1	Standard Coehorn mortar.
Eprouvette	—*	I†	5.655	12.85	13.5**	NA	NA	220	.0625	45	Shot	—	III-3	*Not a weapon, used to test powder. †A few of B. (III-4). **Muzzle face to E end of breech.
8-Inch M 1841	S & G	I	8	16	22.5	6	4	930	1.0625	45	Shell	1200	III-11	Gomer chamber. No ear.
8-Inch M 1861	S & G	I	8	16	22	10	2.5	1010	2	45	Shell	2225	III-14	
10-Inch M 1819	S & G	I	10	23.5v	31.25	8	6	—	—	45	Shell	—	III-6	
10-Inch M 1819	SC	I	10	35.25	45.5	10	9	3860E	—	45	Shell	—	III-7	
10-Inch M 1841	S & G	I	10	20	28	8	5	1852	4	45	Shell	2028	III-12	Gomer chamber. No ear.
10-Inch M 1841-44	SC	I	10	35	46	9	6.5	5775	10	45	Shell	4250	III-8	
10-Inch M 1861	S & G	I	10	20.5	28	12	3.5	1900	4	45	Shell	2064	III-15	
10-Inch M 1861	SC	I	10	32.5	47.5	12	3.5	7300	—	45	Shell	—	III-13	
12-Inch	SC	I	12	—	—	—	—	—	20	45	Shell	4625	—	Experimental.
13-Inch M 1841	SC	I	13	39	53	12	8.5	11500	20	45	Shell	4325	III-10	
13-Inch M 1861	SC	I	13	35	54.5	15	3.5	17120	20	45	Shell	4200	III-16	
16-Inch M 1839	S & G	B	16	26.55	31.55	8	6	1600	1.5	60	Stones*150–250		III-5	*120 lbs. stones
									1	33	Shell† 50–100			†15 6-pdr. shells.

COLUMBIADS CHAPTER IV

Type Weapon	Category	Metal	Bore Diameter	Bore Length	Length Overall	Trunnion Diameter	Trunnion Length	Weight	Charge (Pounds)	Elevation	Projectile	Range (Yards)	Photo Number	Remarks
50-Pdr. M 1811.	—	I	7.25	61	74	6.5	6.25	—	—	—	—	—	IV-1	
8-Inch. M 1844.	SC	I	8	111	124	8	6.5	9240	15	27°30'	Shell	4468	IV-2	
											Shot	4812		
8-Inch. M 1858.	SC	I	8	108.32	123.67	8	6.5	9100	—	—	—	—	IV-7	
8-Inch. M 1861.	SC	I	8	110	119.475	8	3.25	8465	10	30°	Shell	3873	IV-13	
									15		Shot	3224		

COLUMBIADS CHAPTER IV (Continued)

Type Weapon	Category	Metal	Bore Diameter	Bore Length	Length Overall	Trunnion Diameter	Trunnion Length	Weight	Charge (Pounds)	Elevation	Projectile	Range (Yards)	Photo Number	Remarks
8-Inch. M 1861. C.	SC	I	8	108	120.5	8	6.5*	9020	—	—	—	—	IV-20	*Long trunnions.
8-Inch. M 1861. C.	SC	I	8	104.5v	120.5	8	3*	8750	—	—	—	—	IV-21	*Short trunnions.
8-Inch. M 1861. C. R.	SC	I	5.82	108	120.5	8	6.5	—	—	—	—	—	—	Standard model cast and bored to 5.82-Inch Rifle.
10-Inch. M 1844	SC	I	10	111	126	10	9	15400	18 20	35° 39°15′	Shell Shot	4828 5654	IV-3* IV-4*	*Rifled and banded weapons.
10-Inch. M 1858	SC	I	10	101.17	128.82	10	9	15000	—	—	—	—	IV-12	
10-Inch. M 1861*	SC	I	10	120	136.66	10	3.25	15059	15 20	30° 39°15′	Shell Shot	4836 5654	IV-14	*One cast and bored to 8-Inch Rifle
10-Inch. M 1861 R.	SC	I	8 15 x 15 24 x 24	120	136.66*	10	3.25	16000E	—	—	—	—	IV-17	Standard M.1861 sleeved & bored to 8-Inch Rifle. *With oblong cascabel 143.
10-Inch. M 1861 C.	SC	I	10	108	122.5	10	9	13320	—	—	—	—	IV-22	
10-Inch. M 1861 C. R.	SC	I	6.4 5 x 5	108	122.5	10	9	14850	—	—	—	—	IV-23	Standard model cast and bored to 6.4-Inch Rifle.
12-Inch. M 1844–49	SC	I	12	—	—	—	—	—	28	39°	Shell	5761	—	Exp. Probably resembled M.1844.
12-Inch. M.1864. C.	SC	I	12	—	—	—	—	—	—	—	—	—	—	Not completed. Two at Tredegar, March 1865.
13-Inch. M.1864E*	SC	I	13	177.6	155.94	13	—	32731	30	—	—	—	—	*First mention of piece in this year.
15-Inch. M.1861 (first)	SC	I	15	165	190	15	6.5	49099	40	30°	Shell	5018	IV-15	One cast, bored to 12-Inch & rifled.
15-Inch. M.1861 (later)	SC	I	15	167	192	15	4.5	50000E	40	—	—	—	—	Data average of several weapons.
20-Inch. M.1864	SC	I	20	210	243.5	18	6.5*	115200*	200	25°	Shot	8001	IV-16	*Specified, but see Fig. IV-16.

DAHLGRENS & SHELLGUNS CHAPTER V

Type Weapon	Type Carriage	Metal	Bore Diameter	Bore Length	Length Overall	Trunnion Diameter	Trunnion Length	Weight	Charge (Pounds)	Elevation	Projectile	Range (Yards)	Photo Number	Remarks
12-Pdr. Boat Howitzer, Rifle	BT F	B	3.4 12 x 12	55.23	63.5	NA	NA	880	1	5	Shell	1770	V-8	
20-Pdr. Howitzer, Rifle	D	B	4	—	—	—	—	1340	2	5	Shell	1960	V-9	
30-Pdr. Rifle	BS	I*	4.2 10 x 10	—	92	4	3.5	—	—	—	—	—	V-24	*Trunnions, Trunnion Band B.
12-Pdr. Boat Howitzer (Small)	BT F	B	4.62	—	—	NA	NA	300	—	—	—	—	—	
12-Pdr. Boat Howitzer (Light)	BT F	B	4.62	44	51.75	NA	NA	430	.625	—	—	—	V-3	
12-Pdr. Boat Howitzer (Medium)*	BT F D	B	4.62	55.23	63.5	NA	NA	750†	1	5	Shell Case	1085 1150	V-2	*Also called "Heavy." †Weight also listed as 760.
50-Pdr. Rifle	BS	I*	5.1 12 x 12	88.5	107	5.25	5.25	—	—	—	—	—	V-26	*Trunnions, Trunnion Band B.
24-Pdr. Boat Howitzer (Some Rifled)	BT D	B	5.82	58.20	67	NA	NA	1310	2	5	Shell Case	1270 1308	V-1	
80-Pdr. Rifle	BS P	I*	6E	—	—	—	—	—	—	—	—	—	—	*Trunnions, Trunnion Band B.
32-Pdr. of 4500 Lbs., M.1864.	BS	I	6.4	92.25v	107.5–109.25	6.4	3	4500	6	—	—	—	V-22	
150-Pdr. Rifle	P	I*	7.5	119E	140E	—	—	16000	—	—	—	—	V-27	*Trunnions, Trunnion Band B.

Type Weapon	Type Carriage	Metal	Bore Diameter	Bore Length	Length Overall	Trunnion Diameter	Trunnion Length	Weight	Charge (Pounds)	Elevation	Projectile	Range (Yards)	Photo Number	Remarks
8-Inch of 6500 Lbs., M.1864	BS	I	8	98v	115.5	7	3	6500	7	10	Shell	2600	V-21	
9-Inch	BS P	I	9	107	131.5	7.25	7.25	9,000	13	15	Shell	3450	V-10	
10-Inch (Standard)	BS P	I	10	119.5	146E	—	—	12000	12.5	11	Shell	3000	—	
10-Inch (Super 10)* Also called 125-Pdr. and 130-Pdr.	†	I	10	117.75	—	—	—	16500	40‡	—	Shot	—	—	*Classified as Gun. †Probably P. ‡By 1866 reduced to 18 lbs.
11-Inch	P T BS	I	11	132	161	10	9	15700	15 20	15	Shell	3400 3650	V-12	
11-Inch Sleeved to 8-Inch Rifle.	P	I	8 15 x 15	129	158	12	5	17330	25 35	—	—	—	V-16	
13-Inch	T	I	13	130	—	—	—	36000	40	—	—	—	—	
15-Inch (Passaic Class)	T	I	15	130	162E	—	—	42000	35	7	Shell	2100	V-17	
15-Inch (Tecumseh Class)	T	I	15	146E	178E	—	—	42000	35	7	Shell	2100	V-17	
15-Inch, Cast & Bored to 12-Inch Rifle.	*	I	12	146E	178E	—	—	45500	—	—	—	—	—	*Not in service. Only three made.
20-Inch	T	I	20	163	204	16	6	100000	100E	—	—	—	—	

SHELLGUNS, MISCELLANEOUS

Type Weapon	Type Carriage	Metal	Bore Diameter	Bore Length	Length Overall	Trunnion Diameter	Trunnion Length	Weight	Charge (Pounds)	Elevation	Projectile	Range (Yards)	Photo Number	Remarks
8-Inch, 63 Cwt. M 1841	BS	I	8*	102	117	8.5	6.5	7056	—	—	—	—	V-19	*Flared to 8.25.
8-Inch, 55 Cwt. M 1845	BS	I	8	95.4	114.5	—	—	6160	7	10	Shell	2600		
8-Inch, 63 Cwt. M 1845	BS	I	8	100.3	119.31	7	6.4	7056	8	5	Shell	1770	V-20	
9-Inch. C.	*	I	9	107E	131.5	7	7.1	9480	—	—	—	—	V-23	*Probably used afloat and ashore.
10-Inch, 86 Cwt. M 1841	P	I	10*	106	123.5E	—	—	9632	—	—	—	—	—	*Probably flared as 8-Inch, 63 Cwt. M 1841.

PARROTTS CHAPTER VI

Type Weapon	Category	Metal	Bore Diameter	Bore Length	Length Overall	Trunnion Diameter	Trunnion Length	Weight	Charge (Pounds)	Elevation	Projectile	Range (Yards)	Photo Number	Remarks
2.9-In. M.1861*	F	I	2.9 3 x 3	70	78	3.67	2.75	890	1	10° 20°	Shell	3200 5000	VI-1	*With muzzle swell.
3-In. M.1863	F	I	3 3 x 3	70	78	3.67	2.75	890	1	10°	Shell	2970	VI-3	
3.3-In. M.1861*	F	I	3.3 12 x 12†	70	78	3.67	2.75	904	—	—	—	—	VI-4	*Perhaps 1860. †Hook-slant.
3.67-In. M.1861*	F S & G	I	3.67 5 x 5	79	89.5	4.62	3.5	1750	2	15°	Shell	4400	VI-7	*With muzzle swell.
3.67-In. M.1861*	N	I	3.67 5 x 5	79	91.5	4.62	3.5	1750	2	15°	Shell	4400	VI-5	*With muzzle swell.
3.67-In. M.1863	F S & G	I	3.67 5 x 5	79	89.5	4.62	3.5	1750	2	15°	Shell	4400	VI-6	
3.67-In. M.1863	N	I	3.67 5 x 5	79	91.5	4.62	3.5	1750	2	15°	Shell	4400	VI-5	
4.2-In. M.1861*	S & G	I	4.2 5 x 5	120	132.5	5.25	2.75	4200	3.25	15° 25°	Shell	4800 6700	VI-9	*With muzzle swell.
4.2-In. M.1862	S & G	I	4.2 5 x 5	120	132.5	5.25	2.75	4200	3.25	25°	Shell	6700	VI-10	
4.2-In. M.1861*	N	I	4.2 5 x 5	96.8	112	5.6	5	3550	3.25	15°	Shell	4874	VI-11	*With muzzle swell.

PARROTTS CHAPTER VI (Continued)

Type Weapon	Category	Metal	Bore Diameter	Bore Length	Length Overall	Trunnion Diameter	Trunnion Length	Weight	Charge (Pounds)	Elevation	Projectile	Range (Yards)	Photo Number	Remarks
5.3-In. M.1864	N	I	5.3 / 7 x 7	105	124	6	4	5360	6	—	—	—	VI-12	
5.3-In. B.L.R.	N	I	5.3 / 7 x 7	112	112*	6	4	5400TT	—	—	—	—	VI-13	*Without Breech-block.
6.4-In. M.1861	SC / N	I	6.4 / 9 x 9	130	155	8	5	9700	10	25° / 35°	Shell / Shot*	6820 / 8453	VI-14	*Hollow Shot, Wt. 80 Lbs. Shell Wt. 101.
6.4-In. B.L.R.	N	I	6.4 / 9 x 9	139.25	139.25*	8	5	9850TT	—	—	—	—	VI-18	*Without Breech-block.
8-In. M.1861	SC / N	I	8 / 11 x 11	136	162	10	5	16500	16	11°47' / 35°*	Shell	4272 / 8000*	VI-26	*Swamp Angel, see text.
10-In. M.1862	SC	I	10 / 15 x 15	144	177	10	4.5	26500	26	13°30'	Shell	4290*	VI-27	*Not tried for extreme range.

CONFEDERATE PARROTTS

Type Weapon	Category	Metal	Bore Diameter	Bore Length	Length Overall	Trunnion Diameter	Trunnion Length	Weight	Charge (Pounds)	Elevation	Projectile	Range (Yards)	Photo Number	Remarks
2.9-In. C.	F	I	2.9 / 7 x 7*	72.5v	81	3.6	2.9	1500	—	—	—	—	VI-29	*Hook-slant.
2.9-In. C.	N	I	2.9 / 7 x 7*	72.5v	81	NA	NA	—	—	—	—	—	VI-30	*Hook-slant.
3.67-In. C.	S & G	I	3.67 / 7 x 7*	—	—	—	—	—	—	—	—	—	—	*Hook-slant.
4.2-In. C.	S & G	I	4.2 / 5 x 5*	117.75v	132	5.25	4.75	4670	—	—	—	—	VI-32	*Straight.

BROOKE CHAPTER VII

Type Weapon	Category	Metal	Bore Diameter	Bore Length	Length Overall	Trunnion Diameter	Trunnion Length	Weight	Charge (Pounds)	Elevation	Projectile	Range (Yards)	Photo Number	Remarks
4.62-In. Single Band	S & G	I	4.62 / 7 x 7	95E	111.5E	5.85	3	6170	—	—	—	—	VII-5	Brooke, TT.
6.4-In. Single Band	SC / N	I	6.4 / 7 x 7	116.5v	144	7.25	7.25	9120	7–10	—	—	—	VII-4	
6.4-In. Double Band	SC / N	I	6.4 / 7 x 7	115.5v	141– / 144	7– / 7.25	6.5– / 7.25	10700	7–10	—	—	—	VII-3 / VII-9	
7-In. Single Band	SC / N	I	7 / 7 x 7	117.75– / 122.5v	145– / 147.5	8– / 8.5	8– / 8.5	15160	8–13	—	—	—	VII-3	
7-In. Double Band	SC / N	I	7 / 7 x 7	117– / 118v	146.5– / 148*	8– / 8.25	7.25– / 8	14800	8–13 / 10	23	Shell	7900	VII-10	*See text for extra length piece.
7-In. Triple Band	SC / N	I	7 / 7 x 7	126v	153	—*	—*	—	20	—	—	—	VII-11 / VII-12	*Trunnions on Trunnion Band
8-In.	SC / N	I	8 / 7 x 7E	—	—	—	—	—	—	—	—	—	—	
11-In.	SC / N*	I	11	—	—	—	—	24350	—	—	—	—	—	*Use in Navy TT

SMOOTHBORES

Type Weapon	Category	Metal	Bore Diameter	Bore Length	Length Overall	Trunnion Diameter	Trunnion Length	Weight	Charge (Pounds)	Elevation	Projectile	Range (Yards)	Photo Number	Remarks
8-In.* Double Band	SC / N	I	8	11.5vE	142	7.25	6.5	10400	—	—	WI Ball	—	—	*6.4-In. Rifle bored to 8-In. Smooth
10-In.*	SC / N	I	10	—	—	—	—	—	—	—	WI Ball	—	—	*8-In. Rifle bored to 10-In. Smooth.
10-In. Double Band	SC / N	I	10	125v / 126v	150.5 / 158.5	10	6.5	21140 / 21560	—	—	WI Ball	—	VII-6 / VII-7	
11-In. Double Band	SC / N	I	11	136v. / 139v*	170	10.5	7	23612	—	—	WI Ball	—	VII-8	*Two vents.

Type Weapon	Category	Metal	Bore Diameter	Bore Length	Length Overall	Trunnion Diameter	Trunnion Length	Weight	Charge (Pounds)	Elevation	Projectile	Range (Yards)	Photo Number	Remarks
6-Pdr. B.L.R.	Mt N	I	2.5 32 x 32	53	60.15	—	—	336	—	—	—	—	—	Only a few made.
12-Pdr. B.L.R.	F	I	3 38 x 38	73.5	83	—	—	918	1.75	10	Bolt	3961	VIII-5	
12-Pdr. M.L.R.	F	I	3 3 x 3	67.5	76	3.5	3.5	1009	—	—	—	—	VIII-6	
20-Pdr. B.L.R.	F	I	3.75 44 x 44	93	96	—	—	1882	—	—	—	—	VIII-7	Redesignated from 25-Pdr.
40-Pdr. M.1859, Service B.L.R.	S & G N	I	4.75 56 x 56	106.38	120	—	—	3640	—	10°	Bolt	3660	—	
40-Pdr. M.1860, Service B.L.R.	S & G N	I	4.75 56 x 56	106.38	120	—	—	3986	—	10°	Bolt	3688	—	Breech coil added to M.1859
40-Pdr. M.1863E, Export B.L.R.	S & G N	I	4.75 56 x 56	106.5	121	—	—	3696	—	—	—	—	—	
70-Pdr. B.L.R.	SC N	I	6.4 70 x 70	110	—	—	—	6903	9	10°	Bolt	3594	—	Many converted to M.L.R.
70-Pdr. M.L.R.	SC N	I & S	6.4 6 x 6	109	126.5	—	—	7140	11	10	Bolt	3959	—	Ammunition indicates some were 3 x 3.
110-Pdr. B.L.R.	SC N	I	7	—	—	—	—	8400	14	—	—	—	—	100 made. Not issued.
110-Pdr. B.L.R. Service Model	SC N	I	7 76 x 76	99.5	120	—	—	9184	14	—	—	—	VIII-8	Many converted to M.L.R. Some made to weigh 9632.
150-Pdr. M.L.R.	SC N	I & S	8 6 x 6	102.25	131	8	6.25	15737	19–30	—	—	—	VIII-9	West Point Rifle.
150-Pdr. M.L.	SC N	I & S	10 SB	124	156	12	—	26880	50	—	—	—	—	300-Pdr. without rifling.
300-Pdr. M.L.R.	SC N	I & S	10 8 x 8	124	156	12	—	26880	35	—	—	—	—	
600-Pdr. M.L.R.	SC N	I & S	13.3 10 x 10	145.25	183	—	—	51296	70	23°9′	Bolt*	7300	—	*Weight 507 lbs.

WHITWORTH

Type Weapon	Category	Metal	Bore Diameter	Bore Length	Length Overall	Trunnion Diameter	Trunnion Length	Weight	Charge (Pounds)	Elevation	Projectile	Range (Yards)	Photo Number	Remarks
3-Pdr. B.L.R.	Mt*	S	1.5 6 x 6	72	—	—	—	200	8 oz.	—	—	—	—	*TT.
6-Pdr. B.L.R.	F	S	2.15 6 x 6	70	—	—	—	700	—	—	—	—	—	Also listed as M.L.R.
12-Pdr. B.L.R.	F	S	2.75 6 x 6	104	108	3.75	3.5	1100	1.75	35°	Bolt	10000	VIII-13 VIII-14	
12-Pdr. M.L.R.	F	S	2.75 6 x 6	—	86	3.75	3.5	1090	1.75	—	—	—	VIII-14 VIII-15	
32-Pdr. M.L.R.	S & G N	S	4.14* 6 x 6	87	—	—	—	3360	5.25	10°	Bolt	4800	—	*Probably across angles, 3.6E across flats.
70-Pdr. M.L.R.	SC N	S	5 6 x 6	111–114v	132–134	8–8.5	6.5	8580	13	10°	Bolt	5000	VIII-17 VIII-19	Also called 80-Pdr.
120-Pdr. M.L.R.	SC N	S	6.4 6 x 6	144	—	—	—	16660	27	—	—	—	—	Also called 130-Pdr. Weight also 13440, see text.
9-Inch M.L.R.	SC	S	9 6 x 6	—	—	—	—	—	—	—	—	—	—	

BLAKELY

Type Weapon	Category	Metal	Bore Diameter	Bore Length	Length Overall	Trunnion Diameter	Trunnion Length	Weight	Charge (Pounds)	Elevation	Projectile	Range (Yards)	Photo Number	Remarks
12-Pdr. Type 1	F	I	3.5	73.5	84	—	—	—	1.5	7°30′	Bolt	1760	VIII-20	
12-Pdr. Type 2	F	I	3.6 7 x 7	49	58	3.62	2.75	700	—	—	—	—	VIII-22	

BLAKELY (Continued)

Type Weapon	Category	Metal	Bore Diameter	Bore Length	Length Overall	Trunnion Diameter	Trunnion Length	Weight	Charge (Pounds)	Elevation	Projectile	Range (Yards)	Photo Number	Remarks
12-Pdr. Type 3	F	I	3.5 / 6 x 6	55	60.5	3.5	2.62	—	—	—	—	—	VIII-23	
12-Pdr. Type 4	F	I & B	3.6 / 6 x 6	60	66.5	3.6	3	—	—	—	—	—	VIII-24	Trunnions, Trunnion Band B or I, See text.
12-Pdr. Type 5	F	I	3.6 / 7 x 7	49	58	3.62	2.75	—	—	—	—	—	VIII-26	Similar to Type 2 except for band.
12-Pdr. Type 6	F	I	3.5 / 7 x 7	58	67.25	3.25	3	—	—	—	—	—	VIII-28	
18-Pdr. Type 7	F*	I	4 / 6 x 6	65	83	4	3.5	921	—	—	—	—	VIII-29	*S&G also probably
12-Pdr. Type 8	F	I	3.4 / 10 x 10	66.5	73.5	3.75	—	—	—	—	—	—	VIII-30	
12-Pdr. Type 9	F	I	3.5 / 8 x 8	63.5	75	4.5	3	—	—	—	—	—	VIII-31	
10-Pdr.E. Type 10	Mt.	I	2.9 / 6 x 6	26.5	36.5	2.7	2.5	—	—	—	—	—	VIII-32	
4.5-Inch	S & G / N	I & S	4.5 / 7 x 7	76.5v	96	4.62	4.25	—	—	—	—	—	VIII-33	
6.3-Inch*	SC / N	I	6.3 / 8 x 8	73v	88.5	5.75	5.75	—	—	—	—	—	VIII-37	*Probable 32-Pdr. of 32 cwt. Rifled.
100-Pdr.	SC / N	I & S	6.4 / 8 x 8	96	—	—	—	8000	10	—	—	—	—	
120-Pdr.	SC / N	I & S	7 / 9 x 9	100	119.5	7.5	6	9600	12	—	—	—	VIII-34	
150-Pdr. E.*	SC / N	I	7.25—7.5 / 12 x 12	100.62	124	7.5	6	—	—	—	—	—	VIII-36	*Probable 42-Pdr. of 67 cwt. banded and rifled.
200-Pdr.	SC / N	I & S	8 / 3 x 3	119v	136	8.5	6.5	17000*	—	—	—	—	VIII-38 VIII-39	*Weight doubtful
250-Pdr.	SC / N	I & S	9 / 12 x 12	135	150.5	—	—	24000	30	—	—	—	—	
375-Pdr.	SC	S	11 / 12 x 12	—	—	—	—	35000*	37	—	—	—	—	*Weight doubtful
650-Pdr.*	SC	I, S & B	12.75 / 4 x 4	184	194	—	—	60480	55	2	Shell	2200	VIII-40	*Also called 600, 700, and 900-Pdr. Shell weight 470 lbs. Bolt weight 650 lbs.

CANNON MISCELLANEOUS CHAPTER IX

Type Weapon	Category	Metal	Bore Diameter	Bore Length	Length Overall	Trunnion Diameter	Trunnion Length	Weight	Charge (Pounds)	Elevation	Projectile	Range (Yards)	Photo Number	Remarks
2.25-In. Mountain Rifle, M.1862. C.	Mt	B	2.25	40	44	2.7	2.25	200	—	—	—	—	—	
Wiard, 6-Pdr.	F	SS	2.6 / 8 x 8	46.8	53	3.67	3	725*	.0625 / .12 / .75	35°	Shell	800 / 1200 / 7000	IX-11	*Listed Wt. See text.
2.75-In.B.L.R. C.	F	I	2.75	55.38*	61.25†	3	—	—	—	—	—	—	IX-43	*Excludes Chamber. †Excludes Breechblock Link.
Dyer, 2.9-Inch	F	I	2.9 / 8 x 8	44.5	—	—	—	250	1	13°30' *	Shell †	3270 *	—	*Average †Dyer shell, 9 lbs.

Type Weapon	Category	Metal	Bore Diameter	Bore Length	Length Overall	Trunnion Diameter	Trunnion Length	Weight	Charge (Pounds)	Elevation	Projectile	Range (Yards)	Photo Number	Remarks
3-In. Rifle, M.1861	F	WI	3 7 x 7	65	73.3	3.67	2.8	820	1	10° 20°	Shell *	2788 3972	IX-2	Ordnance Rifle *Dyer shell, 9 lbs.
3-In. Rifle, M.1862	F	CS	3 7 x 7	63	73	3.67	2.8	834	—	—	—	—	IX-5	Singer-Nimick
3-In. Rifle, M.1863	F	I	3 7 x 7	—	71.5	3.5	3	—	—	—	—	—	IX-6	HNH No. 1.
3-In. Rifle C.	F	B	3 6 x 6	—	65.5	3.67	2.75	—	—	—	—	—	IX-34	A.B. Rand Bros. Vicksburg, Miss.
3-In. Rifle C.	F	B	3 12 x 12	—	65.5	3.67	3.25	—	—	—	—	—	IX-33	Quinby & Robinson, Memphis, Tenn.
3-In. Rifle C.	F	B	3 12 x 12	57.5	65.5	3.67	2.8	—	—	—	—	—	IX-35	Cast in 6-Pdr. Model 1841 pattern.
3-In. Rifle, M.1861. C.	F	I	3 5 x 5	62.5	72	3.67	2.75	967	—	—	—	—	IX-37	In service but not permanently adopted.
3-In. Rifle C.	F	I	3 12 x 12	62.5	71.5	3.67	2.75	1000	—	—	—	—	IX-38	With muzzle swell.
3-In. Experimental Rifle	Exp.	GS	3 7 x 7	64	73.5	4.2	3.2	1372	—	—	—	—	IX-23	HNH piece at West Point.
3.2-In. B.L.R.	F	WI	3.2 7 x 7	68.75	68.75*	3.67	2.8	820	—	—	—	—	IX-4	Converted Ordnance Rifle *Without Breechblock.
3.3-In. Rifle C.	F	B	3.3 7 x 7	57.5	65.5	3.67	2.8	—	—	—	—	—	IX-36	Cast in 6-Pdr. Model 1841 pattern.
Wiard, 12-Pdr. Rifled Boat Howitzer	N	SS	3.4 12 x 12	—	64.5	NA	NA	783	—	—	—	—	IX-16	
12-Pdr. Rifled Boat Howitzer, C. (TT)	N	I	3.5 12 x 12	54.5	64	NA	NA	—	—	—	—	—	IX-17	
Cameron, 14-Pdr. C.	F	WI	3.56 6 x 6	71	83.5	3.1	2.9	1000*	—	—	—	—	IX-40	*Reported in 1877 newspaper clipping.
Wiard, 12-Pdr.	F	SS	3.6 8 x 8*	57.5v	63.5	4.62	3.5	—	—	—	—	—	IX-9	*Others 12 x 12
Sawyer, 3.67-In.	F	I	3.67 6 x 6	—	—	—	—	—	—	—	—	—	—	
Dyer, 3.67-In.	F	I	3.67 16 x 16	57.5	—	—	—	880	1.25	—	Shell*	—	—	*Dyer shell, 14 lbs.
Read, 3.69-In.	F	I	3.69 3 x 3	103.4	—	—	—	1200	1.5	—	Shell*	—	—	*Read shell, 12 lbs.
Austrian 3.74-In. Rifle.	F	B	3.74 6 x 6*	53	62	3.5	3.25	668– 780†	—	—	—	—	IX-47	*Also smooth-bore †Wt. various weapons
James, 14-Pdr.	F	B*	3.8 10 x 10**	64	73	3.67	2.75	915†	—	—	—	—	IX-18	*A few made of steel. **Some 7 x 7. †Average of several.
4.5-In. Siege Rifle M.1861.	S & G	I	4.5 9 x 9	120	133	5.3	4	3450	3.25	10°	Shell*	3265	IX-8	*Dyer shell, 25.5 lbs.
4.62-In. Siege Rifle M.1862. C.	S & G	I	4.62 7 x 7	106	118	5.82	5	5362	—	—	—	—	IX-39	
Sawyer, 4.62-In.	S & G N	I	4.62 6 x 6	61.5v	78.5	5.5	4	—	—	—	—	—	IX-24	
Read, 4.636-In. Field Rifle	F	I	4.636 7 x 7	74	—	—	—	1900	2	—	Shell*	—	—	*Read shell, 15 lbs.

Type Weapon	Category	Metal	Bore Diameter	Bore Length	Length Overall	Trunnion Diameter	Trunnion Length	Weight	Charge (Pounds)	Elevation	Projectile	Range (Yards)	Photo Number	Remarks
Read, 4.854-In. Siege Rifle	S & G	I	4.854 7 x 7	109	—	—	—	5000	3	—	Shell*	—	—	*Read shell, 22 lbs.
Ames, 50-Pdr. Rifle	N	WI	5.1	92E	106.5E	—	—	5500	3.5	—	Shot*	—	IX-20	*Wt. 37 lbs.
Atwater, 5.85-In.	N	I	5.85 12 x 12	144	—	—	—	11625	—	—	—	—	—	
Sawyer, 5.862-In.	S & G	I	5.862 6 x 6	110	—	—	—	8822	5.5	13°30′	Shell*	4359	—	*Sawyer shell, 45 lbs.
Dimick, 6.4-In.	SC	I	6.4 6 x 6	101	—	—	—	9300	6	—	Shell*	—	—	*Dimick Shell, 51 lbs.
Read, 6.425-In.	SC	I	6.425 3 x 3	110	—	—	—	8500	6	11°30′	Shell*	3665	—	*Read shell, 50 lbs.
Attick, 100-Pdr.*	SC	I	7	110	129	7	6.5	—	14 16	— —	Shell†	—	IX-26	*42-Pdr. Model 1841, Banded & Rifled. †James shell, 100 lbs.
Ames, 125-Pdr.	SC	WI	7*	139	168.13	8	4.5	19400	25	34°30′	Shell†	9230	IX-21	*Later bored to 8-In. †Hotchkiss shell, 106 lbs, 8 oz.

SMOOTHBORES

Type Weapon	Category	Metal	Bore Diameter	Bore Length	Length Overall	Trunnion Diameter	Trunnion Length	Weight	Charge (Pounds)	Elevation	Projectile	Range (Yards)	Photo Number	Remarks
Improvised Cannon C.	Exp	I*	1.5x 6.5†	—	71.5	4.75	3.25	—	—	—	—	—	V-24	*Bands WI †Rectangular
Hughes B.L. C.	F	B*	1.5—2	—	34†	—	—	80†	—	—	Lead Ball	5000E	—	*Also made of WI †Average
Bomford, 3-In. B.L.	Exp.	I	3	64	64*	3.67	2.5	—	—	—	—	—	IX-30	*To missing cascabel
Gilleland 4-Pdr.	Exp.	I	3.13	46.5	56.5	4.2	3	—	—	—	—	—	IX-41	Double-Barreled.
Pate, tappey and Lumsden 3.13-In. Revolving Cannon	Exp.	I	3.13	48*	70	—	—	—	—	—	—	—	IX-44 IX-42	*plus 13.5-inch cylinder
Griffen, 6-Pdr. M.1855.	F	WI	3.67	63.25	72.25	3.67	2.75	1030	—	—	—	—	IX-1	
James, 6-Pdr.	F	B	3.67	64	73	3.67	2.75	—	—	—	—	—	IX-19	
Austrian 3.74-In.	F	B	3.74*	53	62	3.5	3.25	668 780†	—	—	—	—	‡	*Also rifled. †Wts. various pieces. ‡See IX-47.
Wiard, 12-Pdr. Howitzer	F	SS	4.62	—	—	—	—	725	—	—	—	—	IX-10	
Bishop, 12-Pdr. B.L.	F	I	4.62	52	59.5*	5	4	—	—	—	—	—	IX-28	*To end breech-block hinge.
Austrian 5.87-In. Howitzer	F	B	5.87	50.5	59.5	3.67	3.25	632	—	—	—	—	IX-46	
Treadwell, 32-Pdr.	SC N	WI	6.4	—	84.5	4.75	4.25	—	—	—	—	—	IX-22	
Carronade, 32-Pdr.	N	I	6.4*	49	65	5†	4.75†	2200E	—	—	—	—	—	*Flared to 7. †Some had loops
Carronade, 42-Pdr.	N	I	7*	57	71.5†	NA	NA	3000E	—	—	—	—	V-19	*Flared to 7.9 at muzzle. †Another is 68.75.
Bomford, 12-In. M. 1846*	SC	I	12	116.2	134	12	10E	25510	28	—	Shell†	5800	IX-29	*Banded with WI, 1862 †Shell Wt. 181 lbs.
Stockton, 12-In.	N	WI	12	144	169	8.5E	8E	16700	45	—	Shot*	—	IX-32	*Shot Wt. 224 lbs.
Ericsson, 13-In.	N	WI	13	—	152	—	—	47000	—	—	—	—	—	

Condensed list of specifications from the U.S. Ordance Manual of 1861. (Dimensions in inches, weights in pounds).

		GUNS			HOWITZERS	
	6-Pdr.	12-Pdr. 1841	12-Pdr. 1857	12-Pdr.	24-Pdr.	32-Pdr.
FIELD CARRIAGES						
Length, front of wheel to end of trail.	116.6	122.75	122.75	116.6	122.75	122.75
Weight, carriage without limber.	900	1,175	1,128	900	1,128	1,175
Length, limbered, muzzle face to front of pole.	279.1	294	287.63	272.1	283.78	291
Diameter of wheel.	57	57	57	57	57	57
Width of track.	60	60	60	60	60	60
Weight limber, chest empty, without interior divisions.	860	860	860	860	860	860
Weight carriage, tube, limber, chest with ammunition and necessary implements.	3,178	4,428	3,839E	3,173	4.002	4,544
CAISSON						
Length without limber.	125.5	125.5	125.5	125.5	125.5	125.5
Length limbered.	274.7	274.7	274.7	274.7	274.7	274.7
Weight with limber loaded and with necessary implements.	3,509	3,806	3,767E	3,782	3,986	3,755
Number rounds caisson and limber.	150	96	96	117	69	45

FORGE (Same for all batteries)	
Length without limber.	130
Length limbered	279
Weight with limber loaded	3,684
BATTERY WAGON (Same, all batteries)	
Length without limber.	154
Length limbered.	303.13
Weight limbered and loaded.	3,750
MOUNTAIN HOWITZER CARRIAGE	
Length, front of wheels to end of trail.	71.8
Length of shafts.	73
Weight, carriage without implements.	287
Weight of shafts.	30
Diameter of wheels.	38
Track of wheels.	30.2
Weight of pack saddle and harness.	47
PRAIRIE CARRIAGE	
Length, front of wheels to end of trail.	83
Length of carriage limbered.	216
Weight of carriage without limber.	363
Diameter of wheels.	42
Track of wheels	42.5
Weight of limber, chests empty.	343
Weight carriage, tube, limber, chests with ammunition and implements.	1,205
PRAIRIE AMMUNITION CART	
Length of cart.	127
Weight, empty.	434
Weight, loaded with ammunition and implement chest.	940

Condensed list of specifications from the U.S. Ordnance Manual of 1861. (Dimensions in inches, weights in pounds).

	GUNS			HOWITZERS	
	12-Pdr.	18-Pdr.	24-Pdr.	8-Inch	Mortar Wagon
SIEGE CARRIAGES					
Length, front of wheels to end of trail.	141	142	142	142	—
Weight carriage without limber.	2,248	2,350	2,522	2,522	1,792
Length	—	—	—	—	143.6
Length of carriage limbered	278.9	280.9	280.9	280.9	287.85
Length, muzzle face of gun in traveling position to end of pole.	285.15	291.42	290	—	—
Weight limber complete	1,393	1,393	1,393	1,393	1,393

Weight carriage and limber.	3,641	3,743	3,915	3,915	3,185
Weight carriage, tube, limber (Howitzer Model 1841)	7,231	8,656	9,705	6,529	—
Wheels, diameter and track	60	60	60	60	60

	8-Inch Siege	10-Inch Siege	Coehorn
MORTAR BEDS (1841)			
Length	42	51.8	31
Exterior width, including maneuvering bolts.	34	40	15
Weight	920	1,830	132

Condensed list of specifications from the U.S. Ordnance Manual of 1861. (Dimensions in inches, weights in pounds).

	12-Pdr. Gun	18-Pdr. Gun	24-Pdr. Gun	32-Pdr. Gun & 8-In. How.	42-Pdr. Gun
SEACOAST CARRIAGES					
BARBETTE, FRONT PINTLE, WOOD					
Distance between inside of trunnion plates	14.9	16.9	18.1	20.8	22.1
Diameter trunnion holes	4.65	5.35	5.85	6.45	7.05
Height, axis of trunnions, in battery, above traverse circle.	71.76	71.76	73.45	75.77	77.47
Vertical field of fire:					
Above horizontal (degrees)	11	11	11	11	11
Below horizontal (degrees)	5	5	5	5	5
Length top carriage from front of wheels to rear of lunette.	89.5	89.5	90.75	90.75	92.05
Whole length of chassis.	184.06	184.06	183.38	182.86	182.71
Width of chassis between outside rails.	43	43	45	51.3	53.5
Center of pintle to front of rails.	9.5	9.5	9.5	9.5	9.5
Center of pintle to rear of chasis.	174.3	174.3	174.22	173.76	173.66
Center of pintle to center of traverse wheels.	120.33	120.33	120.33	120.33	120.33
Center of pintle to face of piece in battery. Gun:	59	63.15	63.29	63.7	65.3
Howitzer:				52.5	
Diameter of top carriage rollers.	13	13	13	13	13
Diameter of top carriage wheels.	43.5	43.5	43.5	43.5	43.5
Diameter of traverse wheels.	15	15	15	15	15
Weight, top carriage complete	1,666	1,686	1,959	2,213	2,308
Weight, chassis complete and pintle.	1,311	1,311	1,631	2,047	2,211

Condensed list of specifications from the U.S. Ordance Manual of 1861. (Dimensions in inches, weights in pounds).

	8-In. Columbiad	10-In. Columbiad
SEACOAST CARRIAGES		
BARBETTE, CENTER PINTLE, WOOD		
Distance between inside of trunnion plates.	25.2	31.2
Diameter of trunnion holes.	8.05	10.05
Height, axis of trunnions, in battery, above traverse circle.	61	63.2
Vertical field of fire:		
Above horizontal (degrees)	30.5	28
Below horizontal (degrees)	4	3
Length of top carriage.	74	76
Whole length of chassis.	165	165
Width of chassis between outside of rails.	46.2	57.2
Center of pintle to front of chassis.	74	74.42
Center of pintle to rear of chassis.	91	90.58
Center of pintle to center traverse wheels.	64	64
Center of pintle to face of piece in battery.	132.56	133.57
Diameter of top carriage trucks.	13	13
Diameter of chassis traverse wheels.	12	12
Weight, top carriage complete.	2,324	3,142
Weight, chassis complete and pintle.	3,481	4,215

Condensed list of specifications from the U.S. Ordnance Manual 1861. (Dimensions in inches, weights in pounds).

		Front Pintle		Center Pintle	
	10-Inch	8-Inch & 42-Pdr.	32-Pdr. 24-Pdr.	10-Inch	8-Inch
SEACOAST CARRIAGES					
BARBETTE, FRONT & CENTER PINTLE, IRON.					
Distance between inside of trunnion plates.	32.2	25.8	20.8	32.2	25.8
Diameter of trunnion holes	10.05	8.05	6.45	10.05	8.05
Height, axis of trunnions, in battery, above traverse circle.	79.72	77.47	77.47	61	63.2

Vertical field of fire:					
Above horizontal (degrees)	30	30	14	30	30
Below horizontal (degrees)	6	6	6	6	6
Length top carriage to rear of shoe.	75.4	75.6	75.6	75.4	75.6
Whole length of chassis	173	173	173	173	173
Width chasis between outside of rails.	42.75	36.35	31.35	42.75	36.35
Center of pintle to front of rails.	24.25	20.5	9.42	77.09	77.09
Center of pintle to rear end chassis.	166.13	165.47	163.58	95.65	95.65
Center of pintle to center of rear traverse wheels.	120.33	120.33	120.33	64	64
Center of pintle to center of front traverse wheels.	—	—	—	64	64
Center of pintle to face of piece in battery.	66.38	65.28	60.08	134.38	134.18
Diameter top carriage trucks	12	12	12	12	12
Diameter rear traverse wheels (mean).	18	18	18	14.6	14.6
Diameter front traverse wheels (mean).	—	—	—	11.63	11.63
Weight top carriage complete.	1,947	1,860	1,758	1,947	1,860
Weight chassis complete and pintle.	3,084	3,039	3,022	2,679	2,679

Condensed list of specifications from the U.S. Ordnance Manual 1861. (Dimensions in inches, weights in pounds).

SEACOAST CARRIAGES

		CASEMATE			FLANK CASEMATE
CASEMATE & FLANK CASEMATE, WOOD.	24-Pdr. Gun	32-Pdr. Gun	42-Pdr. Gun	8-Inch Columbiad	24-Pdr. Howitzer
Distance between inside of trunnion plates.	18.52	21.26	22.56	25.1	12.95
Diameter trunnion holes.	5.85	6.45	7.05	8.05	4.65
Height, axis of trunnions, in battery, above traverse circle.	48.75	49.95	50.65	50.65	48.25
Vertical field of fire:					
Above horizontal (degrees)	9	8	8	8	—
Below horizontal (degrees)	4	4	4	4	—
Length top carriage from front of cheeks to rear of roller.	67.35	67.35	67.35	67.2	48.25
Whole length of chassis (including 3 inches for tongue fork).	189.15	189.15	189.15	189.15	151
Width of chassis between outside of rails.	40	44.5	46.76	49.16	22
Center of pintle to front of rails.	49.94	49.94	49.94	49.94	7
Center of pintle to rear of chassis.	235	235	235	235	144
Center of pintle to center of traverse wheels Front:	62.5	62.5	62.5	62.5	—
Rear:	194.5	194.5	194.5	194.5	120
Center of pintle to face of piece in battery.	.52	1.03	2.73	4.83	25.6
Diameter top carriage truck wheel.	20	20	20	20	3.8
Diameter rear traverse wheels (mean)	15.9	15.9	15.9	15.9	6
Diameter front traverse wheels (mean)	7.84	7.84	7.84	7.84	—
Weight, top carriage complete.	1,354	1,510	1,566	1,574	620
Weight, chassis complete and pintle.	2,470	2,780	2,925	2,950	710

Condensed list of specifications from the U.S. Ordnance Manual of 1861. (Dimensions in inches, weights in pounds).

SEACOAST CARRIAGES
CASEMATE, IRON

	8-Inch & 42-Pounder	32-Pounder 42-Pounder
Distance between inside of trunnion plates.	25.8	20.8
Diameter of trunnion holes	8.05	6.45
Height, axis of trunnions, in battery, above traverse circle.	50.65	50.65
Vertical field of fire:		
Above horizontal (degrees)	7	10
Below horizontal (degrees)	6	
Length top carriage to rear of shoe.	65.38	65.38
Whole length of chassis, excluding tongue.	164	164
Width of chassis between outside of rails.	36.35	31.35
Center of pintle to front of rails.	49	48.1
Center of pintle to rear end of chassis.	212	211.8
Center of pintle to center rear traverse wheels.	194.5	194.5
Center of pintle to center front traverse wheels.	62.5	62.5
Center of pintle to face of piece in battery.	10.61	.46
Diameter, top carriage trucks.	12	12
Diameter, rear traverse wheels (mean).	15.85	15.85
Diameter, front traverse wheels (mean).	7.85	7.85
Weight, top carriage complete.	1,485	1,454
Weight, chassis complete and pintle.	2,267	2,245

CHAPTER XII AMMUNITION SHOT — SHELL — SPHERICAL CASE

Caliber	15-In.	13-In.	12-In.	11-In.	10-In.	9-In.	8-In.	42-Pdr.	32-Pdr.	24-Pdr.	18-Pdr.	12-Pdr.	9-Pdr.	6-Pdr.	4-Pdr.	3-Pdr.	1-Pdr.
Diameter:	14.85	12.87	11.87	10.85	9.87	8.85	7.88	6.84	6.25	5.68	5.17	4.52	4.10	3.58	3.12	2.84	1.95
Weight:																	
Shot	440	282.84	222	—	127.5	—	65	42.5	32.4	24.3	18.3	12.25	9.14	6.1	4.07	3.05	1
Shot, Cored.	400																
Shot, Navy		276*		166	124	90			32.5								
Shell, Common	352		176		101.67		49.75	31.3	22.5	16.8	13.45	8.34					
Shell, Motar		218	200		88.42		44.12										
Shell, Navy		216.5		135.5	101.5	73.5	52.75		26.5								
Case, Army ·					**		59.5	39	32.7	24.6	16.3	12.1		5.7			
No. balls, lead, .69-In. Diameter.							486	306	245	175	120	78		41			
Case, Navy	358			141	101	75	52		32	24		12					
No. balls, lead .65-In. Diameter									235	175		80					
No. balls, Iron 1-Inch.	1000																
No. balls, Iron .85-Inch				625	435	350	220										

*Difference is weights of Army and Navy shot due to slightly greater windage (approximately .05) used by the Navy thus Army 15-Inch diameter is listed as 14.85 compared to a mean of 14.80 for the Navy. (the 13-inch was 12.87 and 12.80 respectively).

**10-Inch, experimental mortar spherical case weighed 104 pounds with 27 iron balls varying from 1.49 to 1.46 diameter.

CHAPTER XII AMMUNITION CANISTER

Caliber	15-In.	11-In.	10-In.	9-In.	8-In. S.C. How.	8-In. Siege How.	42-Pdr.	32-Pdr.	32-Pdr. Field How.	24-Pdr.	24-Pdr. Field How.	18-Pdr.	12-Pdr. S & G Gun	12-Pdr. Field Gun	12-Pdr. Field How.	12-Pdr. Mt. How.	6-Pdr.
Weight					54.5	53.5	48	37	28.5	29	21.25	23	15	14.8	10.8	11.2	7.32
Length Complete					12.35	12.03	8.7	8.1	10.5	7.35	9.55	6.8	6	8	8.75	6.85	6.75
No. Balls, Iron.					48	48	27	27	48	27	48	27	27	27	48	—	27
Diam. Largest					1.87	1.87	2.26	2.06	1.49	1.87	1.35	1.70	1.49	1.49	1.08	—	1.17
Diam. Smallest					1.84	1.84	2.22	2.02	1.46	1.84	1.32	1.67	1.46	1.46	1.05	—	1.14
No. Balls, Lead															148		
Diameter															0.69		

NAVY

	15-In.	11-In.	10-In.	9-In.	8-In. S.C. How.				32-Pdr. Field How.		24-Pdr. Field How.		12-Pdr. S & G Gun				
Weight	207	120	98	70	50				30		14.55*		7.75†				
No. Balls Iron	600	315	290	230	162				100		39		39				
Diam. Balls	1.3	1.3	1.3	1.3	1.3				1.3		1.3		1				

*Also used 1.3-inch lead balls (39) to give a weight of 22 pounds.

†Also used 1-inch lead balls (39) to give a weight of 11 pounds.

CHAPTER XII AMMUNITION GRAPE — CARCASSES

Caliber	13-In.	11-In.	10-In.	9-In.	8-In.	42-Pdr.	32-Pdr.	24-Pdr.	18-Pdr.	12-Pdr.
GRAPE, ARMY:										
Weight					75.5	51.3	39.8	30.6	22.2	14.8
Length of stand					9.9	8.8	8.2	7.5	6.8	5.8
No. shot in iron stand					9	9	9	9	9	9
Diam. largest shot					3.60	3.17	2.90	2.64	2.40	2.06
Diam. smallest shot					3.54	3.13	2.86	2.60	2.36	2.02
GRAPE, NAVY:										
Weight		125.08	98.62	74.1	53.25	33.5				
No. shot in stand		15	15	18	18	12				
Diam. of shot (mean)		3.55	3.34	2.80	2.50	2.50				
CARCASSES										
Weight	194		87.6		43.6	29.5	21.6	15.8	12.2	8

Index